STATISTICS,
AN INTRODUCTORY ANALYSIS

TARO YAMANE
DEPARTMENT OF ECONOMICS, SAN DIEGO STATE COLLEGE

Statistics, An Introductory Analysis

HARPER & ROW, PUBLISHERS • NEW YORK, EVANSTON, AND LONDON

to MIYAKO

CONTENTS

PREFACE:
NOTE ON USES AND ORGANIZATION

This is a textbook mainly for students in business and economics but it has also been designed so that with appropriate selections of chapters it may be used by students in other disciplines. The first 15 chapters are designed for an undergraduate level, and the remaining chapters for upper divisions courses or an introductory statistics course for graduate students.

Recently most colleges have included statistics as a required course in their economics and business curriculums, and for the majority of students, this will probably be the only statistics course they will ever take. Hence the book is planned to cover a wide and balanced variety of topics in one semester.

A second viewpoint that was adopted by the author was, that in college, the main emphasis should be on the theoretical aspects of statistics, that is, the emphasis should be on the "why" rather than the "how." Hypothetical examples have been used and deliberately kept simple so that the statistical process does not become submerged in a jungle of calculations.

In accordance with these views, five topics are covered in the first 15 chapters which are intended as a basic one semester statistics course. Chapters 1–4 are the traditional descriptive statistics covering frequency distributions, various means, and measures of dispersion.

Chapters 5–10 are on statistical inferences starting with a discussion of probability and including a discussion of the traditional objective approach and the more recent subjective approach to probability theory.

This is followed by a discussion of testing hypotheses and estimation. A chapter on using the subjective approach to statistical problems has also been included to acquaint the student with this new approach.

Chapters 11–13 are on index numbers and time series and have been presented in an orthodox manner.

Chapters 14–15 are on linear regression and correlation analysis; emphasis has been placed on theoretical aspects.

The sequence of topics is such that Chapters 1–4 may be considered as a warmup—getting the student acclimatized to the subject and preparing him for Chapters 5–10. These chapters are usually the hardest for the student to grasp conceptually because of the new and subtle concepts and will probably require maximum effort. Chapters 11–13 are relatively easy for the student to grasp conceptually, and allow the student to relax his pace a little. However, in Chapters 14 and 15, the student once again encounters new concepts and is taxed, although not so much as in Chapters 5–10.

Each instructor probably has his own way of teaching an elementary statistics course. I have found in my own experience that this coverage and sequence of topics provided an optimum pace and also a desirable change of pace for the student. I hope some instructors will also find it agreeable.

Chapters 15–21 discuss the basic distributions for further study of statistics, and Chapters 22–23 discuss multiple regression and the second part of time series. These chapters are mainly for advanced students who are planning to take further courses in statistics or to undertake independent study.

One of the inconveniences I experienced when using various statistics texts was that the tables were attached to the back of the book. This was especially inconvenient for exams, and I suspect there are other instructors who have also had the laborious experience of preparing tables for exams. To alleviate this inconvenience, the tables for this text have been made into a separate booklet which I hope will be of help to instructors.

ACKNOWLEDGMENTS

A textbook such as this owes its existence to many statisticians, economists, and mathematicians whose work forms the basis of the book,
and also to those who have provided me with the opportunity to teach
the course on various occasions. I am indebted to Dean Erwin Gaum-
nitz, School of Commerce, University of Wisconsin for the initial opportunity to teach statistics. The basic sequence of topics of the first
15 chapters was originally formulated at that institution. I am also
indebted to the Department of Economics, School of Commerce, New
York University where I had the opportunity to test various parts of the
material, and in particular to the Economics Department, Graduate
School of Arts and Science, New York University where I had the
opportunity to use the entire text in abbreviated ditto form in the
introductory statistics course. Lectures in the Graduate School were
given once a week for two hours, and the course was for two semesters.
Chapters 1–15 were covered during the first semester, and Chapters 16–
23 were covered during the second. This introductory course was followed by such courses as sampling theory, regression analysis, time
series, quality control, and advanced statistical techniques. The Department of Economics of the Graduate School and Professor Emanuel Stein
provided an ideal environment for this project and generously provided
all the necessary secretarial work without which it would have been
impossible to complete this project. I am also grateful to the Department of Industrial Engineering and Department of Mathematical
Statistics at Columbia University for the opportunities that were

generously given to me to extend my studies and interest in the field of statistics.

I also wish to express my special appreciation to Miss Cecilia Liang, Mrs. Andrée Yamamura, and Miss Yukiko Honda for their excellent job of typing the manuscript many times.

I am indebted to Sir Ronald A. Fisher, F.R.S., Cambridge, and to Dr. Frank Yates, F.R.S., Rothamsted, also to Messrs. Oliver & Boyd, Ltd., Edinburgh, for permission to reprint parts of Tables III, IV, and VIII from their book *Statistical Tables for Biological, Agricultural and Medical Research,* and to the other authors and publishers who are mentioned throughout the book for their kind permission to reproduce the various tables.

TARO YAMANE

STATISTICS,
AN INTRODUCTORY ANALYSIS

INTRODUCTION

1

The theory and methods of collecting, tabulating, and analyzing numerical data comprise the study and application of statistics as the subject will be discussed in this book. The expression "analyzing numerical data" cannot be defined in a simple, brief statement that can in any way relieve the student of the chore of digesting text content. Although the expression is an abstract term, its implication may be demonstrated to some extent by example. But even this device is no more than a clue to the student at this point of study, for he must develop his own philosophical understanding of analytic statistics as he reads through the book and learns the techniques of analysis and interpretation of data.

In nontechnical terms, our object in this study is to acquire a kit of tools that will enable us to interpret and analyze data, a necessary complement to the increasingly complex activities of our daily lives. Over the past half-century, the need to use numerical data as a means of expressing information quantitatively has become very important, both economically and sociologically. For instance, 30 years ago the average person was identified by name only, but today he has many numbers associated with that name. He has a social security number, a driver's license number, an insurance policy number, a store account number, an income tax file number, and various other identifying numbers. If he has a business, he uses quantitative data to analyze the financial status of that business. When he reads about the national economy, he interprets its condition in terms of figures for national income, taxes, prices, rates of production, and similar data, and he uses these figures to describe and analyze the overall national resources and prosperity.

A cursory check of other disciplines such as the biological, physical, and social sciences will also quickly reveal the extent to which numerical data are used for description and analysis. It is apparent immediately that statistics provides a kit of tools that has common use among the diversified activities of our society.

1.1. Statistical Techniques

Techniques such as graphs, charts, frequency distributions, and averages may be used for description and these have much practical use. However, the most important utility of statistics is the analysis of numerical data by statistical techniques.

As mentioned above, the analysis of numerical data by statistical techniques is an abstract expression. It is the purpose of this book to give it concrete content. We start out with the fact that the essential characteristic common to the various techniques is the element of "statistical inference." We define this as a process of inferring from data for the part, a statement relative to the whole and provide a measure of the uncertainty of the inference that has been made. For example, we may have the problem of estimating the proportion of voters in favor of a certain proposal. The reader probably knows that, in solving this problem, a sample of the voters is taken and the proportion of voters in favor is calculated. Suppose 60 percent in the sample are in favor. Then, using this sample proportion, we may infer that 60 percent of *all* voters are in favor of the proposal. But since we are using only a portion of the information to infer about the whole, we cannot be absolutely certain of the conclusion that 60 percent of *all* voters are in favor of the proposal. In other words, there is a degree of uncertainty associated with our conclusion and by using statistical techniques, we wish to provide a measure for this uncertainty.

If, as mentioned before, statistics may be considered a common kit of tools for describing and analyzing data of various disciplines, in this sense, statistics is neutral and therefore the same sampling technique may be used in economics, business, education, and other disciplines. However, statistics has developed certain techniques peculiar to the field of application. In business and economics, for example, such topics as index numbers and time series have been developed to a greater extent than in education or sociology. In these latter disciplines, the techniques of factor analysis have been developed extensively. In the biological sciences, the statistical techniques of experimental designs have developed, and in industry, techniques of quality control are most important.

In this book we shall discuss the basic ideas of statistics and show its applications to business and economics. In Chapters 2–4, we shall discuss descriptive statistics; Chapters 5–10, the basic ideas of statistical inference will be explained; Chapters 11–14 will discuss index numbers, time series, regression analysis, and correlation analysis; and finally, Chapters 15–23 will be mainly concerned with basic distributions. But first let us discuss in the remainder of this chapter a special topic that is much used in practical work, namely, statistical tables.

1.2. Statistical Tables

In the subsequent several hundred pages, various statistical techniques will be presented, but for the majority of students the first few pages concerning statistical tables may turn out to be the topic most used from a practical standpoint. Whether in business, government, or schoolwork, one frequently has to present results of reports or investigations. A problem confronted by the reporter is: How can the results be presented most effectively?

Certain standard forms of presentations have been devised, and they may be broadly classified as tabular form and graphic presentation. Let us start with tabular form.

The tabular form is a table consisting of the following components: the title, the stub, the caption, the body, and the source. Table 1.1 is an example of the simplest form of such a table and is called a one-way

	TABLE 1.1. Production in the U.S., Selected Years	
Title:		
Caption:	Year	Number
	1790	3,929,214
	1890	62,947,714
Stub:	1920	105,710,620
	1940	131,669,275
	1960	178,464,236
Source:	SOURCE: *Statistical Abstract of the U.S.*, 1961, U.S. Department of Commerce, p. 5.	Body

classification table. Two-way, three-way, and further orders of classification may be obtained by subdividing the stub and caption. Table 1.2 is a two-way and Table 1.3 is a three-way classification table.

TABLE 1.2. (Two-way Classification Table)
Motor Vehicles—Summary of Selected Items
(Unit: 1000 cars)

Item	1950	1955	1958
Passenger car factory sales, total	6666	7920	4258
Trucks and bus factory sales	1337	1249	877
Vehicles scrapped	3234	4392	4173

SOURCE: *Statistical Abstract of the U.S.*, 1961, U.S. Department of Commerce, Table No. 754, p. 556.

TABLE 1.3. (Three-way Classification Table)
Motor Vehicles—Summary of Selected Items
(Unit: 1000 cars)

Item	1950	1955	1958
Passenger car factory sales, total	6666	7920	4258
4-door sedans	3247	3044	1481
2-door sedans, coaches and coupes	2794	1691	705
Others	626	3186	2072
Truck and bus factory sales	1337	1249	877
Vehicles scrapped, total	3234	4392	4173
Passenger cars	2598	3773	3635
Trucks and buses	636	619	538

SOURCE: *Statistical Abstract of the U.S.*, 1961, U.S. Department of Commerce, Table No. 754, p. 556.

The rationale of constructing cross classification tables is to first determine what is to have primary emphasis, then what is to have secondary emphasis, and so forth. The data with primary emphasis are put in columns, and those with secondary emphasis are put in rows; for higher-order tables, this process is repeated. It is usually easier to see data when numbers follow one another in a column rather than when they follow one another in a row. Check for yourself with the following numbers:

23,546	23,546	87,125	67,311
87,125			
67,311			

Example.   Prepare the outline of a triple cross classification table that is to display the following information:

a. According to period employed: less than 5 years, from 5 years to 10 years, over 10 years.
b. According to sex: male, female.
c. According to occupation: teaching, administrative, service.

Give principal emphasis to the period employed, secondary to the sex, and tertiary to the occupation.

(Title)

Period Employed and Occupation	Male	Female
Less than 5 years		
Teaching		
Administrative		
Service		
Total		
From 5 years to 10 years		
Teaching		
Administrative		
Service		
Total		
Over 10 years		
Teaching		
Administrative		
Service		
Total		

SOURCE:

1.3.   Graphic Presentation

Another method of presenting data is by using graphs. The main graphs (or charts) are: the arithmetic line diagram, bar charts, pictographs, pie diagrams, and statistical maps. A number of statistical texts[1] devote a large amount of space to the detailed explanation of these charts, and the student who is interested is referred to the references given in the footnote.

---

[1] F. E. Croxton and D. J. Cowden, *Practical Business Statistics,* 3rd ed., Prentice-Hall, 1960. W. A. Spurr, L. S. Kellog, and J. H. Smith, *Business and Economic Statistics,* rev. ed., Richard D. Irwin, 1961. F. E. Croxton and D. J. Cowden, *Applied General Statistics,* 2nd ed., Prentice-Hall, 1955.

FREQUENCY DISTRIBUTION

2

Suppose you are asked the question: How well did the students do in their economics examination? A common answer might be: The average of the class is 75 points. This single number, 75 points, has described the grades of the class and is one of the various available ways to do this. What we propose to do in this and the next chapter is to show how data can be organized in several ways to describe and provide useful information about situations such as that illustrated in the above example. The first concept that needs to be defined for our discussion is the concept of a *variable*.

2.1. The Concept of a Variable

Consider an inequality

$$x + 2 > 5$$

The values of x that satisfy this inequality are (assuming x to be an integer) 4, 5, 6, ... This x, which is an entity that varies, is called a *variable*. The values 4, 5, 6, . . . are the specific values that the *variable* x can take. Thus, for example, speed is a variable associated with cars running on a highway, and the speed of each car is a value that this variable takes. Weight, height, and grades are some variables associated with students.

Let us look at the variable "grades" and denote it by capital X. When there are 5 students and their grades are 75, 63, 82, 90, and 88, we can say that the *variable X* (grades) has 5 *values.* Let us indicate the values by small letters x_i: x_1 for the first value 75, x_2 for the second value 63, and so on.

$$X: \qquad x_1 = 75, \quad x_2 = 63, \quad x_3 = 82, \quad x_4 = 90, \quad x_5 = 88$$

The question, "How well did the students do?", may now be answered by describing and providing information about the variable X, and for that we investigate the various values (that is, the individual grades) of X. We wish to show how these various values of X can be organized and analyzed to provide us with information concerning X. This in turn will give us information about the students.

Before considering this problem, let us discuss two characteristics of a variable. The first is the difference between the possible values and actually observed value of X. The second is the difference between discrete and continuous variables.

The *possible values* of X are all the values that X may take. The *actually observed values* of X are those possible values of X that have actually been observed. Let us illustrate.

Example 1. If the grades of the exam are from 0 to 100 and only in integers, X (the variable "grades") may take on the 101 values: 0, 1, 2, . . . , 99, 100. These are the *possible values* the variable X may take. The 5 values of X that we observed were 75, 63, 82, 90, and 88. These are the *actually observed values* of X.

Example 2. Let X be the number that occurs when a die is tossed. There are 6 *possible values* X may take. Let a 3 occur on the first throw of the die. This 3 is an *actually observed value.*

Assume the die is tossed 24 times and the result is as shown in the following table:

X	Frequency
1	3
2	5
3	4
4	4
5	3
6	5
	24

The table shows that a 1 has occurred 3 times, a 2 has occurred 5 times, and so forth. The 1, 2, 3, . . . , 6 are the *possible values* that X may take. The 24 values that have occurred are the *actually observed values.*

Example 3. Let X be the face of a coin that is tossed and denote a head by 1 and a tail by 0. Then the *possible values* X may take are 1 and 0. Suppose the die is tossed 5 times with the following result:

X	*Number of occurrences*
1	3
0	$\underline{2}$
	5

The *actually observed values* are the 5 values: 1, 1, 1, 0, 0.

Example 4. Suppose the maximum number of letters that may be printed on a page of a certain book is 500. Let X be the number of misprints on a page of the book. Then the *possible values* of X are the 501 values: 0, 1, 2, . . . , 500. $X = 0$ indicates there are no misprints; $X = 1$ indicates there is one misprint, and so forth. If a check of a page shows that there are 6 misprints, this 6 is an *actually observed value*.

A check of 4 pages shows that the number of misprints are 2, 5, 11, and 7 for the respective pages. These 4 values of X are the *actually observed values* of X.

The second characteristic that needs to be discussed is the distinction between *discreteness* and *continuity*. Much thought has been given to these two concepts since the time of the ancient Greek mathematicians.

"From the earliest times two opposing tendencies, sometimes helping one another, have governed the whole involved development of mathematics. Roughly these are the *discrete* and the *continuous*.

"The discrete struggles to describe all nature and all mathematics atomistically, in terms of distinct, recognizable individual elements, like the bricks in a wall, or the numbers, 1, 2, 3, ... The continuous seeks to apprehend natural phenomena—the course of a planet in its orbit, the flow of a current of electricity, the rise and fall of the tides, and a multitude of other appearances which delude us into believing that we know nature—in the mystical formula of Heraclitus: 'All things flow.' Today (as will be seen in the concluding chapter), 'flow,' or its equivalent 'continuity,' is so unclear as to be almost devoid of meaning However, let this pass for the moment.

"*Intuitively* we *feel* that we *know* what is meant by 'continuous motion,' as of a bird or a bullet through the air, or the fall of a raindrop. The motion is *smooth; it does not proceed by jerks; it is unbroken.* In *continuous* motion or, more generally, in the concept of continuity itself, the *individualized* numbers 1, 2, 3, . . . are *not* the appropriate mathematical image. *All* the points on a segment of a straight line, for instance, have no such clear-cut individualities as have the numbers of the sequence 1, 2, 3, . . . , where *the step from one member of the sequence to the next is the same* (namely, 1: $1 + 2 = 3$, $1 + 3 = 4$, and so on); for *between* any two points on a line segment, no matter how close together the points may be, we can always *find,* or at least *imagine,* another point: *there is no 'shortest' step from one point to the 'next.'* In fact there is no *next* point at all.

"The last—the conception of *continuity,* 'no nextness'—when developed in the manner of Newton, Leibniz, and their successors, leads out into the boundless domain of *the calculus* and its innumerable applications to science and technology, and to all that is today called *mathematical analysis.* The other, the *discrete* pattern based on 1, 2, 3, . . . , is the domain of algebra, the theory of numbers, and symbolic logic. Geometry partakes of both the continuous and the discrete.

"A major task of mathematics today is to harmonize the continuous and the discrete, to include them in one comprehensive mathematics, and to eliminate obscurity from both."*

A rigorous definition of continuity is beyond the mathematical level of this book. We shall define it in a nonrigorous manner as follows: A *continuous* variable is a variable whose possible values have no break. For example, let X be the weight of children in a certain class. Assume that the lightest child is 80 lb. and the heaviest to be 150 lb. How many possible values of X are there between 80 lb. and 150 lb.? One can see intuitively that when any two possible values are taken, no matter how close (say, 115.998 lb. and 115.999 lb.), there will always be a possible value between the two. We shall express this by saying that there is "no break" in the values of X and define such a variable as a continuous variable. In this case, as can be seen, there are an infinite number of possible values between 80 lb. and 150 lb. Furthermore, there is an infinite number of possible values between any two possible weights, no matter how close they are.

A *discrete* variable is a variable whose values have breaks or jumps. For example, let X be the number of cows on farms in a certain region. The possible values of X are 0, 1, 2, . . . , 1000, etc. There is a jump or break between; for example, 15 and 16. The variable X (the number of cows) does not have a value such as 15.087.

For another example, consider X as the amount of money a student

---

* E. T. Bell, *Men of Mathematics,* New York: Simon and Schuster, Inc., 1937 (paperback printing, 1961), pp. 13–14. By permission of author and publishers.

has in his pocket. The possible values of X are 0¢, 1¢, 2¢, . . . , $1.00, . . . , $1.95, . . . , etc. There is a break between $1.15 and $1.16. That is, there is no value between $1.15 and $1.16 that X takes. The variable X cannot have a value, say, $1.155589.

Let us now return to our original task of organizing and analyzing the various, actually observed, values of X.

2.2. Frequency Distribution

Suppose 50 students have taken an exam in economics. The grade of the exam is the variable X. Let the 50 individual grades (the values) of this variable X be as given in Table 2.1.

TABLE 2.1.

60,	33,	85,	52,	65,	77,	84,	65,	57,	74,
71,	81,	35,	50,	35,	64,	74,	47,	68,	54,
80,	41,	61,	91,	55,	73,	59,	53,	45,	77,
41,	78,	55,	48,	69,	85,	67,	39,	76,	60,
94,	66,	98,	66,	73,	42,	65,	94,	89,	88,

Now a friend has asked you to describe how the students performed in the economics exam. This may be answered in a number of ways.

You may, for instance, start from the grade of the first student and enumerate the grade of each student. You may arrange the grades from the lowest to the highest and describe, or you may modify it one step further and say so many grades were between 30 and 39 points, so many were between 40 and 49, and so forth. That is, you may describe the situation by enumerating the number of occurrences of the grades in each class of 10 points. The number of occurrences in each class is called *the frequency* in each class, or simply "class frequency."

In any one of these cases, our object is to give a description about the grades (that is, the variable X). When there are only 50 students, it is possible to give the grade of each student, but when there are 100 or 200 students, this method becomes cumbersome. It is simpler to resort to the last method mentioned, where we obtained the frequency of the grades in each class. When these class frequencies (or simply, frequencies) are presented in table form, this table is called a *frequency table*.

Furthermore, when the values of the variable are assembled as a frequency table, it enables us to obtain, by various statistical techniques, further characteristics about the variables that are discussed in Chapter 3.

Let us now tally the raw data and construct a frequency table. There is no grade below 30, so we start from 30 and group the grades as shown in Table 2.2.

TABLE 2.2. Tally Sheet

Class	Tally	Frequency
30–39	||||	4
40–49	ⅢⅡ |	6
50–59	ⅢⅡ |||	8
60–69	ⅢⅡ ⅢⅡ ||	12
70–79	ⅢⅡ ||||	9
80–89	ⅢⅡ ||	7
90–99	||||	4

From Table 2.2 we obtain a frequency table, shown in Table 2.3.

TABLE 2.3.

Class	Frequency
30–39	4
40–49	6
50–59	8
60–69	12
70–79	9
80–89	7
90–99	4
	50

Table 2.3 shows that there are 4 grades between 30 and 39 (the class frequency is 4); 6 grades between 40–49 (the class frequency is 6), etc.

Note that although the description of the grades by the frequency table has simplified the presentation, information of the individual grades has been lost.

The groupings of 30–39, 40–49, etc., are called *class intervals*. The 30, 40, etc., are called the *lower limits,* and 39, 49, etc., are called the *upper limits* of the class intervals. The following points should be noted about class intervals.

1. When a frequency table has too many class intervals, although it gives us more information about the data than one with less, it defeats the purpose of simplification. Generally, it is convenient to have about 7–15 intervals. There is no fixed rule, and it is probably best to exercise one's own judgment. In some cases it may be advisable to have as many as 20 class intervals.

2. The class intervals need not be equal. Here, again, there is no fixed rule, and one must use his judgment in connection with what he wishes to describe. For an example, consider a frequency table of income distribution (Table 2.4) compiled by the U.S. Department of Commerce. We know that the majority of people earn approximately $6000, and very few earn over $25,000. On the other hand, we know that some families earn as much as $1,000,000. If we attempt to keep the class intervals equal at $1000 and consider income brackets up to $1,000,000, we get a frequency table with 1000 class intervals. Unless there is special and specific interest in the number and level of high income families, such a frequency distribution is usually very cumbersome for describing the income distribution. Common sense would indicate that the presentation of Table 2.4, using unequal class intervals, is probably sufficient for describing the distribution of income.

Also note that in our example of grades (Table 2.2), the last interval is 90–99 instead of 90–100. Since there was no one with a grade of 100, the interval was set as 90–99 to keep it equal with the other intervals. However, we may, if we wish, let the last interval be 90–100. Table 4.5 of Chapter 4 lets the last interval be 90–100. Or, as an alternative, we may let the last two intervals be:

	f
90–99	4
100	0

3. The variable X in Table 2.4 is family personal income and is a discrete variable. The actually observed values of a discrete variable are called *discrete data*.

When the data are discrete, the class intervals are shown as in Table 2.4. For example,

$1000–$1999
$2000–$2999

TABLE 2.4.   Distribution of Consumer Units by Income Brackets

Family Personal Income	Number of Families and Unattached Individuals (thousands), 1955
Under $1,000	2,918
$ 1,000– 1,999	5,327
2,000– 2,999	6,272
3,000– 3,999	7,275
4,000– 4,999	7,117
5,000– 5,999	6,363
6,000– 7,499	6,940
7,500– 9,999	5,186
10,000–14,999	3,017
15,000–19,999	852
20,000–24,999	356
25,000–49,999	433
50,000–and over	114
Total	52,170

SOURCE: *U.S. Income and Output,* U.S. Department of Commerce, 1958, p. 161.

Why is this not shown as

$$\$1000.00–\$1999.00$$
$$\$2000.00–\$2999.00 \ ?$$

This is because the variable X (family personal income) has been defined in dollar units. Furthermore, an amount less than $1.00 is very small compared with, say, $2000, and ignoring an amount less than $1.00 has, for practical purposes, little if any effect on the use of the table; also it has the merit of simplifying the use of the table.

Expression of class intervals when the data are discrete is no problem because there is a definite break in the values of the variable. For continuous data, however, there is no break, and therefore it is necessary to create a break while reminding the user of the table that the data are continuous. Letting X be the weight of children, assume for example, two class intervals:

$$70 \ \text{lb.}–79.99 \ . \ . \ .$$
$$80 \ \text{lb.}–89.99 \ . \ . \ .$$

The 79.99 . . . shows that the 9's continue indefinitely. In most cases, this is abbreviated as

$$70 \ \text{lb.}–79.99 \ \text{lb.}$$

omitting the ". . .". It is sometimes simplified further as

$$70 \text{ lb.--}80 \text{ lb.}$$
$$80 \text{ lb.--}90 \text{ lb.}$$

with the understanding that, when written in this fashion, it represents continuous data. We must also assume that all values of X from 70 lb. up to (but excluding) 80 lb. are in the 70–80 lb. class interval, and all values of X from 80 lb. up to (but excluding) 90 lb. are in the 80–90 lb. class interval.

4.   The *midpoint* of a class interval is obtained by adding the lower and upper class limits and dividing by 2. For example, the midpoint of the discrete class interval 30–39 is

$$\frac{30 + 39}{2} = 34.5$$

Note that the midpoint has a decimal place, even though the data (grades) are in whole numbers, and that it is a theoretical value representing the values in the class interval.

For the continuous class interval 30–40, the midpoint is

$$\frac{30 + 40}{2} = 35$$

5.   The term *class interval* is also used to indicate the number of units between two class limits. In our discrete case of grades, 30–39 will have a class interval of 10 points. Note that it is not 9 points because 30 is included as a grade.

The continuous class interval 30–40 (such as weight) will have a class interval of 40–30 = 10 (for example, 10 lb.).

The frequency table shows the distribution of the frequencies of the values of the variable X among various classes. This distribution is called the *frequency distribution* of the variable X. Table 2.3 shows the frequency distribution of the grades of 50 students, and Table 2.4 shows the frequency distribution of consumer units by income brackets. The term *frequency distribution* is usually abbreviated as simply *distribution*. Thus, for example, we say "the distribution of grades" or the "distribution of consumer units by income brackets."

2.3.   Graphic Presentation

In many cases a graphic presentation of a frequency table gives more concise and clear information about a frequency distribution. There are three types of graphic presentation: the *histogram*, the *frequency poly-gon*, and the *frequency curve*.

(i)   A histogram

Using Table 2.3, the frequency table, let us draw a histogram (Fig. 2.1). The first thing we need to do is to enter the scale of the variable X (that is, grades) on the horizontal axis. Since the data are dis-crete, there is a gap between the class interval 20–29 and 30–39. In such a case the dividing point between the two intervals will be $(29 + 30) \div 2 = 29.5$, and similarly for the other dividing points. By doing this, we avoid gaps between the bars. Note also that the dividing points from 0–29.5 have been skipped. It is not necessary to have those dividing points to which there are no corresponding frequencies (such as 9.5, 19.5), but the origin 0 must be indicated on the scale for the vertical axis.

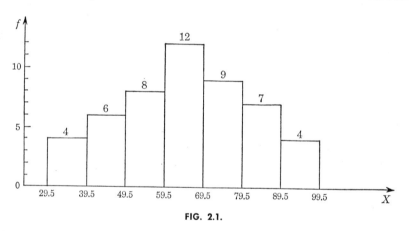

FIG. 2.1.

The second thing we need to do is to plot the bars so that their heights correspond to the frequencies of the classes they represent. The first bar has a height of 4, which corresponds to the frequency 4 in the first class interval, and similarly for the other bars. When the class intervals are unequal, the height of the bars needs to be adjusted. This is explained later.

An alternative way of drawing the histogram is as follows: First, find the midpoints of the class intervals. In our present case they are

$$\frac{30 + 39}{2} = 34.5$$

44.5, 54.5, . . . , 94.5. Second, draw a vertical line (dashed lines of Fig. 2.2) at these points, with heights that correspond to the frequencies

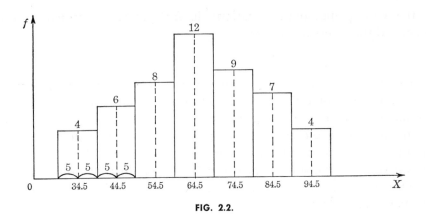

FIG. 2.2.

of the classes. Third, take half the length of the class interval on both sides of these vertical bars and draw the histogram. The construction process is shown in Fig. 2.2.

It can be seen from the graph that, since half the length of an interval is

$$10 \div 2 = 5$$

the bar constructed around the vertical bar at 34.5 is from 29.5 ($= 34.5 - 5$) to 39.5 ($= 34.5 + 5$) and is the same as that obtained in Fig. 2.1, and similarly for the other bars.

The height of a bar shows the density of the frequency per class interval. Students are probably familiar with the concept of density in discussions of population. The population density of India is high (320 persons per square mile), and the population density of the United States is low (49 persons per square mile). The point to note is that the concept of density is on a per unit basis, such as "per square mile."

In our present case, the standard unit is the class interval and the height of a bar shows the frequency on a per interval basis. This concept of frequency per interval is called the *density of the frequencies,* or the *frequency density.*

In Fig. 2.1 the first bar has a height of 4, and this shows that the frequency density for the class interval 30–39 is 4; that is, there are 4 actually observed values of the variable X in the interval 30–39. Hence, when the height of the bar is 4, it should be interpreted as

$$4f/\text{int}$$

with the unit f/int (frequency per interval).

If the frequency density (height of the bar) is multiplied by the length of the interval, we get

$$(4f/\text{int}) \times (\text{interval}) = 4 \text{ frequency}$$

But multiplying the height of a bar by its basis (that is, the interval) is finding the *area* of a bar. Thus we may conclude that the *area* of a bar shows the frequency in that interval.

In our present case, the intervals are all of the same length. Thus the frequency density $4f/\text{int}$, and the frequency in the interval, namely, 4 frequency, have the same value 4 when the units are disregarded.

This distinction between the *height* of a bar, which shows the frequency density, and the *area* of a bar, which shows frequency, becomes important when we have unequal class intervals. The explanation for this is that when we have unequal class intervals, such as those in the accompanying table, we see that the interval 40–59 is twice that of

Class	f	Frequency/interval = frequency density
30–39	4	4
40–59	14	$14/2 = 7$
60–69	3	3
	21	

30–39. If the 30–39 class interval (that is, 10 points) is considered as our standard interval, the 40–59 is equivalent to 2 standard intervals. Since the frequency for the 40–59 class interval is 14, the frequency on a per standard interval basis is $14/2 = 7$. That is, the frequency density (the *height* of the bar) in the 40–59 class interval is 7, as shown in Fig. 2.3.

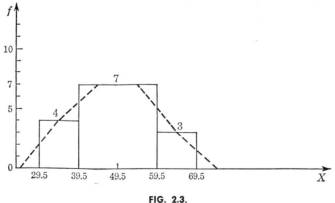

FIG. 2.3.

The *area* under the bar over the 40–59 class interval is, since 40–59 is 2 standard intervals

$$7f/\text{int} \times 2 \text{ int} = 14 \text{ frequency}$$

That is, the *area* under the bar represents the frequency in that interval.

If a class interval is 3 times the standard interval, we divide the frequency by 3 and find the frequency density, which becomes the height of the bar.

(ii) *Frequency polygon*

When the midpoints of the class intervals are linked, we obtain a *frequency polygon* as in Fig. 2.4. For example, the midpoint for the 40–49 class interval is

$$(40 + 49) \div 2 = 44.5$$

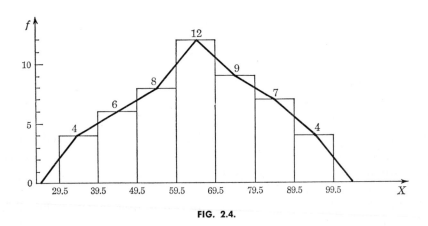

FIG. 2.4.

This is consistent with the way in which the histogram has been drawn. That is, the midpoint between the two vertical lines at 39.5 and 49.5 is also

$$(39.5 + 49.5) \div 2 = 44.5$$

Note that a straight line is drawn to connect the midpoints of the 30–39 and the 20–29 class interval, although there are no frequencies in the 20–29 class interval, and similarly for the last interval. If there should be a class interval in-between (for example, 60–69) that has no frequencies, it would be treated in the same manner.

Note also that the area under the frequency polygon is equal to the area under the histogram in Fig. 2.4.

(iii) Frequency curve

The frequency curve is a graphic presentation of a theoretical frequency distribution. But since it is difficult to give a full discussion of a theoretical frequency distribution at this point, we shall say as a first approximation that a frequency curve is a smoothed frequency polygon.

Certain forms of frequency curves have been given specific names to correspond with specific types of frequency distributions.

The rectangular distribution. If the grades of the students are as in Table 2.5, then the distribution is as in Fig. 2.5. The shape of the distribution is rectangular, and is called a rectangular distribution; it is used mainly in theoretical discussions.

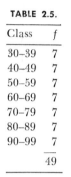

TABLE 2.5.

Class	f
30–39	7
40–49	7
50–59	7
60–69	7
70–79	7
80–89	7
90–99	7
	49

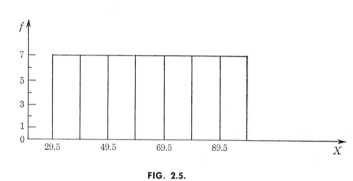

FIG. 2.5.

The normal distribution. A normal distribution is a symmetric distribution about the mean, with a frequency curve that is bell-shaped, as in Fig. 2.6. This will be discussed again in Chapter 6. IQ's of children,

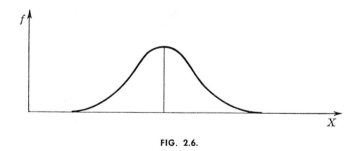

FIG. 2.6.

for example, have a normal distribution. It is the main distribution that we shall use in subsequent discussion.

Skewed distribution. If the grades are not symmetrically distributed about the mean, we say the distribution is *skewed*. Table 2.6 gives a skewed distribution.

TABLE 2.6.

Class	f
30–39	1
40–49	3
50–59	6
60–69	10
70–79	12
80–89	15
90–99	3
	50

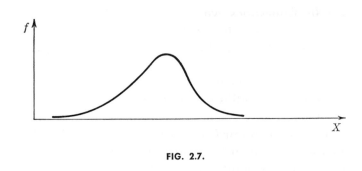

FIG. 2.7.

When the skew has a long tail to the left, as in Fig. 2.7, it is said to be skewed to the left (negatively). When the long tail is to the right, it is skewed to the right (positively).

The distribution of income shown in Table 2.4 is skewed to the right. That is, the majority have incomes around $3000–$5000, and then the distribution gradually tapers off as incomes become higher. Other examples are: The number of farms by size in the United States (skewed to the right); the number of retail stores by sales volume in the United States (skewed to the right); and the distribution of grades in a law school (usually skewed to the left).

Bimodal distribution. A frequency distribution with two peaks (modes), as in Fig. 2.8, is called a *bimodal* distribution; a distribution

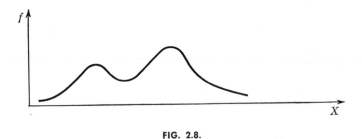

FIG. 2.8.

with three peaks is called a *trimodal* distribution, and so forth.

The distribution of grades in a freshman mathematics class that is made up of a group of good and a group of poor students sometimes shows a bimodal distribution.

2.4. Cumulative Frequency Distribution

Suppose that you are asked the questions: How many students received a grade above 60, or how many students received a grade below

40? Such questions, where one wishes to know the frequency above or below a certain value of a variable X, occur frequently. For example, one may wish to know how many salesmen were able to sell *more than* a certain amount; or, of the numerous sections in a department store, how many sections had a sales amount of *less than* a certain amount; or, how many radios in a shipment had more than five defects, and so forth.

To answer this problem, we shall organize the data into a cumulative frequency table and cumulative frequency curve. Let us illustrate this process with a simple example.

(i) Cumulative frequency table

Suppose 10 students take an exam for which the grades are from 0 to 10, and no fractional grades are given. Let the results of the exam be those given in Table 2.7. The variable X shows the possible values of the grades, and f shows the frequencies.

TABLE 2.7.

(a)			(b)	
X	f		X	Cumulative f
0 points	0		less than 0	0
1 points	1		less than 1	1
2 points	3		less than 2	4
3 points	0		less than 3	4
4 points	0		less than 4	4
5 points	0		less than 5	4
6 points	3		less than 6	7
7 points	2		less than 7	9
8 points	0		less than 8	9
9 points	1		less than 9	10
10 points	0		less than 10	10
	10			

Table 2.7(b) is an "equal to or less than" cumulative frequency table obtained by cumulating the frequencies of Table 2.7(a). The cumulative frequencies in the cumulative column show the number of students who have a grade equal to or less than the corresponding grade. For example, the 1 in the cumulative column means that there is 1 student who has a grade equal to or less than 2 points. The 4 in the cumulative column means there are 4 students who have grades equal to or less than 3 points. But note that the grade 4 points also corresponds to a 4 in the cumulative column. Hence we may also say that there are

4 students who have grades equal to or less than 4 points (that is, 0, 1, 2, 3, and 4 points).

The term "equal to or less than" has been abbreviated to "less than" in Table 2.7(b).

Instead of cumulating the frequencies, we may decumulate the frequencies and construct a decumulative frequency table as shown in Table 2.8(a) and (b). For example, the 9 in the decumulative column that corresponds to the 1 point means that there are 9 students who have a grade of more than 1 point.

TABLE 2.8.

(a)		(b)	
X	f	X	Decumulative f
0 points	0	more than 0	10
1 points	1	more than 1	9
2 points	3	more than 2	6
3 points	0	more than 3	6
4 points	0	more than 4	6
5 points	0	more than 5	6
6 points	3	more than 6	3
7 points	2	more than 7	1
8 points	0	more than 8	1
9 points	1	more than 9	0
10 points	0	more than 10	0

Note that we have used the term "more than" instead of "or more." We do this because we used the term "equal to or less than," in the "less than" cumulative frequency table. Hence we have, for example, 1 student who has a grade equal to or less than 1 point, in which case the 1 point is included. If in the "more than" cumulative frequency table we said 1 point "or more," we should also have to include the 1 point. Thus, if the terms "equal to or less than" and "or more" are used, we include the 1 point in both cases. To avoid this duplication, we have used the term "more than" for the decumulative case.

Let us now combine Tables 2.7 and 2.8 as Table 2.9. We have labeled the cumulative and decumulative columns "less than" and "more than," respectively. Note how the sum of the frequencies in the "equal to or less than" and "more than" columns always add up to 10, the total number of students.

Let us now draw a bar chart of Table 2.7, as shown in Fig. 2.9. The

TABLE 2.9.

X	f	Equal To or Less Than	More Than
0 points	0	0	10
1	1	1	9
2	3	4	6
3	0	4	6
4	0	4	6
5	0	4	6
6	3	7	3
7	2	9	1
8	0	9	1
9	1	10	0
10	0	10	0
	10		

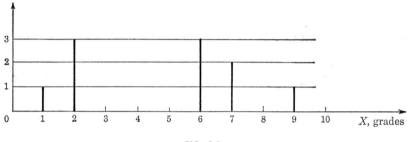

FIG. 2.9.

vertical bars show the frequency densities corresponding to the respective grades. Note that the intervals are points in this case, and the vertical bars are now vertical lines.

Our next task is to draw a cumulative frequency curve, using the "less than" column of the frequency table. This is shown in Fig. 2.10, and the curve shown by the heavy line is the "less than cumulative frequency curve." The height of the curve over a certain grade shows the number of students who have grades equal to or less than that grade. For example, the height of the curve over the grade 6 points is 7. This means that there are 7 students with grades equal to or less than 6 points.

The shape of the cumulative frequency curve shows the distribution of the frequencies. For example, the frequencies of the grades in Table 2.10 are evenly distributed. The "less than" cumulative frequency curve is shown in Fig. 2.11, and as can be seen, the curve ascends evenly, step by step.

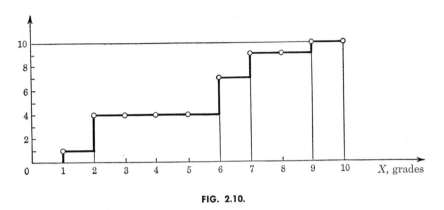

FIG. 2.10.

The grades in Table 2.11 are mostly high. Fig. 2.12 is the corresponding "less than" cumulative frequency curve, and as can be seen, the curve ascends sharply near the upper end of the X scale.

The grades in Table 2.12 are mostly low. Fig. 2.13 is the corresponding "less than" cumulative frequency curve, and as can be seen, the curve ascends sharply near the lower end of the X scale.

Let us summarize our results as follows. Fig. 2.14(a) is a cumulative curve, which shows that the frequencies of the actually observed values are distributed evenly over the range of possible values of the variable X. In Fig. 2.14(b) the frequencies are concentrated near the upper end of the possible values of X, and in Fig. 2.14(c) they are concentrated near the lower end of the possible values of X.

TABLE 2.10.

X	f	Less Than
0	0	0
1	1	1
2	1	2
3	1	3
4	1	4
5	1	5
6	1	6
7	1	7
8	1	8
9	1	9
10	1	10
	10	

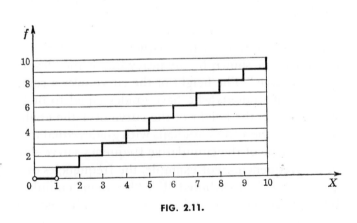

FIG. 2.11.

TABLE 2.11.

X	f	Less Than
0	0	0
1	0	0
2	0	0
3	0	0
4	0	0
5	0	0
6	0	0
7	4	4
8	4	8
9	2	10
	10	

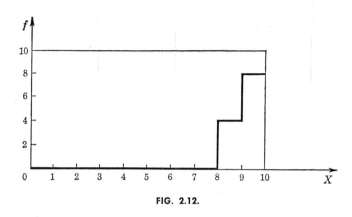

FIG. 2.12.

(ii) Cumulative frequency table—grouped data

Using Table 2.3, we can construct a cumulative frequency table for grouped data, as shown by Table 2.13.

First it is necessary to decide whether to use the lower or upper limits of class intervals as the dividing criteria. Let us use the upper class limits. Then, for example, "less than 39 points" is an abbreviation of "equal to or less than 39 points" and will mean the number of students who have grades up to and including 39 points. In our present case, the number of such students is 4. The number of students who have "less than 49 points" is 10, and so forth.

"More than 39 points" means the number of students who have more

TABLE 2.12.

X	f	Less Than
0	4	4
1	4	8
2	2	10
3	0	10
4	0	10
5	0	10
6	0	10
7	0	10
8	0	10
9	0	10
10	0	10
	10	

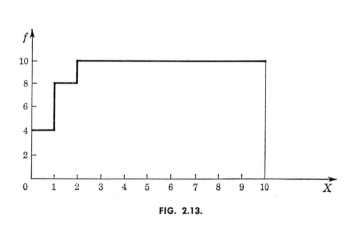

FIG. 2.13.

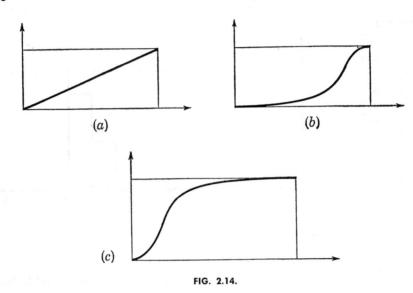

(a)

(b)

(c)

FIG. 2.14.

than 39 points and excludes the students who have 39 points (that is, the number of students who have 40 points or more). In our present case it is 46 students. The number of students who have "more than 49 points" is 40, and so forth.

Note that the corresponding frequencies in the "less than" and "more than" columns add up to 50.

TABLE 2.13. Cumulative Frequency Table
(Using Upper Class Limits)

Class	f	Less Than	More Than
30–39	4	4	46
40–49	6	10	40
50–59	8	18	32
60–69	12	30	20
70–79	9	39	11
80–89	7	46	4
90–99	4	50	0
	50		

(iii) Cumulative frequency curve

Let us now graph the cumulative frequency table. Let the vertical axis show the cumulative frequencies and the horizontal axis show the grades. Then we can plot the "less than" and the "more than" curve as shown in Fig. 2.15.

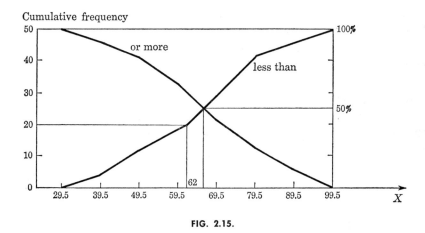

FIG. 2.15.

To graph the "less than" cumulative frequency curve, we first plot the points 29.5, 39.5, . . . , 89.5, and 99.5, which were the dividing points of the bars in the histogram (Fig. 2.1). According to Table 2.11, there are no students with grades less than 29, so we plot a point at height 0 over 29.5. Next, there are 4 students with grades less than 39. So we plot a point at height 4 over 39.5, and similarly for the other points as shown in Fig. 2.15. When these points are linked by straight lines, we have the "less than" cumulative frequency curve.

To graph the "more than" cumulative frequency curve, we note from Table 2.11 that there are 50 students with grades more than (higher than) 29. Recall that the term "more than 29" excludes the grade 29 and starts from 30. So we plot a point at height 50 over 29.5. The next point is at height 46 over 39.5, and so forth. When these points are linked, we obtain the "more than" cumulative frequency curve.

The cumulative frequency curves may be used in two ways. By using the less-than curve, let us illustrate. In the first way we start from the horizontal axis and go to the vertical axis. For example, select a grade 62. Then, as the graph shows, the corresponding frequency is about 20. This means that there are about 20 students with grades equal to or less than 62 points.

In the second way, we start from the vertical axis and go to the horizontal axis. For this method let us convert the cumulative frequencies on the vertical axis into percentages, as shown on the right-hand vertical axis. Then we may find, for example, the grade below which there are 50 percent of the students. The graph shows it to be about 66 points. Similarly, we can find the grade below which there will be 25, 75, or any other percentage of the students. Similar readings can be obtained by using the "more than" curve.

Note that the two curves cross at the 50 percent level. As an exercise, explain why this is so.

(iv)   The Lorenz curve

As an illustration of the cumulative frequency curve, let us discuss the Lorenz curve. Assume there are 10 students and each has $1.00. Then, if we take the cumulative number of dollars on the horizontal axis and the cumulative number of students on the vertical axis, we have Fig. 2.16. Note that we have taken the cumulative frequencies on both axes.

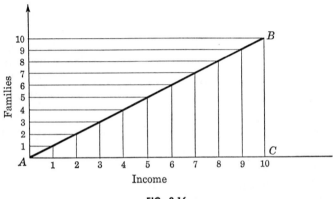

FIG. 2.16.

The curve we have is a straight line AB, which shows that 2 students have a cumulative total of $2.00, 3 students have $3.00, and so forth.

If, on the other hand, the tenth student has $10.00 and the remaining 9 students have nothing, the curve becomes ACB. This shows that up to a total of 9 students, the cumulative income is zero, and then with the addition of the tenth student, the curve jumps up from C to B.

As can be seen, the curve AB shows an equal distribution of income, whereas ACB shows complete inequality. When this is applied to income data, the shape of the Lorenz curve is usually found to be as shown by the curve ADB in Fig. 2.17. The cumulative percent of income is on

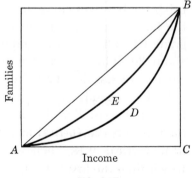

FIG. 2.17.

the horizontal axis and the cumulative percent of families is on the vertical axis.

Suppose AEB is a Lorenz curve after taxes. Then, since it has come closer to AB, we may say that the distribution of income after taxes is more nearly equal than is the distribution of income before taxes.

2.5. Relative Frequencies

(i) Relative frequency table

When the frequencies of a table are expressed in proportional terms, we have a relative frequency table. Since relative frequency tables will be used frequently in subsequent chapters, let us give a brief explanation in this section.

Suppose a coin is tossed 5 times with the results shown in Table 2.14. The relative frequency for heads is $3/5 = 0.6$ and that for tails is $2/5 =$

TABLE 2.14.

Outcome	Frequency	Relative Frequency
Head	3	0.6
Tail	2	0.4
	5	1.0

0.4. We shall compute relative frequencies so that the total of the relative frequencies is always 1.

Table 2.14 may be shown graphically as Fig. 2.18, where the vertical scale is in terms of relative frequencies. The height of the vertical bars shows the relative frequencies. Note that this is *not* a histogram.

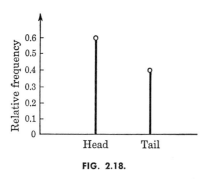

FIG. 2.18.

As another example, let the distribution of misprints per page in a 20-page brochure be as in Table 2.15. Fig. 2.19 is the graph of the table. The height of the bar corresponds to the relative frequencies.

Fig. 2.20 is a histogram made from Fig. 2.19. The vertical dashed lines in Fig. 2.20 correspond to the vertical bars in Fig. 2.18. The width of a bar in Fig. 2.20 is 1. For example, the width of the first bar is from -0.5 to $+0.5$, and the next bar is from 0.5 to 1.5, etc.

TABLE 2.15.

Number of Misprints	f	Relative Frequency
0	8	0.40
1	4	0.20
2	3	0.15
3	2	0.10
4	2	0.10
5	1	0.05
	20	1.00

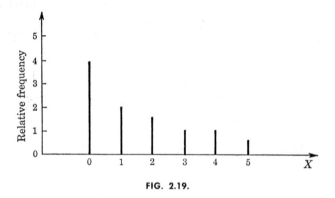

FIG. 2.19.

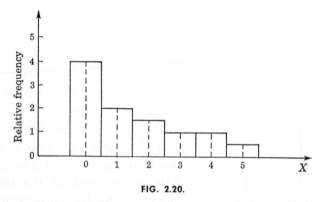

FIG. 2.20.

We have stated previously that the *height* of a bar in a histogram shows frequency per interval, and the *area* shows the frequency in that interval. In our present case, the *height* of a bar shows the relative frequency per interval, and the *area* of a bar shows the relative frequency in that interval. Let us show this relationship in table form, as in Table 2.16.

TABLE 2.16.

Number of Misprints	f	Relative Frequency	Width of Interval	Area, (height) × (width)
0	8	0.40	1	0.40
1	4	0.20	1	0.20
2	3	0.15	1	0.15
3	2	0.10	1	0.10
4	2	0.10	1	0.10
5	1	0.05	1	0.05
	20	1.00		1.00

As the table shows, the total area of the histogram in relative terms is 1. This result will be explained again in Chapter 6 and is fundamental for our discussion after Chapter 6.

(ii)   Unit width intervals

In our example of grades, class intervals were 30–39, 40–49, etc., and the width of an interval was 10 points. In Table 2.15 (showing the number of misprints), the width of intervals was 1 misprint.

In terms of a graph such as Fig. 2.21, we have frequencies on the

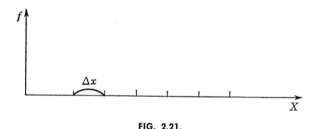

FIG. 2.21.

vertical axis and the variable X (grades, number of misprints) on the horizontal axis. Let us denote an interval on the horizontal axis by Δx. Δ is the Greek letter *delta* and corresponds to d; d in turn may be thought of as an abbreviation of *difference*, and hence Δx may be interpreted as a small difference or small change in X. In the case of grades, Δx was 10 points. In the case of misprints, Δx was 1 misprint. In Table 2.4 of income distribution, Δx was $1000.

Let us now make Δx smaller. In our example of grades, we may let Δx express 1 point. Then $10 \cdot \Delta x = 10$ points expresses the width of the class intervals 30–39, 40–49, etc. In the case of the number of misprints, making Δx smaller than 1 misprint is not very meaningful, and we may consider this to be Δx's smallest unit. As for the income distribution case, we may let $\Delta x = \$1.00$. Then a class interval such as \$2000–\$2999 is expressed as $1000 \cdot \Delta x$.

The point to note is that we may vary the interval Δx.

Now the question that arises is: If the interval Δx may vary, at what width should it be set? Is there a basic unit width?

When we have a continuous variable X, such as weight, speed, or temperature, we may let Δx become as small as we wish. In advanced mathematical statistics where calculus is used, we often let $\Delta x \rightarrow 0$ for purposes of analysis.

However, in practical applications where observed values of X have to be measured, the instruments we use impose a physical limitation on the measurements we can make. For example, a weight scale may give us readings down to only an ounce, a speedometer only in terms of miles, and a thermometer only to a Fahrenheit degree. In such cases, the variable, although theoretically continuous, may be regarded as discrete for practical calculations.

In other words, even though variables such as weight, speed, and temperature may be continuous from a theoretical standpoint, in reality the *possible values* that we can actually measure will be *discrete*.

Based on this practical limitation, we shall define *an interval of unit width* to be equal to the difference between two successive possible values of a variable. Hence, for example, the 1 point of grades, the 1 misprint, or 1 Fahrenheit degree are the unit width intervals Δx of the respective distributions we are considering.

Let us next construct relative frequency tables and histograms, using unit-width intervals. The importance of such frequency tables and histograms is in their relation to probability, which will become clear after Chapter 5. For the moment, let us show only the construction procedure.

(iii)   *Histograms of relative frequencies based on unit width intervals*

By using Table 2.3, we may construct a relative frequency table as shown in Table 2.17. The third column shows the relative frequencies per interval that add up to unity.

The possible values of the variable are, for example, 30, 31, 32, etc., and the difference between two successive values is 1 point. That is, the unit-width interval in this case is $\Delta x = 1$ point, and there are 10 unit widths (10 points) per class interval. This is shown in column 4. Hence

TABLE 2.17.

(1) Class	(2) f	(3) Relative Frequency	(4) Width	(5) Relative Frequency per Unit Width	(6) Area (4) × (5)
30–39	4	0.08	10	0.008	0.08
40–49	6	0.12	10	0.012	0.12
50–59	8	0.16	10	0.016	0.16
60–69	12	0.24	10	0.024	0.24
70–79	9	0.18	10	0.018	0.18
80–89	7	0.14	10	0.014	0.14
90–99	4	0.08	10	0.008	0.08
	50	1.00			1.00

the relative frequencies per unit-width interval is obtained by dividing the relative frequencies by 10. The result is shown in column 5.

By using these relative frequencies per unit width, we may now draw a histogram as shown in Fig. 2.22. A bar of height 0.008 is placed over

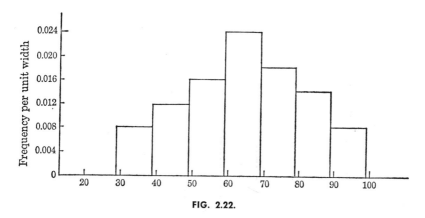

FIG. 2.22.

the interval 29.5–39.5, a bar of height 0.012 is placed over 39.5–49.5, etc.

The area of a bar is (height) × (width). Thus, for the first bar, we have

$$(0.008) \times (10) = 0.08$$

and for the second bar

$$(0.012) \times (10) = 0.12$$

and so forth. The results are given in column 6, which adds up to unity.

Two points should be carefully noted. The first is that the histogram is made from the relative frequencies per unit width, and the second is that because of this construction, the area under the histogram is unity.

Also note that in Table 2.16 we have a special case where the class interval is 1 misprint and the unit width is also 1 misprint; that is, where the class interval is equal to the unit width. Hence the relative frequencies are equal to the relative frequencies per unit width, and they become the height of the bars in the histogram.

Let us give one more example, using unequal class intervals and the distribution of grades in Table 2.18.

TABLE 2.18.

Class	f	Relative Frequency	Width	Relative Frequency per Unit Width	Area
30–39	5	0.25	10	0.025	0.25
40–59	12	0.60	20	0.030	0.60
60–69	3	0.15	10	0.015	0.15
	20	1.00			1.00

Following our previous example, we find the relative frequencies, the width of the intervals, the relative frequency per unit width, and the area. Figure 2.23 is the frequency histogram based on the relative fre-

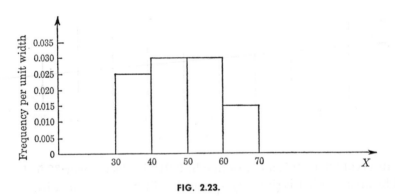

FIG. 2.23.

quency per unit width, and as the last column in Table 2.18 shows, the area of this histogram is unity, 1.

MEASURES OF LOCATION

3 In Chapter 2 the question was asked: How well did the students do in the economics examination? To answer this, the raw data were organized into a frequency table (Table 2.3), which showed the distribution of the frequencies of grades. This distribution of frequencies was called a frequency distribution and was shown graphically by a histogram, frequency polygon, or frequency curve. The frequency distribution and its graphical presentations gave us information about the performance of students in their economics exam.

Now suppose we have two classes *A* and *B,* which have taken an economics exam. The results are shown schematically as in Fig. 3.1

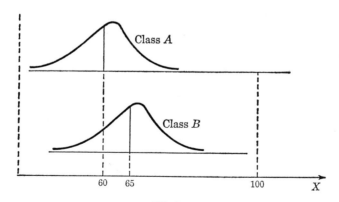

FIG. 3.1.

where the scale of the variable X (grades) is common to both frequency curves. Let us assume that the grades in both classes have a similar distribution, as shown in the figure. But note that the frequency curve of class B is to the right of that of class A. The average grade in class A is 60 and that in B is 65.

The point to note is that we may differentiate these two similar distributions by saying that the distribution of grades of class A has an average of 60 points and that of B has an average of 65 points. We are representing the frequency distribution of class A by the single value 60 and that of B by 65.

As another example, consider the score of a student A at a rifle shooting contest. Let the scores be from 0 (the edge of the target) to 10 (the center of the target). The variable X is the score of a shot, and it has 11 possible values, namely 0, 1, 2, . . . , 10. Suppose the student shoots 20 times. Then the variable X has 20 actually observed values, and we shall have a frequency distribution of X.

To describe the shooting performance of this student A, we may use the frequency distribution of X. However, we may also use the average score to represent his shooting performance. That is, we may use the average of X to represent the distribution of X. If there is a student B, and we wish to compare the scores of A and B, we may compare the average scores of A and B instead of the frequency distributions of their scores.

Our problem in this and the next chapter is to find characteristics, such as the average mentioned above, that will concisely characterize (or locate) a frequency distribution. If we can find adequate characteristics that will characterize a frequency distribution, we may use these characteristics, instead of the frequency distribution itself, to explain the performance of the students in an economics exam or the shooting performance of a student.

The characteristics in which we shall be interested are the measures of location (Chapter 3) and measures of dispersion (Chapter 4) of a distribution. Measures of location will be divided into measures of central location and other measures of location. By measures of central location we mean central points of a frequency distribution that will characterize the distribution. These will be the arithmetic mean, the median, and the mode of a distribution. Other measures of location that we shall not consider are quartiles and percentiles of a distribution. But before considering these measures of location, let us first digress for a moment and define quantitative and qualitative variables.

A *quantitative variable* is one expressed numerically. For example, the variables weight, height, speed, rent, and income are quantitative variables.

A *qualitative variable* is one expressed by a nonnumerical property. For example, heads or tails of a coin, defect or nondefect of a light bulb, poor, average, or superior of a painting, and satisfaction or dissatisfaction of a customer are the possible outcomes of qualitative variables.

Let us define one more term, namely, a parameter of a distribution. A *parameter* of a distribution is a value (a constant) of the distribution that characterizes the distribution. The mean, median, and mode are parameters of a distribution.

3.1. The Arithmetic Mean

Table 2.3 shows the frequency distribution of grades of 50 students (say, of class A). Suppose there is another class B, with 50 students who have a similar distribution of grades. That is, the shapes of the frequency curves look alike. You are asked to compare and describe the grades of the two classes. This may be done by directly comparing the two frequency distributions. However, since the two distributions are similar, may we not select some specific value (parameter) of the distribution and compare these parameters instead of the frequency distribution? The answer is, "yes."

If a frequency distribution can be represented by some central value, we may compare the central values of the two distributions instead of the distributions themselves. One such central value is the arithmetic mean. Let us first define the arithmetic mean before proceeding with our discussion.

Let X be a variable and $x_1, x_2, \ldots, x_n$ be the n actually observed values of X. Then the arithmetic mean of the frequency distribution is defined as

$$\bar{X} = \frac{\text{sum of } n \text{ values}}{n}$$

where $\bar{X}$ represents the arithmetic mean. By using symbols, the definition may be expressed as

$$(1) \qquad \bar{X} = \frac{x_1 + x_2 + \cdots + x_n}{n} = \frac{1}{n} \sum_{i=1}^{n} x_i$$

The arithmetic mean is also simply called the *mean,* or the *average.*

Example 1.   Let X be the variable weight (lb.) of 3 students, and the actually observed values be

$$x_1 = 120, \quad x_2 = 130, \quad x_3 = 140$$

Then the mean $\bar{X}$ is

$$\bar{X} = \frac{1}{n} \sum_{i=1}^{n} x_i = \frac{1}{3}(120 + 130 + 140) = 130 \text{ lb.}$$

Example 2.   The $\bar{X}$ of the 50 grades of Table 2.3 is

$$\bar{X} = \frac{1}{50}(60 + 33 + \cdots + 89 + 88) = 65.2$$

Suppose the mean of the grades of the 50 students in class B is 70. Then, since the two distributions are similar, we may compare the frequency distributions of grades of classes A and B by comparing the means 65.2 points and 70 points. The frequency distributions have been represented by a single value (a parameter). The means, of course, do not give us as much information as the frequency distribution, but it is much simpler.

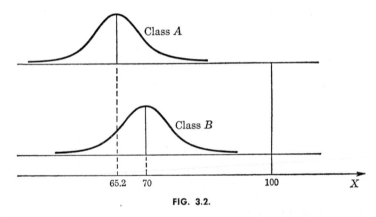

FIG. 3.2.

Let us show the situation schematically with graphs. Figure 3.2 shows the frequency distributions (frequency curves) of classes A and B. The horizontal scale of the variable X is common to both frequency curves. Assuming that these curves are similar to each other (say for simplicity that both are normal distributions), we may differentiate the two by their means, 65.2 points and 70 points.

In similar manner, if we have classes A, B, C, D, E, and the distributions of grades are normal for each class, we may differentiate these five normal distributions by their respective means.

If the distributions are not similar (one may be bell shaped and the other bimodal), it will probably be necessary to compare the two distributions to make a comparison.

Geometrically, the mean of a frequency distribution is the center of gravity. If the frequency curve in Fig. 3.3 is considered as a plate of some kind, it will balance at the mean.

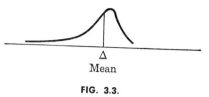

FIG. 3.3.

A main characteristic of the mean for purposes of application is that it must be affected by all the actually observed values. As a result, it will also be affected by extreme values. If there are 5 students with grades

$$60, 60, 60, 60, 100$$

the mean is

$$\bar{X} = \frac{1}{5} (60 + 60 + 60 + 60 + 100) = 68$$

Evidently the single grade 100 has raised the mean by 8 points. If someone were to ask, "what is the average of the 5 students?" and he is told that it is 68 points, he would probably assume that the grades were scattered around 68 points. But as computed above, the 68 points do not adequately represent the distribution of the grades.

Is there a measure of central location that will represent the frequency distribution more adequately than does the mean when the distribution has extreme values and is skewed? In many cases the median discussed in Section 3.2 will be more appropriate. But before considering the median, let us discuss several computational formulas for the mean.

Note also that the mean has other desirable mathematical properties, which will be discussed as the occasion arises.

(i) Ungrouped data—unweighted case

This is the basic formula (1) previously expressed as the definition of arithmetic mean.

(ii) Ungrouped data—weighted case

Suppose a student has taken three tests and earned grades of 50, 80, and 70. The first test took a half-hour, the second took 1 hr., and the third took $1\frac{1}{2}$ hr. In finding the average grade, this student would probably attach different degrees of importance to the three tests. If left to himself, he might rationalize in some way that the first and last tests were of no importance and only the middle test had importance.

However, another student with grades 90, 50, 70 may argue that only the first test was important and the other two were of no importance.

In deciding the relative importance of these tests, we must be "reasonable." Unfortunately, what is reasonable to one person may not be reasonable to another. Nevertheless, in many practical cases, it is possible to decide the relative importance of events (the results of the test) that will be acceptable to a majority of people. In our present case, let us suppose the instructor decides that the relative importance of the tests will be according to the lengths of the tests, that is, $1:2:3$. Then the weighted average is found as shown in Table 3.1.

TABLE 3.1.

(1) Grades	(2) Weights	(3) (1) × (2)
50	1	50
80	2	160
70	3	210
	6	420

Weighted average $= 420/6 = 70$ points.

By using symbols, we may define the weighted arithmetic mean as

$$(2) \qquad \bar{X} = \frac{x_1 w_1 + x_2 w_2 + x_3 w_3}{w_1 + w_2 + w_3} = \frac{\Sigma\, x_i w_i}{\Sigma\, w_i}$$

where $x_1 = 50$, $x_2 = 80$, $x_3 = 70$, and the weights are $w_1 = 1$, $w_2 = 2$, and $w_3 = 3$.

Examples of uses of weights in computing averages may be found in various index numbers. Index numbers are discussed in Chapter 11, but for the moment let us give only some actual examples of weights without computing the index numbers.

Example 3. Dow-Jones commodity-futures price index. Commodity weights based on proportionate value, 1927–1931, were

Wheat	19.5
Corn	8
Oats	5
Rye	4
Wool tops	5.5
Cotton	23.0
Cottonseed oil	4.5
Coffee	7
Sugar	8.5
Cocoa	5
Rubber	6
Hides	4
	100.0

The weights in the table are expressed in percentage terms. The price index is a weighted arithmetic mean, with certain adjustments.

Example 4. Consumer price index, relative importance of major groups.

Groups	1947–1949	1950 January	1952 December
Food	42.7	33.3	29.9
Apparel	12.6	12.8	9.4
Housing	26.9	25.1	32.2
Transportation	7.1	11.4	11.3
Medical care	3.3	5.2	4.8
Personal care	2.5	2.4	2.1
Reading and recreation	2.8	5.8	5.3
Other goods and services	2.1	4.0	5.0

These are the weights used to calculate the consumer price index (or cost of living index), and they are expressed in percentage terms. The consumer price index is a weighted arithmetic mean, with certain adjustments. As the table shows, the weights have been revised every several years to reflect the changes in the consumer's spending pattern. The drop in the importance of food as an expense in the consumer's budget and a rise in the importance of expenses on various services is a salient feature of these weights, which are expressed in percentage terms.

Let us construct an artificial example and show that it makes no difference whether weights are in percentage terms, proportional terms, or some other form. Suppose three tests were taken, with results as shown in the table here.

(1) Grades	(2) Weights	(3) Proportional Weights	(4) Percentage Weights	(5) (1) × (3)
50	10	0.20	20	10
80	15	0.30	30	24
70	25	0.50	50	35
	50	1.00	100	69

The weighted average grade is, using the proportional weights of column 3,

$$\bar{X} = \frac{69}{1} = 69 \text{ points}$$

We divide by 1 because the sum of the weights is 1.

If we use column 4 as weights, we have

$$\bar{X} = \frac{6900}{100} = 69 \text{ points}$$

If we use column 2, we have

$$\bar{X} = \frac{3450}{50} = 69 \text{ points}$$

When proportional weights are used, the sum of the weights is unity, and this eliminates the necessity of dividing by the sum of weights. In our subsequent discussions we shall mainly use this type of weighting procedure.

(iii) Grouped data case

When data are given as a frequency table, the individual values of the variable are unknown, and thus we cannot use the previous formulas for the mean. But by making an assumption, discussed below, we can calculate the mean of a distribution, which in most cases is a good approximation of the true mean. An example follows.

TABLE 3.2.

Lb.	f	m	fm	Actual Values	True Mean	$f\times$(Mean)
30–40	3	35	105	32, 33, 37	34	102
40–50	2	45	90	44, 48	46	92
	5		195		194	194

Let X be the variable weight with a frequency distribution as shown in Table 3.2. We make the assumption that the midpoint of the class interval adequately represents the mean value of that class. For example, if the three actual values in the class 30–40 lb. are 32, 33, and 37, the true mean is $(32 + 33 + 37)/3 = 34$ lb. The assumption is that the midpoint 35 is a good approximation of the true mean 34 lb. of that class.

By using this assumption, we can further assume that $3 \times 35 = 105$ is a good approximation of the sum of the values in that class. We see that the true sum is $32 + 33 + 37 = 102$ lb., and there is a discrepancy of $105 - 102 = 3$ lb.

By applying this reasoning to each class, we can find a good approximation of the sum of the values in each class if we multiply the midpoint by the frequency for each class. In our example we have 105 and 90.

Then, by summing these results, we obtain a good approximation of the sum of *all* the values of X. We have $105 + 90 = 195$. As shown in Table 3.1, the true total is 194.

The mean of X is then obtained by dividing this total by the total number of frequencies. We have

$$\frac{195}{5} = 39 \text{ lb.}$$

The true mean is

$$\frac{194}{5} = 38.8 \text{ lb.}$$

The assumption that the midpoint of the class interval adequately represents the mean value of that class interval is in turn based on the assumption that the values are distributed fairly evenly throughout the interval. When a large number of frequencies occur, this assumption is usually acceptable.

Let us now convert our discussion into a formula. The mid-points are $m_1 = 35$ and $m_2 = 45$. The frequencies are $f_1 = 3$ and $f_2 = 2$. Thus the mean of X is

$$\bar{X} = \frac{m_1 f_1 + m_2 f_2}{f_1 + f_2} = \frac{35 \times 3 + 45 \times 2}{3 + 2}$$

$$= \frac{195}{5} = 39 \text{ lb.}$$

By using the summation notation, this becomes

$$\bar{X} = \frac{\sum\limits_{i=1}^{2} m_i f_i}{\sum\limits_{i=1}^{2} f_i}$$

In general, when we have n class intervals,

(3)
$$\bar{X} = \frac{\sum\limits_{i=1}^{n} m_i f_i}{\sum\limits_{i=1}^{n} f_i}$$

Then the mean of the grades is

$$\bar{X} = \frac{\sum m_i f_i}{\sum f_i} = \frac{3255}{50} = 65.1 \text{ points}$$

where $i = 1, 2, \ldots, 7$, that is, it is the number of class intervals. The true mean calculated on page 38 was 65.2 points.

Example 5. The frequency table shows the distribution of grades of students.

Worksheet 3.1.

Class	f	m	fm
30–39 points	4	34.5	138.0
40–49	6	44.5	267.0
50–59	8	54.5	436.0
60–69	12	64.5	774.0
70–79	9	74.5	670.5
80–89	7	84.5	591.5
90–99	4	94.5	378.0
	$\overline{50}$		$\overline{3255.0}$

(iv) Short method of calculation

Calculations may be simplified by shifting the origin. Let us explain this by an example of ungrouped data. Consider three numbers, 1, 2, and 3. The mean is $\bar{X} = 2$. Let $A = 5$ be called the assumed mean, and subtract and add this to each number:

$$1 - 5 + 5, \quad 2 - 5 + 5, \quad 3 - 5 + 5$$

Then, obviously, the mean is still 2. That is,

$$\bar{X} = \frac{(1 - 5 + 5) + (2 - 5 + 5) + (3 - 5 + 5)}{3}$$

$$= \frac{(5 + 5 + 5) + (1 - 5) + (2 - 5) + (3 - 5)}{3}$$

$$= 5 + \frac{(1 - 5) + (2 - 5) + (3 - 5)}{3}$$

$$= 5 + (2 - 5) = 2$$

This may be rewritten in symbols as

$$\bar{X} = \frac{(A + A + A) + (x_1 - A) + (x_2 - A) + (x_3 - A)}{3}$$

$$= A + \frac{d'_1 + d'_2 + d'_3}{n} = A + \frac{\Sigma d'_i}{n}$$

where d'_i is the difference between the individual values x_i and the assumed mean A. The result may be stated as a formula:

(4)
$$\bar{X} = A + \frac{\Sigma d'_i}{n}$$

Apply this to the following example and find the mean of 1561, 1562, and 1563. Let $A = 1560$; then

$$d'_1 = x_1 - A = 1561 - 1560 = 1$$

$$d'_2 = x_2 - A = 1562 - 1560 = 2$$

$$d'_3 = x_3 - A = 1563 - 1560 = 3$$

Then $\bar{X}$ is

$$\bar{X} = A + \frac{\Sigma d'}{n} = 1560 + \frac{1 + 2 + 3}{3} = 1562$$

When applying this property to *grouped data,* formula (3) becomes

(5)
$$\bar{X} = A + \frac{\sum\limits_{i=1}^{n} f_i d_i}{\Sigma f_i} \times c$$

where A is the assumed mean; d_i is called the class deviation (and is different than d'_i); and c is the class interval. Since this formula is derived from formula (3), the answer obtained by either method is the same.

Let us illustrate its use by an example. Consider the frequency distribution of the grades of students again as shown in Worksheet 3.2.

Worksheet 3.2.

Class	f	m	d	fd
30–39 points	4		−3	−12
40–49	6		−2	−12
50–59	8		−1	− 8 (−32)
60–69	12	64.5	0	0
70–79	9		1	9
80–89	7		2	14
90–99	4		3	12 (+35)
	50			3

One of the midpoints is selected and designated as the assumed mean A. Let us select 64.5 points. Any midpoint may be selected for A, but it will be convenient to select the midpoint where computations are less cumbersome. This point is usually near the middle of the distribution so that the $+fd$'s and $-fd$'s, when summed, will approximately cancel each other, as in Worksheet 3.2 (where we have $+35$ and -32). The class deviation d_i is the number of class deviations from the assumed mean A. Since d_i is set equal to 0 at A, we take minus class deviations up in the direction where grade points are lower and plus deviations down in the direction where the grade points are higher. For instance, the 30–39 class interval is -3 class deviations away from A.

Thus, after working out the worksheet, we find

$$\bar{X} = A + \frac{\Sigma f_i d_i}{\Sigma f_i} \times c = 64.5 + \frac{3}{50} \times 10 = 64.5 + 0.6 = 65.1$$

which is the same answer as that obtained from formula (4).

Select a different A and recalculate. You should get the same answer.

REFERENCE

Formula (5) is derived by use of the following simple illustration. The mean according to formula (3) is

$$\bar{X} = \frac{f_1 m_1 + f_2 m_2 + f_3 m_3}{f_1 + f_2 + f_3}$$

Class	f	m	d	
10–20	f_1	m_1	d_1	$m_1 = A + d_1 c$
20–30	f_2	m_2	d_2	$m_2 = A$
30–40	f_3	m_3	d_3	$m_3 = A + d_3 c$

Let c be the class interval, that is, $c = 10$. Select the midpoint $m_2 = 25$ as the assumed mean A. Then $m_1 = 15$ can be shown as

$$m_1 = A + d_1 c = 25 + (-1)(10) = 15$$

where $d_1 = -1$. The $m_3 = 35$ is

$$m_3 = A + d_3 c = 25 + (1)(10) = 35$$

If we let $d_2 = 0$, then the mean becomes

$$\bar{X} = \frac{m_1 f_1 + m_2 f_2 + m_3 f_3}{f_1 + f_2 + f_3}$$

$$= \frac{f_1(A + d_1 c) + f_2(A + d_2 c) + f_3(A + d_3 c)}{f_1 + f_2 + f_3}$$

$$= \frac{A\,(f_1 + f_2 + f_3) + (f_1 d_1 + f_2 d_2 + f_3 d_3)c}{f_1 + f_2 + f_3}$$

$$= A + \frac{\Sigma\, f_i d_i}{\Sigma\, f_i} \times c$$

3.2.   The Median

Suppose you are interested in describing the income of graduates of K University, five years after graduation. Let X be the variable income. Suppose further that the frequency distribution of incomes shows that most of the graduates have an income around $7,000, but that there are a few who have incomes in excess of $50,000. That is, the distribution is skewed to the right. It is known that K University always has a number of students whose parents own large companies, and so upon graduation they immediately become executives and receive large salaries. Under such circumstances, is the mean an adequate measure of central location to represent this frequency distribution?

A main characteristic of the mean is that it is affected by all the values. In particular, it is affected by extreme values. Assume four graduates of a school with the following incomes:

$$\$6,000, \quad \$6,000, \quad \$6,000, \quad \$42,000$$

The mean is

$$\bar{X} = \frac{1}{4}\,(6,000 + 6,000 + 6,000 + 42,000) = \$15,000$$

The mean of the first three incomes is $6,000, but with the inclusion of the extremely high income of $42,000, the mean becomes $15,000. But, as is seen, this mean of $15,000 does not adequately characterize the frequency distribution of incomes.

In such cases where the frequency distribution is skewed and has extreme values, a measure of central location called a *median* is in many cases more suitable. First let us define this parameter.

A *median* of a frequency distribution is a value that divides the frequency distribution into two equal parts. Let us first illustrate with a theoretical distribution. Figures 3.4(a) and (b) show a continuous frequency curve and its corresponding cumulative frequency curve. A median is a value that divides the area of the frequency curve (Fig. 3.4(a)) into two equal parts. In the graph of the cumulative fre-

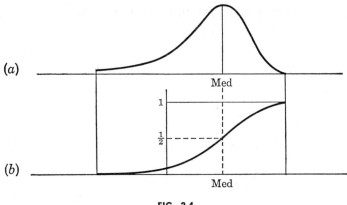

FIG. 3.4.

quency curve, a value of X that corresponds to the point where the curve is of height $\frac{1}{2}$, is a median. Graphically, this is found at the intersection of the horizontal line that is of height $\frac{1}{2}$ (that is, 50 percent) and the cumulative frequency curve.

The student may have noticed that we have said *a* median instead of *the* median. The distinction occurs when there are situations where a median is indeterminate. Suppose we have the following four incomes (Fig. 3.5):

$$\$5, \quad 6, \quad 7, \quad 8$$

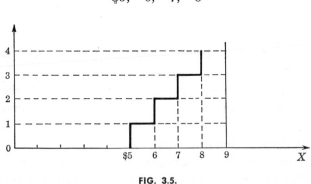

FIG. 3.5.

As the cumulative graph shows, every value between $6.00 and $7.00 is a median. In such cases, the midvalue $(6 + 7)/2 = \$6.5$ is taken as the median. This is just a convention that is usually adopted.

As has been mentioned, a median may be indeterminate, and therefore the application of the preceding definition must be exercised with caution.

Several other points should be noted. Suppose we have five persons with the following incomes (Fig. 3.6):

$$\$2, \quad 3, \quad 4, \quad 5, \quad 6$$

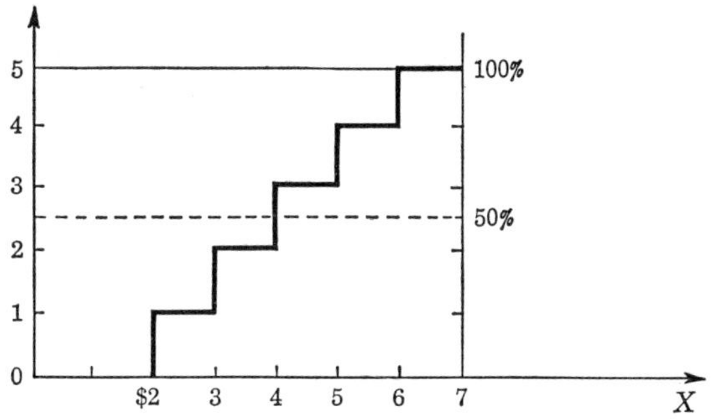

FIG. 3.6.

In this group, the median is $4.00. Although a person cannot be split in half, we may think that half of the person with $4.00 belongs to the lower half of the distribution, and the other half of him belongs to the upper half.

Suppose we have seven persons with incomes (Fig. 3.7):

$$\$3, \quad 4, \quad 5, \quad \underline{5}, \quad 5, \quad 6, \quad 7$$

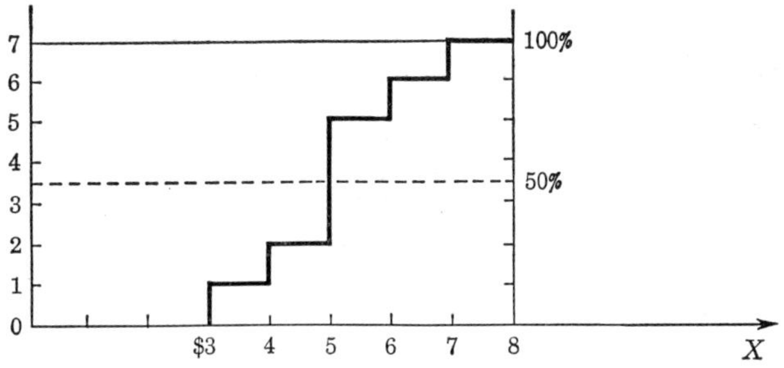

FIG. 3.7.

As the graph shows, the median is $5.00. But it is the second $5.00 underlined that divides the distribution into two equal parts. We may think that half of this person with the second $5.00 belongs to the lower half of the distribution, while the other half belongs to the upper half of the distribution.

For grouped data, we use linear interpolation. For example, if we use our previous frequency distribution of grades, we know (since we have 50 students) that the median value of the variable X (grade point) will be between the 25th and 26th student. It will be the 25.5th student. To find the 25.5th student, we first have to find in which class the 25th and 26th students will be. Since there are 18 students up to the 50–59 class and 30 students up to the 60–69 class, the 25th and 26th students are in the 60–69 class. Secondly, since there are 18 students up to this class, the 25.5th student will be the 7.5th student (25.5 − 18 = 7.5) in this 60–69 class. If we assume that the grades of the students are evenly distributed in this class, then (since there are

TABLE 3.3.

Class	f		
30–39	4		
40–49	6	7 students	
50–59	8		
60–69	12	19, 20, 21, 22, 23, 24, 25, 26, 27, 28, 29, 30	
70–79	9		
80–89	7		
90–99	4		
	50		

12 students in this class interval) the grade of the 7.5th student will correspond to the grade that is 7.5/12 of the way between 60–69. Because the class interval is 10 points, we have

$$60 + 10 \times \frac{7.5}{12} = 66.25$$

Thus 66.25 points is considered the median of the grades.

Illustrations of the use of the median may be found in income statistics. Let us give an illustration. Table 3.4 is the mean and median income of spending units by occupational groups.

As the table shows, the mean income is higher than the median income. We may interpret this to imply that there are extremely high incomes pulling the mean up. That is, the distribution of incomes is skewed to the right. A visual check shows that the discrepancy between the mean and median income of the managerial spending units is larger than that of the clerical-sales spending units. We may interpret this to mean that the distribution of income of managers is more skewed

TABLE 3.4.

	1950	1955	1958
Mean income			
All spending units	$3520	$4650	$5150
Managerial	6580	8280	9170
Clerical-sales	3910	4980	5600
Median income			
All spending units	3000	3960	4400
Managerial	4950	6760	7690
Clerical-sales	3200	4300	5010

SOURCE: *Statistical Abstract of the U.S.*, U.S. Department of Commerce, 1961, pp. 323, Table No. 441.

to the right than that of clerks and salesmen. That is, there are extremely high managerial salaries pulling up the managerial mean incomes.

3.3.   The Mode

A third measure of location of a frequency distribution is the mode of a distribution. The *mode* of a distribution is any value at which the frequency density is at a maximum. Or we may say that it is any value of the variable that occurs most frequently. The definition implies that if the frequency curve has one peak (that is, one maximum) as in Fig. 3.8(a), there is only one mode, whereas if the frequency curve

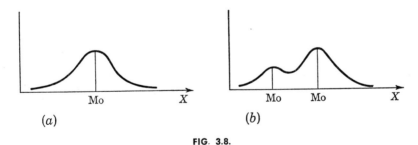

(a)   (b)

FIG. 3.8.

has two (or more) peaks (that is, two or more maximums) as in Fig. 3.8(b), the distribution has two (or more) modes. On the other hand, if we have a rectangular distribution, there is no mode. To illustrate this, let us suppose that a student took five economics tests during the semester, with the results:

$$60, \quad 75, \quad 75, \quad 80, \quad 90$$

Then the mode is 75 points, which occurs twice, whereas the other values occur only once.

If the results of the tests are

$$60, \quad 74, \quad 82, \quad 85, \quad 90$$

there is no mode.

For grouped data, there are several ways of computing the mode. But it is usually sufficient for practical purposes to use the midpoint of the modal class. Let us use the distribution of grade points and illustrate. From Table 3.5(a) we see that the class interval 60–69 has the most frequencies. This class is called the *modal class*. In some cases, it will suffice to say that the mode is between 60 and 69. But there may be occasions when we need to decide what value between 60 and 69 we shall take as the mode. For most practical cases it will be sufficient to take the midpoint, which is 64.5.

TABLE 3.5.

(a)		(b)	
Class	f	Class	f
30–39	4	30–39	2
40–49	6	40–49	10
50–59	8	50–59	6
60–69	12	60–69	12
70–79	9	70–79	9
80–89	7	80–89	7
90–99	4	90–99	4
	50		50

In Table 3.5(b) there are two modal classes, 40–49 and 60–69.

In dealing with grouped data, the mode is affected by the way class intervals are taken. When the class intervals become very small, a mode may disappear. When the class intervals are unequal, such as in Table 2.4 of the distribution of income, the intervals need to be converted on a per interval basis; that is, we need to find the frequency densities before determining the mode.

The characteristics of a mode are that it is easy to compute and may be applied to qualitative as well as quantitative data. One may be investigating, for example, consumer preferences of five brands of soap, $A, B, C, D,$ and E. Let the preferences be

$$A = 20$$
$$B = 30$$
$$C = 25$$
$$D = 50$$
$$E = 40$$

In this case, the modal preference is soap D. Note that the above preferences do not show two modes; that is, B is not a second mode. This is because we may rearrange the sequence of soaps in any order we wish.

As another example of the application of the mode, assume a store wishes to stock men's shirts. An investigation shows that size 16 has the greatest demand. This is the modal value of the distribution of shirt sizes.

As another example, consider the number of passengers who use a subway in a certain city. Let the variable X be the hour of the day and f be the number of passengers. An investigation may show that there are two modes, one in the morning around 8:30 A.M. and one in the evening around 5:30 P.M. We have a bimodal distribution.

The mean and the median were of interest in locating the distribution. That is, the interest was in characterizing the distribution. The mode, as the examples above show, is usually of interest in itself. We are interested in the most typical value, or the most prevalent value, in a distribution.

3.4.   Comparison of the Mean, Median, and Mode

The relationship between the mean, median, and mode when we have a unimodal frequency distribution is shown in Fig. 3.9.

When a distribution is symmetrical, the mean, median, and mode coincide. When a distribution is skewed to the right, then (Fig. 3.9(b))

mean (68 points) > median (65) > mode (63)

For example, income distribution is frequently skewed to the right, where the majority of families have incomes between \$4000 and \$8000, and then the number of families tapers off as the income goes up. In this case, the mean is pulled up by the extreme high incomes and the relation among the three measures is as stated above.

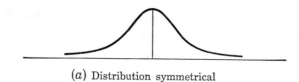

(a) Distribution symmetrical

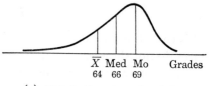

(b) Distribution skewed to right   *(c)* Distribution skewed to left

FIG. 3.9.

When a distribution is skewed to the left, then (Fig. 3.9(c))

$$\text{mode } (69) > \text{median } (66) > \text{mean } (64)$$

The grades of a class where the majority have high grades with a few low grades is an example. Here the mean is pulled down below the median by the extremely low grades.

Note that the median is always in the middle. Another way to remember these relations is that the mean, median, and mode are in the order in which they appear in a dictionary when the distribution is skewed to the left, and the order reverses itself when skewed to the right.

Conversely, when given the mean and median of a unimodal distribution, we can determine whether it is skewed to the left or right. When mean > median, it is skewed to the right; when median > mean, it is skewed to the left. This relationship was used when explaining Table 3.3.

3.5. The Geometric Mean

Three measures of location, the mean, median, and mode have been discussed. By the mean we meant the arithmetic mean. However, there are two other means that are used occasionally in business and economics. They are the geometric mean and the harmonic mean. Of these two, the geometric mean is more important and is used for averaging rates of change and constructing index numbers. We shall discuss only the geometric mean.

(i) Definition

Let us first define the geometric mean (GM) by use of a simple example, and then explain its application. If we have three numbers, 1, 3, and 9, the GM is defined as

$$GM = \sqrt[3]{1 \times 3 \times 9} = \sqrt[3]{27} = \sqrt[3]{3^3} = 3$$

In general, if we have n numbers, the geometric mean is defined as

$$(1) \qquad GM = \sqrt[n]{X_1 \cdot X_2 \cdots \cdot X_n}$$

Logarithms are used to calculate the nth root. For instance, if we have three numbers, 2, 4, 8, then

$$GM = \sqrt[3]{2 \times 4 \times 8}$$

By taking the logarithms on both sides, we find

$$\log\ GM = \log \sqrt[3]{2 \times 4 \times 8} = \log(2 \times 4 \times 8)^{\frac{1}{3}}$$

$$= \frac{1}{3}\ [\log 2 + \log 4 + \log 8]$$

$$\log 2 = 0.3010$$
$$\log 4 = 0.6021$$
$$\log 8 = \underline{0.9031}$$
$$1.8062$$

$$\log GM = \frac{1}{3}(1.8062) = 0.60206$$

Therefore $\qquad\qquad GM = 4$

Formula (1) can be written in terms of logarithms as

$$(2) \qquad\qquad \log GM = \frac{1}{n} \Sigma \log X_i$$

(ii) Applications—averaging rates of change and the compound interest formula

Assume the rate of production has increased 25 percent from the first year to the second and 40 percent from the second to the third year, as follows:

1st	year,	100	
2nd	year,	125	25 percent change (increase)
3rd	year,	175	40 percent change (increase)

What is the average rate of increase during these two years? We see that the second year is 125 percent of the first year and the third year is 140 percent of the second year. Thus

$$\text{GM} = \sqrt{1.25 \times 1.40} = 1.323$$

or the average rate of increase is 32.3 percent.

If we square both sides of the above equation, it becomes

$$(\sqrt{1.25 \times 1.40})^2 = (1.323)^2$$
$$1.25 \times 1.40 = (1 + .323)^2$$

Now, $1.25 \times 1.40 = 1.75$. Then

$$1.75 = (1 + 0.323)^2$$

Let $P_2 = 1.75$, $P_0 = 1$, and $r = 0.323$. Then the above equation may be written as

$$P_2 = P_0 (1 + r)^2$$

which is the familiar compound-interest formula.

We have shown that the average rate of change r found by the geometric mean is the rate of interest in the compound-interest formula.

This result may be stated in general terms as follows: If an initial investment of P_0 (dollars) becomes P_n (dollars) after n years, the geometric mean r of the rates of increase of the n years is found by solving

$$(3) \qquad P_n = P_0 (1 + r)^n$$

Let $P_n = \$175$, $P_0 = \$100$, and $n = 2$ years. Then

$$175 = 100 (1 + r)^2$$

$$(1 + r)^2 = \frac{175}{100}$$

$$r = \sqrt{\frac{175}{100}} - 1$$

where $\sqrt{175/100}$ is calculated by logarithms. We find

$$r = 1.323 - 1 = 0.323$$

Thus $r = 0.323$, or 32.3 percent, is the geometric mean of the rates of increase of the $n = 2$ years. In terms of the compound-interest formula, $r = 32.3$ percent is the rate of interest at which $P_0 = \$100$ is compounded $n = 2$ years.

In general, we may write

(4)
$$r = \sqrt[n]{\frac{P_n}{P_0}} - 1$$

Example.   The GNP has grown from \$400,000,000,000 in 1956 to \$500,-
000,000 in 1960. What is the average rate of growth? Using formulas (3) and
(4), we have

$$500 = 400 (1 + r)^4$$

$$r = \sqrt[4]{\frac{500}{400}} - 1$$

Let
$$x = \sqrt[4]{\frac{500}{400}} = \sqrt[4]{\frac{5}{4}}$$

$$\log x = \frac{1}{4} \log \frac{5}{4} = \frac{1}{4} [\log 5 - \log 4]$$

$$= \frac{1}{4} [0.6990 - 0.6021]$$

$$= \frac{1}{4} \times 0.0869 = 0.0217$$

Therefore
$$x = 1.052$$

Thus r becomes

$$r = 1.052 - 1 = 0.052$$

That is, the average rate of growth is 5.2 percent annually.

REFERENCE

(iii) Discounting, capitalization

From the compound interest formula (3), we have

(5)
$$P_0 = \frac{P_n}{(1 + r)^n}$$

This may be interpreted as follows: If the future income is P_n dollars, and
the present rate of interest is $100r$ percent, then the present value of the P_n
dollars will be P_0 dollars, as given by the above formula. For example, if we
have a machine that has a life of 25 years and is expected to yield a net
income of \$100 per year, and at the end of 25 years the machine becomes

worthless, then the machine is worth (that is, its present value is)

$$\frac{100}{1+r} + \frac{100}{(1+r)^2} + \frac{100}{(1+r)^3} + \cdots + \frac{100}{(1+r)^{25}}$$

This process of obtaining the present value of future income by use of the interest rate is called *discounting*.

Now let us assume we have a piece of land that will give us a net income of $100 per year *forever*. Then the present value of this piece of land is

$$\frac{100}{1+r} + \frac{100}{(1+r)^2} + \cdots + \frac{100}{(1+r)^n} + \cdots$$

It can be shown by use of mathematics pertaining to series that since

$$\frac{1}{(1+r)^n} < 1$$

this sums up to

$$\$100 \times \left\{ \frac{1 - \left(\frac{1}{1+r}\right)^\infty}{1 - \frac{1}{1+r}} - 1 \right\}$$

This $[1/(1+r)]^\infty$ is, for practical purposes, equal to zero. Thus

$$\$100 \times \left\{ \frac{1}{1 - \frac{1}{1+r}} - 1 \right\} = 100 \times \frac{1}{r} = \frac{100}{r}$$

If the going rate of interest is 4 percent, then the land is worth

$$\frac{\$100}{0.04} = \$2500$$

This $2500 is called the *capital value* of the piece of land. In general, the capital value is

(6) $$V = \frac{y}{r}$$

where V is the capital value, r is the rate of interest, and y is the annual income.

The above was a hypothetical situation in which we assumed that the stream of future income continued *forever*. But even if it continued only for a long number of years, that is, if n is large, then $[1/(1+r)]^n$ will be close to zero, and the idea of capitalization, $V = y/r$, will be applicable.

MEASURES OF DISPERSION

4

After surveying the grades of a group of 50 students, they were arranged into a frequency distribution that provided us with a more orderly picture of the characteristics of the variable X (grades). The mean of the variable X was then computed, which located the distribution, and the frequency distribution was represented by this one value.

But it could have been that all the grades were just about equal, or that some were very low and others were very high. In the first case, the scatter of the variable X (grades) would be small, and in the second case, the scatter would be large. We should like to find a measure for this scatter of X, which is called *dispersion* in statistics.

When the dispersion of X is known in addition to the arithmetic mean, the description of the distribution of the grades will be greatly improved. When asked, "how well did the students do?", we should answer by giving the arithmetic mean *and* the dispersion of X. In this chapter, three measures of dispersion—the range, the mean deviation, and the standard deviation—are considered.

4.1. The Range

The simplest measure of dispersion is the range. It is the difference between the maximum value and the minimum value of the data. Suppose that there are two classes of students, A and B. Both classes have a mean of 70 points. From the information given to us by the mean, it appears that there is no great difference between the two classes.

But if we are given the additional information that the highest and lowest grade in class A is 99 and 25, while in class B it is 73 and 66, we can see immediately that although both classes have the same mean of 70 points, there is a wide difference in the variability of the grades. The range in class A is 99–25 = 74 points, whereas in B, it is 73–66 = 7 points.

This observation assumes that in class A the remainder of the grades are scattered between 99 and 25. But it could be that there is only one grade of 99 and one grade of 25 and the other grades are between 69 and 74 points. The range does not give us this information because it is based on the two extreme values only.

4.2. Mean Deviations

Another measure of dispersion that includes the variability of all the items is the mean deviation. It is the average of deviations from some central value, such as the mean or median of a distribution. When the mean is used as the central value, we have the mean deviation from (or about) the mean, and when the median is used, we have the mean deviation from (or about) the median. Other points such as the mode may be used as the central value, but in most cases, the term *mean deviation* is used to indicate the mean deviation from the mean. In our subsequent discussion, we shall follow this convention. Let us explain this concept by use of an example.

Assume we have students with grades

$$50, \quad 55, \quad 60, \quad 70, \quad 75, \quad 80$$

In order to measure the dispersion of these grades, the mean is selected, from which the variability of the grades is measured and then the average variability is derived. The deviations from the mean become, since the mean is 65,

$$-15, \quad -10, \quad -5, \quad 5, \quad 10, \quad 15$$

This is shown graphically in Fig. 4.1.

The minus signs indicate that the *direction* of the deviations is to the left. But since we are interested in the amount of variability, that

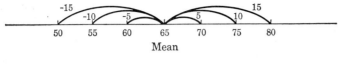

FIG. 4.1.

is, in the *distance* of the deviations, the minus signs are disregarded when finding the average variability. (*Note that the sum of the signed deviations from the mean is always zero.*) Thus we have

$$\frac{15 + 10 + 5 + 5 + 10 + 15}{6} = \frac{60}{6} = 10$$

That is, the mean deviation is 10 points, and is the average of the *distances* (ignoring the *directions*) of the deviations from the mean. This measure of dispersion takes into consideration all the items in the frequency distribution and is relatively simple to compute. In general, when there are n observations, the mean deviation is given by

$$(1) \qquad\qquad \text{Mean deviation} = \frac{\sum_{i=1}^{n} |x_i - \bar{X}|}{n}$$

where the two vertical lines that enclose $x_i - \bar{X}$ mean that the minus signs are ignored. (We have taken the *absolute value* of the deviations.)

Instead of the mean ($\bar{X}$), the median (med) may be used. Then the measure of dispersion becomes

$$(2) \qquad \text{Mean deviation from the median} = \frac{\sum |x_i - \text{med}|}{n}$$

We state without proof that this deviation is always less than, or equal to, the mean deviation.

Only the case for ungrouped data has been considered. There are formulas for grouped data also, but this mean deviation is very rarely used. It was discussed here to lead up to the standard deviation, which is considered next.

4.3.   The Standard Deviation

The third measure of dispersion to be considered is the standard deviation. It is similar to the mean deviation in that the deviations are measured from the mean. The reason why the standard deviation is favored over the mean deviation or the range is that it has desirable mathematical properties. Some of these properties will be explained in later chapters. We shall first redefine the term *deviation* more precisely, then define the concept of a variance, and finally define the standard deviation.

(i) Deviation

The difference between an individual value x_i and the mean $\bar{X}$ is called the *deviation* of x_i from $\bar{X}$. That is,

(1) $e = \text{deviation} = x_i - \bar{X}$

It is customary to subtract the $\bar{X}$ from x_i; that is, $x_i - \bar{X}$, and not the other way (not $\bar{X} - x_i$). For example, let the average grade be $\bar{X} = 70$ points and an individual grade be $x = 60$ points; then the deviation is $e = 60 - 70 = -10$ points. As our discussion of statistics develops, the student will realize that a great part of our effort will be devoted to the analysis of deviations.

(ii) Variance

Consider the example of five grades given in Table 4.1. The second column shows the deviation $x_i - \bar{X}$. The third column is the square

TABLE 4.1.

	X	$X - \bar{X} = e$	$(X - \bar{X})^2$
	50	$50 - 65 = -15$	225
	55	$55 - 65 = -10$	100
	60	$60 - 65 = - 5$	25
	70	$70 - 65 = 5$	25
	75	$75 - 65 = 10$	100
	80	$80 - 65 = 15$	225
Sum	390	0	700
Mean	65		116.5

of the deviations; that is $(x_i - \bar{X})^2$. The sum of these squared deviations is

$$\sum_{i=1}^{6} e_i^2 = \sum_{i=1}^{6} (x_i - \bar{X})^2 = 700$$

The arithmetic mean of the squared deviations is

$$\frac{\sum (x_i - \bar{X})^2}{n} = \frac{700}{6} = 116.5$$

This average (or mean) of the squared deviations $(x_i - \bar{X})^2$ is called the *variance* and is stated in formula form as follows:

(2) $$\text{Variance of } X = \frac{\sum\limits_{i=1}^{n} (x_i - \bar{X})^2}{n}$$

The following terms are used interchangeably: the variance of the distribution of X; the variance of the distribution; the variance of X; and just simply, the variance. The context of the discussion usually allows us to say simply "the variance" without causing any confusion. It is abbreviated symbolically as

(3) $$\text{Var}(X) = \frac{\sum (x_i - \bar{X})^2}{n}$$

The Greek letter σ squared (that is, σ^2) is also used to denote the variance in formulas. Thus

(4) $$\text{Var}(X) = \sigma^2$$

The quantity

(5) $$\sum\limits_{i=1}^{n} (x_i - \bar{X})^2$$

will appear over and over again in subsequent discussions. It is called the *sum of the squared deviations.*

(iii) The standard deviation

The variance is a measure of dispersion. But note that the deviations have been squared. This means that if the grades of students are considered, the unit of the variance is (points)^2. To correct this inadequacy and obtain a measure of dispersion for the grades, which will be in terms of "points," the square root of the variance is taken. The square root of the variance is called the *standard deviation* of the variable X.

(6) $$\text{Standard deviation} = \sqrt{\text{variance}} = \sqrt{\frac{700}{6}} = \sqrt{116.5} = 10.7 \text{ points}$$

Therefore, one standard deviation is 10.7 points. The standard deviation is denoted by σ. In symbols,

(7) $$\sigma = \sqrt{\frac{\sum (x_i - \bar{X})^2}{n}}$$

In theoretical statistics the variance is the parameter that is mainly used, but in applied statistics, it is the standard deviation. After applications of the standard deviation have been discussed in Chapters 6 and 7, its meaning will become clearer. In the present section let us concentrate on the computational procedures.

(iv)   Ungrouped data

Our object is to change formula (7) so that computational procedures will become simpler and suitable for machine calculation. The change is performed as follows: Formula (5) becomes (see preceding Reference)

$$(8) \qquad \Sigma (x_i - \bar{X})^2 = \Sigma x_i^2 - \frac{(\Sigma x_i)^2}{n}$$

We can illustrate the use of this formula (8) by the data in Table 4.2.

TABLE 4.2.	
X	X²
50	2500
55	3025
60	3600
70	4700
75	5625
80	6400
390	26050

Substituting the results of Table 4.2 into formula (8), we get

$$\Sigma (x_i - \bar{X})^2 = \Sigma x_i^2 - \frac{(\Sigma x_i)^2}{n}$$

$$= 26{,}050 - \frac{(390)^2}{6} .$$

$$= 700$$

which is what was obtained in Table 4.1.

By combining formulas (7) and (8), we get

$$(9) \qquad \sigma^2 = \frac{\Sigma (x_i - \bar{X})^2}{n}$$

$$= \frac{\Sigma x_i^2 - \frac{(\Sigma x_i)^2}{n}}{n}$$

This is the computational formula that we seek for ungrouped data. In terms of our example, we get

$$\sigma = \sqrt{\dfrac{26{,}050 - \dfrac{(390)^2}{6}}{6}} = \sqrt{\dfrac{700}{6}} = 10.7 \text{ points}$$

REFERENCE

$$\Sigma (x_i - \bar{X})^2 = \Sigma (x_i^2 - 2x_i\bar{X} + \bar{X}^2)$$
$$= \Sigma x_i^2 - 2\bar{X} \Sigma x_i + n\bar{X}^2$$
$$= \Sigma x_i^2 - 2n\bar{X}^2 + n\bar{X}^2$$
$$= \Sigma x_i^2 - n\bar{X}^2$$

Also, since

$$\bar{X} = \frac{\Sigma x_i}{n}$$

$$n\bar{X}^2 = n\left(\frac{\Sigma x_i}{n}\right)^2 = \frac{(\Sigma x_i)^2}{n}$$

Thus,

$$\Sigma (x_i - \bar{X})^2 = \Sigma x_i^2 - \frac{(\Sigma x_i)^2}{n}$$

Substituting this into formula (7) gives formula (9).

(v) Shifting the origin

The origin from which the grades are measured is zero. (The origin from which the deviations are measured is the mean.) What happens to the dispersion of a variable if an origin other than zero is used? The answer is: There will be no change. This can be explained heuristically as follows: Assume there are three students with grades 70, 80, and 90. There is a 10-point difference between the successive grades.

Next subtract an arbitrary number (say, 50) from each grade. Then the grades measured from the origin 50 will be

$$70 - 50 = 20, \quad 80 - 50 = 30, \quad 90 - 50 = 40$$

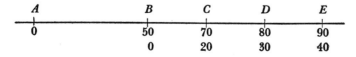

A		B	C	D	E
0		50	70	80	90
		0	20	30	40

Graphically, we are measuring the distance of the points C, D, and E from $B = 50$ rather than $A = 0$. This shows that the differences between the successive grades in terms of the new origin are still 10 points. In general, the difference between the successive grades (points) will always be 10 points, no matter what value is selected as the origin. That is, the scatter between the grades is the same (invariant) no matter where the origin is. In symbols this is stated as follows:

(10) $$\text{Var}(X) = \text{Var}(X + a)$$

where a is an arbitrary number.

Using the data of Table 4.2, let us subtract 60 from each X. That is, let $a = -60$ in formula (10). The result is shown in Table 4.3. The

TABLE 4.3.

$X - 60$	$(X - 60)^2$
-10	100
$-\ 5$	25
0	0
10	100
15	225
20	400
30	850

grades -10, -5, 0, 10, 15, 20 are based on the origin 60 rather than 0. The variance of these grades is

$$\text{Var}(X - 60) = \frac{\Sigma\,(x - 60)^2 - \dfrac{(\Sigma\,(x - 60))^2}{n}}{n}$$

$$= \frac{850 - \dfrac{30^2}{6}}{6}.$$

$$= \frac{700}{6}$$

which is the same as the variance prior to shifting the origin. Thus

$$\text{Var}(X) = \text{Var}(X - 60)$$

Obviously, this procedure simplifies computations considerably when the numbers are large. For example, the variance of three numbers 1001, 1002, and 1003 is the same as the variance of 1, 2, and 3.

$$
\begin{array}{cc}
X & X^2 \\
1001 - 1000 = 1 & 1 \\
1002 - 1000 = 2 & 4 \\
1003 - 1000 = 3 & 9 \\
\hline
6 & 14
\end{array}
$$

$$
\sigma^2 = \frac{14 - \dfrac{6^2}{3}}{3} = \frac{14 - 12}{3} = \frac{2}{3}
$$

As a further check, subtract 1002 instead of 1000, and find the variance. Also check that

$$
\mathrm{Var}(X) = \mathrm{Var}(X - 50)
$$

using the data of Table 4.2. Note that

$$
\mathrm{Var}(X) = \mathrm{Var}(X - 60) = \mathrm{Var}(X - 50)
$$

REFERENCE

$$
\frac{\Sigma\,(x + a)}{n} = \frac{\Sigma\,x + na}{n} = \bar{X} + a
$$

Therefore

$$
\mathrm{Var}(X + a) = \frac{\Sigma\,[(x + a) - (\bar{X} + a)]^2}{n}
$$

$$
= \frac{\Sigma\,(x - \bar{X})^2}{n}
$$

$$
= \mathrm{Var}(X)
$$

(iii)   Grouped data

For a frequency distribution where the individual values are not known, such as in Table 4.2, a formula that gives an approximate value for the standard deviation of the distribution is used. It is

(11)
$$
\sigma = \sqrt{\frac{\displaystyle\sum_{i=1}^{k} f_i\,(m_i - \bar{X})^2}{n}}
$$

where m_i is the midpoint of the class intervals; $\bar{X}$ is the mean of the distribution; f_i is the frequency of each class; n is the total number of frequencies (that is, $n = \Sigma\,f_i$); and k is the number of classes.

The assumption on which this formula is based is that all actually observed values in a class interval are equal to the midvalue m_i of that class. Then the deviation $(m_i - \bar{X})$ is obtained and squared. Since there are f_i observations in that class, the sum of the squared deviations for the ith class interval will be

$$f_i(m_i - \bar{X})^2$$

and since we want the sum of the squared deviations for *all* the k classes, we find the sum for all the classes by

$$\sum_{i=1}^{k} f_i(m_i - \bar{X})^2$$

Thus $\sum f_i(m_i - \bar{X})^2/n$ is the sum of the squared deviations divided by n, which is the variance. The square root of this is the standard deviation.

This formula requires that the mean $\bar{X}$ be calculated and that deviations $(m_i - \bar{X})$ be obtained. To avoid this inconvenience, we can derive a formula from (11) that does not require these calculations:

$$(12) \qquad \sigma = c \sqrt{\dfrac{\sum\limits_{i=1}^{k} f_i d_i^2}{n} - \left(\dfrac{\sum\limits_{i=1}^{k} f_i d_i}{n}\right)^2}$$

where c is the class interval; f_i is the frequency of the ith class; d_i is the deviation of the ith class from an assumed origin; and n is the total number of observations. To repeat, this is derived from the preceding formula (11) and thus gives us the same result. Let us explain its use by the example in Table 4.4.

TABLE 4.4.

Class	f	d	fd	d^2	fd^2
30–39	4	−3	−12	9	36
40–49	6	−2	−12	4	24
50–59	8	−1	− 8	1	8
60–69	12	0	0	0	0
70–79	9	1	9	1	9
80–89	7	2	14	4	28
90–99	4	3	12	9	36
	50		3		141

First, an assumed origin 0 at the 60–69 class interval is selected. Then minus class deviations are taken upward (in the direction where the grades become lower) and plus deviations downward (in the direction where the grades become higher). Thus, for example, the class 30–39 is -3 class deviations away. The reason that 60–69 was selected as the origin is because observation of the data indicated computations would be least cumbersome. If observation of the data shows that computations are least cumbersome when the origin 0 is placed at the 70–79 class interval, we shall select that class.

The remainder of the computation in Table 4.4 is obvious. After putting our calculated values in formula (12), we obtain

$$\sigma = 10\sqrt{\frac{141}{50} - \left(\frac{3}{50}\right)^2} = 10\sqrt{2.8164} = 16.78 \text{ points}$$

Carry out the computations by setting the 70–79 class as zero. You should get the same answer.

REFERENCE

We know from Chapter 3 that

$$\bar{X} = A + \frac{\Sigma f_i d_i}{n} \times c$$

$$m_i = A + d_i c$$

Substituting this into $\Sigma f_i (m_i - \bar{X})^2$, we find

$$\Sigma f_i(m_i - \bar{X})^2 = \Sigma f_i (A + d_i c - A - \frac{\Sigma f_i d_i}{n} \times c)^2$$

$$= \Sigma f_i \left(d_i c - \frac{\Sigma f_i d_i}{n} \times c \right)^2$$

$$= c^2 \left[\Sigma f_i d_i^2 - 2n \left(\frac{\Sigma f_i d_i}{n} \right)^2 + n \left(\frac{\Sigma f_i d_i}{n} \right)^2 \right]$$

$$= c^2 \left[\Sigma f_i d_i^2 - n \left(\frac{\Sigma f_i d_i}{n} \right)^2 \right]$$

Thus the variance becomes

$$\text{Var}(X) = \frac{\Sigma f_i (m_i - \bar{X})^2}{n}$$

$$= c^2 \left[\frac{\Sigma f_i d_i^2}{n} - \left(\frac{\Sigma f_i d_i}{n} \right)^2 \right]$$

and the square root of this is formula (12).

(iv) Grouped data—unequal class-interval case

When class intervals are unequal, we may use formula (12) by adjusting the value of d, but to avoid this, we shall use formula (11). Fortunately (11) can be expanded as follows to simplify calculations:

$$(13) \qquad \sigma = \sqrt{\dfrac{\Sigma f_i m_i^2 - \dfrac{(\Sigma f_i m_i)^2}{n}}{n}}$$

The worksheet for this formula is shown in Table 4.5.

TABLE 4.5.

Class	f	m	fm	m^2	fm^2
30–39	4	34.5	138.0	1190.25	4,761.00
40–49	6	44.5	267.0	1980.25	11,881.50
50–59	8	54.5	436.0	2970.25	23,762.00
60–69	12	64.5	774.0	4160.25	49,923.00
70–79	9	74.5	670.5	5550.25	49,952.25
80–89	7	84.5	591.5	7140.25	49,981.75
90–100	4	95	380.0	9025.00	36,100.00
	$n = 50$		3257.0		226,361.50

Thus, from formula (13), we find

$$\sigma = \sqrt{\dfrac{226{,}361.50 - \dfrac{10{,}608{,}049}{50}}{50}}$$

$$= \sqrt{284.028} = 16.85$$

The difference arises because we use 95 as the midpoint instead of 94.5.

If the last class interval is 90–99 instead of 90–100, the answer will be the same, whether formula (12) or (13) is used. As an exercise, find the standard deviation, using formula (13), when the last class is 90–99, and show that it is equal to the standard deviation obtained from formula (12).

REFERENCE

We know that

$$\bar{X} = \dfrac{\Sigma f_i m_i}{n}$$

Substituting this into $\Sigma f_i(m_i - \bar{X})^2$, we find

$$\Sigma f_i(m_i - \bar{X})^2 = \Sigma f_i\left(m_i - \frac{\Sigma f_i m_i}{n}\right)^2$$

$$= \Sigma f_i m_i^2 - 2\frac{(\Sigma f_i m_i)^2}{n} + \frac{(\Sigma f_i m_i)^2}{n}$$

$$= \Sigma f_i m_i - \frac{(\Sigma f_i m_i)^2}{n}$$

Thus the variance of X is

$$\mathrm{Var}(X) = \frac{\Sigma f_i(m_i - \bar{X})^2}{n}$$

$$= \frac{\Sigma f_i m_i^2 - \dfrac{(\Sigma f_i m_i)^2}{n}}{n}.$$

and the square root of this is formula (13).

(v)   Comments on the standard deviation

The meaning of the standard deviation will become clearer in Chapters 6 and 7. For the present, we may say that the standard deviation is a unit of measurement for dispersion, just as the pound is a unit of measurement for weight or the inch is a unit of measurement for length.

As an illustration, suppose that there are two classes A and B, which have the same mean grade of 70 points, and that both classes have a bell-shaped, symmetrical frequency curve. Furthermore assume that the grades of class A are concentrated near the mean, while those of class B are scattered throughout the range of the grades. We may assume that the standard deviation of class A is smaller than that of class B. Then the frequency curves may look like those drawn in Fig. 4.2.

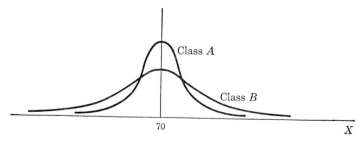

FIG. 4.2.

The curve for class A is slimmer and taller, and the curve for class B is shorter and flatter. The smaller the standard deviation, the smaller the scatter (dispersion), and the larger the standard deviation, the larger the scatter (dispersion).

(vi) *Standardized value*

In Fig. 4.3, assume that the standard deviation of the variable X is 10 points ($\sigma = 10$ points), the mean of the variable X is 70 points

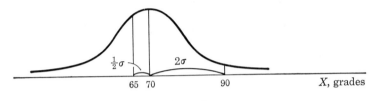

FIG. 4.3.

($\bar{X} = 70$ points), and an individual grade is 90 points ($x_i = 90$ points). Then the individual grade is 20 points above the mean. Or, in terms of the standard deviation, it is 2 standard deviations above the mean. If another student has a grade of 65 points, he is 5 points below the mean. That is, it is half a standard deviation below the mean:

$$\frac{x - \bar{X}}{\sigma} = \frac{90 - 70}{10} = \frac{20}{10} = 2 \text{ standard deviations}$$

$$\frac{x - \bar{X}}{\sigma} = \frac{65 - 70}{10} = \frac{-5}{10} = -\frac{1}{2} \text{ standard deviation}$$

We can always translate the difference between the mean and an individual value into units of standard deviations. We say the deviation $x_i - \bar{X}$ has been *standardized*.

In general, when the variable X is divided by its standard deviation,

$$\frac{X}{\sigma} : \frac{x_1}{\sigma}, \frac{x_2}{\sigma}, \quad \dots \quad , \frac{x_n}{\sigma}$$

we say the variable X has been standardized.

This procedure will enable us to make comparisons of the dispersion of individual values in different distributions. For example, assume that an individual got a 90 on the test, the mean of the class was 70, and the $\sigma = 10$ points. In a second test he got 600, the mean of the class was 560 points, and the $\sigma = 40$ points in this class. In the first case he received 20 points above the average ($90 - 70 = 20$), and in the second case he earned 40 points above the average $(600 - 560 = 40)$. Was he better off in the first or second test?

When the differences are standardized, we find

First test: $\dfrac{90 - 70}{10} = \dfrac{20}{10} = 2$ standard deviations

Second test: $\dfrac{600 - 560}{40} = \dfrac{40}{40} = 1$ standard deviation

Thus he is further above the mean in the first test than in the second test. He was much better off in the first test. We shall calculate how much better off he was, after discussion of the normal area table in Chapter 6.

(vii)   Unit distribution

The standard deviation of the distribution of a standardized variable

$$\frac{X}{\sigma} : \frac{x_1}{\sigma}, \frac{x_2}{\sigma}, \ldots, \frac{x_n}{\sigma}$$

is unity. In theoretical statistics, distributions with mean $= 0$ and standard deviation (or variance) $= 1$ are usually used to facilitate analysis. Such distributions will be called *unit distributions*. For example, the normal area table which is explained in Chapter 6 is calculated from a normal distribution with mean $= 0$ and $\sigma^2 = 1$. We shall, in this section, show how a unit distribution is constructed by shifting the origin to the mean and standardizing the variable, by use of a simple illustration.

Suppose there are three numbers x_1, x_2, and x_3. The variance of these numbers is

$$\text{Var}(X) = \sigma^2 = \frac{1}{3} \sum_{i=1}^{3} (x_i - \bar{X})^2$$

Hence, these numbers may be standardized by

$$\frac{x_1}{\sigma}, \frac{x_2}{\sigma}, \frac{x_3}{\sigma}$$

The variance of the standardized variable is

$$\text{Var}\left(\frac{X}{\sigma}\right) = \frac{1}{3} \sum_{i=1}^{3} \left(\frac{x_i}{\sigma} - \frac{\bar{X}}{\sigma}\right)^2 = \frac{1}{\sigma^2}\left\{\frac{1}{3} \sum (x_i - \bar{X})^2\right\}$$

$$= \frac{1}{\sigma^2} \cdot \sigma^2 = 1$$

That is, the variance of the standardized variable is unity.

Example. Let us use the data in Table 4.1 as an example. The sum of the squared deviations for the standardized variable X/σ is shown in the accompanying Table 4.6.

TABLE 4.6.

X/σ	$(X/\sigma - \bar{X}/\sigma)$	$(X/\sigma - \bar{X}/\sigma)^2$
$50/\sigma$	$-15/\sigma$	$225/\sigma^2$
$55/\sigma$	$-10/\sigma$	$100/\sigma^2$
$60/\sigma$	$-\ 5/\sigma$	$25/\sigma^2$
$70/\sigma$	$5/\sigma$	$25/\sigma^2$
$75/\sigma$	$10/\sigma$	$100/\sigma^2$
$80/\sigma$	$15/\sigma$	$225/\sigma^2$
		$700/\sigma^2$

Thus the variance of the standardized variable X/σ is

$$\text{Var}\left(\frac{X}{\sigma}\right) = \frac{\dfrac{700}{\sigma^2}}{6} = \frac{700}{6} \times \frac{1}{\sigma^2}$$

But since $\text{Var}(X) = \sigma^2 = 700/6$, we find

$$\text{Var}\left(\frac{X}{\sigma}\right) = \frac{700}{6} \times \frac{6}{700} = 1$$

Using the result obtained above, we may now construct a unit distribution. This is performed in two steps. The first is to shift the origin to the mean and the second is to standardize the adjusted variable. Let the values be x_1, x_2, x_3. The origin is shifted to the mean by

$$x_1 - \bar{X}, \qquad x_2 - \bar{X}, \qquad x_3 - \bar{X}$$

Since $\text{Var}(X) = \text{Var}(X - \bar{X}) = \sigma^2$, these adjusted values are standardized by dividing by the standard deviation σ:

$$z_1 = \frac{x_1 - \bar{X}}{\sigma}, \qquad z_2 = \frac{x_2 - \bar{X}}{\sigma}, \qquad z_3 = \frac{x_3 - \bar{X}}{\sigma}$$

where we have set the standardized values equal to z_1, z_2, and z_3 for brevity.

The mean of z_1, z_2, and z_3 is

$$\bar{Z} = \frac{z_1 + z_2 + z_3}{3}$$

$$= \frac{1}{3}\left\{\frac{x_1 - \bar{X}}{\sigma} + \frac{x_2 - \bar{X}}{\sigma} + \frac{x_3 - \bar{X}}{\sigma}\right\}$$

$$= \frac{1}{3} \times 0 = 0$$

The variance of Z is

$$\mathrm{Var}(Z) = \mathrm{Var}\left(\frac{X - \bar{X}}{\sigma}\right)$$

$$= \mathrm{Var}\left(\frac{X}{\sigma} - \frac{\bar{X}}{\sigma}\right)$$

$$= \mathrm{Var}\left(\frac{X}{\sigma}\right)$$

$$= 1$$

Hence, the variable Z has a unit distribution.

To summarize: Given a distribution of values $x_1, x_2, \ldots, x_n$, its mean $\bar{X}$, and its standard deviation σ, the distribution of

$$\frac{x_1 - \bar{X}}{\sigma}, \quad \frac{x_2 - \bar{X}}{\sigma}, \ldots, \frac{x_n - \bar{X}}{\sigma}$$

has a mean of 0 and standard deviation of unity.

4.4. Relative Dispersion (Coefficient of Variation)

Assume that a group of students took two tests. The first test has an average of 60 points and a standard deviation of 6 points, with a maximum of 100 points. The second test has an average of 700 points and a standard deviation of 7 points, with a maximum of 1000 points. Which of the two tests has a larger scatter (dispersion)? Here we are comparing the dispersion of two frequency distributions.

One can readily see that from an *absolute* standpoint, the 7 points is a larger scatter than the 6 points, but from a *relative* standpoint, we can see that the students were much closer together in the second test. To bring this idea out explicitly, a measure of *relative* dispersion has been formulated. The *coefficient of variation* of a distribution, as it is called, is defined as

(1)
$$V = \frac{\sigma}{\bar{X}}$$

Thus in our present situation, we have

First test, $V = \dfrac{6}{60} = \dfrac{1}{10}$

Second test, $V = \dfrac{7}{700} = \dfrac{1}{100}$

We observe that the relative dispersion of the second test is only $1/10$ of the first.

By use of the cofficient of variation, the dispersion of different frequency distributions can be compared.

When the coefficient of variation is squared, we find

$$V^2 = \frac{\sigma^2}{\bar{X}^2} = \frac{\dfrac{\Sigma (x_i - \bar{X})^2}{n}}{\bar{X}^2}$$

which becomes

(2)
$$V^2 = \frac{\Sigma \left(\dfrac{x_i - \bar{X}}{\bar{X}} \right)^2}{n}$$

The $e = x_i - \bar{X}$ is sometimes called the *absolute* deviation. Thus

$$\frac{x_i - \bar{X}}{\bar{X}}$$

is the *relative deviation*. Hence V^2 as given by formula (2) may be considered as the variance in relative terms, and therefore it is called the *relative variance*.

Instead of discussing dispersion in terms of the absolute deviation $e = x_i - \bar{X}$ and the standard deviation σ, we may discuss it in terms of the relative deviation and the coefficient of variation. That the two are equivalent is easily seen in the following:

$$\frac{\text{Absolute deviation}}{\text{Standard deviation}} = \frac{x_i - \bar{X}}{\sigma}$$

$$\frac{\text{Relative deviation}}{\text{Coef. of variation}} = \frac{\dfrac{x_i - \bar{X}}{\bar{X}}}{\dfrac{\sigma}{\bar{X}}} = \frac{x_i - \bar{X}}{\sigma}$$

Other applications of the V are its use in checking experimental results and in estimating the standard deviation. In a number of cases the $\bar{X}$ and σ change together so that the V is approximately constant. In such a situation, if there are several sets of experimental data that involve calculation of $\bar{X}$ and σ, calculating their V's and comparing them with the given V as well as with each other will serve as a check.

Also, if V is given from previous data and $\bar{X}$ is known for a new batch of data, the σ may be estimated by $\sigma = \bar{X}V$.

Snedecor gives a value of 3.75 percent for the stature of male and female V and also points out that experimental animals and plants have, in many cases, stable V's.[1]

Other examples of the use of V may be found in sampling, where it is used to check the reliability of an estimated variance. Since this involves concepts that have not been discussed, we shall simply point out that when we have skewed distributions, it is desirable to check the reliability of the standard deviation, and the V may be used for this purpose. Roughly speaking, when the data are very skewed, the V tends to be large, and a large amount of data becomes necessary to get a reliable standard deviation.

---

[1] G. W. Snedecor, *Statistical Methods*, 5th ed., Ames: Iowa State College Press, 1956, p. 62.

PROBABILITY THEORY

5

In Chapters 1 to 4, we discussed descriptive statistics, which was mainly concerned with organizing data and describing a given situation in an orderly way. In the subsequent six chapters, Chapters 5 to 10, we shall consider the topic of statistical inference, which is a procedure of selecting a sample of data and making inferences about the original body of data from which the sample was taken. A well-known example is the opinion poll in which a small group of individuals selected at random from a large group is used to infer an opinion that the large group may have. The Gallup opinion poll concerning presidential elections is a typical example.

As we shall see, the link between the sample and the original body of data is based on probability theory. Hence, to discuss statistical inference, we need a certain amount of preliminary knowledge of probability theory. But a formal discussion of this theory is very difficult at this point in our study, so we shall confine our discussion to that portion of immediate usefulness to us and take up the details more formally in Chapter 15.

In our discussion of probability theory, we shall distinguish between the interpretation of probability and the calculus of probability. The interpretation of probability is a problem of methodology and deals with the question: What do we mean by probability and how should we interpret it? For example, the probability of a head occurring when a coin is tossed is 1/2. How should this statement be interpreted?

There are two main schools of thought concerning the interpretation of probability. One may be called the *objective* (or objectivist, or objectivistic) school, and it has been the main one in statistics up to the present time. The second one may be called the *subjective* (or subjectivist, or subjectivistic) school and is currently gaining importance in statistics. This emphasis on the subjective approach was brought to the attention of statisticians by the work of L. J. Savage* and by R. Schlaifer.** Both books are on an advanced level.

We shall discuss both approaches very briefly in this chapter and again at a slightly more advanced level in Chapter 16.

The calculus of probability deals with the mathematical deductions obtained from the basic postulates of probability. We shall find, for example, the multiplication rule of probabilities from the basic postulates.

5.1 Preliminary Ideas

Before discussing probability theory, a few preliminary ideas that are used in the subsequent discussions will be presented. The first is the concept of an event.

Consider an experiment of tossing a die, and let the variable X be the 6 possible outcomes $x_1, x_2, \ldots, x_6$. Each of these outcomes is called an *elementary*, or *simple*, *event*. That is, a simple event is a possible outcome of the variable X, the characteristic of which is that it cannot be decomposed into a combination of other events. The simple events are denoted by E_i. Then, for the die example, the 6 simple events are denoted as $E_1, E_2, \ldots, E_6$, where E_1 is the occurrence of a 1, E_2 is the occurrence of a 2, and so forth.

In contrast to the simple events, consider an event A, which is to be the occurrence of a 1 or 2. Clearly, this event A can be decomposed into 2 simple events, E_1 and E_2. An event that can be decomposed into simple events is called a *compound event*.

The collection of all possible outcomes of an experiment is a collection of simple events. For example, the collection of all possible outcomes of tossing a die is shown by the collection of simple events

$$\{E_1, \quad E_2, \quad \cdots, \quad E_6\}$$

Instead of the word "collection," we may also use the word "set."

---

* L. J. Savage, *Foundations of Statistics*, New York: John Wiley & Sons, Inc., 1954.
** R. Schlaifer, *Probability and Statistics for Business Decisions*, New York: McGraw-Hill, 1959.

Example 1. Consider the experiment of tossing 2 coins. There are $2 \times 2 = 4$ possible outcomes, which are shown in Fig. 5.1. Each of the 4 outcomes

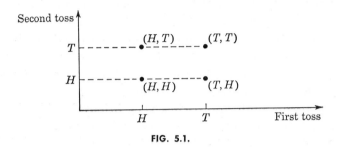

FIG. 5.1.

$$(H, H), \quad (H, T), \quad (T, H), \quad (T, T)$$

is a simple event and may be denoted by E_1, E_2, E_3, and E_4. Then the collection (or set) of these 4 simple events,

$$\{E_1, E_2, E_3, E_4\}$$

shows all possible outcomes of the experiment. Braces are used to indicate a collection or set of events.

The event of just 1 head is given by the 2 events $E_2 = (H, T)$ and $E_3 = (T, H)$. Let this event be denoted by A. Then

$$A = \{E_2, E_3\}$$

and this is a compound event.

Example 2. Consider an economics test given to 500 students where the minimum grade is zero and the maximum is 100. Then there are 101 possible outcomes: $E_0 = 0$, $E_1 = 1$, $E_2 = 2$, ... , $E_{100} = 100$. All possible outcomes of the test are shown by the set

$$S = \{E_0, E_1, \cdots, E_{100}\}$$

The event of 95 points or more is shown by

$$A = \{E_{95}, E_{96}, \cdots, E_{100}\}$$

and this A is a compound event.

Example 3. The grades of the 500 students for the course are $A, B, C, D,$ and F. Then, when the grades of students are checked, there are 5 possible outcomes: $E_1 = A, E_2 = B, E_3 = C, E_4 = D,$ and $E_5 = F$.

All possible outcomes of this experiment concerning 500 students are shown by the set

$$S = \{E_1, E_2, \cdots, E_5\}$$

The event of a grade of C or better is

$$A = \{E_1, E_2, E_3\}$$

which is a compound event.

Example 4.   A group of 2000 people are checked on their smoking habits and are classified as heavy, average, light, and nonsmokers. There are thus 4 possible outcomes, which may be denoted by E_1, E_2, E_3, and E_4, where E_1 categorizes the heavy smoker. The set of all possible outcomes of the 2000 people is

$$\{E_1, E_2, E_3, E_4\}$$

The examples considered so far have had only a *finite* number of simple events. But let us now consider a group of 500 students who weigh between 140 and 190 lb. How many possible outcomes are there? Since the weights between 140 and 190 lb. can be divided into as many parts as we wish, there are an infinite number of possible outcomes. That is, there are an infinite number of simple events.

A careful examination of this illustration shows that the following four elements may be distinguished:

1. There are an infinite number of possible outcomes: that is, an infinite number of simple events.
2. The entities with which we are concerned and with which measurements or attributes are associated are the 500 students. Each student is called an *elementary unit*.
3. The *variable* x associated with the elementary unit (student) is weight.
4. There are 500 *values* of the variable x and 1 value, x_i, for each elementary unit (student). These 500 values are also called *observations*. The number of elementary units and the number of observations are the same.

With these distinctions in mind, we observe that for each observation x_i, there is a corresponding simple event E_i, and for each simple event E_i, there may be none, one, or more than one corresponding x_i. If we let $x_i = 150$ lb., then there is a corresponding $E_i = 150$ lb., but there may be another student, say $x_j = 150$ lb. Then $E_i = 150$ lb. also corresponds to x_j. That is, the simple event $E_i = 150$ lb. has two observations, x_i and x_j, corresponding to it. On the other hand, there may be no students weighing $E_k = 152$ lb., in which case there are no observations corresponding to E_k.

Our discussion has become slightly involved, but the main points the reader should understand are:

1. The simple event that denotes a possible outcome of an experiment.
2. The elementary unit; that is, the student, car, laborer, TV set.
3. The variable x associated with the elementary unit, such as weight, speed, wages, price.
4. The number of values or observations of x, and the relation between simple events and observations.

The reader may wonder, "why are we making all these fine distinctions?" The reason is that we shall start the discussion of probability by using the idea of events. Then we shall reinterpret these results in terms of variables. Finally, using the ideas related to variables and observations, we shall proceed into a discussion of statistical inference.

Example 5. The die example in Section 5.1 has the following results:

$$x_1: \frac{70}{600} \qquad x_2: \frac{80}{600} \qquad x_3: \frac{90}{600}$$

$$x_4: \frac{100}{600} \qquad x_5: \frac{110}{600} \qquad x_6: \frac{150}{600}$$

a. The simple events are the 6 possible outcomes.
b. The elementary unit is the face of the die that appears. Since the die is tossed 600 times, we have 600 elementary units.
c. The variable x is the outcome of the toss.
d. Each of the 600 elementary units generates an observation that is a value of the variable. There are thus 600 values: for example, the $x_1 = 1$ may occur 70 times, the $x_2 = 2$ may occur 80 times, the $x_3 = 3$ may occur 90 times, and so forth.

Example 6. Consider a box with red and green beads. Perform an experiment of drawing a bead and then replacing it. Repeat this 600 times, observing the color of the bead at each draw. Assume the results are

$$\begin{array}{ll} \text{Red:} & 200 \\ \text{Green:} & \underline{400} \\ & 600 \end{array}$$

a. The simple events are the occurrence of a red or green bead.
b. The elementary unit is the bead and there are 600 elementary units.
c. The variable x is the outcome of a draw that is red or green.
d. Each of the 600 elementary units generates an observation that is a value (or attribute) of the variable. There are 600 observations.

Example 7. There are 600 hogs and we are interested in their weights.

    a. The simple events are the possible weights of the hog. Let us assume that the lightest hog weighs 100 lb. and the heaviest one weighs 200 lb. The possible weights that range between these two weights are infinite. That is, there is an infinite number of simple events in this case.

    b. The elementary unit is the hog, and there are 600 elementary units.

    c. The variable x is the weight of the hogs.

    d. Each of the 600 elementary units (hogs) generates an observation, which in this case is a specific weight.

Example 8. A penny and a dime are tossed together 600 times.

    a. We are interested in the simple events for which there are 4 possible outcomes:

	Penny	Dime
1st outcome:	H	H
2nd outcome:	H	T
3rd outcome:	T	H
4th outcome:	T	T

    b. The elementary unit is the combination of faces that appears when the penny and dime are tossed. There are 600 elementary units.

    c. The variable x is the outcome of a toss.

    d. There are 600 values of x, that is, 600 observations. There may be 140 of (H, H), 160 of (H, T), 155 of (T, H), and 145 of (T, T).

Example 9. Consider a box with 10 balls in it, numbered 1 to 10. Take 1 ball out, record the number, and then replace it. After 3 such drawings, sum the numbers. Then repeat the process. For example, assume 2, 3, and 7 are drawn. Then the total is $2 + 3 + 7 = 12$. The smallest sum is $1 + 1 + 1 = 3$ and the largest sum is $10 + 10 + 10 = 30$. Assume that this experiment is repeated 600 times.

    a. The simple event is the sum of the 3 drawings. As can be seen, the possible outcomes are 3, 4, . . . , 30; that is, there are 28 possible outcomes, or 28 simple events.

    b. An elementary unit is a combination of 3 balls that have been drawn. (1, 1, 1) or (1, 2, 1), etc., are examples of the elementary unit, and 600 such combinations have been drawn. For example, the combination (1, 1, 1) may have been drawn 15 times, (1, 2, 1) may have been drawn 25 times, and so forth.

    c. The variable x is the 28 possible outcomes.

d. There are 600 values (observations) of X. The sum 3 may occur 15 times, the sum 4 may occur 25 times, etc.

Let us now define two relations between events A and B. Consider an experiment of tossing a die and let $E_1, E_2, \ldots, E_6$ be the 6 possible outcomes. Let A be the compound event

$$A = \{E_1, \quad E_3, \quad E_5\}$$

That is, A is the event of an odd number occurring. Let B be the compound event of

$$B = \{E_4, \quad E_5, \quad E_6\}$$

That is, B is the event of a number equal to or greater than 4 occurring. Then we have the following two relations between A and B.

1. Both A and B occur together. We have this situation when the event E_5 occurs. This is written AB, or $A \cap B$, or $A \& B$, and $A \cap B$ is read "A intersection B." We shall use all three notations.
2. Either A or B or both occur. In our present example, this is the compound event $\{E_1, E_3, E_4, E_5, E_6\}$. This is written $A \cup B$, or "A or B," and $A \cup B$ is read "A union B."

If A and B have no events in common, then the event $A \& B$ is impossible. For example, let $A = E_1$ and $B = \{E_3, E_4\}$. Then the event $A \& B$ is the event that a 1 and 3, 4 occur together, which is clearly impossible. In this case we write

$$A \& B = 0 \qquad \text{or} \qquad AB = 0$$

and say A and B are *mutually exclusive events*. The 0 is a symbol and not the number zero in our present case. It indicates a set with no events; it is an empty set.

Example 10.   Let A be the event that a student is 20 years old. Let B be the event that a student is a smoker of cigarettes. Then the event "$A \& B$" is the event of a student who is both 20 years old *and* is a smoker. "A or B" is the event of a student who is either 20 years old *or* is a smoker.

Example 11.   Let A be the event that a person is a college graduate, B be the event that a person earns more than \$10,000, C be the event that he is married, and D be the event that he has children. Then "$A \& B$" is the event that a person is a college graduate *and* earns more than \$10,000. "A or B" is the event that a person is a college graduate *or* a person who earns more than \$10,000. "$A \& B \& C$" is the event that a person is a college graduate *and* earns more than \$10,000 *and* is married. "A or B or C" is the event that a person is a college graduate *or* earns more than $10,000 *or* is married. What is the event *"A & B & C & D"*? What is the event *"A or B or C or D"*?

Let us define three more concepts that we shall be using in our discussion of probability theory. They are discussed briefly because they will be explained again in Chapter 7.

A *population* (or *universe*) is defined as the aggregate (totality) of the elementary units. Since the number of elementary units is equal to the number of observations, we may say that a population is the aggregate of the observations. For example, assume that there are 600 hogs and we are interested in the variable X, the weight of the hogs. Each hog is an elementary unit, and hence the population is the 600 hogs. Or we may say that 600 observations (that is, the 600 weights) is the population.

The size of a population is usually denoted by capital N.

A *sample* is a set of n observations (elementary units) drawn from the population. This n is called the *size* of the sample. As an illustration, if we select 20 hogs from the population of 600 hogs, we have a sample of size $n = 20$. Or we may say that we select 20 *observations* (weights) from the population of 600 observations (weights).

Depending on how a sample is drawn from the population, we get different kinds of samples, such as simple random sampling, systematic sampling, and cluster sampling. In this book we shall consider only simple random sampling. Before we can define simple random sampling, we must first discuss the various processes of sampling.

If the process of sampling is such that the elementary unit (hog) drawn can be replaced (or returned) in the population so that it can be drawn again, we have *sampling with replacement.* If the elementary unit (hog) is removed from the population so that it cannot be drawn again, we have *sampling without replacement.*

As an example, consider a box with 10 balls in it, numbered 1 to 10. The 10 balls may be considered as the population, and the variable X is the number on a ball. A ball is drawn, say, a ball numbered 7, and is set aside. It is replaced in the box by another new ball numbered 7. This is sampling with replacement. Instead of replacing the ball numbered 7 by another ball also numbered 7, we may return the ball we drew, in which case it will still be *sampling with replacement.* If a ball is drawn and is not replaced or is not returned so that a ball numbered 7 cannot be drawn again, we have *sampling without replacement.*

A *simple random sample* of size n is a sample selected from a population in such a way that all possible samples of size n have the same chance or probability of being selected. We shall explain this in more detail later. For the present moment, let us consider only samples of size $n = 1$. Then a simple random sample of size $n = 1$ is a sample selected from the population such that each sample (each elementary unit in our present case) has the same chance of being selected.

In our subsequent discussion, when the term *random sample* is used, it will mean simple random sample.

Also, when we say that an item has been selected *at random,* it may be interpreted as meaning "selecting a sample of size $n = 1$ by the simple random sampling process."

Notation.   For subsequent discussions we shall distinguish between the characteristics of a population and a sample by using Greek letters for the population parameters and Latin letters for sample statistics. Thus, the mean and standard deviation of the population are denoted by μ and σ, and for the sample, they are denoted by $\bar{X}$ and s. The $\bar{X}$ and s derived from the sample are called *statistics*. Note that there is only one μ and σ, whereas the number of $\bar{X}$'s and s's will depend on the number of samples selected.

5.2.   The Objective Approach to Probability

In this section we shall discuss three different approaches to probability. The first is an approach based on the principle of insufficient reason, the second is the frequency theory of probability, and the third is an approach similar to the second one but with an important difference, which we shall explain.

(i)   The principle of insufficient reason

The principle of insufficient reason (or principle of indifference) was used by the famous Swiss mathematician Jacob Bernoulli (1654–1705) to define probabilities. Suppose a fair die is tossed and a student is asked the probability that a 2 will occur. He will probably give the answer $1/6$. If a fair coin is tossed and he is asked the probability that a head will occur, he will probably give the answer $1/2$. However, if he is asked why he answered $1/6$ or $1/2$, he may have trouble giving a precise reason.

The principle of insufficient reason proposes that when there is no basis for preferring any one of the possible events (outcomes) to any other, then all should be treated as if they were equally likely to occur. Hence, in the case of a fair die, each number is considered equally likely to occur, and thus the probability that a 2 will occur is $1/6$.

The famous French mathematician P. S. Laplace (1749–1827) stated this principle in his book, *A Philosophical Essay on Probabilities,* as follows: "The theory of chance consists in reducing all the events of the same kind to a certain number of cases equally possible, that is to say, to such as we may be equally undecided about in regard to their existence, and in determining the number of cases favorable to the event whose probability is sought. The ratio of this number to that of all the cases possible is the measure of probability, which is thus simply a fraction whose numerator is the number of favorable cases and whose denominator is the number of all the cases possible."[*]

This principle of insufficient reason has several characteristics, one of which is that it assumes symmetry of events. Thus we have a *fair* die, or a *fair* coin, or a *fair* deck of cards. A second characteristic is that it is based on abstract reasoning and does not depend on experience.

The assumption of symmetry restricts the application of this principle because, as we shall see later, many outcomes of problems (such as those in business and economics) do not have symmetry.

On the other hand, since computations of probability do not depend on experience, it allows us to compute the probabilities without conducting a large number of trials. This type of computation is sometimes called *a priori* computations of probabilities. For a number of problems such as die tossing and coin tossing, which satisfy the requirements for the application of this principle, we shall use the a priori method to determine the probabilities.

(ii) The first frequency theory approach to probability

The basic reference to this approach is the famous Russian mathematician A. N. Kolmogorov's book, *Foundations of the Theory of Probability* (1933).[**] Let us explain this approach with an illustration. Consider an experiment of tossing a fair coin. There are 2 possible outcomes (events), E_1 (heads) and E_2 (tails). Let us repeat this experiment 200 times under uniform conditions. The results are given in Table 5.1.

The column labeled H shows the number of heads per 10 tosses. The column $m = \Sigma H$ is the cumulative sum of heads. The column m/n is the relative frequency of heads for n tosses. For example, in the third row, $m/n = 14/30 = 0.47$ is the relative frequency of heads in 30 tosses.

---

[*] P. S. Laplace, *A Philosophical Essay on Probabilities,* translated by F. W. Truscott and F. C. Emory, New York: Dover Publications, Inc., 1951, pp. 6–7. Reprinted by permission.

[**] A. N. Kolmogorov, *Foundations of the Theory of Probability,* translated by N. Morrison, New York: Chelsea Publishing Co., 1956.

TABLE 5.1.

	1	2	3	4	5	6	7	8	9	10	H	$m = \Sigma H$	$\dfrac{m}{n} = \dfrac{\Sigma H}{n}$
1	T	H	H	H	T	T	H	T	H	H	6	6	0.60
2	T	T	H	T	T	T	T	H	T	T	2	8	0.40
3	H	H	H	T	T	H	T	H	H	T	6	14	0.47
4	T	H	T	T	H	H	H	H	T	T	5	19	0.48
5	H	T	H	T	T	H	H	H	T	H	6	25	0.50
6	T	H	T	H	H	T	H	T	H	H	6	31	0.52
7	T	H	H	H	H	H	H	T	H	T	7	38	0.54
8	H	H	T	T	H	T	H	H	T	T	5	43	0.54
9	T	T	H	T	H	H	T	T	T	T	3	46	0.51
10	H	T	H	T	H	H	T	H	T	T	5	51	0.51
11	H	T	T	H	T	H	T	H	T	H	5	56	0.51
12	T	H	H	T	H	T	H	H	H	H	7	63	0.53
13	H	T	T	T	H	T	H	T	H	H	5	61	0.52
14	T	T	H	H	T	T	T	H	H	T	4	72	0.51
15	T	H	T	H	T	T	H	T	T	T	3	75	0.50
16	T	T	H	T	T	T	H	T	H	T	3	78	0.49
17	H	T	T	T	H	H	H	T	T	H	5	83	0.49
18	H	T	H	H	T	T	H	H	T	H	6	89	0.48
19	T	H	T	H	T	H	T	H	H	H	6	95	0.50
20	H	T	H	T	T	H	H	T	H	H	6	101	0.51

Note the following points of this experiment:

1. We have an experiment ϵ (tossing a coin), which is repeated over and over again (200 times) *under uniform conditions.* The n ($=200$) shows the number of repetitions of ϵ.

2. There are two possible outcomes (events) in our example and we have computed the *relative frequency* of the event heads for different n's.

3. The fluctuations of the relative frequencies of heads, m/n, fluctuate considerably when n is small, but as n becomes large, the amplitude of the fluctuations decreases. This phenomenon is expressed by saying: *The relative frequency becomes stable,* or *the relative frequency shows statistical regularity,* as n becomes large.

Let us show item 3, about statistical regularity, in terms of a graph. In Fig. 5.2, we have relative frequencies on the vertical axis and the number of tosses n on the horizontal axis. We see from the figure that

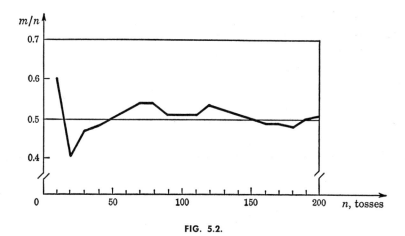

FIG. 5.2.

the amplitude of the fluctuations gradually decreases as n becomes larger and, in our present case, tends to fluctuate around the value 0.5.

Note carefully that although we have said it tends to fluctuate around 0.5, it could well fluctuate around 0.53 or 0.47, or some other value. The reason why 0.5 is used is that we are assuming a fair coin and are tacitly using the principle of insufficient reason.

However, our main interest at this point is not whether the probability is 0.53 or 0.47 or 0.5, but that as the number of repetitions of the experiment increases, the relative frequency of heads will become stable and tend toward a certain value. From this we may conjecture (form an opinion or judgment on insufficient evidence) that when the experiment ϵ is repeated a large number of times, the relative frequency of an event would, with a high degree of certainty, be practically (almost, approximately) equal to a number P.

Based on this line of reasoning, we construct an idealized abstract mathematical model of this experiment and postulate as follows: Given an experiment ϵ (tossing a coin) and an event A (heads), we may assign a number P (say, $1/2$) to the event A (heads), which will be called the *probability* of event A. This P has the following characteristics: When the experiment is repeated a very large number of times (n), and the event occurs m times, the relative frequency m/n will be practically (approximately, almost) equal to this number P.

The number P, which we have called the probability of event A, is also written $P(A)$. We shall mainly use this latter notation.

In terms of our present example, the probability $P(A) = 1/2$ is a number such that the relative frequency m/n ($= 101/200 = 0.505$ for

200 tosses) will be practically equal to $P(A) = 1/2$ when n is very large.

Let us give one more example. Suppose the coin is bent with a pair of pliers and then tossed 400 times. The result of 400 repetitions of this experiment is given in Table 5.2, where the relative frequency of the event of A (heads) shows a tendency to fluctuate between 0.46 and 0.44. Figure 5.3 is a graph of the relative frequencies. The graph shows

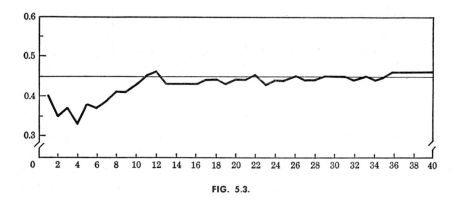

FIG. 5.3.

that as the number of repetitions n increases, the relative frequency shows statistical regularity.

TABLE 5.2.

	1	2	3	4	5	6	7	8	9	10	H	m	m/n
1	H	T	H	T	T	H	T	H	T	T	4	4	0.40
2	T	T	T	T	T	H	T	T	H	H	3	7	0.35
3	H	T	H	T	H	T	H	T	T	T	4	11	0.37
4	H	T	T	T	T	H	T	T	T	T	2	13	0.33
5	T	H	T	H	H	T	H	H	T	H	6	19	0.38
6	H	T	T	T	T	T	T	H	T	H	3	22	0.37
7	T	H	H	T	H	H	T	T	T	H	5	27	0.39
8	H	H	T	T	H	H	H	T	T	H	6	33	0.41
9	T	T	H	T	H	T	T	H	T	H	4	37	0.41
10	H	H	H	H	T	H	T	H	T	T	6	43	0.43
11	T	H	H	H	T	T	T	H	H	H	6	49	0.45
12	T	T	H	H	H	H	T	H	T	H	6	55	0.46
13	T	T	H	T	T	T	T	T	T	T	1	56	0.43
14	T	T	T	H	T	T	H	T	H	H	4	60	0.43
15	T	H	T	H	T	H	T	T	H	T	4	64	0.43

TABLE 5.2. (Continued)

	1	2	3	4	5	6	7	8	9	10	H	m	m/n
16	T	T	T	H	T	H	H	T	H	H	5	69	0.43
17	H	T	H	T	T	H	H	H	H	T	6	75	0.44
18	H	H	T	T	H	T	H	T	H	T	5	80	0.44
19	T	H	T	T	T	T	H	T	T	T	2	82	0.43
20	T	H	H	T	H	H	T	H	T	H	6	88	0.44
21	H	H	H	T	T	T	T	H	T	T	4	92	0.44
22	T	T	H	T	T	T	T	H	T	H	3	95	0.45
23	T	T	T	H	H	T	H	H	T	H	5	100	0.48
24	T	H	T	T	H	T	H	H	H	H	6	106	0.44
25	T	T	T	T	T	H	T	H	H	H	4	110	0.44
26	II	H	H	H	T	H	H	H	H	T	8	118	0.45
27	T	T	T	T	H	T	T	T	T	H	2	120	0.44
28	T	T	T	T	T	T	H	H	H	H	4	124	0.44
29	T	T	H	H	T	H	H	H	T	H	6	130	0.45
30	T	H	T	T	H	H	H	T	T	H	5	135	0.45
31	T	T	T	H	H	H	T	T	T	T	3	138	0.45
32	T	H	T	T	T	H	H	T	T	H	4	142	0.44
33	H	T	H	H	T	T	H	T	T	H	5	147	0.45
34	H	H	T	H	T	T	H	T	T	T	4	151	0.44
35	H	H	H	H	T	T	H	H	T	T	6	157	0.45
36	H	T	H	H	H	H	H	T	T	H	7	164	0.46
37	T	H	H	T	H	T	H	T	H	T	5	169	0.46
38	T	T	H	T	H	H	H	H	H	T	6	175	0.46
39	H	T	T	T	T	H	H	T	H	T	4	179	0.46
40	H	H	H	T	T	T	H	T	H	T	5	184	0.46

With this much evidence, we conjecture that when the experiment is repeated a large number of times, the relative frequency of this event A (heads) would, with a high degree of certainty, be practically equal to a number $P(A)$. We shall assign this number $P(A)$ to the event A (heads) and call it the probability of event A.

Note that in this case we cannot use the principle of insufficient reason, and hence cannot compute a priori the probability $P(A)$. However, our definition of $P(A)$ tells us that when n is large, the relative frequency m/n should be approximately equal to $P(A)$.

The question that immediately arises is: What is the value of $P(A)$? Since we cannot compute a priori the probability $P(A)$, we shall *estimate* $P(A)$. And, from our definition of $P(A)$, it is natural for us to estimate $P(A)$ by the relative frequency of event A. That is, we shall use m/n as an estimate of $P(A)$. In our present example,

$$P(A) = \frac{m}{n} = \frac{184}{400} = 0.46$$

Note carefully that the probability of event A, $P(A)$, and the relative frequency of event A, m/n, are not the same thing. However, when n is large, and when $P(A)$ is not known, m/n is used as an *estimate* of $P(A)$, and is frequently called the probability of A.

Note the following points about this definition of probability. First that $m \leq n$. That is, the number of occurrences of heads (m) is less than or equal to the number of repetitions (n). Hence the relative frequency m/n is less than or equal to unity. That is,

$$\frac{m}{n} \leq 1$$

Second, if the number of occurrences of heads is zero, then $m = 0$ and

$$\frac{m}{n} = 0$$

Hence

$$0 \leq \frac{m}{n} \leq 1$$

Thus it is natural for us to conjecture that $0 \leq P(A) \leq 1$, and in fact we shall postulate that

$$0 \leq P(A) \leq 1$$

This postulate is rather tricky and requires further explanation. If we have an impossible event A, then clearly $P(A) = 0$. If we have a box of 10 black balls, the probability of selecting a white ball is zero.

However, when we have $P(A) = 0$, this does not necessarily mean that event A is an impossible event. From the definition of $P(A)$ we see that $P(A) = 0$ means; in a large number of trials n, the relative frequency m/n of the event A is approximately equal to zero. Hence $P(A) = 0$ means that event A may be an impossible event *or* that it occurs so infrequently that it may be considered as an impossible event. Or we may say that when the experiment is performed once, its occurrence is practically impossible, and when the experiment is repeated a large number of times, it occurs so infrequently that it may be considered as an impossible event.

If an event always occurs, $P(A) = 1$. An event that always occurs is called a *certain event*. For example, if we have a box of 10 black balls, the probability of selecting a black ball is unity. The event of selecting a black ball is a certain event.

However, $P(A) = 1$ does not necessarily mean that event A always occurs. From our definition, $P(A) = 1$ means that, in a large number of trials n, the relative frequency m/n of event A is approximately (almost, practically) equal to unity. Hence $P(A) = 1$ means that event A occurs always or almost always, and hence may be considered from a practical point of view as a certain event.

Or we may say that when the experiment is performed once, the occurrence of the event is almost (practically) certain, and that when the experiment is repeated a large number of times, it occurs so frequently that it may be considered as a certain event.

Four of the characteristics of this approach are:

1. It assumes a large number of trials.
2. It assumes statistical regularity.
3. $P(A)$ is estimated by the relative frequency of A.
4. It is based on experience.

Most of the statistics developed during the past 50 years were based on this approach to probability theory and were mainly developed in England and America. The statistical theory based on this approach to probability has proved very useful in applications, as we shall see later in this book.

However, certain limitations of this approach to probability, and hence limitations on the statistical theory that has been developed, have also been recognized. In particular, the first two characteristics we mentioned above become restrictions. There are cases where we evaluate events without their actual occurrence, and where we cannot repeat experiments. For instance, one hears such statements as "there is a 50–50 chance that a rocket will hit the moon," even though the event has not actually occurred. Or one sees a statement such as "chances of negotiating new contracts between the U.S. Steel Workers of America and the steel industry are rated about 50–50." Or, when there is a boxing match between two boxers who have never met before, there are certain odds. As these illustrations show, there are many cases that have probabilities attached to them even though there are no repetitions of experiments or actual frequency of occurrences.

Let us see if the subjective approach to probability, which we consider next, will be able to assign probabilities to cases such as those mentioned above. But before that, let us briefly discuss a second frequency theory approach.

(iii)   The second frequency theory approach to probability

This second frequency theory approach is similar to the first approach in that it starts with the relative frequency m/n of event A. But it differs from the first as follows: The first approach assigned a number $P(A)$ to the event A and called it the probability of event A. This $P(A)$ had the characteristic that when the number of trials was large, m/n and $P(A)$ were almost (practically, approximately) equal.

The second approach defines the probability of event A as the *limit* of m/n *as* n *tends to infinity*. Thus we may write

$$P(A) = \frac{m}{n} \qquad \text{as } n \to \infty$$

Note carefully that in the first approach, we said merely that $P(A)$ and m/n were practically equal when n was large, whereas in the second approach, we say $P(A)$ *is* the *limit* of m/n as n tends to infinity.

In the first approach, we assigned a number $P(A)$ to event A and called it the probability of A. In the second approach, $P(A)$ *is the limit of a limiting process.*

In the first approach, $P(A)$ is an idealization of the statistical regularity of the relative frequency of an event. The second approach requires the existence of a limit for the relative frequency of an event.

As mentioned previously, we shall use the first approach. It will suffice if the student knows that there is this second approach and recognizes it when it is being used by other writers.

5.3.   The Subjective Approach

As mentioned at the beginning of this chapter, the subjective approach to probability was brought to the attention of statisticians by Professor Savage:

"Personalistic views hold that probability measures the confidence that a particular individual has in the truth of a particular proposition, for example, the proposition that it will rain tomorrow. These views postulate that the individual concerned is in someways 'reasonable,' but they do not deny the possibility that two reasonable individuals faced with the same evidence may have different degrees of confidence in the truth of the same proposition."*

Professor Savage uses the term personalistic instead of subjective (or subjectivistic).

As the quotation shows, the probability of an event A is interpreted as a measure of confidence that a reasonable person assigns to the event A. This approach allows the weights we assigned, when computing the weighted arithmetic mean, to be interpreted as probabilities. By using the example of three exams of Section 3.1, we have Table 5.3. The weights assigned were a measure of confidence or importance that the instructor assigned to the three exams.

TABLE 5.3.

(1) Grades	(2) Weights	(3) Proportional Weights	(4) (1) × (3)
50	10	0.20	10
80	15	0.30	24
70	25	0.50	35
	50	1.00	69

As we found before, the weights may be expressed in proportional terms so that they always add up to unity. These proportional (or relative) weights may be considered as the probabilities assigned to the events (exams).

As another example, consider the case where the chances are rated 50–50 for a contract between steel workers and the steel industry, given in Table 5.4. The relative weights may be considered as the probabilities assigned to the events.

TABLE 5.4.

Event	Weights	Relative Weights
Contract	50	0.5
No contract	50	0.5
	100	1.0

As can be seen, this subjective approach may be applied to events that have not yet occurred, or to events that occur only once, and does

---

* *Op. cit.*, p. 3. By permission of the author and publisher.

not require an experiment with a large number of trials or the assumption of statistical regularity. Furthermore, the first frequency theory approach may also be interpreted in terms of this subjective approach as follows:

Recall that the first frequency theory approach assigned a number $P(A)$ to event A, which had the characteristic that the relative frequency m/n of event A (when the experiment is repeated a large number of times) is practically (almost) equal to $P(A)$. Recall also that in the subjective approach, $P(A)$ was a measure of confidence that a reasonable person assigns to the event A. Hence we shall argue that if a person feels confident that an event A will occur with relative frequency m/n when the experiment is repeated a large number of times, he will assign this relative frequency m/n to the event as its probability of occurrence.

The relative frequency m/n of an event A was considered as an estimate of $P(A)$ in the frequency theory discussion. We are now simply assigning this m/n to the event A as an estimate of the probability of event A if we are confident that the event A will occur with relative frequency m/n when n is large.

This subjective approach is evidently very flexible and may be applied to a wide variety of situations. Various illustrations of this approach will be given in subsequent discussion. For the moment let us proceed with our study of probability and next consider the calculus of probability.

5.4. Postulates of Probability Theory

With its background as outlined to this point, we shall first state the postulates of probability theory and then deduce various rules for the calculus of probabilities. The word "postulate" is used instead of "axioms" to avoid the impression that these postulates are sometimes a priori. They are man-made basic assumptions. The three postulates are as follows:

(a) Given an experiment ϵ with mutually exclusive possible outcomes (simple events) $E_1, E_2, \ldots, E_n$, a nonnegative number,

$$(1) \qquad\qquad P(E_i) \geqq 0$$

is assigned to each outcome and is called the probability of event E_i.

(b) The sum of the probabilities of all possible mutually exclusive events is unity:

$$(2) \qquad\qquad P(E_1) + P(E_2) + \cdots + P(E_n) = 1$$

(c) The probability of either of two mutually exclusive events E_i or E_j occurring is equal to the sum of their probabilities:

(3) $$P(E_i \text{ or } E_j) = P(E_i) + P(E_j)$$

Let us first illustrate the meaning of these three postulates in terms of the frequency theory approach. Suppose a die is tossed 200 times with the results shown in Table 5.5. If we have a fair die we may compute the probabilities a priori by use of the principle of insufficient reason. But let us assume that the die is not fair.

TABLE 5.5.

Events	f	Relative Frequency
1	32	0.16
2	28	0.14
3	30	0.15
4	36	0.18
5	34	0.17
6	40	0.20
	200	1.00

The mutually exclusive possible outcomes are E_1, E_2, E_3, E_4, E_5, E_6. We assign nonnegative numbers $P(E_1)$, $P(E_2)$, ... , $P(E_6)$ to the events. In our present case, we shall use the relative frequencies as estimates of $P(E_i)$. Thus, as the table shows,

$$P(E_1) = 0.16, \qquad P(E_2) = 0.14, \cdots, \qquad P(E_6) = 0.20$$

Furthermore, the sum of probabilities of all possible mutually exclusive events is, as Table 5.5 shows,

$$P(E_1) + P(E_2) + \cdots + P(E_6) = 0.16 + 0.14 + \cdots + 0.20 = 1$$

Finally, the probability that two mutually exclusive events, either E_1 or E_2, will occur is

$$P(E_1 \text{ or } E_2) = P(E_1) + P(E_2) = 0.16 + 0.14 = 0.30$$

In terms of the subjective approach, we may be using weights to express the relative importance of an event. We have seen that when weights are expressed in relative terms, the calculus of these weights follow the preceding three postulates. Hence the weights may be treated as probabilities.

Let us next generalize the third postulate. E_1 and E_2 are the events of a 1 and 2 occurring. Let A denote the compound event of a 1 or 2 occurring. Thus

$$P(A) = P(E_1 \text{ or } E_2) = P(E_1) + P(E_2)$$

E_3 is the event of a 3 occurring. Then, clearly, A and E_3 are mutually exclusive events. Thus, from the third postulate,

$$P(A \text{ or } E_3) = P(A) + P(E_3)$$

But this may be rewritten as

$$P(E_1 \text{ or } E_2 \text{ or } E_3) = P(E_1) + P(E_2) + P(E_3)$$

By repeating this process, we have in general the following result: If $E_1, E_2, \ldots, E_n$ are mutually exclusive events,

$$P(E_1 \text{ or } E_2 \text{ or } \cdots \text{ or } E_n) = P(E_1) + P(E_2) + \cdots + P(E_n)$$

This is called the *addition rule*.

Example 1.   Suppose we have a box with 2 red, 3 black, and 5 green balls. Each time a ball is drawn, it is returned to the box. Hence the probabilities of drawing a specific colored ball are

$$P(\text{red}) = 0.2, \qquad P(\text{black}) = 0.3, \qquad P(\text{green}) = 0.5$$

The probability of drawing either a red or black ball is, since they are mutually exclusive events,

$$P(\text{red or black}) = P(\text{red}) + P(\text{black}) = 0.2 + 0.3 = 0.5$$

The probability of drawing either a red or green ball is

$$P(\text{red or green}) = P(\text{red}) + P(\text{green}) = 0.2 + 0.5 = 0.7$$

Example 2.   Of every 100 students who are selected, we find, on the average:

> 10 students who have a grade of A
> 20 students who have a grade of B
> 40 students who have a grade of C
> 20 students who have a grade of D
> 10 students who have a grade of F

There are 5 outcomes (events) and the probabilities of these events are

$$P(\text{grade } A) = 0.10, \qquad P(\text{grade } B) = 0.20, \qquad P(\text{grade } C) = 0.40$$
$$P(\text{grade } D) = 0.20, \qquad P(\text{grade } F) = 0.10$$

The probability of selecting a student who has either grade A or B is, since they are mutually exclusive events,

$$P(A \text{ or } B) = P(A) + P(B) = 0.1 + 0.2 = 0.3$$

The probability of selecting a student who has either grade C, D, or F is

$$P(C \text{ or } D \text{ or } F) = P(C) + P(D) + P(F) = 0.4 + 0.2 + 0.1 = 0.7$$

We can use these postulates to derive other rules of the calculus of probabilities. We shall first define conditional probabilities and then use this to find a multiplication rule. We shall then define statistical independence and find a second multiplication rule.

5.5. Conditional Probabilities

Suppose we have an urn with ten balls numbered 1 to 10. The first 3 balls (1 to 3) are colored red, and the other balls are colored green. Let us perform an experiment of drawing a ball at random and returning it to the urn. We shall assign a probability of 0.1 to each ball, as shown in Table 5.6.

TABLE 5.6.

Events	Probability	Compound Event	Probability	Conditional Probability
1	0.1 ⎫			$0.1/0.3 = 1/3$
2	0.1 ⎬	Red	0.3	
3	0.1 ⎭			
4	0.1 ⎫			
5	0.1 ⎪			
6	0.1 ⎪			
7	0.1 ⎬	Green	0.7	
8	0.1 ⎪			
9	0.1 ⎪			
10	0.1 ⎭			
	$\overline{1.0}$		$\overline{1.0}$	

Suppose now that a ball has been drawn and we are told that it is a red ball. Given this change in the conditions under which the experiment is performed, what probability should be assigned to the event of drawing a ball numbered 3?

From the additional information that it is a red ball, we know that the ball that was drawn is one of the three balls numbered 1, 2, or 3.

In terms of the concept of a population, this may be interpreted as follows: The population is the totality of the elementary units, that is, the 10 balls. By providing the additional information and changing the initial conditions, we have restricted the population to a subpopulation of red balls only. This is shown graphically in Fig. 5.4. The left graph, (a), shows the total population; the right graph, (b), shows the subpopulation made up only of red balls.

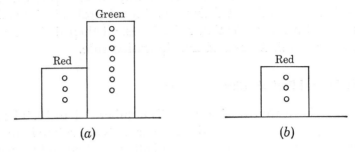

Green

Red

Red

(a)

(b)

FIG. 5.4.

The question now is: What probability should be assigned to the three red balls in the subpopulation?

According to the postulates stated in Section 5.4, the total probability has to be 1. We also know that the original probabilities were 0.1 for each ball. Thus we wish to assign new probabilities to these three balls (events) such that the proportion between the probabilities does not change, but the probabilities add up to 1.

Obviously, this is a simple problem of taking proportions. All we have to do is to first find the total probability of the subpopulation and then divide each probability of the events in the subpopulation by this total. The total probability of the subpopulation is

$$P(1) + P(2) + P(3) = 0.1 + 0.1 + 0.1 = 0.3$$

Then the new probabilities we assign are

$$P(1 \mid r) = \frac{P(1)}{0.3} = \frac{0.1}{0.3} = \frac{1}{3}$$

$$P(2 \mid r) = \frac{P(2)}{0.3} = \frac{0.1}{0.3} = \frac{1}{3}$$

$$P(3 \mid r) = \frac{P(3)}{0.3} = \frac{0.1}{0.3} = \frac{1}{3}$$

where, for example, $P(1 \mid r)$ means the probability of drawing a ball numbered 1, given a red ball (see Table 5.6).

The total of these new probabilities we have assigned is

$$\frac{1}{3} + \frac{1}{3} + \frac{1}{3} = 1$$

The probabilities obtained after we had changed the initial conditions are called *conditional probabilities.*

The two points to note in this discussion are as follows:

1.   By changing the initial conditions under which an experiment is performed, we restrict the events to be considered to a subpopulation.

2.   The probabilities assigned to the events in this subpopulation are such that the ratios of the probabilities between the events are the same as in the original population, but they add up to unity.

Let us now state our results as a formula. We had

$$P(1 \mid r) = \frac{0.1}{0.3}$$

where 0.3 was the probability of a red ball; that is,

$$P(\text{red}) = 0.3$$

This is the total probability of the subpopulation of red balls; and 0.1 is the probability of the joint event of a red ball that is numbered 1. Recall that a joint event was shown by 1 & red. Hence we have,

$$P(1 \ \& \ \text{red}) = 0.1$$

Thus our result is

$$P(1 \mid r) = \frac{P(1 \ \& \ r)}{P(\text{red})}$$

$$= \frac{\text{prob. of joint event } 1 \ \& \ r}{\text{prob. of the subpop.}}$$

Let us apply this result to the question: What is the probability of selecting a 5, given a green ball?

$$P(5 \mid \text{green}) = \frac{P(5 \ \& \ \text{green})}{P(\text{green})} = \frac{0.1}{0.7} = \frac{1}{7}$$

In similar manner we may find

$$P(5 \mid \text{red}) = \frac{P(5 \ \& \ \text{red})}{P(\text{red})} = \frac{0}{0.3} = 0$$

Obviously, 5 & red is an impossible event.

Example 1.   Given an urn with 10 balls numbered 1 to 10, what is the probability of selecting the ball numbered 5 after drawing a ball that is not numbered 5?

In the original state, each ball is assigned a probability of $1/10 = 0.1$ (Fig. 5.5). To add the condition that a ball not numbered 5 is drawn and not re-

(a)   (b)

FIG. 5.5.

placed is to restrict the population to the subpopulation of 9 balls. Hence the probabilities we assign to the balls in this subpopulation are obtained by dividing the probability of each ball (0.1) by the total probability of the subpopulation (0.9). Thus,

$$P(5 \mid \text{not } 5) = \frac{0.1}{0.9} = \frac{1}{9}$$

$P(5 \mid \text{not } 5)$ is read as the probability of selecting a 5, given (assuming) that a ball not numbered 5 is selected first.

In terms of our formula we have

$$P(5 \mid \text{not } 5) = \frac{P(5 \ \& \ \text{not } 5)}{P(\text{not } 5)}$$

The event "5 & not 5" is equal to the event 5. Thus

$$P(5 \ \& \ \text{not } 5) = P(5) = 0.1$$

and hence

$$P(5 \mid \text{not } 5) = \frac{0.1}{0.9} = \frac{1}{9}$$

With this much background, let us now define conditional probability as follows: If A is an event with positive probability, the conditional probability of B, given A, is defined as

$$P(B \mid A) = \frac{P(B \ \& \ A)}{P(A)}$$

We have restricted the total population by a hypothesis A and have formed a subpopulation from which we calculate the probability of B.

Example 2.   Let B be the event that the person is a male. Then the probability of selecting a person who has tuberculosis, given he is a male, is

$$P(B \mid A) = \frac{P(B \ \& \ A)}{P(A)}$$

where $P(B \ \& \ A)$ is the probability of selecting a person who has tuberculosis and is a male. $P(A)$ is the probability of selecting a male.

For example, assume the probabilities of the events are as shown in Table 5.7.

TABLE 5.7.

Events	Probability	Compound Event	Probability	Conditional Probability
Male, TB Male, NTB	0.05 ⎫ 0.45 ⎭	Male	0.50	⎰ 0.05/0.5 = 0.1 ⎱ 0.45/0.5 = 0.9
Female, TB Female, NTB	0.10 ⎫ 0.40 ⎭	Female	0.50	⎰ 0.1/0.5 = 0.2 ⎱ 0.4/0.5 = 0.8
	1.00		1.00	

The NTB in the table means non-TB. The conditional probability we seek is

$$P(\text{TB} \mid \text{male}) = \frac{P(\text{TB \& male})}{P(\text{male})}$$

In terms of frequencies, this may be shown as computed in Table 5.8. We assume 700 persons have been selected.

TABLE 5.8.

Events	Frequency	Relative Frequency	Compound Event	Frequency	Relative Frequency
Male, TB Male, NTB	35 315	0.05 ⎫ 0.45 ⎭	Male	350	0.5
Female, TB Female, NTB	70 280	0.10 ⎫ 0.40 ⎭	Female	350	0.5
	700			700	

The relative frequencies are used as estimates of the probabilities. The computational results of the conditional probability $P(\text{TB} \mid \text{male})$ is the same as above.

Example 3. Let B be the event that a person has an IQ over 110 and A be the event that the person chosen is a college graduate. The probability that a person chosen at random has an IQ over 110, given that he is a college graduate, is

$$P(B \mid A) = \frac{P(B \ \& \ A)}{P(A)}$$

where $P(B \& A)$ is the probability that the person chosen has an IQ over 110 and is a college graduate. $P(A)$ is the probability of choosing a person who is a college graduate.

As an illustration, assume that the probabilities are as given in Table 5.9.

TABLE 5.9.

Events	Probability	Compound Event	Probability	Conditional Probability
College, over 110	0.3 ⎫	College	0.4	⎧ 0.3/0.4 = 0.75
College, under 109	0.1 ⎭			⎩ 0.1/0.4 = 0.25
Non-college, over 110	0.2 ⎫	Non-College	0.6	⎧ 0.2/0.6 = 0.33
Non-college, under 109	0.4 ⎭			⎩ 0.4/0.6 = 0.64
	$\overline{1.0}$		$\overline{1.0}$	

The conditional probability we seek is

$$P(\text{over } 110 \mid \text{college}) = \frac{P(\text{over } 110 \& \text{college})}{P(\text{college})} = \frac{0.3}{0.4} = 0.75$$

This is shown graphically in Fig. 5.6.

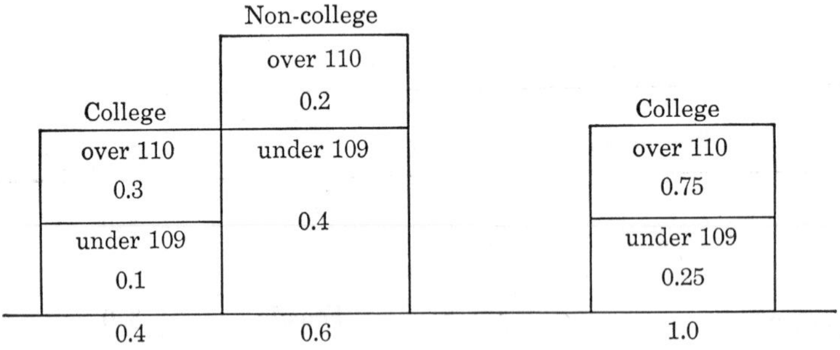

FIG. 5.6.

Example 4. Using the probabilities of Example 3, let us find the conditional probability of selecting a college student, given a person with an IQ over 110. That is, find $P(\text{college} \mid \text{over } 110)$. For this, we construct Table 5.10. The conditional probability we seek is

$$P(\text{college} \mid \text{over } 110) = \frac{P(\text{college} \& 110)}{P(\text{over } 110)} = \frac{0.3}{0.5} = 0.6$$

This result is shown graphically in Fig. 5.7.

TABLE 5.10.

Events	Probability	Compound Event	Probability	Conditional Probability
Over 110, college	0.3 ⎫	Over 110	0.5	⎧ 0.3/0.5 = 0.6
Over 110, non-college	0.2 ⎭			⎩ 0.2/0.5 = 0.4
Under 109, college	0.1 ⎫	Under 109	0.5	
Under 109, non-college	0.4 ⎭			
	$\overline{1.0}$		$\overline{1.0}$	

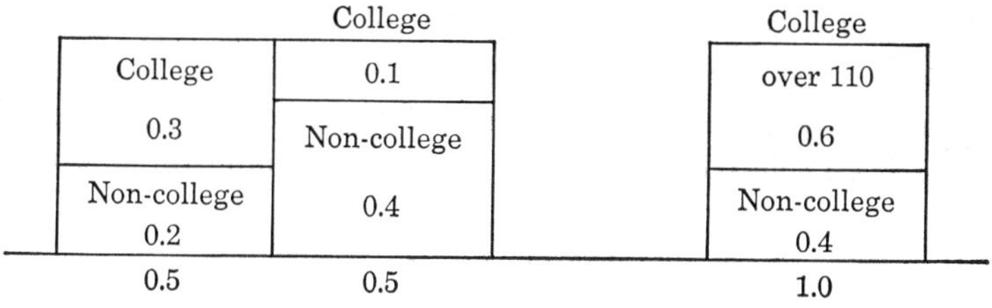

	College
College 0.3	0.1
	Non-college 0.4
Non-college 0.2	
0.5	0.5

College
over 110 0.6
Non-college 0.4
1.0

FIG. 5.7.

5.6.   A Rule for Multiplication of Probabilities

The definition of conditional probabilities has been given as

$$P(B \mid A) = \frac{P(B \text{ \& } A)}{P(A)}$$

From this we find

$$P(B \text{ \& } A) = P(A)P(B \mid A)$$

We also know that

$$P(A \mid B) = \frac{P(A \text{ \& } B)}{P(B)}$$

and hence

$$P(A \text{ \& } B) = P(B)P(A \mid B)$$

The event $A \text{ \& } B$ is the joint event of A and B. It means the event where both A and B occur simultaneously. Clearly, $A \text{ \& } B$ and $B \text{ \& } A$ are equal. Thus

$$P(A \text{ \& } B) = P(A)P(B \mid A) = P(B)P(A \mid B)$$

In words we may say: The probability of the joint event $A \text{ \& } B$ is the product of $P(A)$ and $P(B \mid A)$, or the product of $P(B)$ and $P(A \mid B)$.

Example 1. Of all students, 30 percent receive a grade of C (event A). Of all students who receive C, 40 percent are females (event B). What is the probability of a randomly selected female having a grade C?

The event of a female having a grade C is the joint event A & B. We also know that

$$P(A) = 0.3, \qquad P(B \mid A) = 0.4$$

Then, from our rules, we find

$$P(A \ \& \ B) = P(A)P(B \mid A) = (0.3)\,(0.4) = 0.12$$

Example 2. Suppose we have 5 students. What is the probability of selecting the first and third students in that order? Let us assume each student has equal chance of being selected. Then the probability of selecting the first student (event A) is $P(A) = 1/5$.

The probability of selecting the third student (event B), given the first student has been selected, is (since there are now four students remaining)

$$P(B \mid A) = \frac{1}{4}$$

Thus the probability of the event A & B is

$$P(A \ \& \ B) = P(A)P(B \mid A) = \frac{1}{5} \times \frac{1}{4} = \frac{1}{20}$$

As an exercise in conditional probabilities, let us find $P(B \mid A)$ by use of the conditional probability formula. We have

$$P(B \mid A) = \frac{P(B \ \& \ A)}{P(A)}$$

Let us construct a table showing all the events, Table 5.11. The 1–2, 1–3, etc., in the table means: the order of selection is (1st student–2nd

TABLE 5.11.

Events	Probability	Compound Event	Probability	Conditional Probability
1–2	1/20			1/4
1–3	1/20			1/4
1–4	1/20	1st student	4/20	1/4
1–5	1/20	first		1/4
2–1				
2–3				
2–4				
. . .	. . .			
5–3				
5–4				
	1.0			

student), (1st student–3rd student), etc. From Table 5.11 we find

$$P(B \mid A) = \frac{P(B \& A)}{P(A)} = \frac{\dfrac{1}{20}}{\dfrac{4}{20}} = \frac{1}{4}$$

5.7. Statistical Independence

Suppose a fair coin is tossed once. The event of a head occurring (event A) is $1/2$. Let event B be the event of tossing the coin a second time and getting a head. What is the probability of event B (second head), given event A (first head)? That is, what is $P(B \mid A)$?

We observe that the occurrence of the second head is not influenced by the first head. That is, the occurrence of the second head is independent of the first head. In such a case, we shall say event B is *statistically independent* of event A.

In terms of symbols, we have

(1) $$P(B \mid A) = P(B) = \frac{1}{2}$$

But, since we have from equation

$$P(B \mid A)P(A) = P(B)P(A \mid B)$$

we see that if $P(B \mid A) = P(B)$, then

(2) $$P(A) = P(A \mid B)$$

In other words, if B is statistically independent of A, then A is statistically independent of B. If the occurrence of the second head is independent of the first head, then the occurrence of the first head is independent of the second head.

Hence we shall say: *If formula (1) or (2) holds, events* A *and* B *are statistically independent.*

The conditional probability formula is

(3) $$P(B \mid A) = \frac{P(B \& A)}{P(A)}$$

If A and B are *statistically independent*, then from formulas (1) and (3),

(4) $$P(B \& A) = P(B)P(A)$$

and also, from formulas (2) and (3),

(5) $$P(A \& B) = P(A)P(B)$$

Formulas (4) and (5) show that *the probability of the joint occurrence of statistically independent events* A *and* B *is equal to the product of the probabilities of these events*. We have thus derived a rule for the multiplication of probabilities for independent events.

Let us substitute formulas (4) and (5) into (3). Then

(6) $$P(B \mid A) = \frac{P(B \,\&\, A)}{P(A)} = \frac{P(B)P(A)}{P(A)} = P(B)$$

In similar manner, when we have

(7) $$P(A \mid B) = \frac{P(A \,\&\, B)}{P(B)}$$

and substitute formula (4) or (5) into this formula, we get

(8) $$P(A \mid B) = P(A)$$

Our result shows that formulas (4) and (5) imply statistical independence.

Therefore we shall say: *If formula (4) or (5) holds, events* A *and* B *are statistically independent*.

This rule for multiplication of independent events may be generalized to any number of events. For example, let event A be heads on the first toss of a fair coin, event B be heads on the second toss, and let event C be heads on the third toss. We observe that all three events are mutually independent. In particular, the joint $A \,\&\, B$ is independent of C. Hence, applying our rule, we find the probability of the joint event $A \,\&\, B \,\&\, C$ (that is, getting a head on the first, second, and third toss) is

$$P(A \,\&\, B \,\&\, C) = P(A \,\&\, B)P(C)$$

But

$$P(A \,\&\, B) = P(A)P(B)$$

Therefore

(9) $$P(A \,\&\, B \,\&\, C) = P(A)P(B)P(C)$$

and in our present case, we have

$$P(A \,\&\, B \,\&\, C) = \frac{1}{2} \times \frac{1}{2} \times \frac{1}{2} = \frac{1}{8}$$

This formula (9) may be generalized in similar manner to more than three events.

Example 1. Machine A has a probability of 0.1 of stopping because of a breakdown. Machine B has a probability of 0.2 of stopping. Machines A and B are assumed to be statistically independent of each other. What is the probability that both machines will stop at the same time?

$$P(A \text{ stops } \& B \text{ stops}) = P(A \text{ stops}) \times P(B \text{ stops})$$
$$= 0.1 \times 0.2 = 0.02$$

Example 2. There are three typists in an office and each has a probability of 0.2 of being absent. Assuming the events of being absent are independent, what is the probability that all three secretaries will be absent on the same day? Let A, B, and C be the events that the respective secretaries are absent. Then

$$P(A \& B \& C) = P(A)P(B)P(C) = (0.2)\,(0.2)\,(0.2) = 0.008$$

Example 3. Given an urn that has 10 red, 20 black, and 70 green balls. Four balls are selected at random, one at time, and returned to the urn. What is the probability of selecting a red, black, green, green in that order?

$$P(\text{red } \& \text{ black } \& \text{ green } \& \text{ green}) = 0.1 \times 0.2 \times 0.7 \times 0.7 = 0.0098$$

Note carefully the proviso, "in that order." The case where the order is disregarded is discussed in Chapter 7.

The astute reader may now raise the question: Are these probabilities that have been obtained from the multiplication rule legitimate probabilities? To be legitimate probabilities, they must satisfy the basic axiom, which stated that the probabilities must be nonnegative and also add up to unity. That they are nonnegative is obvious, since they are the product of nonnegative probabilities. What we need to check is whether they add up to unity.

Consider as an illustration, a loaded penny, where

$$P(H) = P_1 \qquad P(T) = P_2$$

Since the penny is loaded, we assume $P_1 \neq \frac{1}{2}$, $P_2 \neq \frac{1}{2}$, $P_1 + P_2 = 1$.
Let another loaded dime have probabilities

$$P(H) = P_3 \qquad P(T) = P_4$$

where $P_3 \neq \frac{1}{2}$, $P_4 \neq \frac{1}{2}$, and $P_3 + P_4 = 1$. When the penny and dime are tossed together, there are four possible outcomes (that is, simple events), as shown in Fig. 5.8. The outcomes are:

$$(H, H), \qquad (H, T), \qquad (T, H), \qquad (T, T)$$

Using the mulitplication rule, we may now assign probabilities to these four simple events. They are as follows:

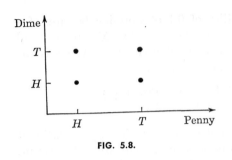

FIG. 5.8.

$$P(H, H) = P(H)P(H) = (P_1)\,(P_3)$$
$$P(H, T) = P(H)P(T) = (P_1)\,(P_4)$$
$$P(T, H) = P(T)P(H) = (P_2)\,(P_3)$$
$$P(T, T) = P(T)P(T) = (P_2)\,(P_4)$$

It is obvious that each of these probabilities is nonnegative. Let us next check to find whether they add up to unity.

$$P_1P_3 + P_1P_4 + P_2P_3 + P_2P_4 = P_1(P_3 + P_4) + P_2(P_3 + P_4)$$
$$= P_1 \cdot 1 + P_2 \cdot 1 = P_1 + P_2 = 1$$

That is, the probabilities we assigned to the four simple events, using the multiplication rule, satisfy both requirements of the basic axiom, and hence are legitimate probabilities.

It turns out that this holds true in general. Thus we may proceed and use the multiplication rule to assign probabilities to simple events that have been generated by statistically independent experiments.

5.8. Mathematical Expectation and Random Variable

Before concluding this chapter, let us consider two more ideas, mathematical expectation and random variable, which we shall be using over and over again in our subsequent discussions. The mathematical expectation of a variable X, as we shall see, is simply its weighted arithmetic mean presented in terms of probability. First we shall illustrate this new concept.

Suppose you get \$2.00 if a head occurs and \$3.00 if a tail occurs when a fair coin is tossed. How much do you *expect* to get per toss when this game is played over and over again? Assume the game is played 10 times and there are 4 heads and 6 tails. Then the total amount of money you get is

$$\$2 \times 4 + \$3 \times 6 = \$26$$

The average per game is

$$\frac{\$2 \times 4 + \$3 \times 6}{10} = 2 \times \frac{4}{10} + 3 \times \frac{6}{10} = 2.6$$

These $4/10$ and $6/10$ are the relative frequencies of getting a head and a tail. When this game is played many times, these relative frequencies will approach $1/2$. Thus we may say: If the game is played a large number of times, the average amount of money you get per game will be approximately

$$\$2 \times \frac{1}{2} + 3 \times \frac{1}{2} = \$2.5$$

We restate the results in terms of symbols: The variable X is the amount of money received, and the values it takes are $x_1 = \$2.00$ and $x_2 = \$3.00$. When the game is played a large number of times, there are a large number of observations, but they are either $x_1 = \$2.00$ or $x_2 = \$3.00$. Let $P(H) = 1/2$ and $P(T) = 1/2$. Then the result may be stated as

$$x_1 P(H) + x_2 P(T) = \$2 \times \frac{1}{2} + 3 \times \frac{1}{2} = \$2.5$$

We may now formalize this idea as follows:

Let X be a variable with outcomes x_1 and x_2, which occur with probability $P(X = x_1)$ and $P(X = x_2)$. The *mathematical expectation* of the variable X, which we denote by $E(X)$, is defined as

(1) $$E(X) = x_1 P(x_1) + x_2 P(x_2)$$

In general, if X has n outcomes, then

(2) $$E(X) = x_1 P(x_1) + x_2 P(x_2) + \cdots + x_n P(x_n)$$

Example 1.   Assume you get $\$1, \$2, \$3, \$4, \$5, \$6$, when a 1, 2, 3, 4, 5, or 6 of a die occurs. Then the variable X has six outcomes: $\$1, \$2, \ldots, \$6$. Thus, assuming a fair die, the expected value of X is

$$E(X) = \$1 \times P(X = 1) + \$2 \times P(X = 2) + \cdots + \$6 \times P(X = 6)$$

$$= \$1 \times \frac{1}{6} \times 2 \times \frac{1}{6} + \cdots + 6 \times \frac{1}{6} = \frac{21}{6} = \$3.5$$

Example 2.   Consider a lottery with 1000 tickets. Each ticket is 25¢ and the prize is $\$100$. The variable X has two outcomes, winning ($\$100$–25¢) or losing 25¢. Thus the mathematical expectation of X is

$$E(X) = (\$100 - 0.25) \times P(\text{win}) + (-0.25) \times P(\text{lose})$$

$$= (\$100 - 0.25) \times \frac{1}{1000} + (-0.25) \times \frac{999}{1000}$$

$$= 10¢ - 25¢ = -15¢$$

That is, the sponsors of the lottery can expect to make 15¢ per ticket. Thus, for 1000 tickets, they make $\$150$. This is consistent with the fact that the total sale of tickets is $\$250$ and the prize is $\$100$.

Example 3. In Example 2, assume that you bought 500 tickets. What is the mathematical expectation? Since 500 tickets will cost you $125,

$$E(X) = (\$100 - 125) \times P(\text{win}) + (-\$125) \times P(\text{lose})$$

$$= (\$100 - 125) \times \frac{500}{1000} + (-\$125) \times \frac{500}{1000}$$

$$= -\$75$$

As is seen, the mathematical expectation of X is the same as finding the weighted mean of X.

We shall define, nonrigorously, a *random variable* as a variable with probabilities associated to it. This will be discussed again in Chapter 16. We shall in many cases use the term *variable* as an abbreviation of "random variable."

Let X be the outcome of a toss of a die. X has 6 possible outcomes and to each outcome there is associated a probability of $1/6$. This X is a random variable.

5.9. Summary

Understand the following five ideas:
1.   When A and B are mutually exclusive events, then

$$P(A \text{ or } B) = P(A) + P(B)$$

2.   The conditional probability of B, given A, is

$$P(B \mid A) = \frac{P(B \& A)}{P(A)}, \qquad P(A) > 0$$

3.   When A and B are not statistically independent, then

$$P(B \& A) = P(A)P(B \mid A)$$

4.   When A and B are statistically independent, then

$$P(B \mid A) = P(B)$$

and

$$P(A \& B) = P(A)P(B)$$

5.   The expectation of X is

$$E(X) = x_1 P(X = x_1) + x_2 P(X = x_2) + \cdots + x_n P(X = x_n)$$

114

THE NORMAL C

tion, which is a frequency
the center of the distrib
cally. An example is t

THE NORMAL CL
AND NORMAL AREA TABLE

6

6.1. Introduction

For our subsequent discussion of statistical inference, we need two preliminaries: probability, which was discussed in Chapter 5, and the normal curve and normal area table, which are the topics of this chapter. We wish to discuss and learn how to use the normal area table so that we can calculate the probability of an event. However, a formal discussion of the normal curve and normal area table are mathematically too advanced for this book, but nevertheless the meaning and use may be explained without formal mathematical derivations.

As subsequent discussion will reveal, the normal curve holds central importance in statistics because a vast number of phenomena may be explained in terms of the normal distribution, which we shall discuss later. Several mathematicians contributed to its formulation, among whom were Abraham De Moivre (1667–1754), Pierre S. Laplace (1749–1827), and Karl Gauss (1777–1855). Although De Moivre was the first to develop the normal distribution, his work went unnoticed, and it was the work of Gauss, which appeared later, that became better known among mathematicians. As a result, the normal distribution is sometimes called the *gaussian distribution*, although this term is less used nowadays in statistics as discussed here.

The normal curve is the graphical expression of the normal distribu-

distribution that has many frequencies near
ution and then gradually tapers off symmetri-
he distribution of IQ's as shown in Table 6.1.

TABLE 6.1.

IQ	f
60– 69	26
70– 79	56
80– 89	145
90– 99	230
100–109	235
110–119	182
120–129	82
130–139	31
140–149	13
	1000

Figure 6.1 is the frequency histogram and frequency polygon of the
normal distribution in Table 6.1. As we increase the number of observations and make the class intervals smaller, we can see intuitively that
the frequency polygon will become a smooth curve, as shown in Fig. 6.2.
This smooth curve then can be thought of as an ideal model of an actual
situation.

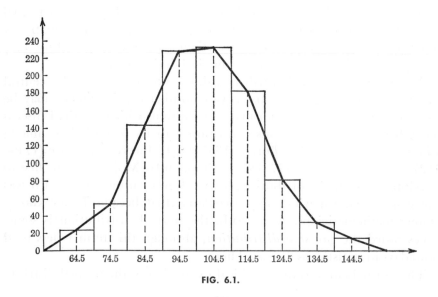

FIG. 6.1.

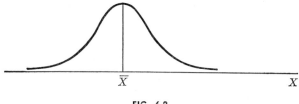

FIG. 6.2.

As was the case in probability theory, where theoretical probabilities were used as models to represent actual situations, the normal curve may also be considered as a theoretical model that we use because of its usefulness to analyze actual situations. This point concerning the usefulness of the normal curve and normal distribution for analysis of various practical situations will become clear as our discussion develops and illustrations are presented.

The properties of this normal curve are:
1. It is symmetrical and bell shaped.
2. As a result, the mean is in the middle and divides the area in half, and the mean, median, and mode are identical.
3. Theoretically, the curve extends in both directions, gradually coming closer to the horizontal axis. It extends out to infinity, but never reaches the horizontal axis.

The third point may puzzle the reader because, in our illustration, the distribution of IQ's has a lower limit of zero, and no one has yet been found to have an IQ over 250. As has been mentioned, the normal curve is an ideal model, and the actual distributions we deal with are approximations and are usually truncated at certain upper and lower limits. Nevertheless they are usually treated as if they were the ideal normal distributions used to calculate the probabilities of events. This approximation is permissible and usually has very little effect on the practical results that are derived.

Our object, as we stated at the beginning, is to learn how to find the probability of an event by using the normal curve and normal area table. Let us now construct a hypothetical distribution and discuss this problem.

6.2. Heuristic Explanation of the Normal Curve and Normal Area Table

In Chapter 5 we stated that the sum of probabilities of all possible events is unity. We also know that the area under a normal curve that represents a frequency distribution shows graphically all possible events.

Hence, to establish a connection between probability theory and a normal curve, we wish to represent the area under a normal curve in terms of proportions and say that the *total area under the curve is unity*. We shall use a hypothetical case to derive this property.

Assume a fixed rifle is shot 200 times at a target that is broken up into vertical stripes of 1 in. (Fig. 6.3). After counting the shots on the target, let us say that we obtained the results shown in Table 6.2.

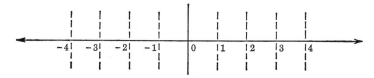

FIG. 6.3.

TABLE 6.2.

Class	Frequency	Relative Frequency
−5 to −4	2	0.01
−4 to −3	4	0.02
−3 to −2	12	0.06
−2 to −1	28	0.14
−1 to −0	48	0.24
0 to 1	52	0.26
1 to 2	32	0.16
2 to 3	16	0.08
3 to 4	4	0.02
4 to 5	2	0.01
	200	1.00

For instance, between 1 and 2 in., there were 32 shots; and so forth. Since there are 200 shots, and 32 of them fell between 1 and 2 in. from the center, the relative frequency of shots falling between 1 and 2 in. is $32/200 = 16/100$, or 0.16.

We use the frequency table to draw a histogram with a vertical scale on the left side, as in Fig. 6.4. Then the area of this histogram will be

$$\text{Area} = (1 \times 2) + (1 \times 4) + (1 \times 12) + \cdots + (1 \times 16) +$$
$$(1 \times 4) + (1 \times 2) = 200$$

That is, the *area* is equal to the total frequencies.

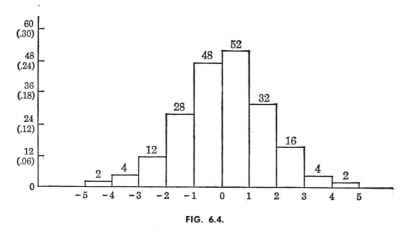

FIG. 6.4.

Since we want the area in terms of proportions, let us divide the total area by $N = 200$, which is the total number of frequencies. Then, in *proportionate terms*, the area of the histogram is 1.00.

Dividing the total area by N is the same as dividing each frequency by N and then summing up. That is,

$$\frac{\text{Area}}{N} = \frac{(1 \times f_1) + (1 \times f_2) + \cdots + (1 \times f_9) + (1 \times f_{10})}{N}$$

$$= \frac{f_1}{N} + \frac{f_2}{N} + \cdots + \frac{f_9}{N} + \frac{f_{10}}{N}$$

$$= 1$$

where $f_1, f_2, \ldots, f_{10}$ are the frequencies. The frequencies divided by N (that is, f_i/N) gives us the relative frequencies. This means that we have plotted a histogram using relative frequencies rather than frequencies. So, all we have to do is to divide the units of our vertical scale by 200. The results are shown in the brackets on the vertical scale of the histogram.

Previously one of the rectangles in the histogram showed the frequency of shots that would fall in that interval. Now it shows the *relative* frequency of shots that would fall in that interval. We shall consider this relative frequency as an *estimate* of the probabilities. For instance, between 1 and 2 in., as we said previously, there would be 32 shots. Now we say that the probability of a shot's (that is, an event) falling between 1 and 2 in. is 0.16. The probability of a shot's falling between 1 and 3 in. will be $0.16 + 0.08 = 0.24$. The probability that a shot will fall somewhere on the target will be the sum of all the rectangles that comprise the whole area, which is 1.

Fit a smooth frequency curve to this histogram and assume that we have been able to fit the curve in such a way that the area under the curve and the area of the histogram are equal. Thus the area under the frequency curve (which we presume to be a normal curve) is equal to 1.00.

As we mentioned before, the midpoint of the normal curve is the mean. The properties of the normal curve are such that we can calculate the *proportions* of the area lying between the mean and the indicated value by using the standard deviation. For example, when the indicated value (x) is one standard deviation away from the mean (μ), the proportion of the area between x_1 and μ (that is, the shaded area in Fig. 6.5) is

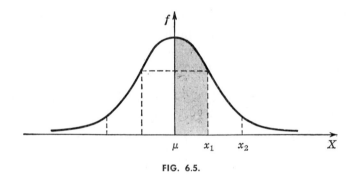

FIG. 6.5.

34.13 percent. When x_2 is 2 standard deviations away, the area between x_2 and μ is 47.73 percent. We always measure the deviation of x from the mean μ. Mathematicians have calculated all these proportions for us and have arranged them in table form. This is known as the *normal area table*.

How to use the normal area table

Let us assume that the distribution of the IQ's of army recruits has a normal distribution, with $\mu = 100$ and $\sigma = 10$. Then what is the proportion of army recruits that have an IQ between 100 and 105? We wish to find diagrammatically the area of the shaded proportion in Fig. 6.6.

The deviation between 100 and 105 in terms of standard deviations is

$$z = \frac{x - \mu}{\sigma} = \frac{105 - 100}{10} = \frac{5}{10} = 0.50$$

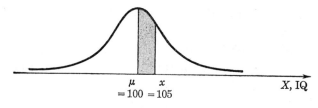

$$\mu \qquad x$$
$$=100 \ =105$$

$$X, IQ$$

FIG. 6.6.

That is, the deviation is 0.5 standard deviation. The deviation has been standardized. We shall use the letter z to show this type of operation.

Let us now show how the normal area table is used to find the shaded proportion. Table 6.3 is a portion of the normal area table. (See Table 1 in Appendix for the full table.) Since the deviation $x - \mu$ is 0.5 standard deviation, we find that the corresponding proportion in the table is 0.3085. This 0.3085 is the proportion of the shaded area in the tail end of Fig. 6.7. Note that the proportions in the normal area table show the area under the *tail end* of the normal curve.

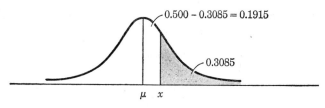

0.500 − 0.3085 = 0.1915

0.3085

$$\mu \quad x$$

FIG. 6.7.

TABLE 6.3.   Normal Area Table

z	0.00	0.01	...
0.0	0.500	0.4960	
0.1	0.4002	0.4562	
...	...	...	
0.5	0.3085	0.3050	
...	...	...	
1.0	0.1587	0.1562	
:			

Since the total area under the normal curve is 1.0, each half is 0.5. Hence the shaded area that we seek in Fig. 6.6 is

$$0.5 - 0.3085 = 0.1915$$

That is, the proportion of the shaded area is 0.1915, or 19.15 percent, of the total area.

What does this mean? First note that the event under consideration is the occurrence of recruits with IQ's between 100 and 105. Let us denote this event by A. Then the probability we seek is the probability of there being recruits with IQ's between 100 and 105. That is, $P(A)$. From our discussion of the area under the normal curve, we see that 0.1915 is this probability; that is,

$$P(A) = 0.1915$$

There are two kinds of normal area tables: One gives the proportion of area of the tail end as shown by the area designated by I in Fig. 6.8;

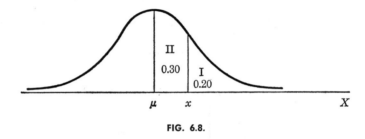

FIG. 6.8.

a second gives the area that is designated by II in Fig. 6.8. If the proportion of I is 0.20, then the proportion given by the second kind of table is $0.50 - 0.20 = 0.30$.

The table used in this book is the first kind because, in our subsequent discussion of statistical inference, we shall usually be concerned with the area in the tail end of the normal curve.

Example 1. What is the proportion of army recruits who have an IQ between 100 and 105.7? We assume $\mu = 100$ and $\sigma = 10$.

$$z = \frac{105.7 - 100}{10} = \frac{5.7}{10} = 0.57$$

From the normal area table we find 0.2843. Thus the proportion we want is

$$0.5000 - 0.2843 = 0.2157$$

That is, 21.57 percent of the recruits have an IQ between 100 and 105.7.

Or, we may say that the probability of there being recruits between 100 and 105.7 is 0.2157.

Example 2. What is the proportion of army recruits between 103 and 105.7? Let us draw a diagram (Fig. 6.9) as a visual aid showing this situation. First find z:

$$z = \frac{103 - 100}{10} = \frac{3.0}{10} = 0.30$$

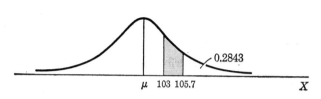

FIG. 6.9.

Then, from the normal area table, the proportion of area in the tail end is 0.3821. We know from Example 1 that the proportion corresponding to 105.7 is 0.2843. Thus the shaded area we seek is

$$0.3821 - 0.2843 = 0.0978$$

Example 3. What proportion of the army recruits have an IQ of less than 83.6? For this we have

$$z = \frac{83.6 - 100}{10} = \frac{-16.4}{10} = -1.64$$

Diagrammatically, it is the tail end of the curve in Fig. 6.10. From the normal area table we find that it is 0.0505. Note that the minus sign indicates that the area is the *left*-hand side of the normal curve. A plus indicates the *right*-hand side of the normal curve.

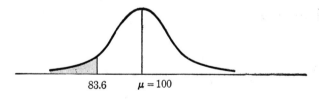

FIG. 6.10.

Example 4. What is the proportion beyond 120? Since

$$z = \frac{120 - 100}{10} = 2$$

we find from the normal area table that the proportion is 0.0228.

Three proportions that will occur over and over again in subsequent discussion are

$$z = 1.28 \cdots 0.1003 \text{ (which is approximately 10\%)}$$
$$z = 1.64 \cdots 0.0505 \text{ (which is approximately 5\%)}$$
$$z = 2.00 \cdots 0.0228$$

It is recommended that the student memorize the first two proportions.

6.3.   Discussion of the Normal Distribution

It was mentioned in Section 6.1 that the normal curve holds central importance in statistics because a vast number of phenomena may be explained in terms of the normal distribution. A question that naturally arises is: Why? To answer this question, we first have to investigate several statistical properties related to the normal distribution.

(i)   Addition of independent normal variables

Let ξ_1 be a variable denoting the IQ of students in school A, and let ξ_2 be a variable denoting the IQ of students in school B. Assume that ξ_1 is normally distributed with mean μ_1 and variance σ_1^2 and that ξ_2 is also normally distributed with mean μ_2 and variance σ_2^2. We shall also assume that ξ_1 and ξ_2 are statistically independent.

We state without proof the following two theorems:

1.   The sum of independent normally distributed variables is itself normally distributed. That is, let

$$\xi = \xi_1 + \xi_2$$

Then ξ is normally distributed. Furthermore, the mean μ and variance σ^2 of ξ are given by

$$\mu = \mu_1 + \mu_2$$
$$\sigma^2 = \sigma_1^2 + \sigma_2^2$$

2.   If ξ is normally distributed, where

$$\xi = \xi_1 + \xi_2$$

then each ξ_1 and ξ_2 is also normally distributed. Although everything has been stated in terms of two variables, the result holds for n variables.

(ii)   Generalization

A question that arises now is: What if the random variables are *not* normally distributed? It turns out that, under certain conditions, the sum of independent random variables is asymptotically normal. Asymptotically normal means that the sum will approach a normal distribution as the number (n) of random variables that are summed becomes large. This, very nonrigorously, will be called the *central limit theorem.*

It is too difficult to discuss the conditions under which this theorem holds true. However, we can very easily discuss how this theorem helps to *explain* why a vast number of phenomena show approximately a normal distribution.

We may illustrate with IQ's that are known to be normally distributed. The IQ's of children may be thought of as a random variable that may be affected by a large number of mutually independent causes (parents, living conditions, location, friends, etc.). Let us assume that these mutually independent causes are random variables that add up and affect the IQ of a child, and furthermore that there are many such contributing random variables and that each contributes only a very small effect. By assuming these effects, the central limit theorem may be used to explain why the IQ is normally distributed. Note carefully that the central limit theorem provides an *explanation* of why the IQ is normally distributed; it does not *prove* that the IQ is normally distributed.

Now let us consider the example of the rifle shots. The random variable was the deviation of the shot from the center of the target. Assuming that there is no systematic bias, we may think that the deviation of a shot is affected by a very large number of mutually independent causes such as a slight change in the wind, a slight change in the atmospheric pressure, a small difference in the weight of the bullet, or a slight change in the physical condition of the shooter. Then, with the central limit theorem in mind, we may conjecture that the deviations of the shots (which are affected by a large number of independent causes, each having a very small effect) may be approximately normally distributed. By taking a sample of the deviations, we can check this experimentally.

Although only two examples have been presented, it is quite easily seen that there are many other examples in technological problems, problems of measurements, biological problems, economic problems, etc., where the random variable is affected by a very large number of mutually independent causes, each having a very small effect. Hence we may infer that a great many distributions will be approximately normal. Experience has shown that this is indeed the case. But note once again that the central limit theorem does not prove the existence of normal distributions such as those mentioned in the examples. It has been used solely to explain or expect (infer, conjecture) the phenomena of approximately normally distributed variables.

(iii) The importance of the normal distribution

In the preceding section, we showed how probabilities of events may be computed by using the normal area table. In this section we showed how we may expect a vast number of phenomena to be approximately normally distributed, and it is known from experience that a vast number of phenomena do have approximately normal distributions. Hence the normal distribution has wide application in statistics and is one of the most important distributions.

Another reason why the normal distribution is important is that it has a number of desirable mathematical properties. Some of these will be described later.

6.4. Continuity Correction

The normal area table is based on a continuous normal distribution, or, we may say, on a continuous normal curve. However, in many practical applications, the data are discrete, and in such cases it is necessary to apply a continuity correction. Let us use an example to explain this.

Suppose the mean of the number of hogs on a farm in a certain county is 120 hogs and the standard deviation is 20 hogs. What is the probability that there are 150 hogs or more on a farm? We shall assume that the distribution of the number of hogs is approximately normal.

Let us first draw a diagram of this problem as a visual aid. From Fig. 6.11(a) we see that the proportion of the area of the curve we are interested in is the shaded part beyond 150 hogs.

However, note that the data are discrete. Hence, when looking at Fig. 6.11(a), we may think that we have fitted a smooth curve to a histogram so that the area under the curve and the histogram is ap-

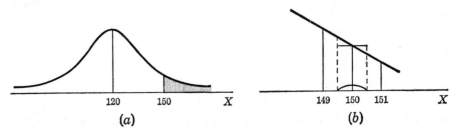

(a) (b)

FIG. 6.11.

proximately equal. But, from our discussion in Chapter 2, we know that when we have discrete data, the bars have to be plotted between midpoints. In our present case, this is shown in Fig. 6.11(b). The bar over 150 hogs is from 149.5 hogs to 150.5 hogs. Therefore, when we want to compute the probability of 150 hogs or more, which means we include 150 hogs, the area we want is from 149.5 to the end of the right tail.

On the other hand, if we want to know the probability of the number of hogs being between 130 and 150 inclusive, we have to find the area between 129.5 and 150.5 where we are including 130 and 150. This is shown schematically in Fig. 6.12.

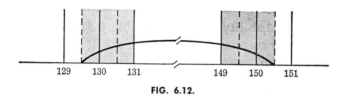

FIG. 6.12.

Obviously, when we have discrete data and use the normal area table, which is based on a continuous distribution, we need a correction of $1/2$ when calculating the probabilities. This is called a *continuity correction*. Whether or not the $1/2$ is to be added or subtracted from the value of X will depend on the nature of the problem. The best thing to do is to sketch a few bars of the diagram and reason out whether to add or subtract the $1/2$. A few illustrations will clarify the procedure.

Using the normal area table, we find for the first example,

$$z = \frac{\left(X - \frac{1}{2}\right) - \mu}{\sigma} = \frac{\left(150 - \frac{1}{2}\right) - 120}{20}$$

$$= \frac{29.5}{20} = 1.475$$

We find from the normal area table that the area we seek is between 0.0708 (for 1.47) and 0.0694 (for 1.48). By linear interpolation we find 0.0701. That is, the probability of there being 150 hogs or more on a farm is 0.0701.

The area (probability) when the continuity correction is not used is 0.0668, since $z = 1.5$.

To find the area (probability) between 130 and 150 inclusive, we approach it in two steps. But first let us draw a diagram for visual aid (Fig. 6.13). Let the area from 130 to the right be A, and let the

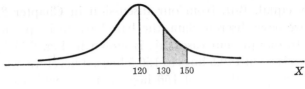

120   130   150 X

FIG. 6.13.

area from 150 to the right be B. Then the area we seek is $A - B$. For area A we find, since 130 is included,

$$z = \frac{\left(130 - \frac{1}{2}\right) - 120}{20} = \frac{9.5}{20} = 0.475$$

Hence the area (probability) is, from the table, 0.3246.

If the continuity correction is not used, z will be 0.5 and the probability will be 0.3085.

For area B we find

$$z = \frac{\left(150 + \frac{1}{2}\right) - 120}{20} = \frac{30.5}{20} = 1.525$$

and the area (probability) is 0.0636.

If the continuity correction is not used, the z will be 1.5 and the area will be 0.0668. Hence the area we seek is

$$A - B = 0.3246 - 0.0636 = 0.2610$$

That is, the probability of the number of hogs' being between 130 and 150 inclusive is 0.2610.

When the continuity correction is not used, the area becomes

$$A' - B' = 0.3085 - 0.0668 = 0.2417$$

That is, the probability of the number of hogs' being between 130 and 150 is 0.2417.

6.5.   Ordinate of the Normal Distribution

Table 2 of the Appendix shows the values of ordinates of the normal distribution.* The first column, showing the values for z, is the same as the area table and shows the distance from the mean in terms of

---

* See Section 16.5, Par. (iv), for illustration of use of ordinates of normal distribution.

standard deviations. For example, $z = 1.3$ means that the distance from the mean is 1.3 standard deviations. The value corresponding to the z's in the body of the table shows the frequency density at that point. For instance, the value corresponding to $z = 1.3$ is 0.1714, which shows the frequency density at $z = 1.3$. We explain the meaning of this table by showing how the area under the normal curve can be calculated by using these ordinate values and intervals.

Table 6.4 shows the values of the ordinates of the normal curve taken from the ordinate table at intervals of 0.5. Fig. 6.14 is a histo-

TABLE 6.4.

z	Height of Bar	Area of Bar
0.0	0.3989	$0.3989 \times 0.25 = 0.099725$
0.5	0.3521	$0.3521 \times 0.5 = 0.17605$
1.0	0.2420	$0.2420 \times 0.5 = 0.1210$
1.5	0.1295	$0.1295 \times 0.5 = 0.06475$
2.0	0.0540	$0.0540 \times 0.5 = 0.0270$
2.5	0.0175	$0.0175 \times 0.5 = 0.00875$
3.0	0.0044	$0.0044 \times 0.5 = 0.0022$
3.5	0.0009	$0.0009 \times 0.5 = 0.00045$
		0.49925

gram that has been drawn from these ordinates: for $z = 0$, the ordinate is 0.3989; for $z = 0.5$, it is 0.3521, etc.

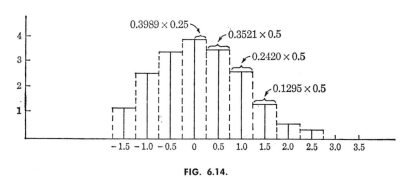

FIG. 6.14.

On the right half of the histogram of Fig. 6.14, the area for the bar at $z = 0.5$ is

$$0.3521 \times 0.5 = 0.17605$$

since the height of the bar (ordinate; that is, frequency density) is 0.3521 and the width of the interval is 0.5. For the bar at $z = 1.0$, it is 0.2420 × 0.5. The areas of the other bars are calculated in similar fashion except for the bar at $z = 0$. The area of the bar at $z = 0$ is half in the left and half in the right side of the histogram, and the area in the right half is

$$0.3989 \times 0.25 = 0.099725$$

since the width is $0.5 \div 2 = 0.25$. Thus the sum of the areas of the bars in the right-hand side of the histogram is (as shown by the calculations in Table 6.4) 0.49925 and is approximately 0.5, as we expected.

The computation is similar for the left-hand side. Thus the total area under the histogram is approximately 1.0.

As the width of the intervals is made smaller, the shape of the histogram will approach the shape of a normal curve having a mean of zero, standard deviation of unity, and area of unity.

SAMPLING DISTRIBUTION

<table>
<tr><td>

7

</td><td>

As a preliminary to the discussion of statistical in-ference, we discussed probability theory, the normal area table, and the central limit theorem. One more important preliminary that we shall discuss in this chapter is the concept of a *sampling distribution of a statistic.* By use of this concept, we shall find a simple

</td></tr>
</table>

way of calculating the probability of selecting a sample from a population.

We shall start our discussion with an explanation of the concept of all possible samples and then consider simple random sampling again. Using these two concepts, we shall show how to calculate the probability of selecting a sample from a population. Next we shall define the concept of a sampling distribution of a statistic and then use the central limit theorem to explain the characteristics of the sampling distribution of the sample mean and the sample proportion. From our discussion of these two sampling distributions, we shall learn a simple way of finding the probability of selecting a sample from a population.

7.1. All Possible Samples

When there are 20,000 army recruits, how many different ways are there of selecting a sample of 100 recruits? Let us start with very simple examples and work toward the answer.

1. Assume there are 4 letters: $A, B, C,$ and D. What are the number of different possible samples of size 2 we can select, when the sampling is with replacement?

Since it is with replacement, we can have samples such as

$$AA, \quad AB, \quad AC, \quad AD$$

and so forth. The first element of the sample can be selected in 4 different ways. Likewise, the second element can also be selected in 4 different ways. Thus the total number of samples of size 2 that can be selected with replacement is

$$4 \times 4 = 4^2 = 16$$

$$
\begin{array}{llll}
A : AA & AB & AC & AD \\
B : BA & BB & BC & BD \\
C : CA & CB & CC & CD \\
D : DA & DB & DC & DD
\end{array}
$$

When we want to select samples of size 3, the number of different possible samples will be

$$4 \times 4 \times 4 = 4^3 = 64$$

In general, when we have n elements, there are n^r different, possible ways of selecting samples of size r.

But note that when 2 letters were selected, we had AB and BA, BC and CB, and so forth. It is clear from the context that we mean AB and BA are different; that is, the *order* of the letters is considered. This is the case of *permutations*.

2. We had in item 1 the condition "with replacement." Now, if it is *without* replacement, there are 4 choices in the first place, and $4 - 1 = 3$ choices in the second place. Thus, for samples of size 2, we have

$$4 \times 3 = 12$$

that is, there are 12 possible samples. The 4 samples AA, BB, CC, and DD are deleted from the 16 samples listed above.

When we select a sample of size 3, without replacement, we have

$$4 \times (4 - 1) \times (4 - 2) = 24$$

that is, there are 24 possible samples.

In general, when we have n elements and select samples of size r without replacement, there will be

$$n \times (n - 1) \times (n - 2) \times \cdots \times (n - r + 1) = (n)_r$$

possible samples. We write $(n)_r$ to indicate the above computations.

3. $r = n$ is the case of finding how many different ways we can order n elements. From our preceding results, it is

$$(n)_n = n \times (n-1) \times (n-2) \times \cdots \times 2 \times 1$$

There is a special symbol for this, namely,

$$(n)_n = n!$$

which is read "n factorial." For example,

$$5! = 5 \times 4 \times 3 \times 2 \times 1 = 120$$
$$3! = 3 \times 2 \times 1 = 6$$

Thus the number of different orderings of n elements is $n!$. If there are 3 students, they may be lined up in $3! = 6$ different ways. If there are 5 students, they may be lined up in $5! = 120$ different ways.

4. When we say *combinations*, we disregard the order. Thus AB and BA are the two orderings of a single combination AB.

When we have a combination ABC, there are $3! = 6$ orderings of these three elements.

When we have n different elements, there is one combination of the n elements, but there are $n!$ different orderings.

5. Now let us put these things together. We have a combination of 4 letters, $ABCD$. We take a sample of size 3. Then there are $(4)_3$ different ways of selecting samples of size 3 without replacement when the order is considered.

Each of the samples of size 3 can be ordered in $3!$ different ways.

Thus the number of samples of size 3 without replacement that can be selected when we *disregard the order* of the letters within each sample will be

$$\frac{(4)_3}{3!} = \frac{4 \times 3 \times 2}{3 \times 2 \times 1} = 4$$

These 4 samples are

$$ABC, \quad ABD, \quad ACD, \quad BCD$$

In general, if we have n elements, there are $(n)_r$ different ways of selecting samples of size r without replacement. Each sample (which is a combination of r different element) has $r!$ different orderings. Thus,

$$\frac{(n)_r}{r!}$$

gives us the number of different ways we can select a sample of size r from n elements without replacement, when we disregard the order within each sample.

There is a special symbol for this operation, namely,

$$\binom{n}{r} = \frac{(n)_r}{r!}$$

We define

$$0! = 1 \quad \text{and} \quad \binom{n}{0} = 1$$

This $\binom{n}{r}$ is known as the *binomial coefficient,* and we shall now proceed to use it.

Example 1.   There are 6 students. A group of 5 students are to be selected to form a basketball team. How many different ways are there of selecting 5 students?

$$\binom{n}{r} = \binom{6}{5} = \frac{(6)_5}{5!} = \frac{6 \times 5 \times 4 \times 3 \times 2}{5 \times 4 \times 3 \times 2 \times 1} = 6$$

That is, there are 6 different ways of selecting a team of 5.

Example 2.   The number of possible different ways of selecting 5 cards from a deck of 52 cards is

$$\binom{52}{5} = \frac{(52)_5}{5!} = \frac{52 \times 51 \times 50 \times 49 \times 48}{5 \times 4 \times 3 \times 2 \times 1} = 2{,}598{,}960$$

Example 3.   The number of possible different hands of 13 cards is

$$\binom{52}{13} = \frac{(52)_{13}}{13!} = 635{,}013{,}559{,}600$$

There is approximately 1 chance in 635 billion of getting a certain bridge hand.

Example 4.   A group of 10 guests are to be divided into 2 groups of 5 each and seated at 2 tables. How many different ways are there of dividing the guests?

$$\binom{10}{5} = \frac{(10)_5}{5!} = \frac{10 \times 9 \times 8 \times 7 \times 6}{5 \times 4 \times 3 \times 2 \times 1} = 252$$

There are 252 different ways of dividing the group.

Example 5. How many different ways are there of seating the 5 guests at a table?

$$5! = 5 \times 4 \times 3 \times 2 \times 1 = 120$$

that is, there are 120 different ways of seating the 5 guests.

6. The binomial coefficient may also be rewritten as follows

$$\binom{n}{r} = \frac{(n)_r}{r!} = \frac{(n)_r}{r!} \times \frac{(n-r)!}{(n-r)!}$$

But note that

$$(n)_r \cdot (n-r)! = n!$$

Thus we find

$$\binom{n}{r} = \frac{n!}{r!(n-r)!}$$

Example 6. The number of ways of selecting 3 students from 5 students are

$$\binom{5}{3} = \frac{(5)_3}{3!} = 10$$

But note that this may be written as

$$\binom{5}{3} = \frac{(5)_3}{3!} = \frac{(5)_3}{3!} \cdot \frac{2!}{2!} = \frac{5!}{3!(5-3)!} = 10$$

7. If we return now to our original question of the number of ways of selecting 100 recruits from 20,000, we find that this will be

$$\binom{n}{r} = \binom{20,000}{100}$$

We shall not attempt to calculate this, but from the preceding examples, it is quite clear that we shall have a very large number of ways.

The results of this section may now be summarized as follows: Given a population of N elementary units, the number of possible ways of selecting samples of size n are

$$\binom{N}{n} = \frac{N!}{n!(N-n)!}$$

7.2. Simple Random Sampling

There are a number of different ways of selecting samples, but we shall consider only one, probability sampling. Probability sampling in turn can be subdivided into simple random sampling, stratified sampling, and cluster sampling. We could add a few more methods of probability sampling, but we shall deal only with simple random sampling.

By *probability sampling,* we mean a sampling plan in which every member of the population has a known probability of being included in the sample. And when each member that has not been previously drawn has an equal probability of being selected, we have what is known as *simple random sampling.*

To illustrate, let us assume there are 6 slips of papers with numbers 1, 2, . . . , 6 in a box. We wish to select a sample of size 3 from the box, without replacement. *Simple random sampling* implies that the probability of a number's being drawn is 1/6 for all 6 numbers; and on the second draw, the probability of a number's being drawn is 1/5 for all the remaining 5 numbers; and so forth. If this should be the case, then each number not previously drawn has an equal probability of being selected.

Now, what is the probability that a member of the population, say, the number 4, will be in the sample? Since we have a sample of size 3, we make 3 draws. Thus the question we are asking may be restated as: What is the probability of picking a 4 on the first, or second, or third draw? Let A be the event of selecting a 4 on the first draw. Then

$$P(A) = \frac{1}{6}$$

The probability of picking a 4 on the second draw is the probability that it is not selected on the first draw multiplied by the probability that it is selected on the second draw, given it was not drawn on the first draw. Let us show this in terms of formulas. We have

$$P(C \,\&\, B) = P(B)P(C \mid B)$$
$$= \frac{5}{6} \times \frac{1}{5} = \frac{1}{6}$$

where B is the event that a 4 is not selected on the first draw, and C is the event that a 4 is selected on the second draw. Hence $P(C \mid B)$ is the probability of a 4 being selected on the second draw, *given* it was not selected on the first draw.

Similarly, the probability of selecting a 4 on the third draw and not on the first two draws is obtained as follows: Let

B: a 4 is not selected on the first draw
D: a 4 is not selected on the second draw
E: a 4 is selected on the third draw

Then

$$P(B \& D \& E) = P(B) \cdot P(D \mid B) \cdot P(E \mid B, D)$$

$$= \frac{5}{6} \times \frac{4}{5} \times \frac{1}{4} = \frac{1}{6}$$

These three events, A, C, E, are mutually exclusive. Thus the probability of the number 4's being in the sample is

$$P(A \text{ or } C \text{ or } E) = \frac{1}{6} + \frac{5}{6} \times \frac{1}{5} + \frac{5}{6} \times \frac{4}{5} \times \frac{1}{4} = \frac{3}{6}$$

Similarly, the probability of, for example, the number 2's being in the sample is $3/6$.

If we have 7 slips of paper and take samples of size 5, the probability of the number 3's being in the sample is $5/7$.

In general (one can see by induction), if the size of the sample is n and the size of the population is N, then when we use simple random sampling, every member of the population has a probability of n/N of being included in the sample. For example, if we have 120 students and we select 10 students at random, and each student has equal probability of being picked, then each of the 120 students has a probability of $10/120$ of being in the sample.

Now let us consider the question we were originally interested in, namely: What is the probability of selecting a sample of size n from a population of size N? Let us use a simple illustration and discuss this problem.

Suppose there are 6 numbers and we draw samples of size 3; then there will be

$$\binom{6}{3} = \frac{6!}{3!(6-3)!} = \frac{6!}{3!3!} = \frac{6 \times 5 \times 4}{3!} = 20$$

or 20 possible samples. When we adopt simple random sampling, each sample has an equal probability of $1/20$ of being selected. This can easily be proved as follows: The probability of selecting the first number is $1/6$; the probability of selecting the second number is $1/5$; and the probability of selecting the third number is $1/4$. Thus the probability of selecting these 3 numbers in a certain order is

$$\frac{1}{6} \times \frac{1}{5} \times \frac{1}{4} = \frac{1}{6 \times 5 \times 4}$$

But when we talk of a sample of 3 numbers, we are not concerned with the order. We have seen that when we have 3 numbers, there are 3!

ways of ordering them. Thus the probability of selecting a sample of size 3 will be

$$\frac{1}{6 \times 5 \times 4} \times 3! = \frac{1}{\dfrac{6 \times 5 \times 4}{3!}} = \frac{1}{\dbinom{6}{3}} = \frac{1}{20}$$

In general we can see by induction that when we select a sample of size n from a population of size N by simple random sampling, the probability of any one of the $\dbinom{N}{n}$ samples' being selected will be

$$\frac{1}{\dbinom{N}{n}}$$

In our subsequent discussion we shall confine ourselves to this simple random sampling.

Note that the preceding discussion was for the case where sampling was without replacement. We can do the same for the case with replacement, but in practical problems we generally use sampling without replacement. Thus, if there are 20,000 new recruits and we wish to select a sample of size 100 by simple random sampling, we obtain the following conclusions:

1. There are $\dbinom{20,000}{100}$ different ways of selecting 100 recruits, that is, there are $\dbinom{20,000}{100}$ different samples.

2. The probability of any of the $\dbinom{20,000}{100}$ samples being selected will be $\dfrac{1}{\dbinom{20,000}{100}}$

3. The probability of any recruit's being included in the sample will be $100/20,000$.

Example.   Let us apply to a simple example the results obtained in the preceding discussion. Consider two urns, A and B, that each have 9 balls with numbers on them as in Fig. 7.1.

A simple random sample of 3 balls is selected from urn A. The numbers on the balls are

$$4, \quad 4, \quad 5$$

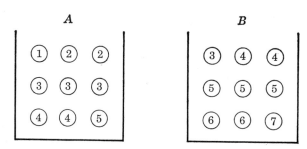

FIG. 7.1.

TABLE 7.1.

Number	Urn A	Urn B
1	1	
2	2	
3	3	1
4	2	2
5	1	3
6		2
7		1
	$\overline{9}$	$\overline{9}$

From our discussion of all possible samples, we know that there are

$$\binom{9}{3} = \frac{9!}{3!6!} = 84$$

possible ways of selecting a sample of size 3. But note that when we say there are 84 possible samples, this reasoning implies that all 9 balls in the urn are different. To allow for this assumption, let us label the balls in urn A as follows:

Urn A: (1) $(2)_1$ $(2)_2$ $(3)_1$ $(3)_2$ $(3)_3$ $(4)_1$ $(4)_2$ (5)

Subscripts have been added to distinguish among the same numbers.

In terms of the sample we selected, that is, (4, 4, 5), we have for urn A:

Urn A: $(4)_1$ $(4)_2$ (5)

We know the probability of selecting a sample size 3 is 1/84. Thus the probability of selecting the sample (4, 4, 5) from urn A is 1/84.

Let us next calculate the probability of selecting the sample (4, 4, 5) from urn B. We have the following samples:

$$(4)_1 \quad (4)_2 \quad (5)_1$$
$$(4)_1 \quad (4)_2 \quad (5)_2$$
$$(4)_1 \quad (4)_2 \quad (5)_3$$

that is, the sample (4, 4, 5) from urn *B* is distinguished and counted as 3 samples, but for practical purposes, it is the same sample counted 3 times. Thus the probability of selecting the sample (4, 4, 5) from urn *B* is

$$\frac{1}{84} \times 3 = \frac{3}{84}$$

We were able to calculate these probabilities because simple random sampling (or more generally, probability sampling) was used.

7.3.   Some Practical Problems

Now that we have decided on how we are going to select the sample, namely, by simple random sampling, we have the practical problem of selecting a sample of size *n*. Let us assume that we wish to find the amount of rent paid by families in a certain block. We first have to decide what we mean by families. Once this has been decided, the whole population can be subdivided into these family units, which are called *ultimate units*.

Now we can make a *list* of all the ultimate units (that is, families), one by one. Or we can combine several families that live close together and make a *list* of such combinations. Each item on the list will contain several families, and each family will be in only one item of the list. A list that splits up the population into items made up of the ultimate units is called a *frame*. Each item in the frame is called a *sampling unit*. Each sampling unit may contain one or more of the ultimate units.

When we engage in simple random sampling, we select the *sample units* from the frame and obtain a sample. We need to select the sample units so that the probability of selecting any one sampling unit will be equal. For this we may use the *random number table*. Let us explain by use of an example.

Assume that there are 500 students and we wish to select a simple random sample of 30 students. For this we use the random number table; a portion of it is given below and the complete table is given in Table 13 of the Appendix. We start down the line, taking 3 digits at a time, since 500 is a 3-digit number. The first number we see is 231. Thus we select the 231st student.

The next number is 055. Thus we select the 55th student. This process is continued until we have selected 30 students. When we run into a number that is greater than 500 (for example, 682), we skip it.

If the same number occurs twice, we skip it. The random number table is designed so that the probability of any student's being selected will be equal.

There are many practical problems in defining an ultimate unit, a sampling unit, and a frame. These will not be discussed at this point so as not to digress from the main topic of sampling distributions. Now let us now get back to the main line of discussion.

7.4. Sampling Distribution

We have seen how a simple random sample is selected and how the probability of selecting a sample is calculated, given a certain population. This was explained in terms of a simple hypothetical problem. But in practical problems, where the sample size and population are large and hence the number of all possible samples is large, this becomes very difficult.

A question naturally arises: Is there any way of simplifying this process of obtaining probabilities for samples? It turns out that this may be done by using the central limit theorem. By using this theorem, we shall find that we may use the sample mean to represent the sample and calculate the probability of the occurrence of the sample mean, instead of calculating the probability of occurrence of a sample from a given population.

Let us start with a rediscussion of the central limit theorem.

Random Number Table
1–4

1	23 15
2	05 54
3	14 87
4	38 97
.	.. ..
.	.. ..
.	.. ..

(i)   The central limit theorem

In Chapter 6 the central limit theorem was stated as: When given n independent random variables $X_1, X_2, \ldots, X_n$, which all have the *same* distribution (no matter what the distribution), then

$$X = X_1 + X_2 + X_3 + \cdots + X_n$$

is asymptotically normal. The mean μ and variance σ^2 of X are

$$\mu = \mu_1 + \mu_2 + \cdots + \mu_n = n\mu_i$$

$$\sigma^2 = \sigma_1^2 + \sigma_2^2 + \cdots + \sigma_n^2 = n\sigma_i^2$$

where μ_i and σ_i^2 are the mean and variance of X_i.

Let us explain the assumption *same distribution* as follows: Suppose there are two schools, A and B, and X_1 and X_2 are random variables denoting the IQ's of students of each school. Let μ_1 and σ_1^2 be the mean and variance of X_1, and μ_2 and σ_2^2 be the mean and variance of X_2. When we say that the random variable X_1 and X_2 have the *same distribution*, we mean that:

1. Both X_1 and X_2 have similar distributions; say, both have normal distributions, or rectangular distributions, or binomial distributions, etc.
2. The means μ_1 and μ_2 are equal; that is, $\mu_1 = \mu_2$.
3. The variances σ_1^2 and σ_2^2 are equal; that is, $\sigma_1^2 = \sigma_2^2$.

Let us show this graphically. Figure 7.2(a) shows the case where both

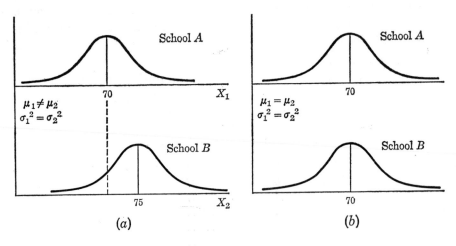

(a)   (b)

FIG. 7.2.

X_1 and X_2 have normal distributions in which $\sigma_1^2 = \sigma_2^2$ but $\mu_1 = 70$ and $\mu_2 = 75$, and hence X_1 and X_2 do not have the same distribution. In Fig. 7.2(b), $\mu_1 = \mu_2 = 70$, and $\sigma_1^2 = \sigma_2^2$, and this is the case where X_1 and X_2 have the *same* distribution.

As can be seen, we may also interpret this assumption, *same distribu-*

tion, as follows: Suppose we are given a population of N students. Select (with replacement) a student and let X_1 be a random variable IQ. Select a second student and let X_2 be a random variable IQ. Then, since X_1 and X_2 came from the same population, X_1 and X_2 will have the same distribution. If we select 3 students (with replacement), we may interpret this as having three independent random variables X_1, X_2, X_3, all having the same distribution.

In general, when we select a *random sample of size n* from a population, we shall have n independent random variables

$$X_1, \quad X_2, \quad \ldots, \quad X_n$$

all having the *same* distribution. In our subsequent discussion, when a *sample of size n* is selected, we shall always assume this interpretation.

Strictly speaking, only when a random sample is selected with replacement will the random variables X_1, X_2, ..., X_n be independent. However, in most practical problems where the population is large and the sample is relatively small, the random variables X_1, X_2, ..., X_n that have been selected without replacement may be treated as if they were independent.

Note carefully that we have two ways of observing a sample of size n. The first approach is as follows: Suppose a sample of size $n = 5$ students is selected and the random variable X is weight. Then we may express the sample as

$$X: \quad x_1, \quad x_2, \quad x_3, \quad x_4, \quad x_5$$

where X is the random variable and the lower case letters $x_1, x_2, \ldots, x_5$ show the 5 *values* of X.

The second approach is to consider the weight of each student as an independent random variable. Then the *sample* of 5 students may be shown by

$$X_1, \quad X_2, \quad X_3, \quad X_4, \quad X_5$$

that is, by the 5 random variables (not the specific values). The *values* of the variables are shown by small letters:

$$X_1 = x_1, \quad X_2 = x_2, \quad X_3 = x_3, \quad X_4 = x_4, \quad X_5 = x_5$$

But, since the 5 students came from the same population, the random variables $X_1, \ldots, X_5$ all have the *same* distribution.

In our present case, where the X_i have the same distribution, the first and second approaches are equivalent, but when the variables

$X_1, X_2, \ldots, X_n$ do *not* have the same distribution, the two approaches are *not* equivalent. Since we shall only consider cases where the X_i all have the same distribution, both approaches will be used interchangeably.

We now return to the central limit theorem and state it as follows: When a random sample of size n is taken from a population (with mean μ and variance σ^2), we have n independent random variables $X_1, X_2, \ldots, X_n$, all having the same distribution. Let

$$\bar{X} = \frac{1}{n} (X_1 + X_2 + \cdots + X_n)$$

where $\bar{X}$ is the sample mean. Then (we state without proof) $\bar{X}$ is asymptotically normal with mean and variance:

$$E(\bar{X}) = \mu$$

$$\mathrm{Var}(\bar{X}) = \frac{\sigma^2}{n} \sqrt{\frac{N-n}{N-1}}$$

Let us illustrate this result with an example.

Suppose that of six students, the first student has \$1.00, the second has \$2.00, and so forth up to the sixth student, who has \$6.00. Let us consider the 1, 2, $\ldots$, 6 dollars as the population and find its mean and standard deviation as shown in Table 7.2.

TABLE 7.2.

X	X²
\$ 1	1
2	4
3	9
4	16
5	25
6	36
21	91

$$\mu = \frac{21}{6} = \$3.5$$

$$\sigma = \sqrt{\frac{1}{N} \Sigma (X - \mu)^2}$$

$$= \sqrt{\frac{\Sigma X^2}{N} - \left(\frac{\Sigma X}{N} \right)^2}$$

$$= \sqrt{\frac{91}{6} - \left(\frac{21}{6} \right)^2}$$

$$= \sqrt{\frac{17.5}{6}}$$

Two students are selected as a sample. The number of possible samples of size 2 that can be selected is

$$\binom{6}{2} = \frac{6!}{2!4!} = 15$$

Let us denote $\binom{N}{n} = M$ to avoid confusion.

These $M = 15$ samples are as follows:

(1)	$1, 2	(6)	2, 3	(10)	3, 4	(13)	4, 5	(15)	5, 6
(2)	1, 3	(7)	2, 4	(11)	3, 5	(14)	4, 6		
(3)	1, 4	(8)	2, 5	(12)	3, 6				
(4)	1, 5	(9)	2, 6						
(5)	1, 6								

The probability of any one of these samples being selected is 1/15.

Let us now find the sample mean of each sample. Given in the same order as the samples above, they are:

(1)	$1.5	(6)	2.5	(10)	3.5	(13)	4.5	(15)	5.5
(2)	2.0	(7)	3.0	(11)	4.0	(14)	5.0		
(3)	2.5	(8)	3.5	(12)	4.5				
(4)	3.0	(9)	4.0						
(5)	3.5								

The probability of occurrence of any one of these samples means is the same as the probability of the sample from which it was derived, and hence the probability is also 1/15.

But note that

Sample:	(5)	(8)	(10)
	$1,6	2,5	3,4
$\bar{x}$:	$3.5	3.5	3.5

That is, for the fifth, eighth, and tenth sample, the sample means are equal ($\bar{x} = \$3.5$) although we have three different samples. Hence the probability of $\bar{x} = \$3.5$ occurring is

$$\frac{1}{15} \times 3 = \frac{3}{15}$$

Let us attach probabilities to the other sample means in a similar manner and show the results in Table 7.3.

Figure 7.3 is a bar chart of Table 7.3. Note that the variable on the horizontal axis is $\bar{X}$ and not X.

It is this distribution of the sample means that we are seeking, and one that is a cornerstone of statistical inference. Let us now investigate the characteristics of this distribution. The first characteristic we notice is that the distribution is unimodal and symmetric, which is an interesting result because the population we started out with is a rectangular distribution.

TABLE 7.3.

$\bar{X}$	f	Probabilities
$1.5	1	1/15
2.0	1	1/15
2.5	2	2/15
3.0	2	2/15
3.5	3	3/15
4.0	2	2/15
4.5	2	1/15
5.0	1	1/15
5.5	1	1/15
	15	1.00

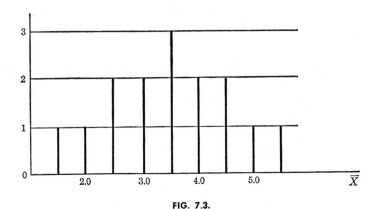

FIG. 7.3.

Second, the mean of the distribution is

(1) $$\bar{\bar{X}} = \frac{\bar{x}_1 + \bar{x}_2 + \cdots + \bar{x}_{15}}{15} = \$3.5$$

where the double bar over X indicates that it is the mean of the sample means. This result is obtained from the following worksheet. The important point here is the relation between $\bar{\bar{X}}$ and μ; that is, $\bar{\bar{X}} = \$3.5$ is equal to the population mean $\mu = \$3.5$.

Third, calculations show that the standard deviation of this distribution is

(2) $$\sigma_{\bar{x}} = \sqrt{\frac{1}{M} \Sigma (\bar{x}_i - \bar{\bar{x}})^2} = \sqrt{\frac{17.5}{15}}$$

where the subscript $\bar{x}$ of $\sigma_{\bar{x}}$ indicates that it is the standard deviation of the distribution of the sample means. The important point here is the

Worksheet

$\overline{X}$	f	d	fd	d^2	fd^2
$1.5	1	-4	-4	16	16
2.0	1	-3	-3	9	9
2.5	2	-2	-4	4	8
3.0	2	-1	-2	1	2
3.5	3	0	0	0	0
4.0	2	1	2	1	2
4.5	2	2	4	4	8
5.0	1	3	3	9	9
5.5	1	4	4	16	16
	$\overline{15}$		$\overline{0}$		$\overline{70}$

$$\overline{X} = A + \frac{\Sigma\, fd}{M} \times C = \$3.5 + \frac{0}{15} \times (0.5) = \$3.5$$

$$\sigma_{\bar{x}} = C \sqrt{\frac{1}{M}\left[\Sigma\, fd^2 - \frac{(\Sigma\, fd)^2}{M}\right]}$$

$$= 0.5 \sqrt{\frac{1}{15}[70 - 0]} = \sqrt{\frac{17.5}{15}}$$

relation between σ and $\sigma_{\bar{x}}$. This relation, which is not obvious, is as follows:

(3) $$\sigma_{\bar{x}} = \frac{\sigma}{\sqrt{n}} \cdot \sqrt{\frac{N-n}{N-1}}$$

Let us check this relation between σ and $\sigma_{\bar{x}}$. We have already calculated σ as

$$\sigma = \sqrt{\frac{17.5}{6}}$$

By substituting this into formula (3), we find

$$\sigma_{\bar{x}} = \frac{\sigma}{\sqrt{n}} \sqrt{\frac{N-n}{N-1}} = \frac{\sqrt{\frac{17.5}{6}}}{\sqrt{2}} \sqrt{\frac{6-2}{6-1}} = \sqrt{\frac{17.5}{15}}$$

which is the same result as that obtained directly from the worksheet, and hence shows that the formula holds true for our example. This will be discussed again later.

The *central limit theorem* we are interested in tells us that the results just obtained may be generalized. We may state it in a nonrigorous manner as follows: Let N be the size of a population with μ and σ. Let n be the sample size. Then there are $M = \binom{N}{n}$ possible samples, and hence there are $M = \binom{N}{n}$ sample means $\bar{x}_i$: $i = 1, 2, \ldots, \binom{N}{n}$. These sample means will generate a distribution of sample means with the following characteristics (Fig. 7.4):

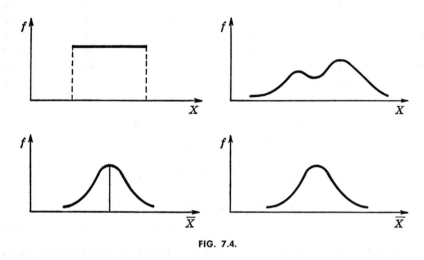

FIG. 7.4.

1.   If the population is large and normally distributed, the distribution of the sample mean will be normal.

2.   If the population is large but not normally distributed, the distribution of the sample mean will *approach* a normal distribution, provided the sample size is large (especially if it is larger than 30). For example, we may have a rectangular distribution, or a bimodal distribution, or any other kind of distribution, and as long as the sample size is large enough (say, greater than 30), the distribution of the sample mean $\bar{X}$ will approach a normal distribution.

3.   The mean of the distribution of the sample mean is equal to the population mean. This is expressed as follows:

(4) $$E(\bar{X}) = \mu$$

where $E(\bar{X})$ is the expected value of $\bar{X}$.

4.   The standard distribution of this distribution is

(5) $$\sigma_{\bar{x}} = \frac{\sigma}{\sqrt{n}} \sqrt{\frac{N-n}{N-1}}$$

To distinguish it from the standard deviation of the population σ and the standard deviation of the sample, s, it is called the *standard error* and denoted by the symbol $\sigma_{\bar{x}}$.

We can see that $\sigma_{\bar{x}}$ is smaller than σ, and as n becomes larger, $\sigma_{\bar{x}}$ becomes smaller. This means that the dispersion of the distribution of the sample mean $\bar{X}$ is smaller than that of the population and will become smaller as the sample size increases. A little reflection should bring out the common sense of this. As an illustration, assume that there are 200 students and that their grades are scattered from 20 points to 100 points. Let the mean be $\mu = 60$ points. Then, if we take samples of 10 students and calculate their sample means, the scatter of the sample means will be less than the scatter of the individual grades in the population.

If we take samples of size 20, the sample means will become closer to μ and the scatter of the sample means will become even narrower. If we take samples of size 199, we can see intuitively that the sample means will be concentrated close to μ.

This distribution of the sample mean is called a *sampling distribution*. Or, expressed more completely, we should say "the *sampling distribution of the sample mean $\bar{X}$*," because if we had taken, for example, other statistics such as the sample median instead of the sample mean, we could have constructed the sampling distribution of the median. As we shall see in later chapters, we can construct various other sampling distributions of statistics obtained from the sample.

Thus we have three important conclusions due to the central limit theorem. By assuming large samples and a large population, we conclude that:

1. The sampling distribution of the sample mean $\bar{X}$ is a normal or approximately normal distribution.

2. $E(\bar{X}) = \mu$.

3. $\sigma_{\bar{x}} = \dfrac{\sigma}{\sqrt{n}} \sqrt{\dfrac{N-n}{N-1}}.$

The assumption that we are using probability sampling should not be forgotten. Only when we have this assumption will we be able to make probability statements.

Let us summarize the main points of our discussion in Table 7.4. The p and π in the last row of Table 7.4 denote the sample proportion and population proportion. This will be discussed later.

TABLE 7.4.

	Variable	Distribution	Mean	Variance
Population	X	Any kind	$E(X) = \mu$ $= \dfrac{1}{N} \sum\limits_{i=1}^{N} x_i$	$\mathrm{Var}(X) = \sigma^2$ $= E(x - \mu)^2$ $= \dfrac{1}{N} \sum\limits_{i=1}^{N} (x_i - \mu)^2$
Sample	X	Any kind	$\bar{X} = \dfrac{1}{n} \sum\limits_{i=1}^{n} x_i$	$s^2 = \dfrac{1}{n} \Sigma\, (x_i - \bar{X})^2$
Sampling distribution of the $\bar{X}$	$\bar{X}$	Approximately normal	$E(\bar{X}) = \mu$	$\sigma_{\bar{x}}^2 = \dfrac{\sigma^2}{n} \cdot \dfrac{N-n}{N-1}$
Sampling distribution of p	p	Approximately normal	$E(p) = \pi$	$\sigma_p^2 = \dfrac{\pi(1-\pi)}{n} \cdot \dfrac{N-n}{N-1}$

We can also show the various relations schematically as in Fig. 7.5, which assumes a population of $N = 13$ and samples of size $n = 5$. There

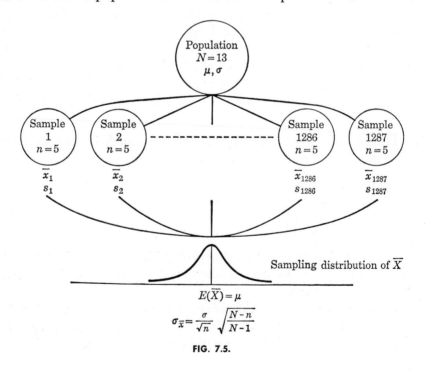

Sampling distribution of $\overline{X}$

$$E(\overline{X}) = \mu$$

$$\sigma_{\overline{x}} = \frac{\sigma}{\sqrt{n}} \sqrt{\frac{N-n}{N-1}}$$

FIG. 7.5.

are thus $\binom{13}{5} = 1287$ possible samples, and hence 1287 possible sample means. These sample means form the sampling distribution of the sample mean, which approaches a normal distribution when n is large.

We may now proceed to see how the central limit theorem may be used to simplify calculating the probabilities of the occurrence of samples.

(ii)   *How the probability of selecting a sample from a given population is calculated by the sampling distribution of the sample mean*

Table 7.3 and Fig. 7.3 are reproduced here as Table 7.5 and Fig. 7.6, for convenience.

TABLE 7.5.

$\bar{X}$	f	Samples	Probabilities		
\$1.5	1	(1,2)	1/15		
2.0	1	(1,3)	1/15		
2.5	2	(1,4), (2,3)	1/15	1/15	
3.0	2	(1,5), (2,4)	1/15	1/15	
3.5	3	(1,6), (2,5), (3,4)	1/15	1/15	1/15
4.0	2	(2,6), (3,5)	1/15	1/15	
4.5	2	(3,6), (4,5)	1/15	1/15	
5.0	1	(4,6)	1/15		
5.5	1	(5,6)	1/15		
	15		1.00		

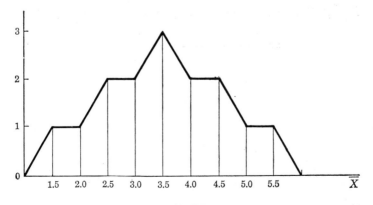

FIG. 7.6.

The central limit theorem required that the population and sample be large if the sampling distribution of the sample mean were to approach a normal distribution. But recall that our hypothetical population was a small rectangular population $\{\$1, 2, \ldots, 6\}$, and the sample size was $n = 2$. Thus the sampling distribution of the sample mean in Table 7.5 is still quite different from a normal distribution and the frequency polygon of Fig. 7.6 is also quite different from a normal curve. But, for brevity and purposes of explaining the ideas, let us assume that they are normal. We shall give more realistic examples later.

Now let us ask the question: What is the probability of selecting a sample with a sample mean of $\bar{x} = \$5.5$? From Table 7.5 and Fig. 7.6, this is easily seen as $1/15$ and may be expressed in symbols as

$$P[\bar{X} = \$5.5] = \frac{1}{15}$$

The probability of selecting a sample with a sample mean of $\bar{x} = \$5.5$ in our present example means specifically the probability of selecting the sample $(5, 6)$.

What is the probability of selecting samples with a sample mean of $\bar{x} = \$4.5$? This, we see, is

$$P[\bar{X} = \$4.5] = \frac{2}{15}$$

The probability of selecting samples with a sample mean of $\bar{x} = \$4.5$ means specifically the probability of selecting the samples $(3,6)$ or $(4,5)$.

What is the probability of selecting samples with a sample mean greater than or equal to $\bar{x} = \$4.5$? This is

$$P[\bar{X} \geqq \$4.5] = P[\bar{X} = 4.5] + P[\bar{X} = 5.0] + P[\bar{X} = 5.5]$$

$$= \frac{2}{15} + \frac{1}{15} + \frac{1}{15} = \frac{4}{15}$$

This means that the probability of selecting the samples $(5,6)$, $(4,6)$, (3.6), or (4.5) is $4/15$.

The probabilities were obtained from Table 7.5. But if the population and sample had been large, the sampling distribution of the sample mean would have been approximately normal, and then the normal area table could have been used to calculate the probabilities. Although we shall not get accurate results, let us show how this works, using our present example.

The probability of selecting samples with a sample mean greater than or equal to $4.5 is obtained by finding the shaded area under the normal curve in the tail end beyond $4.5 $- 1/2 \times 1/n$, as shown schematically in Fig. 7.7. The $-1/2 \times 1/n$ is the continuity correction, and in our

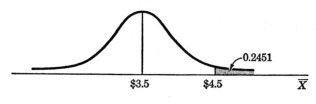

FIG. 7.7.

present case it is $-1/2 \times 1/2 = -0.25$. Thus $4.5 - 0.25 = 4.25.

Recall that the standard error is

$$\sigma_{\bar{x}} = \sqrt{\frac{17.50}{15}} = \sqrt{1.1666} = \$1.08$$

Thus the deviation of $4.25 from the mean is

$$\bar{X} - \mu = \$4.25 - 3.5 = \$0.75$$

which, when standardized, becomes

$$z = \frac{\bar{X} - \mu}{\sigma_{\bar{x}}} = \frac{\$0.75}{\$1.08} = 0.694$$

From the normal area table we find that, when $z = 0.694$, the area under the tail end is 0.2451; that is,

$$P[\bar{X} \geq 4.5] = 0.2451$$

According to Table 7.5, the probability $P[\bar{X} \geq \$4.5]$ is $4/15 = 0.2666$, and thus there is approximately a 1 percent $(0.2666 - 0.2451 = 0.01)$ absolute discrepancy. The relative discrepancy is approximately 4.3 percent:

$$\frac{0.2666 - 0.2451}{0.2666} = \frac{0.0115}{0.2666} = 4.3\%$$

This discrepancy between 0.2451 and 0.2666 has occurred because the requirements for the central limit theorem, namely, a large population and a large sample, were not satisfied.

However, our main purpose was to show the reasoning process by a simple hypothetical problem. Let us summarize this before we proceed to give more realistic examples.

1. From a given population of size N we can select $M = \binom{N}{n}$ samples of size n, and hence there will also be $M = \binom{N}{n}$ sample means.

2. The distribution of these sample means will approach a normal distribution if n is large (say, larger than 30). If the original population is normal, the distribution of the sample means will be normal no matter how small the sample.

3. From the normal sampling distribution of the sample mean $\bar{X}$, we can calculate the probability of selecting samples with sample means greater than or equal to, say, $\bar{X}_0$. This is done by finding

$$z = \frac{\bar{X}_0 - \mu}{\sigma_{\bar{x}}}$$

where

$$E(\bar{X}) = \mu, \qquad \sigma_{\bar{x}} = \frac{\sigma}{\sqrt{n}} \sqrt{\frac{N - n}{N - 1}}$$

and by using the normal area table.

4. Note that when applying the continuity correction to the sampling distribution of the sample mean, it is $1/2 \times 1/n$ instead of simply $1/2$, as was explained in Chapter 6.

Example 1.   Consider a group of 13 students with a distribution of grades as shown in Table 7.6. Let $A = 5$, $B = 4$, $C = 3$, $D = 2$, and $F = 1$ honor points.

TABLE 7.6.

Grade	f	$X - \mu$	$(X - \mu)^2$	$f(X - \mu)^2$
A (5)	1	$5 - 3 = 2$	4	4
B (4)	3	$4 - 3 = 1$	1	3
C (3)	5	$3 - 3 = 0$	0	0
D (2)	3	$2 - 3 = -1$	1	3
F (1)	1	$1 - 3 = -2$	4	4
	13			14

Then, for example, a straight A student will be a student with an average of 5 honor points. The mean and standard deviation of this distribution is

$$\mu = 3 \text{ honor points}, \qquad \sigma = \sqrt{\frac{14}{13}} = 1.076 \text{ honor points}$$

Simple random samples of 3 students are selected, without replacement. The number of such samples that can be selected are

$$\binom{13}{3} = \frac{13!}{3!10!} = 286$$

But note carefully that this calculation assumes all 13 grades to be different. For example, Table 7.6 shows that 3 students have B's. Each B is considered different. Let this be denoted by B_1, B_2, and B_3. Then (A, B_1, B_2), (A, B_1, B_3), and (A, B_2, B_3) are considered as 3 different samples. The number of samples may be calculated as follows: First find

$$\begin{array}{ccc} A & B & B \\ 1 \times 3 & \times & 2 = 6 \end{array}$$

This shows that there is only 1 choice for the A, 3 choices for the first B, and 2 choices for the second B. The six samples are

$$\begin{array}{cccccc} A & B_1 & B_2 & \quad A & B_2 & B_3 \\ A & B_1 & B_3 & \quad A & B_3 & B_1 \\ A & B_2 & B_1 & \quad A & B_3 & B_2 \end{array}$$

Evidently, for example, this assumes that $(A\ B_1\ B_2)$ and $(A\ B_2\ B_1)$ are different; that is, the order of the B's is considered. But the $M = 286$ possible samples consider only *combinations;* that is, (A, B_1, B_2) and $(A, B_2 B_1)$ are the same and are counted only once in the $M = 286$ samples. Thus we need to make the following correction:

$$\begin{array}{ccc} A & B & B \\ 1 \times 3 \times 2 \div 2! = 6 \div 2! = 3 \end{array}$$

That is, there are 2! ways of ordering B_1B_2, and hence we divided 6 by 2!.

Let us now enumerate all the samples, using the above method of calculation. First we present all the possible combinations:

(1) $A\ B\ B$ (3)		(10) $B\ B\ B$ (1)		(19) $C\ C\ C$ (10)		(24) $D\ D\ D$ (1)
(2) $A\ B\ C$ (15)		(11) $B\ B\ C$ (15)		(20) $C\ C\ D$ (30)		(25) $D\ D\ F$ (3)
(3) $A\ B\ D$ (9)		(12) $B\ B\ D$ (9)		(21) $C\ C\ F$ (10)		$\overline{4}$
(4) $A\ B\ F$ (3)		(13) $B\ B\ F$ (3)		(22) $C\ D\ D$ (15)		
(5) $A\ C\ C$ (10)		(14) $B\ C\ C$ (30)		(23) $C\ D\ F$ (15)		
(6) $A\ C\ D$ (15)		(15) $B\ C\ D$ (45)		$\overline{80}$		
(7) $A\ C\ F$ (5)		(16) $B\ C\ F$ (15)				
(8) $A\ D\ D$ (3)		(17) $B\ D\ D$ (9)				
(9) $A\ D\ F$ (3)		(18) $B\ D\ F$ (9)				
$\overline{66}$		$\overline{136}$				

$$66 + 136 + 80 + 4 = 286$$

Second, the number of possible samples for each combination is found (see reference, p. 158) and is shown on the right side of each sample in the brackets. There is a total of $M = 286$ samples.

Third, we calculate the average grade of each sample; for instance:

$$\frac{A + B + B}{3} = \frac{5 + 4 + 4}{3} = \frac{13}{3} = 4.33 \text{ points}$$

$$\frac{A + B + C}{3} = \frac{5 + 4 + 3}{3} = \frac{12}{3} = 4.0 \text{ points}$$

and so forth. The results are given in the same order as the list of numbered samples above:

(1)	$\frac{13}{3}$	(10)	$\frac{12}{3}$	(19)	$\frac{9}{3}$	(24)	$\frac{6}{3}$
(2)	$\frac{12}{3}$	(11)	$\frac{11}{3}$	(20)	$\frac{8}{3}$	(25)	$\frac{5}{3}$
(3)	$\frac{11}{3}$	(12)	$\frac{10}{3}$	(21)	$\frac{7}{3}$		
(4)	$\frac{10}{3}$	(13)	$\frac{9}{3}$	(22)	$\frac{7}{3}$		
(5)	$\frac{11}{3}$	(14)	$\frac{10}{3}$	(23)	$\frac{6}{3}$		
(6)	$\frac{10}{3}$	(15)	$\frac{9}{3}$				
(7)	$\frac{9}{3}$	(16)	$\frac{8}{3}$				
(8)	$\frac{9}{3}$	(17)	$\frac{8}{3}$				
(9)	$\frac{8}{3}$	(18)	$\frac{7}{3}$				

Note, for example, that:

(7)	A	C	F	$\frac{9}{3}$	5 samples
(8)	A	D	D	$\frac{9}{3}$	3 samples
(13)	B	F	F	$\frac{9}{3}$	3 samples
(15)	B	C	D	$\frac{9}{3}$	45 samples
(16)	C	C	C	$\frac{9}{3}$	10 samples
					$\overline{66}$

That is, there are 66 samples that have an average of $9/3 = 3$ points. Similar computations can be made for the other sample means. The results are in Table 7.7.

TABLE 7.7.

$\bar{X}$	f	d	fd	d^2	fd^2
5/3	3	−4	−12	16	48
6/3	16	−3	−48	9	144
7/3	34	−2	−68	4	136
8/3	57	−1	−57	1	57
9/3	66	0	0	0	0
10/3	57	1	57	1	57
11/3	34	2	68	4	136
12/3	16	3	48	9	144
13/3	3	4	12	16	48
	286		0	60	770

$$\bar{X} = A + \frac{\Sigma fd}{M} \cdot C = 3 + \frac{0}{286} \cdot \frac{1}{3} = 3$$

$$\sigma_{\bar{x}} = C \sqrt{\frac{\Sigma fd^2}{M} - \left(\frac{\Sigma fd}{M}\right)^2} = \frac{1}{3} \sqrt{\frac{770}{286}} = \frac{1}{3} \sqrt{\frac{35}{13}} = 0.5496$$

The mean and standard error of this sampling distribution are calculated in Table 7.7. Let us check $\sigma_{\bar{x}}$ with the formula given in Table 7.4. We have

$$\sigma = \sqrt{\frac{14}{13}}$$

Thus the $\sigma_{\bar{x}}$ becomes

(1) $$\sigma_{\bar{x}} = \frac{\sigma}{\sqrt{n}} \sqrt{\frac{N-n}{N-1}} = \frac{\sqrt{\frac{14}{13}}}{\sqrt{3}} \sqrt{\frac{13-3}{13-1}}$$

$$= \sqrt{\frac{14}{13 \times 3} \times \frac{10}{12}} = \frac{1}{3} \sqrt{\frac{35}{13}}$$

and is the same as the results of direct computations in Table 7.7. Since we had $\sigma = \sqrt{14/13}$, we could have used formula (1) instead of actually calculating $\sigma_{\bar{x}}$ as we did in Table 7.7. In fact, when N and n become large, we shall have to use formula (1); otherwise we shall have a problem of trying to find a very large number of sample means.

Figure 7.8 is a frequency polygon of this distribution, where the distribution looks more like a normal curve than that of Fig. 7.3, although it is still only a rough approximation.

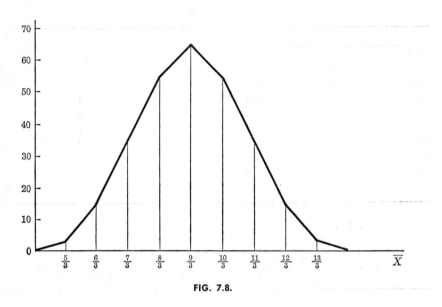

FIG. 7.8.

Let us now calculate the probabilities of selecting samples. The samples are characterized (that is, represented) by their sample means. Thus, using the sample mean, let us ask: What is the probability of selecting a sample with a sample mean of $\bar{x} = 12/3 = 4$ points? From Table 7.7 we see that

$$P[\bar{X} = 4] = \frac{16}{286}$$

That is, there are 16 chances in 286 of selecting a sample of size 3 with a sample mean of 4 points, given our population.

Or, to state it another way, we are saying that 16 samples in the possible 286 samples have a sample mean of $\bar{x} = 4$ points. We know that these samples are

(2)	*A*	*B*	*C*	15
(10)	*B*	*B*	*B*	1
				—
				16

where there are 15 samples of (*A* *B* *C*) and 1 sample of (*B* *B* *B*).

Let us now calculate the probability of selecting samples with sample means greater than or equal to 4 points. From Table 7.7 we find

$$P[\bar{X} \geq 4] = P[\bar{X} = 4] + P\left[\bar{X} = \frac{13}{3}\right]$$

$$= \frac{16}{286} + \frac{3}{286} = \frac{19}{286}$$

Instead of calculating probabilities directly as we have done above, we may use the central limit theorem and the sampling distribution of the sample mean and calculate it indirectly. This will give us an approximate value. The probability we seek is the shaded area under the sampling distribution shown in Figure 7.9, which is (approximately) a normal distribution. We find

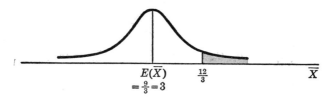

FIG. 7.9.

$$z = \frac{\bar{X} - \mu}{\sigma_{\bar{x}}} = \frac{\frac{12}{3} - \frac{1}{2} \times \frac{1}{3} - \frac{9}{3}}{0.5469} = \frac{\frac{5}{6}}{0.5469} = 1.525$$

From the normal area table, we find 0.064 (approximately).

Our direct calculations above show the probability to be

$$\frac{19}{286} = 0.066$$

and there is about a 0.2 percent $(0.066 - 0.064 = 0.002)$ absolute difference. The relative difference is about 3 percent:

$$\frac{0.002}{0.066} = \frac{2}{66} = \frac{1}{33} = 0.03$$

As the sample size becomes larger, this discrepancy becomes smaller.

The interpretation of $P[\bar{X} \geq 4] = 19/286$ is: The probability of selecting a sample with a sample mean greater than or equal to 4 points is 19/286. The reader should be able to identify these 19 samples from the tables.

The 286 possible samples are enumerated in the Reference.

REFERENCE

(1) A　B　B : $\dfrac{1 \times 3 \times 2}{2!} = \dfrac{6}{2!} = 3$

(2) A　B　C : $1 \times 3 \times 5$ 　　　 $= 15$

(3) A　B　D : $1 \times 3 \times 3$ 　　　 $= 9$

(4) A　B　F : $1 \times 3 \times 1$ 　　　 $= 3$

(5) A　C　C : $\dfrac{1 \times 5 \times 4}{2!} = \dfrac{20}{2!} = 10$

(6) A　C　D : $1 \times 5 \times 3$ 　　　 $= 15$

(7) A　C　F : $1 \times 5 \times 1$ 　　　 $= 5$

(8) A　D　D : $\dfrac{1 \times 3 \times 2}{2!} = \dfrac{6}{2!} = 3$

(9) A　D　F : $1 \times 3 \times 1$ 　　　 $= 3$

(10) B　B　B : $\dfrac{3 \times 2 \times 1}{3!} = \dfrac{6}{3!} = 1$

(11) B　B　C : $\dfrac{3 \times 2 \times 5}{2!} = \dfrac{30}{2!} = 15$

(12) B　B　D : $\dfrac{3 \times 2 \times 3}{2!} = \dfrac{18}{2!} = 9$

(13) B　B　F : $\dfrac{3 \times 2 \times 1}{2!} = \dfrac{6}{2!} = 3$

(14) B　C　C : $\dfrac{3 \times 5 \times 4}{2!} = \dfrac{60}{2!} = 30$

(15) B　C　D : $3 \times 5 \times 3$ 　　　 $= 45$

(16) B　C　F : $3 \times 5 \times 1$ 　　　 $= 15$

(17) B　D　D : $\dfrac{3 \times 3 \times 2}{2!} = \dfrac{18}{2!} = 9$

(18) B　D　F : $3 \times 3 \times 1$ 　　　 $= 9$

(19) C　C　C : $\dfrac{5 \times 4 \times 3}{3!} = \dfrac{60}{3!} = 10$

(20) C　C　D : $\dfrac{5 \times 4 \times 3}{2!} = \dfrac{60}{2!} = 30$

(21) C　C　F : $\dfrac{5 \times 4 \times 1}{2!} = \dfrac{20}{2!} = 10$

(22) C　D　D : $\dfrac{5 \times 3 \times 2}{2!} = \dfrac{30}{2!} = 15$

(23) C　D　F : $5 \times 3 \times 1$ 　　　 $= 15$

(24) D　D　D : $\dfrac{3 \times 2 \times 1}{3!} = \dfrac{6}{3!} = 1$

(25) D　D　F : $\dfrac{3 \times 2 \times 1}{2!} = \dfrac{6}{2!} = 3$

$$3 + 15 + 9 + \cdots + 15 + 1 + 3 = 286$$

Example 2. Given a group of $N = 90$ wage earners with a distribution of wages as in Table 7.8, find the probability of selecting a sample of size $n = 16$ with an average wage greater than $77.

TABLE 7.8.

Wages	f	d	fd	d^2	fd^2
$ 40	3	-3	-9	9	27
50	12	-2	-24	4	48
60	18	-1	-18	1	18
70	24	-0	0	0	0
80	18	1	18	1	18
90	12	2	24	4	48
100	3	3	9	9	27
	90		0	28	186

$$E(X) = \mu = A + \frac{\Sigma fd}{N} \cdot C$$

$$= \$70 + \frac{0}{90} \cdot 10 = \$70$$

$$\sigma = C \sqrt{\frac{\Sigma fd^2}{N} - \left(\frac{\Sigma fd}{N}\right)^2}$$

$$= 10 \sqrt{\frac{186}{90} - 0}$$

$$= 10 \sqrt{2.066} = 10 \times 1.437 = \$14.37$$

If we try to solve this problem as we did in Example 1, we first need to find all possible samples. This will be

$$\binom{90}{16} = \frac{90!}{16! \ 74!}$$

It is quite obvious that this will be a very large number, and for practical purposes, it is a prohibitive task to find the probabilities of the samples and sample means. But from the central limit theorem we know that the sampling distribution of the sample mean is approximately a normal distribution, as shown in Fig. 7.10. Finding the probability of selecting samples with sample means greater than or equal to $77 is equivalent to finding the

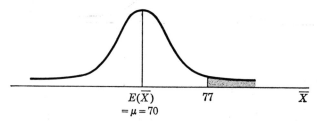

$$E(\overline{X}) = \mu = 70 \qquad 77 \qquad \overline{X}$$

FIG. 7.10.

probability of sample means greater than or equal to $77 in the sampling distribution of the sample mean. Since we have a normal distribution, this is found by calculating z:

$$z = \frac{\bar{X} - \mu}{\sigma_{\bar{x}}} = \frac{77 - \frac{1}{2} \times \frac{1}{16} - 70}{3.294} = 2.12$$

where $\sigma_{\bar{x}}$ is obtained from

$$\sigma_{\bar{x}} = \frac{\sigma}{\sqrt{n}} \sqrt{\frac{N - n}{N - 1}}$$

$$= \frac{\$14.37}{\sqrt{16}} \sqrt{\frac{90 - 16}{90 - 1}}$$

$$= \$3.592 \times 0.917$$

$$= \$3.294$$

From the normal area table, the proportion that corresponds to $z = 2.12$ is 0.0170. That is, the probability of finding a sample mean greater than or equal to $77 is 0.0170. This may also be stated as: The probability of selecting samples with sample means greater than or equal to $77 is 0.0170.

Although we cannot specifically identify these samples with sample means greater than or equal to $77, we have found the approximate probability of selecting them. The probability of 0.017 shows that there are approximately only 1.7 chances in 100 of selecting such a sample.

Note that the continuity correction $1/2 \times 1/n$, where $n = 16$, has very little effect on the result.

Example 3. Data for the production of wheat per acre of 101 farms are available. The mean is $\mu = 15$ bushels per acre and the standard deviation is $\sigma = 4$ bushels. Find the probability of selecting samples of size $n = 25$ with sample means less than or equal to $\bar{x} = 13.5$ bushels. The sampling distribution of the sample mean is shown in Fig. 7.11.

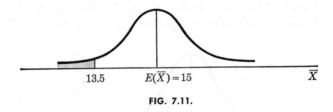

FIG. 7.11.

The probability of sample means being less than or equal to 13.5 bushels is obtained by finding the shaded area in the tail end of the curve. We find (omitting the continuity correction $1/2 \times 1/n$, where $n = 101$):

$$z = \frac{\bar{X} - \mu}{\sigma_{\bar{x}}} = \frac{13.5 - 15}{0.6976} = -2.15$$

where $\sigma_{\bar{x}}$ is obtained from

$$\sigma_{\bar{x}} = \frac{\sigma}{\sqrt{n}} \sqrt{\frac{N - n}{N - 1}} = \frac{4}{\sqrt{25}} \sqrt{\frac{101 - 25}{101 - 1}} = 0.6976 \text{ bushels}$$

By using $z = -2.15$, we find 0.0158 from the normal area table; that is,

$$P\,[\bar{X} \leq 13.5] = 0.0158$$

Thus the probability of finding sample means less than or equal to 13.5 bushels is 0.0158. Or we may state this as: The probability of selecting samples with sample means less than or equal to 13.5 bushels is 0.0158. This may also be stated as: There are $1.6(0.0158 \cong 0.016)$ chances in 100 of selecting a sample with a sample mean less than or equal to 13.5 bushels from a population where $\mu = 15$ bushels.

7.5. Comments on the Standard Error Formula

The formula for the standard error is

(1) $$\sigma_{\bar{x}} = \frac{\sigma}{\sqrt{n}} \sqrt{\frac{N - n}{N - 1}}$$

and it assumes a finite population of size N. The factor

$$\sqrt{\frac{N - n}{N - 1}}$$

is called the *finite population correction* (fpc).

We see that when we have an infinite population, the fraction $(N - n)/(N - 1)$ approaches 1.00, and hence the fpc also approaches 1.00. Then formula (1) becomes, simply,

(2) $$\sigma_{\bar{x}} = \frac{\sigma}{\sqrt{n}}$$

Whenever sampling is with replacement, we have an infinite population. For example, consider a box with 5 beads in it. If, when a sample is taken, the beads are replaced each time they are drawn, we have an infinite population. We can draw samples of size $n = 10$, or $n = 100$, or whatever size we wish. Other examples of infinite populations will be specified later in examples.

We can also see that when N is large relative to n, the fraction

$$\frac{N-n}{N-1} = \frac{1 - \dfrac{n}{N}}{1 - \dfrac{1}{N}}$$

will approach 1.00, and hence the fpc will also be close to 1.00. Thus, when N is large relative to n, we may use formula (2).

How large should N be relative to n before we can use formula (2)? Some say that n should be less than 5 percent of N; others say that n should be less than 10 percent. We shall adopt the 10 percent rule. If there should be any doubt about the accuracy of the result, a simple calculation of the fpc will dispose of the doubt.

7.6.   The Sampling Distribution of the Sample Proportion

Our discussion up to now has been restricted to the sampling distribution of the sample mean $\bar{X}$. We shall now discuss in similar fashion the distribution of the sample proportion p and find the $E(p)$, $\text{Var}(p)$, and the nature of the sampling distribution of p. An illustration is used to derive these properties.

Suppose we have a box that has 4 white and 6 black beads. The 10 beads are considered as the population and the proportion of white beads is $4/10 = 0.4$. This proportion is called the *population proportion* and is denoted by $\pi = 0.4$.

Let us next select samples of size $n = 5$ from this population. There are

$$\binom{10}{5} = \frac{10!}{5!5!} = 252$$

possible samples. Recall that this assumes all 10 beads to be different. But since our samples consider any white bead as the same or any black bead as the same, the number of possible samples may be found as follows: Let $\bigcirc$ denote a white bead and $\oplus$ denote a black bead. Then:

$$\overset{\bigcirc}{4} \times \overset{\bigcirc}{3} \times \overset{\bigcirc}{2} \times \overset{\bigcirc}{1} \times \overset{\oplus}{6} \div 4! = 6$$

This shows that in the 252 possible samples, 6 of them are samples that have 4 white and 1 black bead. In similar fashion, we find

$$\overset{\bigcirc}{4} \times \overset{\bigcirc}{3} \times \overset{\bigcirc}{2} \times \overset{\oplus}{6} \times \overset{\oplus}{5} \div (3!)(2!) = 60$$

$$\overset{\bigcirc}{4} \times \overset{\bigcirc}{3} \times \overset{\oplus}{6} \times \overset{\oplus}{5} \times \overset{\oplus}{4} \div (2!)(3!) = 120$$

$$\overset{\circ}{4} \times \overset{\oplus}{6} \times \overset{\oplus}{5} \times \overset{\oplus}{4} \times \overset{\oplus}{3} \div (4!) \quad = 60$$

$$\overset{\oplus}{6} \times \overset{\oplus}{5} \times \overset{\oplus}{4} \times \overset{\oplus}{3} \times \overset{\oplus}{2} \div (5!) \quad = 6$$

and

$$6 + 60 + 120 + 60 + 6 = 252$$

Thus the probability of selecting a sample with 4 white and 1 black beads is

$$P[4w, \quad 1b] = \frac{6}{252}$$

and likewise:

$$P[3w, \quad 2b] = \frac{60}{252}$$

$$P[2w, \quad 3b] = \frac{120}{252}$$

$$P[1w, \quad 4b] = \frac{60}{252}$$

$$P[0w, \quad 5b] = \frac{6}{252}$$

Let p be the proportion of white beads in a *sample*. Then, for 4 white and 1 black beads,

$$p = \frac{4}{5} = 0.80$$

This p is called the *sample proportion*, and it is a statistic.

The results may now be presented in table form as shown in Table 7.9. This frequency distribution of the sample proportion is called the *sampling distribution of the sample proportion*. The bar chart in Fig. 7.12 shows this sampling distribution.

TABLE 7.9.

Sample	p	f	$p - \pi$	$(p - \pi)^2$	$(p - \pi)^2 f$
0w, 5b	$p = 0.0$	6	−0.4	0.16	0.96
1w, 4b	$p = 0.2$	60	−0.2	0.04	2.40
2w, 3b	$p = 0.4$	120	0.0	0.0	0.0
3w, 2b	$p = 0.6$	60	0.2	0.04	2.40
4w, 1b	$p = 0.8$	6	0.4	0.16	0.96
		252			6.72

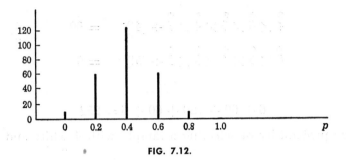

FIG. 7.12.

When we have a frequency distribution, we wish to know two things: its mean and standard distribution. From Table 7.9 the mean is found by the weighted mean formula as

(1) $\bar{p} = \dfrac{(6 \times 0.0) + (60 \times 0.2) + (120 \times 0.4) + (60 \times 0.6) + (6 \times 0.8)}{6 + 60 + 120 + 60 + 6}$

$$= \left(0.0 \times \frac{6}{252}\right) + \left(0.2 \times \frac{60}{252}\right) + \left(0.4 \times \frac{120}{252}\right)$$
$$+ \left(0.6 \times \frac{60}{252}\right) + \left(0.8 \times \frac{6}{252}\right)$$

$$= 0.4$$

That is, the mean of the sampling distribution of p is equal to $\pi = 0.4$. More generally, we state that the expected value of p is equal to π; that is

(2) $\qquad E(p) = p_1 \cdot P[X = p_1] + p_2 \cdot P[X = p_2]$
$$+ \cdots + p_5 \cdot P[X = p_5]$$
$$= 0.0 \times \frac{6}{252} + 0.2 \times \frac{10}{252} + \cdots + 0.8 \times \frac{6}{252}$$

$$= 0.4$$

Therefore

(3) $\qquad\qquad\qquad\qquad E(p) = \pi$

The variance is, using the calculation results in Table 7.9,

$$(4) \qquad \mathrm{Var}(p) = \frac{\Sigma\,(p - \pi)^2 f}{\Sigma f}$$

$$= \frac{6.72}{252} = \frac{0.08}{3}$$

where the sum $\Sigma\,(p - \pi)^2 \cdot f$ is taken over all possible samples. For our simple problem, finding $\mathrm{Var}(p)$ was easy. But when we have larger samples and populations, this becomes a very laborious task. Fortunately there is a simple formula that gives us the same results. It is

$$(5) \qquad \mathrm{Var}(p) = \frac{\pi(1 - \pi)}{n} \cdot \frac{N - n}{N - 1}$$

where $\sqrt{(N - n)/(N - 1)}$ is the fpc. For the present problem we find

$$\mathrm{Var}(p) = \frac{\pi(1 - \pi)}{n} \cdot \frac{N - n}{N - 1}$$

$$= \frac{(0.4)(0.6)}{5} \times \frac{10 - 5}{10 - 1}$$

$$= \frac{0.24}{9} = \frac{0.08}{3}$$

That is, we have obtained the same result as in formula (4). Therefore we shall use formula (5) instead of formula (4).

The results may be summarized and generalized as follows: Given a population of size N with a population proportion π, the sampling distribution of the sample proportion p for samples of size n will have a mean and variance as follows:

$$(3) \qquad E(p) = \pi$$

$$(5) \qquad \mathrm{Var}(p) = \frac{\pi(1 - \pi)}{n} \cdot \frac{N - n}{N - 1}$$

A characteristic of the sampling distribution of the sample mean $\bar{X}$ is that it approaches a normal distribution when n is large. This enabled us to find the probabilities of selecting samples with certain sample means. Can something similar to this be said about the sampling distribution of the sample proportion p? The answer is: Yes, when n is large, the sampling distribution of p will be a normal distribution.

How large must n be to be able to use the normal distribution? This is discussed in Chapter 19, but we shall state for the present that the normal distribution should be used only when $n \geqq 25$.

Thus we now have the following results: The mean and variance of the sampling distribution of p is given by

$$E(p) = \pi$$

$$\text{Var}(p) = \frac{\pi(1-\pi)}{n} \cdot \frac{N-n}{N-1}$$

and furthermore, the sampling distribution is approximately normal when n is large.

The square root of $\text{Var}(p)$ is the standard deviation of the sampling distribution of p and is called the *standard error*. It is denoted by

$$\sigma_p = \sqrt{\frac{\pi(1-\pi)}{n}} \cdot \sqrt{\frac{N-n}{N-1}}$$

We are now in a position to apply these results to practical problems.

Example 1. In a population of families, 20 percent subscribe to magazine K. What is the probability of selecting a random sample of size $n = 225$ with a sample proportion $p = 0.16$ or less?

Let us first interpret the problem in terms of a figure. As Fig. 7.13 shows,

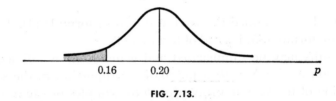

| 0.16 | 0.20 | p |

FIG. 7.13.

we want the shaded area in the left tail. By using the normal approximation, this is easily found as follows:

$$z = \frac{p - \pi}{\sigma_p} = \frac{0.16 + \dfrac{1}{2} \times \dfrac{1}{225} - 0.20}{0.026}$$

$$= \frac{-0.04 + 0.002}{0.026} = -1.4615$$

where σ_p *is*

$$\sigma_p = \sqrt{\frac{\pi(1-\pi)}{n}} = \sqrt{\frac{(0.20)(0.80)}{225}}$$

$$= \frac{0.40}{15} = 0.026$$

Note that we have assumed fpc $= 1$ and the continuity correction as

$$\frac{1}{2} \times \frac{1}{n} = \frac{1}{2} \times \frac{1}{225} = 0.0022$$

Since $z = -1.46$, we find from the normal area table that

$$P[p \leq 0.16 \mid \pi = 0.20] = 0.0721$$

The interpretation is: There are about 7.2 chances in 100 of selecting samples with a sample proportion less than or equal to 0.16 from a population where $\pi = 0.20$.

Example 2.   Of 2000 dealers, 40 percent indicated that they planned to increase their orders for dishwashers. What is the probability of selecting a simple random sample of 400 dealers with a sample proportion of $p = 46\%$ from this population?

In diagrammatic terms, we have Fig. 7.14 and we want the shaded area in

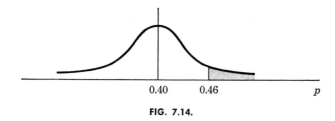

0.40   0.46 p

FIG. 7.14.

the right tail:

$$z = \frac{p - \pi}{\sigma_p} = \frac{0.46 - \frac{1}{2} \times \frac{1}{400} - 0.40}{0.0217} = 2.70$$

where

$$\sigma_p = \sqrt{\frac{\pi(1 - \pi)}{n}} \sqrt{\frac{N - n}{N - 1}} = \sqrt{\frac{(0.4)(0.6)}{400}} \sqrt{\frac{2000 - 400}{2000 - 1}} = 0.0217$$

Since $z = 2.70$, we find from the normal area table that

$$P[p \geq 0.46 \mid \pi = 0.40] = 0.0035$$

The interpretation is: There are about 3.5 chances in 1000 of selecting samples of size 400 with sample proportions greater than or equal to 0.46 from a population where $\pi = 0.40$.

TESTING HYPOTHESES

8

Now that we have a background of probability theory and sampling distributions, we are ready to discuss the topic of testing hypotheses. We shall do these in steps: first, introduce new terminology that will be used in subsequent discussion; second, explain type I and type II errors; third, explain tests concerning null and simple alternative hypotheses; and fourth, generalize the discussions of the third step, explain simple decision problems, and derive OC curves.

8.1. Introduction of New Terminology

Suppose we are given 2 urns, A and B, with red and green balls in them as follows:

	Urn A	Urn B
Red	2	7
Green	8	3

A ball is selected from one of the urns; assume that it is a red ball. The statistician does not know from which urn it was selected. However, based on this red ball, he wishes to decide from which urn the ball was selected.

Let us analyze this simple problem, using statistical terminology. First, the 2 urns will be called *states of nature* or *states of the world.* These will be denoted by w_1 and w_2. Obviously the *worlds,* w_1 and w_2, are the objects (that is, the urns) about which the statistician is concerned, and the term *states of the world* describe the world. In our present problem, w_1 has 2 red and 8 green and w_2 has 7 red and 3 green balls. We shall use w_1 and w_2 to denote both worlds and states of the world. A characteristic of the states of the world is that they should be exclusive and exhaustive. That is, there are no other states of the world other than w_1 and w_2 in our present experiment.

If there are 3 urns, each with a different number of red balls, there are 3 states of the world. In our present example, where we have only 10 balls (red and green) in an urn, the number of red balls are either 0, 1, . . . , or 10. Hence there are 11 possible states of the world. However, in our present problem, we have defined our experiment to have only 2 urns with 2 red in one urn and 7 red in the other.

Second, the statistician performs an *experiment* ϵ, which in the present case is selecting a ball.

Third, the *outcomes* of the experiment ϵ are denoted by the variable X. In our present case, the outcomes of the experiment (that is, drawing a ball) are red or green. Recall that these outcomes were also called *events.* We may also show these outcomes diagrammatically as in Fig. 8.1. This line is a 1-dimensional space, and the 2 points on it indicate the 2 outcomes, red and green. This space, which shows the possible outcomes of

Red   Green X

FIG. 8.1.

X, is called a *sample space*. The outcomes (red or green ball) may be considered as a sample of size 1, and these 2 points, which represent samples, are called *sample points*.

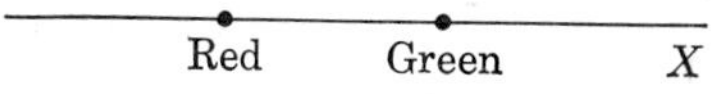

As another illustration, let us assume that 2 balls are drawn, with replacement, from an urn. Then the possible outcomes of this experiment of taking a sample of 2 balls are

$$(r, r), \quad (r, g), \quad (g, r), \quad (g, g)$$

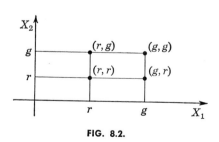

FIG. 8.2.

That is, there are 4 possible outcomes. This may be shown diagrammatically, as in Fig. 8.2. This diagram represents the sample space associated with the experiment. We see that we have a 2-dimensional sample space and that there are $2^2 = 4$ sample points.

Note that the two samples (r, g) and (g, r) have been considered as being different. But for practical problems they are the same sample.

If a sample of size 3 is drawn, we have a 3-dimensional sample space with $2^3 = 8$ sample points. If a sample of size 4 is drawn, we have a 4-dimensional sample space with $2^4 = 16$ sample points. If a sample of size n is taken, and there are only 2 possible outcomes for each draw, we shall have an n-dimensional space with 2^n sample points.

Now let us assume there are red, green, and black balls in the urns. That is, there are 3 possible outcomes per draw, instead of 2 possible outcomes per draw. Then, when 1 ball is drawn, the sample space is as in Fig. 8.3. We have a 1-dimensional sample space with 3 sample points.

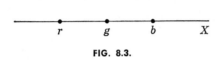

FIG. 8.3.

If we take a sample of size 2, the sample space is as in Fig. 8.4. It is a 2-dimensional sample space with $3^2 = 9$ sample points. If we take a sample of size 3, we have a 3-dimensional sample space with $3^3 = 27$ sample points. By induction we see that if we take a sample of size n, we shall have an n-dimensional sample space with 3^n sample points.

With regard to our main line of discussion, we have so far explained: first, the term states of the world; second, an experiment ϵ; third, a sample space, and sample points associated to ϵ. The fourth element in our problem to be explained is an *act*, which the statistician selects.

We shall give further explanation about acts later on, but for the

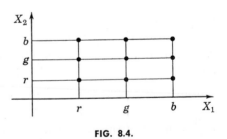

FIG. 8.4.

moment let us say A_1 is an action taken, assuming that w_1 is true; and A_2 is an action taken, assuming that w_2 is true. In our present example, A_1 is to select urn A, and A_2 is to select urn B.

The fifth and last element in our problem may be explained as follows: How does the statistician decide whether to adopt action A_1 or A_2? This, as we have seen, is based on the ball (that is, the outcome; or we may say, the sample) that has been drawn.

In our present example, a red ball has been drawn. Which action should the statistician take, A_1 or A_2? Suppose a green ball has been drawn. Which action should he take, A_1 or A_2? It will be convenient if a *rule* were to be set up in advance so that we can tell which action to take when a certain outcome is observed. For example, let us set up the following *rule:*

Outcome	Rule
Red	A_1
Green	A_2

This rule says: When the outcome is a red ball, take action A_1, and when the outcome is a green ball, take action A_2.

The fifth element of the problem is this rule (or, we may say, a function) that tells which *action* to take when given an *outcome*. This can be shown schematically as

$$\text{(Outcome)} \longrightarrow \text{(rule)} \longrightarrow \text{(action)}$$

We shall call this rule a *decision rule.*

An alternative way of expressing this is

$$\text{(Sample space)} \longrightarrow \text{(decision rule)} \longrightarrow \text{(action space)}$$

because the sample space is the space that shows all possible outcomes. This latter interpretation is the one we shall mainly use for our theoretical discussion. Figure 8.5 gives an illustration in which a sample of size 2 has been drawn.

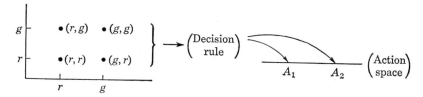

FIG. 8.5.

A question that immediately arises is: Why did we set up the decision rule? Are there any other decision rules? Let us first investigate whether there are any other decision rules.

Since we have 2 outcomes and 2 actions, we have the following $2^2 = 4$ decision rules, which are shown by d_1, d_2, d_3, d_4. The decision rule listed above is d_2.

TABLE 8.1.

Outcome	d_1	d_2	d_3	d_4
Red	A_1	A_1	A_2	A_2
Green	A_1	A_2	A_1	A_2

If we have 3 outcomes and 2 actions, there will be $2^3 = 8$ decision rules. For example, assume there are 3 colors: red, green, and black. Then we have the decision rules in Table 8.2.

TABLE 8.2.

Outcome	d_1	d_2	d_3	d_4	d_5	d_6	d_7	d_8
Red	A_1	A_1	A_1	A_2	A_2	A_2	A_1	A_2
Green	A_1	A_1	A_2	A_1	A_2	A_1	A_2	A_2
Black	A_1	A_2	A_1	A_1	A_1	A_2	A_2	A_2

Decision rule d_2 shows that when a red or green ball is drawn, take action A_1; when a black ball is drawn, take action A_2.

In general, if there are n outcomes and 2 actions, there will be 2^n decision rules.

A question that arises is: Why did we select the decision rule d_3? Is d_3 the only decision rule we should select as our criterion? These questions will be discussed later. For the present, let us confine ourselves to the meaning of the various new terms.

To summarize, we have the following 5 elements:

1. States of the world.
2. Experiment ϵ.
3. Sample space and sample point.
4. Action A_1 and A_2.
5. Decision rules.

With this much background, let us now proceed to the next topic, type I and type II errors.

8.2. Type I and Type II Errors

The statistician was faced with a problem of deciding whether a ball that was drawn came from urn $A(w_1)$ or from urn $B(w_2)$. If the statistician rejects w_1 (urn A) when in fact it is true (that is, the ball actually came from urn A), the statistician has made the type I error (or error of the first kind). In our present problem, rejecting urn A implies accepting urn B, and accepting urn B was called "taking action A_2." Hence we may say: If the true state of nature is w_1 (urn A) and the statistician takes action A_2 (that is, selects urn B), he makes a type I error. This type I error is also called the α error.

If the statistician rejects w_2 (urn B) when in fact it is true (that is, the ball actually came from urn B), the statistician has made the type

II error (or error of the second kind). In our present problem, rejecting urn B implies accepting urn A, and accepting urn A was called "taking action A_1." Hence we may say: If the true state of nature is w_2 (urn B) and the statistician takes action A_1 (that is, selects urn A) he makes a type II error. This type II error is also called the β error.

The relation between states of nature and actions may be shown schematically as follows (Table 8.3): The upper left-hand corner shows the relation where the true state of nature is w_1 and the action taken by the statistician (or decision maker) is A_1; hence it is a correct decision.

TABLE 8.3.A.

	States of Nature	
Action	w_1, Urn A	w_2, Urn B
A_1	Correct decision	Incorrect decision, β error
A_2	Incorrect decision, α error	Correct decision

The lower left-hand corner shows the relation where the true state of nature is w_1 and the action taken is A_2; hence it is an incorrect decision (the α error).

The upper right-hand corner shows the relation where the true state of nature is w_2 and the action taken is A_1; hence it is an incorrect decision (the β error).

The lower right-hand corner shows the relation where the true state of nature is w_2 and the action taken is A_2; hence it is a correct decision.

Several more examples of type I (α) and type II (β) errors are presented as follows: Assume w_1 is the state of nature where we have good students (that is, students with grades A, B, C, or D), and w_2 is the state where we have poor students (that is, students with grades F). Let the two actions A_1 and A_2 be "to pass" or "to flunk" a student, respectively. Then we can show the situation schematically as follows:

TABLE 8.3.B.

	States of Nature	
Action	w_1, Good Students	w_2, Poor Students
A_1, pass	Correct decision	Incorrect decision, β error
A_2, fail	Incorrect decision, α error	Correct decision

The α error is made when a good student has been failed. The β error is made when a poor student has been passed.

Another example is: w_1 is good weather; w_2 is rain; A_1 is "do not take umbrella"; A_2 is "take umbrella." The situation is as follows:

TABLE 8.3.C.

	States of Nature	
Action	w_1, Fair	w_2, Rain
A_1, do not take umbrella		β error
A_2, take umbrella	α error	

The last example may be changed as follows: w_1 is rain; w_2 is fair; A_1 is "take umbrella"; A_2 is "do not take umbrella." Then the schema becomes:

TABLE 8.3.D.

	States of Nature	
Action	w_1, Rain	w_2, Fair
A_1, take		β error
A_2, do not take	α error	

Now the α error is not taking an umbrella when it rains. In the previous case it was taking the umbrella when it was fair. The α and β errors have reversed themselves.

This points out that the α error and β error will depend on how we select our w_1, w_2, A_1, and A_2. As a convention, we usually take our w_1, w_2, A_1, and A_2 so that the α error is the one we are mainly interested in avoiding. If not taking an umbrella when it rains is the more serious error than taking an umbrella when it is fair weather, we should adopt the second schema.

It is also recommended that the schema be set up so that the α error will always be in the lower left-hand cell and (consequently) the β error will be in the upper right-hand cell. This will avoid confusion. We shall follow this rule.

8.3. Testing Hypotheses

We shall now apply the various previous results to the classical problems of testing hypotheses. The adjective "classical" is used because the test we are about to discuss was developed during the past half-century and may be contrasted with a new approach that has been developed recently. We shall discuss this new approach in Chapter 9.

The simplest case may be outlined as follows: We wish to determine whether or not a sample came from population (state of nature) w_1. Let us assume that the mean of the population is μ_0 and the mean of the sample is $\bar{X}$. Then we ask the question: What is the probability of selecting a sample with sample mean $\bar{X}$ or greater from a population with mean μ_0? Let us assume that the probability is α (say, 3 percent). This means that there are 3 chances in 100 of selecting a sample with a sample mean $\bar{X}$ or greater from a population with mean μ_0.

Hence, if we conclude that the sample did *not* come from the population, the probability of being incorrect is 0.03. Or, we may say, the probability of being incorrect by deciding the sample did not come from the population, when in fact it did, is 0.03.

We have assumed that the population has a mean of μ_0. This, then, is our hypothesis; that is,

Hypothesis: The mean of the population is μ_0

which is usually abbreviated

$$H_1: \qquad \mu = \mu_0$$

and is called the *null hypothesis*. It is the hypothesis that we are interested in testing.

We use this term "null hypothesis" and state our conclusion as follows: The probability of rejecting the null hypothesis (H_1) when in fact it is true is 0.03. Or, we may say that 0.03 is the probability of taking action A_2, given H_1. In symbols this is

$$P(A_2 \mid H_1)$$

But note that this rejection of the null hypothesis is simply the type I (α) error. The α error is the error of rejecting the state of nature w_1 (H_1) when in fact it is true. In other words, 0.03 is the *risk* of making an error of the first kind. We shall use α to denote this risk. In symbols we have

$$\alpha = P(A_2 \mid H_1) = 0.03$$

Because of random fluctuations in sample selection, there is always a risk of making an error, although by making the samples large, this risk may be reduced. This point is explained later.

Let us give an illustration. Suppose a company has 160 secretaries and the distribution of their typing speed is as shown in Table 8.4. The variable X is the typing speed.

TABLE 8.4.

Typing Speed, X	Freq., f	Midpoint, m	d	df	d²	fd²
45—	10		−3	−30	9	90
50—	20		−2	−40	4	80
55—	30		−1	−30	1	30
60—	40	62.5	0	0	0	0
65—	30		1	30	1	30
70—	20		2	40	4	80
75—	10		3	30	9	90
	160			0		400

$$\mu = A + \frac{\Sigma \, fd}{N} \times C = 62.5 + \frac{0}{160} \times 5 = 62.5$$

$$\sigma = C \sqrt{\frac{\Sigma \, fd^2}{N} - \left(\frac{\Sigma \, fd}{N}\right)^2} = 5 \sqrt{\frac{400}{160}} = 7.79$$

We find the population mean to be $\mu = 62.5$ words per minute, and the population standard deviation to be $\sigma = 7.79$ words per minute.

A secretarial school claims that by instructing the secretaries on company premises for several days, the typing speed will increase. The company hires the secretarial school to perform its services.

After the instructions have been given, the company decides to have a statistician check the results. The statistician selects a random sample of 16 secretaries and finds the sample mean to be 66.2 words per minute. He asks: How probable is it to select a sample with a sample mean greater than or equal to 66.2 from the original population H_1?

We learned in Chapter 7 how to use the sampling distribution of the sample mean and the results of the central limit theorem to calculate the probability of selecting a sample. In our present case, the sampling distribution of the sample mean may be shown as in Fig. 8.6.

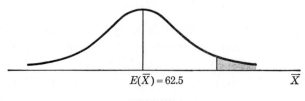

$E(\overline{X}) = 62.5$ $\overline{X}$

FIG. 8.6.

We know that

$$E(\bar{X}) = \mu = 62.5$$

Since the sampling distribution of the sample mean is approximately normal, the area of the shaded part is found by

$$z = \frac{\bar{X} - E(\bar{X})}{\sigma_{\bar{x}}} = \frac{66.2 - \frac{1}{2} \times \frac{1}{16} - 62.5}{1.85} \doteq 1.98$$

where the $\sigma_{\bar{x}}$ is obtained from

$$\sigma_{\bar{x}} = \frac{\sigma}{\sqrt{n}} \sqrt{\frac{N - n}{N - 1}} = \frac{7.79}{\sqrt{16}} \sqrt{\frac{160 - 16}{160 - 1}} \doteq 1.85$$

Since $z = 1.98$, the proportion of the shaded area is 0.0239. In symbols this is shown as

$$P[\bar{X} \geq 66.2 \mid \mu = 62.5] = 0.0239$$

The interpretation is: There are about 2 chances in 100 of selecting samples with sample means greater than or equal to 66.2 from population H_1.

This may also be interpreted as follows: The *risk* of committing the α error of rejecting H_1 when in fact it is true is about 0.02.

The question that arises is: How large a *risk* should be taken to decide whether or not the null hypothesis is to be rejected?

The classical analysis is ambiguous on this point and circumvents this impasse by saying: The level of the risk is to be determined by persons other than the statistician; it is a policy decision and it will suffice if the statistician can provide the policy decision maker with information useful for his policy making.

We shall discuss this problem again, but for the moment let us follow the classical approach and assume that the *risk* the policy decision maker is willing to take of committing the α error is *given*. In most cases, values such as 0.05 (5 percent) or 0.01 (1 percent) are used as the risk the decision maker is willing to accept.

This α risk is also called the *level of significance*. When using this term, the reasoning is sometimes presented as follows: Assume that the null hypothesis is true and that the mean is μ. Let $\bar{X}$ be the sample mean. Then the probability of selecting a sample such that the difference $d = \bar{X} - \mu$ is larger than some value (say, d_0) may be shown by

$$P(\bar{X} - \mu \geq d_0) = \alpha$$

If, for example, $\alpha = 0.05$, this equation may be interpreted to mean that there are approximately 5 chances in 100 of selecting a sample with a sample mean $\bar{X}$ from a population with mean μ such that $\bar{X} - \mu \geq d_0$. We may consider it practically impossible to select in a single trial a sample that will have a sample mean $\bar{X}$ that deviates from the population mean μ by d_0 or more.

What we actually have before us is the sample. The null hypothesis is something we have set up. Thus we conclude that the evidence from the sample does not support the null hypothesis, and hence we reject the null hypothesis. We have not proved that the null hypothesis is wrong, only that the sample evidence does not support the null hypothesis.

This result is usually expressed as follows: If the probability (say, 3 percent) of the deviation between $\bar{X}$ and μ is smaller than or equal to α (say, 5 percent), where α is the predetermined level of significance, we consider the difference between $\bar{X}$ and μ to be *significant* and therefore we *reject* the null hypothesis.

If the probability (say, 10 percent) of the deviation between $\bar{X}$ and μ is larger than α (say, 5 percent), we consider the difference between $\bar{X}$ and μ to be *not significant,* and therefore we *accept* the hypothesis. That is, the deviation of $\bar{X}$ from μ is considered to be due to chance (random) causes.

In our present case, the rejection of H_1 implies that the statistician thinks the sample came from a different population that has a higher average typing speed.

It is important to understand that no causal relationship has been proved. The results simply show that the data support the claim (or the data are consistent with the claim) that the typing speed increases. To use another example, consider the claim that smoking causes cancer. Data are compiled which show that people who smoke have a higher rate of cancer. But this statistical analysis does not prove any causal relationship between smoking and cancer. It shows only that the data are consistent with the claim.

Let us now analyze and summarize the above illustration as follows:

1. The population H_1 that was rejected is the hypothesis under consideration. The important point to note here is that when we say "hypothesis" in statistics, we mean a frequency distribution. To distinguish this from hypotheses that have no frequency distribution, such as "the earth is round," it may be called a *statistical hypothesis.*

The statistical hypothesis that is being tested is called the *null hypothesis* and is denoted by H_1. The statistician wishes to *accept* or *reject* the null hypothesis. If he rejects the null hypothesis, he is implying acceptance of some other hypothesis. This other hypothesis is called the *alternative hypothesis* (or alternative hypotheses, if there is more than one alternative), and is denoted by H_2.

In our present case, the original population (frequency distribution) H_1 is the null hypothesis. The alternative hypotheses H_2 are the frequency distributions with a higher average.

2.   The statistician finds that when the sample mean is $\bar{X} = 66.2$ or greater, the probability is

$$P[\bar{X} \geqq 66.2 \mid \mu = 62.5] = 0.0239$$

It is seen that when the deviation (or difference)

$$d = \bar{X} - \mu$$

becomes larger, the probability of finding a sample with such a sample mean becomes smaller. The statistician thinks that 2 chances in 100 is a very small probability and *rejects* H_1, based on the reasoning that selecting such a sample is *highly improbable*. When the deviation is large and the occurrence of such a sample mean is highly improbable, this may be expressed by saying: The sample mean $\bar{X}$ *differs significantly* from μ. When the deviation is small and the occurrence is probable, this may be expressed by saying: The sample mean $\bar{X}$ *does not differ significantly* from μ.

This leads to the question: Where is the dividing line between improbable and probable, and hence between rejection and acceptance of H_1? This will depend on how certain the statistician wishes to be in not making an incorrect decision of rejecting H_1 when in fact it should be accepted. In our present case, the statistician thinks that 2 chances out of 100 is highly improbable. These 2 chances in 100 are also expressed as 2 percent. In other cases it may be 1, 5, 10 percent or some other percent. This will be discussed again later, so let us for the moment say that the dividing criteria is 5 percent. These dividing criteria are called *levels of significance* and are denoted by α.

Our explanation has been rather long, but once it is understood, the problems may be solved in the following compact manner. The null and alternative hypotheses are

$$H_1: \quad \mu = 62.5$$
$$H_2: \quad \mu > 62.5$$

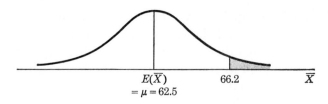

$E(\overline{X})$ $= \mu = 62.5$ 66.2 $\overline{X}$

FIG. 8.7.

where $\sigma = 7.79$. The sample mean is $\overline{X} = 66.2$ (Fig. 8.7). Then

$$z = \frac{\overline{X} - \mu}{\sigma_{\bar{x}}} = \frac{66.2 - \frac{1}{2} \cdot \frac{1}{16} - 62.5}{1.85} = 1.98$$

where

$$\sigma_{\bar{x}} = \frac{\sigma}{\sqrt{n}} \sqrt{\frac{N-n}{N-1}} = \frac{7.79}{\sqrt{16}} \sqrt{\frac{160-16}{160-1}} \doteq 1.85$$

Since $z = 1.98$, we find from the normal area table that

$$P[\overline{X} \geqq 66.2 \mid \mu = 62.5] = 0.0239$$

Thus, there are about 2 chances in 100 of selecting samples with sample means greater than or equal to 66.2. Since we have agreed on the $\alpha = 5$ percent level of significance, there is a significant difference between $\overline{X} = 66.2$ and $\mu = 62.5$, and therefore we reject the hypothesis H_1 that $\mu = 62.5$. This implies that the sample came from H_2, where $\mu > 62.5$.

An alternative way of expressing the conclusion is: The α-risk is 2.39 percent and is less than the permissible level of $\alpha = 0.05$ (that is, 5 percent). Hence we reject the null hypothesis.

To repeat once again, when the hypothesis H_1 is rejected, it means that the *frequency distribution* with $\mu = 62.5$ is rejected. The implication that the sample came from H_2 means that the sample came from a *frequency distribution* with a μ greater than 62.5.

Let us now present several examples. Examples 1, 2, and 3 are illustrations of one-tail tests concerning means. Examples 4 and 5 are one-tail tests concerning proportions. Examples 6 and 7 are two-tail tests concerning means and proportions.

One-tail tests of means

The illustration concerning secretaries was a one-tail test. The null and alternative hypotheses were

$$H_1: \quad \mu = 62.5$$
$$H_2: \quad \mu > 62.5$$

A characteristic of this test is that the alternative hypothesis H_2 is *one-sided;* that is, the statistician is concerned only with values greater than 62.5. The reason for this is that the company was interested only in checking the claim of the secretarial school that the typing speed would increase. It was not necessary to check whether or not the typing speed fell below 62.5 words per minute.

This illustration was a *right-tail test,* but as can be seen, if the alternative hypothesis were concerned only with values of the population mean less than the value of the population mean of the null hypothesis, we should have a left-tail test.

In symbols this becomes

$$H_1: \quad \mu = \mu_0$$
$$H_2: \quad \mu < \mu_0$$

where μ_0 is the value of μ in the null hypothesis.

Example 1. Past records show that the average grade of students taking economics is 65 points, with a standard deviation of 16 points. A new method of teaching is employed and a random sample of 64 students is selected. The sample average is 69 points. Is there a significant difference between the $\mu = 65$ points and the sample mean of 69 points?

This problem implies that we are interested in testing whether or not there has been an *increase* in the average grade, that is, whether the average grade has increased beyond 65 points. Hence we have a one-sided alternative, and the null and alternative hypotheses are

$$H_1: \quad \mu = 65 \text{ points}$$
$$H_2: \quad \mu > 65 \text{ points}$$

where $\sigma = 16$ points; $\bar{X} = 69$ points. Thus

$$z = \frac{\bar{X} - E(\bar{X})}{\sigma_{\bar{x}}} = \frac{69 - 65}{2} = 2$$

where

$$\sigma_{\bar{x}} = \frac{\sigma}{\sqrt{n}} = \frac{16}{\sqrt{64}} = 2$$

and we have assumed that $fpc = 1$; we have also omitted the continuity correction. The situation is shown in Fig. 8.8. Since $z = 2$, we find 0.0228 from the normal area table. In symbols we have

$$P[\bar{X} \geq 69 \mid \mu = 65] = 0.0228$$

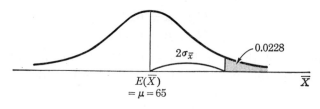

FIG. 8.8.

This means that the chances are about 2/100 of selecting a random sample of 64 students with an average of $\bar{X} = 69$ or greater from a population with $\mu = 65$; or we may say that the α-risk is about 2 percent.

Since we have agreed to set the level of significance at $\alpha = 0.05$, we shall reject the null hypothesis H_1. There is a significant difference between $\bar{X} = 69$ and $\mu = 65$ points. The implication is that the data support the claim that the new teaching method will improve the average.

Example 2. It is known from past records that the average weight of hogs 6 weeks after birth is 100 lb., with a standard deviation of 18 lb. A new diet is given to a large group of hogs and a random sample of 36 hogs is selected. The average weight is found to be 107.5 lb. Has there been a significant increase in the weight of the hogs?

As we were in the previous problem, we are interested in testing whether the average weight of the hogs is over 100 lb. Hence the alternative hypothesis is one-sided. The null and alternative hypotheses are

$$H_1: \qquad \mu = 100 \text{ lb.}$$
$$H_2: \qquad \mu > 100 \text{ lb.}$$

where $\sigma = 18$ lb.; $\bar{X} = 107.5$ lb. Thus

$$z = \frac{\bar{X} - \mu}{\sigma_{\bar{x}}} = \frac{107.5 - 100}{3} = 2.5$$

where

$$\sigma_{\bar{x}} = \frac{\sigma}{\sqrt{n}} = \frac{18}{\sqrt{36}} = 3 \text{ lb.}$$

and we have assumed $fpc = 1$ and have omitted the continuity correction. The situation is shown in Fig. 8.9. Since $z = 2.5$, we find 0.0062 from the

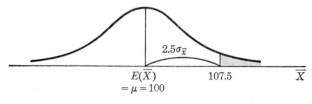

FIG. 8.9.

normal area table. In symbols we have

$$P[\bar{X} \geqq 107.5 \mid \mu = 100] = 0.0062$$

This means that the chances are about $0.6/100$ of selecting a random sample of 36 hogs with an average of $\bar{X} = 107.5$ lb. or greater from a population with $\mu = 100$ lb.; or we may say that the α-risk is about 0.6 percent.

Since $\alpha = 0.05$, we reject the null hypothesis H_1. There is a significant difference between $\bar{X} = 107.5$ and $\mu = 100.0$ lb.

The implication is that the data support the claim that the new diet will increase the average weight of the hogs.

Example 3.   The contents of a bottle of lotion is claimed to be 100 cc. A random sample of 144 bottles is selected and the average amount of lotion per bottle is found to be 99 cc. Assuming that the standard deviation is 4 cc, is there a significant difference between the observed value of 99 cc and the assumed value of 100 cc?

In this case, the inspector is interested in checking whether an insufficient amount of lotion is in the bottle. Hence we have a one-sided test, and the null and alternative hypotheses are

$$H_1 : \qquad \mu = 100 \text{ cc}$$
$$H_2 : \qquad \mu < 100 \text{ cc}$$

and it is a left-tail test. Assuming the population is very large, let $fpc = 1$. Also, since $n = 144$, let us omit the continuity correction. Then

$$z = \frac{\bar{X} - E(\bar{X})}{\sigma_{\bar{x}}} = \frac{99 - 100}{\dfrac{4}{12}} = -3$$

Thus

$$P[\bar{X} \leqq 99 \mid \mu = 100] = 0.0013$$

This means that there are about 1.3 chances in 1000 of selecting a sample of size $n = 144$ with a mean $\bar{X} = 99$ or smaller from a population with a mean $\mu = 100$ cc. Assuming a 5 percent level of significance, we conclude that the difference between $\bar{X} = 99$ cc and $\mu = 100$ cc is significant, and therefore the null hypothesis is rejected.

Note carefully that nothing has been proved. We have found only that the evidence does not support the claim that the volume of contents of the bottle is 100 cc. However, there is an α-risk of about 0.0013.

One-tail test concerning proportions
Example 4.   Previous data show that 20 percent of the families in a certain city subscribe to magazine K. There is some reason to believe there has been a recent drop in the subscription rate. To test whether or not there has been

a change, a random sample of 100 families is selected and the sample proportion is found to be $p = 0.16$ ($=16$ percent).

Since the interest is in checking whether or not there has been a drop, we assume that there has been no drop (that is, $\pi = 20$ percent) and then set up the one-sided alternative that $\pi < 20$ percent. We have

$$H_1: \qquad \pi = 20\%$$
$$H_2: \qquad \pi < 20\%$$

The sample proportion is $p = 16$ percent. Thus

$$z = \frac{p - \pi}{\sigma_p} = \frac{0.16 - \dfrac{1}{2} \times \dfrac{1}{100} - 0.20}{0.04}$$

$$= \frac{-0.04 - 0.005}{0.04}$$

$$= -1.125$$

where σ_p is

$$\sigma_p = \sqrt{\frac{\pi(1 - \pi)}{n}}$$

$$= \sqrt{\frac{(0.20)(0.80)}{100}}$$

$$= \frac{0.40}{10} = 0.04$$

Note that we have assumed $fpc = 1$. Since $z = -1.125$, we find from the normal area table that

$$P[p \le 0.16 \mid \pi = 0.20] = 0.1303$$

This is shown diagrammatically in Fig. 8.10.

The interpretation is: There are about 13.03 chances in 100 of selecting

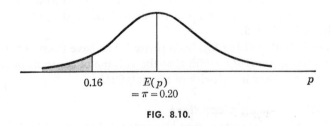

| 0.16 | $E(p)$ | | p |
| | $= \pi = 0.20$ | | |

FIG. 8.10.

samples with a sample proportion less than or equal to 0.16 from a population where $\pi = 0.20$. Since we use $\alpha = 0.05$, we accept the null hypothesis H_1. That is, there is no significant difference between $p = 0.16$ and $\pi = 0.20$, and therefore it is thought that the difference is due to the chance. This means that the data do not support the claim that there has been a decrease in the subscription rate.

We may also say that the α-risk is about 13 percent, and since α is set at $\alpha = 5$ percent, we *accept* the null hypothesis.

Example 5. In January, 40 percent of 2000 dealers indicated that they planned to increase their orders for dishwashers. In March, there was reason to believe that this percentage had increased. A random sample of 400 dealers was selected and the sample proportion was $p = 46$ percent. Has there been a significant increase?

Since we are interested in the increase of orders, we set up the null hypothesis that there has been no increase (that is, $\pi = 40$ percent) and then set up the one-sided alternative that $\pi > 0.40$. The null and alternative hypotheses are shown by

$$H_1: \quad \pi = 0.40$$
$$H_2: \quad \pi > 0.40$$

The $p = 0.46$. Thus

$$z = \frac{p - \dfrac{1}{2} \times \dfrac{1}{n} - \pi}{\sigma_p} = \frac{0.46 - \dfrac{1}{2} \times \dfrac{1}{400} - 0.40}{0.0217} = 2.70$$

where

$$\sigma_p = \sqrt{\frac{\pi(1-\pi)}{n}} \sqrt{\frac{N-n}{N-1}}$$

$$= \sqrt{\frac{(0.40)(0.60)}{400}} \sqrt{\frac{2000-400}{2000-1}}$$

$$= (0.02449)(0.894)$$

$$= 0.0217$$

Since $z = 2.70$, we find from the normal area table that

$$P[p \geq 0.46 \mid \pi = 0.40] = 0.0035$$

This is shown in Fig. 8.11.

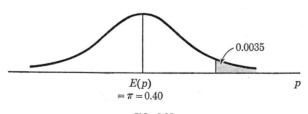

FIG. 8.11.

The interpretation is: There are about 3.5 (0.35) chances in 1000 (100) of selecting samples with sample proportions greater than or equal to 0.46 from a population where $\pi = 0.40$. Since we use $\alpha = 0.05$, we reject the null hypothesis H_1. That is, there is a significant difference between $p = 0.46$ and $\pi = 0.40$. This means that the data support the claim that there has been an increase in the proportion of dealers that plan to increase their orders.

Or we may say the α-risk is about 0.35 percent, and hence we reject the null hypothesis.

Two-tail tests

Example 6.   A process is in control when the average amount of instant coffee that is packed in a jar is 6 oz. The standard deviation is 0.2 oz. A sample of 100 jars is selected at random and the sample average is found to be 6.1 oz. Is the process out of control?

We assume that the process is in control; that is, the null hypothesis is that the population mean is 6.0 oz. ($\mu = 6.0$). The alternative hypothesis is that the population mean is not 6.0 oz. (that is, $\mu \neq 6.0$). In this case the population mean may be either greater than or smaller than 6.0. This is a two-sided alternative. In symbols, this is shown as follows:

$$H_1: \qquad \mu = 6.0$$
$$H_2: \qquad \mu \neq 6.0$$

Furthermore, let us specify the level of significance at 5 percent.

This level of significance is also the α-risk; that is, it is the probability of rejecting the null hypothesis when in fact it is true.

Let us show the situation diagrammatically as in Fig. 8.12(a). We have

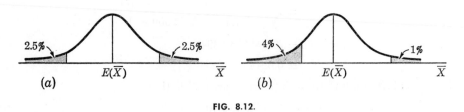

(a)   (b)

FIG. 8.12.

taken 2.5 percent on each tail. We may interpret this to mean that the manufacturer considers it equally important to avoid overfilling or underfilling a jar.

If he should consider the avoidance of underfilling to be 4 times more important than overfilling, he may have, for example, 4 percent in the left tail and 1 percent in the right tail, as shown in Fig. 8.12(b). In our subsequent discussion, unless otherwise stated, we shall always divide the α-risk equally between the upper and lower tails for simplicity. (See Example 5 of Section 8.5.)

The test is as follows:

$$z = \frac{6.1 - 6.0}{\dfrac{0.2}{10}} = 5$$

where we have assumed $fpc = 1$ and have omitted the continuity correction. The result clearly shows that the probability of finding a sample mean as large as 6.1 oz. is less than 2.5 percent. Hence we shall reject the null hypothesis that $\mu = 6.0$ oz. Obviously the process is not in control.

Example 7. In Example 5 we assumed 40 percent of the dealers planned to increase their orders for dishwashers, and in March there was reason to believe that this percentage had increased. Let us now suppose there is no reason to believe there has been an increase or decrease. A random sample of 400 dealers is selected, and the $p = 46$ percent. Has there been a change in the population proportion $\pi = 40$ percent?

In this case, we assume that there has been no change; that is, the null hypothesis is that the population proportion is 40 percent. The alternative hypothesis is that the population proportion is not 40 percent. In symbols we have

$$H_1: \qquad \pi = 40\%$$
$$H_2: \qquad \pi \neq 40\%$$

and furthermore, let us assume that the level of significance is 5 percent.

Since we are assuming that there is no reason to believe the population proportion has changed one way or the other, and since there is no special importance attached to the α-risks of the upper or lower tails, we shall put 2.5 percent in each tail, as shown in Fig. 8.13. The z is

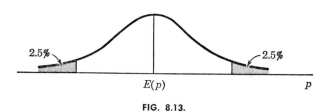

2.5%   2.5%

$E(p)$ p

FIG. 8.13.

$$z = \frac{p - \dfrac{1}{2} \times \dfrac{1}{n} - E(p)}{\sigma_p} = \frac{0.46 - \dfrac{1}{2} \times \dfrac{1}{400} - 0.40}{\sqrt{\dfrac{0.4 \times 0.6}{400}}} \doteq 2.60$$

where we assume $fpc = 1$. Since $z = 2.60$, we find from the normal area table,

$$P[p \geq 0.46 \mid \pi = 0.40] = 0.0047$$

Since the level of significance is set at 2.5 percent for the right-hand tail, we conclude that there is a significant difference, and therefore we reject the null hypothesis $\pi = 40$ percent.

8.4.   Simple Decision Problems

In Section 8.3 the significance tests specified the level of significance, which was the probability of committing the type I (α) error, and nothing was said about the type II (β) error. In this section we shall discuss problems of testing hypotheses that consider both α and β errors, and consideration of the β error will lead to a discussion of the OC curve. Let us start our explanation with a simple illustration.

Suppose a TV sales company wants to decide whether it should undertake a sales campaign for color TV in a certain county. The company believes that it would be worth while, provided the average monthly income of the families is $400 or more, and that it would not be worth while if the average income were less than $400.

There are two approaches to this problem, and the choice of either depends on the way the company considers the α-risk. One approach is that the company is anxious to avoid the error of not starting the campaign when it should. It does not want to miss the opportunity of making money.

The second approach is that the company is anxious to avoid the error of starting the campaign when it should not. The families do not have enough money and the company is anxious to avoid losing a large amount of money on a futile sales campaign. Let us start with the first approach:

Case I—First Approach

(i)   Calculation of decision rule

The hypothesis we are interested in testing, that is, the null hypothesis, is that the average income of the population is $400 or more:

$$H_1: \quad \mu \geq \$400$$

The alternative hypothesis is that the average income is less than $400:

$$H_2: \quad \mu < \$400$$

Then the α and β errors may be shown schematically as follows:

Action	w_1, $\mu = \$400$	w_2, $\mu < \$400$
A_1, start		$\beta = P(A_1 \mid w_2)$
A_2, do not start	$\alpha = P(A_2 \mid w_1)$	

Action A_1 is "to start" the sales campaign, and A_2 is "to not start" the sales campaign. Then the type I error is "to not start" the sales campaign when in fact the average income is $400 or more. The type II error is "to start" the sales campaign when the average income is less than $400.

Clearly, an accurate way of finding the average income of families is to check the income of every family in the county. Then management may decide whether or not to start a sales campaign. However, this job is usually prohibitive in terms of cost.

Is there a simpler way of reaching the decision of starting or not starting a sales campaign? Is there a way of reaching this decision by using *sample data* instead of investigating the whole population? At this point, a statistician is called in and asked to find a decision rule that will tell the company what action to take when a certain sample is observed.

When the decision is based on a sample, however, there is a chance that the results of the sample may be misleading. There is a chance of making wrong decisions, and as identified previously, these are the type I and type II errors. The α- and β-risks associated with these errors are, as before,

$$\alpha = P(A_2 \mid w_1)$$

$$\beta = P(A_1 \mid w_2)$$

Now the question is: What should be the α- and β-risks? In our previous discussion, the α-risk was called the *level of significance* and was set at $\alpha = 0.05$ or 0.01. As to why it is set at 5 percent or 1 percent is usually not explained except to say that it is a policy decision which management makes after considering all the pertinent aspects of the problem on hand; so, let us say $\alpha = 5$ percent and continue our discussion.

We now show how the statistician may find the decision rules for the following two cases:

1. When a sample of size n (say, $n = 100$) is given (that is, predetermined).
2. When a sample of size n is not predetermined, but the β-risk is given.

We shall consider the first case in this section and the second case in Section 8.8. But first let us digress for a moment and explain the terms *acceptance region* and *rejection region,* which we shall be using in our subsequent discussion. In Section 8.1 we explained that a decision rule is a *rule* that tells us whether to take action A_1 or A_2 when a certain sample (outcome) is observed.

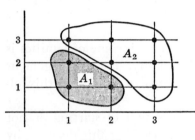

FIG. 8.14.

We also explained that the *sample space* is a space that is made up of all possible samples. For example, suppose we have an urn with 3 balls in it numbered from 1 to 3. A sample of size 2 is selected with replacement. Then the sample space is 2-dimensional and is shown as in Fig. 8.14. There are 9 possible samples (when the order is considered), which are also the outcomes, and these may be shown as in the left-hand column of Table 8.5.

Let us set up a decision rule as shown in the right-hand column of Table 8.5 where action A_1 is to be taken when samples (1,1), (1,2), or (2,1) are observed, and action A_2 is taken when the other samples are observed.

TABLE 8.5.

Outcome	Rule
1, 1	A_1
1, 2	A_1
1, 3	A_2
2, 1	A_1
2, 2	A_2
2, 3	A_2
3, 1	A_2
3, 2	A_2
3, 3	A_2

As we see in Fig. 8.14, this decision rule splits the sample space into two parts: The shaded part, which includes samples that lead to action A_1, and the unshaded part, which includes samples that lead to action A_2. In general, we may say that a *decision rule splits the sample space into two parts, one part that leads to action* A_1 *and another part that leads to action* A_2. The part that leads to action A_1 is called the *acceptance region,* and the part that leads to action A_2 is called the *rejection region* (or critical region).

From our previous discussion we know there are $2^{3^2} = 212$ decision rules. That is, there are 212 ways of splitting this sample space into acceptance and rejection regions. We have shown only one of these 212 ways.

Now the statistician is to select a sample of size n and, based on this sample, decide whether it came from w_1 or w_2. At this point, we use our results of Chapter 7. In Chapter 7 we found a simple way of finding the probability of selecting a sample from a population by using the central limit theorem. The central limit theorem told us that the sampling distribution of the sample mean was approximately normal. By letting the sample mean represent the sample, we were able to calculate the probability of selecting samples.

This simplifies matters considerably because the sampling distribution is 1-dimensional and is approximately normal, whereas the sample space is n-dimensional (assuming a sample size of n).

In our present case we have two populations, w_1 ($\mu = \$400$) and w_2 ($\mu < \$400$), and taking a sample of size n (say, $n = 100$) means generating an n ($=100$) dimensional sample space. But, as just mentioned, instead of working with these n-dimensional sample spaces, we shall use the 1-dimensional sampling distributions of the sample mean generated from w_1 and w_2.

Our problem is therefore reduced to finding a decision rule that splits these 1-dimensional sampling distributions into the acceptance and critical region. Let us now show how this is worked out.

We know that the sampling distribution of the sample mean generated from w_1 ($\mu = \$400$) will be approximately normal, with

$$E(\bar{X}) = \$400$$

$$\text{Var}(\bar{X}) = \frac{\sigma^2}{n}$$

where σ^2 is the population variance.

As for w_2, we have $\mu < \$400$, which includes such values as $399,

$398, . . . , etc. To simplify our discussion, we shall let w_2 be $\mu = \$395$ for the moment and explain the process of finding the decision rule and α- and β-risks. After that we shall consider the other alternative hypotheses and construct an OC curve.

The sampling distribution generated from w_2 ($\mu = \$395$) will also be approximately normal, with

$$E(\bar{X}) = \$395$$

$$\mathrm{Var}(\bar{X}) = \frac{\sigma^2}{n}$$

where we assume for the moment that σ is the same for w_1 and w_2. We shall explain in Chapter 10 why this assumption of equal variances is reasonable.

Figure 8.15 shows the two sampling distributions, w_1 with $\mu = \$400$, and w_2 with $E(\bar{X}) = \$395$.

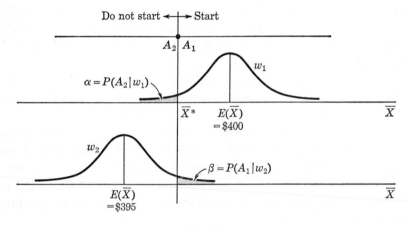

FIG. 8.15.

We can see intuitively that if a sample mean $\bar{X}$ (say, 399) is much larger than 395 and is close to 400, we may conjecture that the sample probably came from w_1 (400) rather than w_2 (395). Conversely, if the sample mean $\bar{X}$ (say, 396) is close to 395 and much smaller than 400, we may conjecture that the sample probably came from w_2 (395) rather than w_1 (400). Note carefully that we do not actually know that w_1 is 400 nor that w_2 is 395. These are hypotheses and we are saying that *if* w_1 and w_2 should be 400 and 395, respectively, we may reason as above.

Following this line of reasoning, the statistician wishes to find a value, say, $\bar{X}^*$, somewhere between 395 and 400 such that when the sample mean $\bar{X}$ is $\bar{X} \geq \bar{X}^*$, he will recommend action A_1 (start campaign) to the company, and when $\bar{X} < \bar{X}^*$, he will recommend A_2 (do not start). This value $\bar{X}^*$ is called the *critical value* and is shown in Fig. 8.15. This critical value $\bar{X}^*$ divides the sampling distribution generated from w_1 into two parts, the *acceptance region*, which is to the right of (greater than or equal to) $\bar{X}^*$, and the *rejection region*, which is to the left of (smaller than) $\bar{X}^*$.

In other words, the statistician has, by selecting a critical value $\bar{X}^*$, selected a decision rule.

A characteristic of this decision rule is that the α-risk must be 5 percent or less. In terms of Fig. 8.15, it means that the shaded part in the left-tail end of the sampling distribution generated from w_1 is to be 5 percent.

We have not specified the β-risk. However, it may be shown graphically. The β-risk is the shaded part in the right-hand tail of the sampling distribution generated from w_2 (see Fig. 8.15).

With this much background we may now interpret the α- and β-risks as follows: Given the state of nature w_1, the probability of selecting a sample such that $\bar{X} < \bar{X}^*$ is 0.05. And since we have decided that when $\bar{X} < \bar{X}^*$, we take action A_2, this may be written in symbols as

$$\alpha = P(\bar{X} < \bar{X}^* \mid w_1)$$
$$= P(A_2 \mid w_1) = 0.05$$

which is the α-risk, and is the probability of committing the type I error.

In similar fashion,

$$\beta = P(\bar{X} \geq \bar{X}^* \mid w_2)$$
$$= P(A_1 \mid w_2)$$

which is the β-risk, and is the probability of committing the type II error.

Let us now summarize our results as follows: If a sample of size n is selected and the sample mean is $\bar{X}$, then when

$$\bar{X} \geq \bar{X}^* \qquad \text{take action } A_1$$
$$\bar{X} < \bar{X}^* \qquad \text{take action } A_2$$

and the risks are α and β.

Our problem now is to find the critical value $\bar{X}^*$, the sample size n, and the β-risk. However, in many cases, such as in quality control, the sample size n is specified. Values such as $n = 2, 3, 4, 5, 7, 10, 15, 20, 30, 40, 50, 75, 100$, etc., are used. When n is given, the β-risk varies according to the value of the alternative hypothesis H_2. That is, when the sample size is predetermined, the value of β depends on H_2.

In other cases, where the alternative hypothesis H_2 is specified, such as $395 in our present example, and management is able to provide a value for β by some nonstatistical policy decision, the sample size becomes automatically fixed.

In our present problem, $\alpha = 5$ percent and $n = 100$ are given, and the problem is to find $\bar{X}^*$ and the β-risk. The null and alternative hypotheses are

$$H_1: \qquad \mu \geq \$400$$
$$H_2: \qquad \mu < \$400$$

Of the various alternative hypotheses $\mu < \$400$, we have selected $395 to start the explanation. Then the sampling distribution generated from w_1 and w_2 will be approximately normal, as shown in Fig. 8.16. $\bar{X}^*$ is the

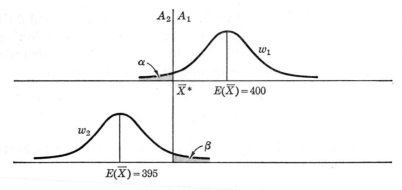

FIG. 8.16.

critical value, the region to the right (larger) of $\bar{X}^*$ is the acceptance region (take action A_1), and the region to the left (smaller) of $\bar{X}^*$ is the rejection region.

Let us assume that from other sources, such as past data, the standard deviation of the population is known to be $\sigma = \$20$. Then the standard error is

$$\sigma_{\bar{x}} = \frac{\sigma}{\sqrt{n}} = \frac{20}{\sqrt{100}} = \$2.00$$

Using the assumption that $\alpha = 5$ percent, we know that the deviation between $E(\bar{X}) = \$400$, and $\bar{X}^*$ is 1.645 from the normal area table. Using this we may find $\bar{X}^*$ as follows:

$$\frac{400 - \bar{X}^*}{2} = 1.645$$

$$\bar{X}^* = 400 - 3.29 = \$396.71$$

Using this $\bar{X}^*$, we may calculate β as follows: From Fig. 8.16 we see that

$$\frac{\bar{X}^* - 395}{2} = \frac{396.72 - 395}{2} = 0.86$$

Therefore

$$\beta = P(A_1 \mid w_2) = 0.1949$$

This $\beta = 19.49$ percent means that the probability of taking action A_1 (that is, accepting the hypothesis that $\mu = \$400$) when the true state of nature is w_2 is 19.49 percent. Hence, there is a pretty good chance of erroneously accepting $\$395$ as $\$400$. In other words, the ability of distinguishing between $\$395$ and $\$400$ is not too good.

The β-risk was calculated for the one value $\mu = \$395$, but in similar fashion we may calculate the β-risk for the other alternative hypotheses. The β-risks for $\mu = \$400$, $\$398.72$, $\$396.72$, $\$394.72$, and $\$392.72$ are tabulated in Table 8.6 and are also shown graphically in Fig. 8.17.

TABLE 8.6.

H	β	$1 - \beta$
$400.00	0.9500	0.05
398.72	0.8413	0.16
396.72	0.5000	0.50
394.72	0.1587	0.84
392.72	0.0228	0.98

We may now state the decision rule we are seeking:
Decision rule.   Take a sample of size $n = 100$. If

$$\bar{X} \geq \$396.72 \qquad \text{take action } A_1 \text{ (start campaign)}$$
$$\bar{X} < \$396.72 \qquad \text{take action } A_2 \text{ (do not start campaign)}$$

Then $\alpha = 5$ percent and the β-risks for various alternative hypotheses are as shown in Table 8.6.

Suppose that the sample mean $\bar{X}$ is $\$397$. Then
Action.   Take action A_1 and start the sales campaign.

As this decision rule and Table 8.6 show, we have a sequence of β-risks for various alternative hypotheses. What we shall do next is to

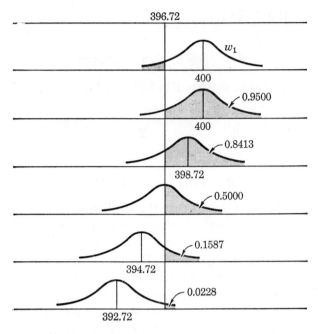

FIG. 8.17.

show these risks as a curve and find a way to express the decision rule in terms of a curve. For this we shall first discuss the concept of a power function and then the OC curve. After we have discussed the OC curve, we shall restate the above decision rule, using an OC curve.

(ii)   The power function

The probability

$$1 - \beta = 1 - P(A_1 \mid w_2) = P(A_2 \mid w_2)$$

is the probability of making the *correct decision* of taking action A_2 when the true state of nature is in fact w_2. This $1 - \beta$ is called the *power of the function*. Clearly, the greater the power of the function, the better the decision rule. Note that

$$1 - \beta = P(A_2 \mid w_2)$$

shows that the power of the function depends on w_2. In our present case, w_2 meant $\mu < \$400$, and as w_2 changes, $1 - \beta$ will change. We may ask: How will it change?

The rationale behind the change of $1 - \beta$ as w_2 changes is simple. We are interested in correctly selecting the true state of nature, given a

sample. The further apart that w_1 and w_2 are, the easier it is to distinguish them. For example, w_1 is $\mu_1 = \$400$, and if w_2 is $\mu_2'' = \$300$ and a
sample is selected, it probably will be easy to tell which population the
sample came from because w_1 and w_2 differ greatly. But if w_2 is $\mu_2'' = \$399$ and a sample is selected, it will be difficult to tell from which popu-
lation the sample came because w_1 and w_2 are so close together. In the
first case, there is very little chance of making an incorrect decision, the
β-risk will be small, and the power $1 - \beta$ (which shows the probability
of selecting w_2 when in fact the true state of nature is w_2) will be large.
In the second case, by similar reasoning, we can clearly see that $1 - \beta$
will be small.

Values of the power function $1 - \beta$ are given for various values of the
alternative hypotheses in Table 8.6. Let us next graph the power function $1 - \beta$ as shown in Fig. 8.18. The curve that is obtained is called the

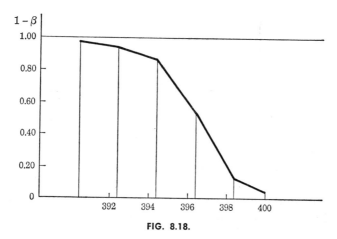

FIG. 8.18.

power curve. It shows the values of $1 - \beta$ (that is, the probability of
making a correct decision), given alternative hypotheses w_2. Remember
that this curve is obtained by keeping $n = 100$, $\bar{X}^* = \$396.72$, and
$w_1 = \$400$ fixed while letting w_2 vary. Therefore this power curve shows
a decision rule where w_2 is allowed to vary. For example, the point that
corresponds to $\$394.72$ tells us:

$$w_1 = \$400 \qquad w_2 = \$394.72$$

Take sample of $n = 100$. If

$$\bar{X} \geqq \$396.72 \qquad \text{take action } A_1$$
$$\bar{X} < \$396.72 \qquad \text{take action } A_2$$

Then $\alpha = 0.05$ and $\beta = 0.1587$.

The curve also shows that as w_2 becomes smaller (that is, as w_1 and w_2 become farther apart), the power of the decision rule increases and the probability of making a correct decision increases.

This leads to the question: If there are two decision rules, could we not compare their power curves and see which is a better decision rule? Before we can answer this question, we need to explain what is meant by a "better" decision rule. Clearly, we mean a decision rule where the probability of making a correct decision is larger; that is, the decision rule that has the larger $1 - \beta$ is better. Graphically, this means that the decision rule whose power curve is higher is better. For example, in Fig. 8.19 the decision rule with the power curve II is better.

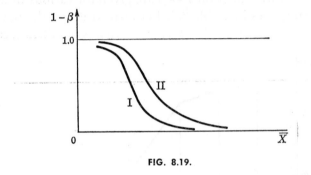

FIG. 8.19.

A question that naturally arises is: Is there a decision rule whose power curve is highest? If there is, we may conclude it is the best decision rule. It has been shown that there is such a decision rule for one-tail tests, and we shall state only the results. Suppose the power curve II in Fig. 8.19 is for a critical region taken in the tail end, as

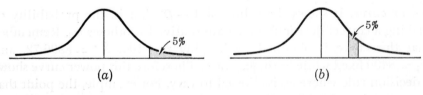

(a)   (b)

FIG. 8.20.

shown in Fig. 8.20(a). Let the power curve I be for the critical region shown in Fig. 8.20(b). We see that it is possible to take the critical region at various places, as long as the area is kept at 5 percent (that is, $\alpha = 5$ percent). It turns out that all power curves based on critical regions other than the one in the tail end (that is, the power curve II) will be below the power curve II as illustrated by the power curve I.

A test that produces a power curve like II and which is highest is called a *uniformly most powerful test*. The one-tail tests we are using are uniformly most powerful tests. Note that in these cases $\alpha = 5$ percent and n are given.

Unfortunately, further discussion of the power curve becomes rather complicated and is omitted. It was presented here as a background to the OC curve, which we discuss next.

(iii)   The OC curve

The OC curve is the reverse of the power curve. That is, where the power curve was the graph of $1 - \beta$, the OC curve is the graph of β.

If this is the case, why is it not sufficient to consider only the power curve? In theoretical statistics, it is indeed sufficient, and the OC curve is generally not considered. But in practical statistics, in certain types of problems, the OC curve is much easier to interpret for practical purposes and hence is extensively used.

What then are these certain types of problems? These usually occur in quality control, especially in the topic of acceptance sampling, and this type of statistical technique is used when, for example, the Armed Forces procures goods. In fact, two of the best-known tables that use acceptance sampling and OC curves are published by the U.S. Department of Defense. They are:

1.   Military Standard Sampling Procedures and Tables for Inspection by Attributes. MIL-STD-105B, 31 December, 1958.
2.   Military Standard Sampling Procedures and Tables for Inspection by Variables for Percent Defective. MIL-STD-414, 11 June, 1957.

These are also used in private industry. Let us first draw the OC curve for our illustration of the TV sales company and then give additional illustrations.

Table 8.6 is reproduced below as Table 8.7 for convenience. The OC

TABLE 8.7.

w_2	β	$1 - \beta$
\$400.00	0.9500	0.05
398.72	0.8413	0.16
396.72	0.5000	0.50
394.72	0.1587	0.84
392.72	0.0228	0.98

curve is obtained by graphing the β values, as shown in Fig. 8.21. Note carefully that this OC curve assumes $n = 100$, $\alpha = 5$ percent, and the

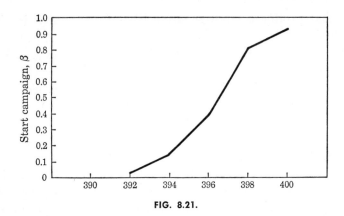

FIG. 8.21.

null hypothesis is $\mu = \$400$. The horizontal scale shows the alternative values $\mu < \$400$ and the vertical scale shows the β values.

The height of the curve shows the β value and is the probability of accepting w_1. Hence, when the curve is high near $400 and low when it deviates away from $400, as shown figuratively in Fig. 8.22(a), it indicates that the ability of the decision rule to distinguish between the

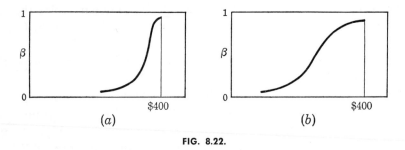

FIG. 8.22.

null and alternative hypotheses is good.

However, if the OC curve should be like the one in Fig. 8.22(b), where it is high for values away from $400 such as $396, $394, as in the figure, the ability of the decision rule to distinguish between the null and alternative hypotheses is not good.

We may now state our decision rule as follows:

Decision rule. Take a random sample of size $n = 100$. If

$$\bar{X} \geqq \$396.72 \qquad \text{take action } A_1 \text{ (start campaign)}$$
$$\bar{X} < \$396.72 \qquad \text{take action } A_2 \text{ (do not start campaign)}$$

Then the α-risk is 5 percent and the β-risks for the alternative hypotheses are as shown in Fig. 8.21.

Suppose a random sample of $n = 100$ families is selected and the sample mean is $\bar{X} = \$394$. Then, according to our decision rule, the action to be taken is:

Action.   Take action A_2 and do not start campaign.

Case III—Second Approach

Let us briefly summarize our discussion of the first approach. A TV sales company wishes to decide whether or not to start a sales campaign. It took a random sample of $n = 100$ and found a decision rule such that $\alpha = 5$ percent and an *OC* curve that shows the β-risks for alternative hypotheses. The characteristics of this decision rule and *OC* curve were that the null and alternative hypotheses and the α- and β-risks were (shown schematically) as follows:

Action	w_1, $\mu_1 = \$400$	w_2, $\mu_2 < \$400$
A_1, start campaign		$\beta = P(A_1 \mid w_2)$
A_2, do not start campaign	$\alpha = P(A_2 \mid w_1)$	

The company was anxious to avoid the error of not starting a sales campaign when it should.

We now shall consider a second approach, in which the company is anxious to avoid the error of starting a sales campaign when it should not. It is anxious to avoid the loss of spending money on a futile sales campaign. In this case, the null and alternative hypotheses are

$$H_1: \quad \mu \leq \$400$$
$$H_2: \quad \mu > \$400$$

and the α- and β-risks may be shown schematically as follows:

Action	w_1, $\mu = \$400$	w_2, $\mu > \$400$
A_1, do not start		$\beta = P(A_1 \mid w_2)$
A_2, start	$\alpha = P(A_2 \mid w_1)$	

It is clear the type I error is the error of starting a sales campaign when it should not be started, and the type II error is the error of not starting when it should be started.

This schema shows that unless there is evidence that the income is above $400, the company will not start the campaign; the company is not anxious to start the campaign. In the first approach, the basis was that unless evidence showed that the income is less than $400, the company would start the campaign.

As in our previous approach, let $\alpha = 5$ percent and $n = 100$. Then the critical value may be obtained as follows (see Fig. 8.23):

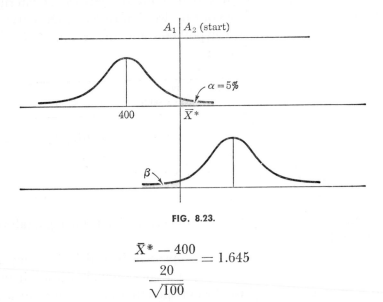

FIG. 8.23.

$$\frac{\bar{X}^* - 400}{\dfrac{20}{\sqrt{100}}} = 1.645$$

$$\bar{X}^* = \$403.29$$

With this critical value, let us find the various β-risks and the OC curve, using Fig. 8.24 as a visual aid. The β values are shown in Table 8.8 and the OC curve in Fig. 8.25.

Note in Fig. 8.25 how the vertical scale shows the probability of not starting, whereas in the previous case (Fig. 8.21) it showed the probability of starting the sales campaign.

The decision rule we seek is:

Decision rule. Take a random sample of size $n = 100$. If

$\bar{X} \leq \$403.29$ take action A_1 (do not start campaign)
$\bar{X} > \$403.29$ take action A_2 (start campaign)

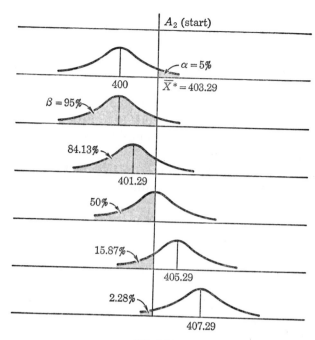

FIG. 8.24.

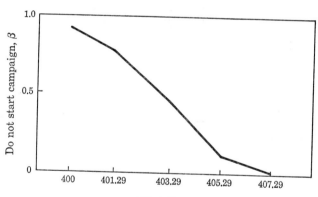

FIG. 8.25.

TABLE 8.8.

w_2	β
$400.00	0.95
401.29	0.8413
403.29	0.50
405.29	0.1587
407.29	0.0228

Then $\alpha = 5$ percent and the β-risks are as shown by the OC curve in Fig. 8.25.

In the first approach, the critical value $\bar{X}^*$ was $396.71; in the second approach, it is $403.29. By comparing these two critical values, we can see heuristically that it will be easier to start the campaign in the first approach.

For example, if we take a random sample of $n = 100$ and the sample mean is $397, the action is:

Action. Take action A_1 and do not start the sales campaign.

Recall that in the first approach the action was to start the sales campaign when the sample mean was $397.

8.5. Examples Using the Sample Mean

Example 1. Suppose a company accepts shipments of cables if the average strength is 200 lb. or more, and rejects shipments if the average strength is less than 200 lb. The statistician is asked to find a decision rule such that $\alpha = 0.05$ and $n = 25$. The $\sigma = 20$ lb. is given. The null and alternative hypotheses are

$$H_1: \qquad \mu \geqq 200 \text{ lb.}$$
$$H_2: \qquad \mu < 200 \text{ lb.}$$

The situation is shown schematically below and also diagrammatically in Fig. 8.26.

Action	w_1, $\mu = 200$ lb.	w_2, $\mu < 200$ lb.
A_1, accept		$\beta = P(A_1 \mid w_2)$
A_2, reject	$\alpha = P(A_2 \mid w_1)$	

In this case the company is anxious to accept the shipment, and unless there is evidence to the contrary, it wishes to accept the shipment. The standard error is

$$\sigma_{\bar{x}} = \frac{20}{\sqrt{25}} = 4 \text{ lb.}$$

Since $\alpha = 5$ percent, we have

$$\frac{200 - \bar{X}^*}{\sigma_{\bar{x}}} = 1.645$$

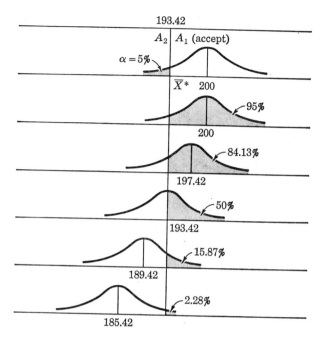

FIG. 8.26.

Therefore

$$\bar{X}^* = 193.42 \text{ lb.}$$

Thus, when the sample mean $\bar{X}$ is less than or equal to 193.42 lb., the α-risk is 5 percent.

Let us now calculate the β-risks for various alternative μ's. For $\mu = 200$ lb., we can see from Fig. 8.26 that

$$\beta = P(A_1 \mid \mu = 200) = 0.95$$

For $\mu = 197.42$, the β is as follows:

$$\frac{197.42 - 193.42}{4} = 1$$

Therefore

$$\beta = P(A_1 \mid \mu = 197.42) = 0.8413$$

In similar manner we can find the values of β for other μ's. The results for selected values of μ are given in Table 8.9 and the *OC* curve is shown in Fig. 8.27.

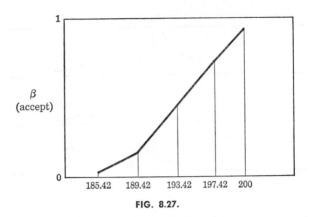

FIG. 8.27.

TABLE 8.9.

w_2 lb.	β
200	0.9500
197.42	0.8413
193.42	0.5000
189.42	0.1586
185.42	0.0228

Decision rule. Take a random sample of size $n = 25$. If

$$\bar{X} \geqq 193.72 \qquad \text{take action } A_1 \text{ (accept shipment)}$$
$$\bar{X} < 193.72 \qquad \text{take action } A_2 \text{ (reject shipment)}$$

Then $\alpha = 5$ percent and the β-risks are as shown by the OC curve in Fig. 8.27.

We see from the OC curve, when the alternative hypothesis is greater than 190 lb., that the β-risk is over 15 percent.

Example 2. In Example 1 we may set the null and alternative hypotheses as

$$H_1: \qquad \mu \leqq 200 \text{ lb.}$$
$$H_2: \qquad \mu > 200 \text{ lb.}$$

Then the situation may be shown schematically as follows:

Action	w_1, $\mu = 200$ lb.	w_2, $\mu > 200$ lb.
A_1, reject		$\beta = P(A_1 \mid w_2)$
A_2, accept	$\alpha = P(A_2 \mid w_1)$	

This shows that the company is anxious to reject the shipment unless there is evidence to the contrary. The situation is shown in Fig. 8.28.

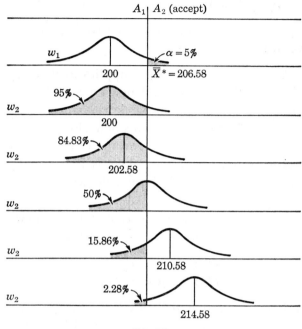

FIG. 8.28.

The critical value $\bar{X}^*$ is

$$\frac{\bar{X}^* - 200}{4} = 1.645$$

Therefore

$$\bar{X}^* = 206.58 \text{ lb.}$$

The β-risks are calculated and shown in Table 8.10 and the OC curve is given in Fig. 8.29.

TABLE 8.10.

w_2 lb.	β
200	0.95
202.58	0.8413
206.58	0.5000
210.58	0.1586
214.58	0.0228

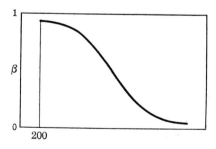

FIG. 8.29.

Decision rule. Take a random sample of size $n = 25$. If

$$\bar{X} \leq 206.58 \text{ lb.} \qquad \text{take action } A_1 \text{ (reject)}$$
$$\bar{X} > 206.58 \text{ lb.} \qquad \text{take action } A_2 \text{ (accept)}$$

Then $\alpha = 5$ percent and β's for the alternative hypotheses are given by the OC curve in Fig. 8.29.

Example 3. A construction company supplies to its employees gloves that have an average life of 90 days. A new type of glove recommended is claimed to last longer and be more convenient although it is more expensive. The company will adopt this new glove if its average life is 120 days or more, but would rather continue to use the present type of glove if the average life of the new glove is less than 120 days. The statistician is asked to find a decision rule with $\alpha = 5$ percent and $n = 36$. The standard deviation is 18 days.

Suppose the company is anxious to change to the new glove. Then the null and alternative hypotheses may be stated as

$$H_1 : \qquad \mu \geq 120 \text{ days}$$
$$H_2 : \qquad \mu < 120 \text{ days}$$

Unless there is evidence that the gloves have an average life of less than 120 days, the company will accept the null hypothesis and accept the new gloves. The α- and β-risks are shown as follows:

Action	w_1, $\mu = 120$ days	w_2, $\mu < 120$ days
A_1, adopt		$\beta = P(A_1 \mid w_2)$
A_2, do not adopt	$\alpha = P(A_2 \mid w_1)$	

The critical value $\bar{X}^*$ is as follows:

$$\frac{120 - \bar{X}^*}{\dfrac{18}{\sqrt{36}}} = 1.645$$

Therefore

$$\bar{X}^* = 115.055$$

The β-risks for various alternative hypotheses are given in Table 8.11 and are also shown in Fig. 8.30. The OC curve based on these β values is shown in Fig. 8.31.

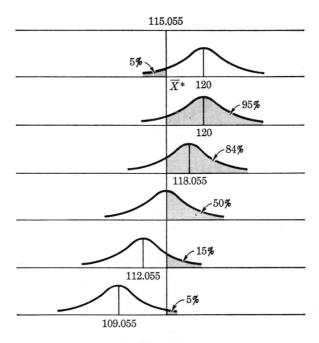

FIG. 8.30.

TABLE 8.11.

w_2	β
120	0.9500
118.055	0.8413
115.055	0.5000
112.055	0.1587
109.055	0.0228
106.055	0.0013

Decision rule.   Take a random sample of size $n = 36$. If

$\bar{X} \geq 115.055$ days	take action A_1 (adopt)
$\bar{X} < 115.055$ days	take action A_2 (do not adopt)

Then $\alpha = 5$ percent and the β-risks for various alternative hypotheses are as shown by the OC curve in Fig. 8.31.

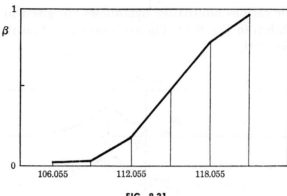

FIG. 8.31.

If a random sample of size $n = 36$ is taken, and $\bar{X} = 119$ days, the action is:

Action. Take action A_1 and adopt the new gloves.

The α-risk is 5 percent, but the β-risk is over 84 percent. However, the company may consider the difference beween 120 days and 119 days, or 118 days, not important and be willing to assume the large β-risk.

Example 4. Suppose in Example 3 that the company is not anxious to change to the new gloves. Then the null and alternative hypotheses are

$$H_1: \quad \mu \leq 120 \text{ days}$$
$$H_2: \quad \mu > 120 \text{ days}$$

Unless there is evidence that the gloves have an average life of more than 120 days, the company will not change to the new gloves. The α- and β-risks are shown as follows:

Action	w_1, $\mu = 120$ days	w_2, $\mu > 120$ days
A_1, reject		$\beta = P(A_1 \mid w_2)$
A_2, accept	$\alpha = P(A_2 \mid w_1)$	

The critical value $\bar{X}^*$ (Fig. 8.32) is as follows:

$$\frac{\bar{X}^* - 120}{3} = 1.645$$

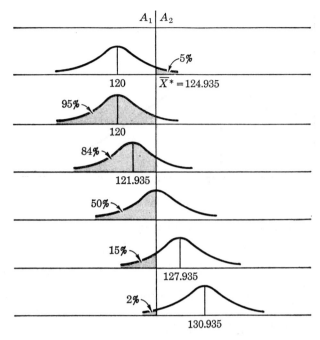

FIG. 8.32.

Therefore

$$\bar{X}^* = 124.935 \text{ days}$$

Based on this $\bar{X}^*$, we find the β values as shown in Table 8.12.

TABLE 8.12.

w	β
120	0.9500
121.935	0.8413
124.935	0.5000
127.935	0.1587
130.935	0.0228

Hence, the decision rule is as follows.

Decision rule.   Take a random sample of size $n = 36$. If

$$\bar{X} \leq 124.935 \qquad \text{take action } A_1 \text{ (reject)}$$
$$\bar{X} > 124.935 \qquad \text{take action } A_2 \text{ (accept)}$$

Then $\alpha = 5$ percent and β is as shown by the OC curve in Fig. 8.33.

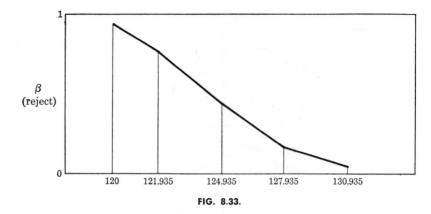

FIG. 8.33.

Example 5. A manufacturer who produces bolts considers his process in control when the average diameter is 10 cm, and out of control when the average is not 10 cm. When the process is out of control, he wishes to stop the process. A statistician is asked to find a decision rule such that $\alpha = 5$ percent. The check is to be made by taking 16 bolts every hour. The standard deviation is known to be 0.2 cm.

The null and alternative hypotheses are

$$H_1 : \qquad \mu = 10 \text{ cm}$$
$$H_2 : \qquad \mu \neq 10 \text{ cm}$$

and the problem may be shown schematically as in the table below and graphically as in Fig. 8.34.

Action	$w_1,$ $\mu = 10$ cm.	$w_2,$ $\mu < 10$ cm.	$w_3,$ $\mu > 10$ cm.
$A,$ continue		β	β
$A,$ stop	$\alpha = 0.05$		

As seen in Fig. 8.34, this is a two-tail test, and we have two critical values, $\bar{X}_1^*$ and $\bar{X}_2^*$. The acceptance region is between $\bar{X}_1^*$ and $\bar{X}_2^*$ and is where the process is continued.

The shaded part in the tail ends of the sampling distribution based on w_1 show the α-risks. A question that immediately arises is: How should the $\alpha = 5$ percent be divided between the two tails? As can be seen, we may have 1 percent in the left tail and 4 percent in the right tail; or 2 percent in the left tail and 3 percent in the right tail; and so forth. There are an infinite number of ways we can divide the $\alpha = 5$ percent.

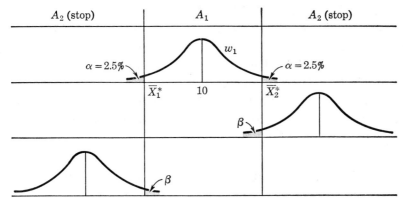

FIG. 8.34.

As mentioned previously, we were able to find a uniformly most powerful test when we had a one-tail test. For a two-tail test, it can be shown that there is no uniformly most powerful test. This may be shown heuristically as in Fig. 8.35. Let μ_0 be the null hypotheses. Then,

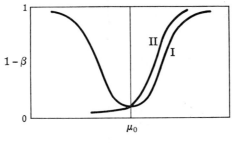

FIG. 8.35.

as the graph shows, for values greater than μ_0, the test shown by II is better than a test shown by I because II has a higher power curve.

But for values less than μ_0, I is better than II because it has a higher power curve.

The characteristic of the power curve I is that its power is minimum at $\mu = \mu_0$ (at the null hypothesis) and it is symmetrical about the value $\mu = \mu_0$.

The other curve, II, has a minimum at a value other than $\mu = \mu_0$ and is not symmetrical around the value $\mu = \mu_0$.

The test that is represented by the power curve I, which has a minimum at $\mu = \mu_0$ is called an *unbiased test*. The other tests are called *biased tests*.

Our question was: how should the α-risk be divided between the two tails? To this we shall answer: If there is no reason to favor one side of the α-risk over the other, we shall use the unbiased test, in which case the α-risk is divided equally between both tails. In our present cause, it will be 2.5 percent in each tail.

Now that we have decided on having 2.5 percent in each tail, we may calculate the $\bar{X}_1^*$ and $\bar{X}_2^*$ as follows: From the normal area table, $z = 1.96$ for 2.5 percent. Thus

$$\frac{\bar{X}_1^* - 10}{\dfrac{0.2}{\sqrt{16}}} = 1.96 \qquad\qquad \frac{\bar{X}_2^* - 10}{\dfrac{0.2}{\sqrt{16}}} = -1.96$$

$$\bar{X}_1^* = 10.098 \qquad\qquad\qquad \bar{X}_2^* = 9.902$$

Let us next calculate the β-risks, using Fig. 8.36 as a visual aid.

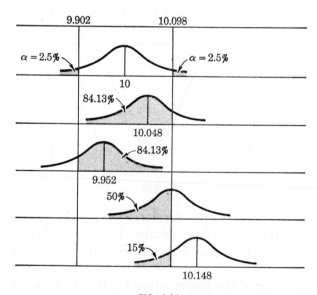

FIG. 8.36.

As Table 8.13 shows, the β-risks are symmetrical around $\mu = 10.000$, shown by the OC curve in Fig. 8.37.

Note also that in the two-tail test case, the way the null and alternative hypotheses are set up is unique and is in contrast to the one-tail tests in Examples 1 to 4.

TABLE 8.13.

w	β
10.198	0.0228
10.148	0.1587
10.098	0.5000
10.048	0.8413
10.000	0.9500
9.952	0.8413
9.902	0.5000
9.852	0.1587
9.802	0.0228

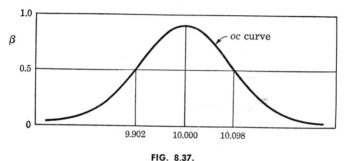

FIG. 8.37.

8.6.   Decision Rules Concerning Proportions

Decision rules concerning proportions may be found by a similar procedure to that of decision rules concerning means. One assumption that changes when dealing with proportions is that the standard error of proportions is different for each sampling distribution. Otherwise the procedure is similar.

Example 1.   A TV manufacturing company wishes to decide whether to use plastic or nonplastic (wood, etc.) material for TV chassis. If 50 percent or less of purchasers prefer plastic, the company will use nonplastic material, and if more than 50 percent prefer plastic, the manufacturer will use plastic. The null and alternative hypotheses are

$$H_1: \qquad \pi \leqq 50\%$$
$$H_2: \qquad \pi > 50\%$$

This setup implies that the company is not anxious to use plastic. That is, unless there is evidence that more than 50 percent of purchasers prefer plastic, it will not use plastic. The α- and β-risks may be shown as follows:

Action	w_1, $\pi = 50\%$	w_2, $\pi > 50\%$
A_1, use nonplastic		$\beta = P(A_1 \mid w_2)$
A_2, use plastic	$\alpha = P(A_2 \mid w_1)$	

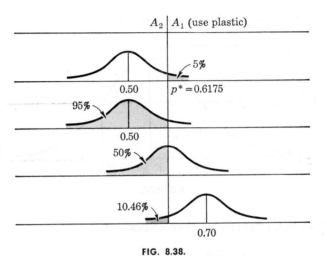

FIG. 8.38.

Let us assume that $\alpha = 5$ percent and the sample size is $n = 49$. Using Fig. 8.38 as a visual aid, we find the critical value p^* as follows:

$$\frac{p^* - 0.50}{\sqrt{\dfrac{0.5 \times 0.5}{49}}} = 1.645$$

$$p^* = 0.6175$$

Using the $p^* = 0.6175$, let us find the β-risks for several alternative w_2's. For $\pi = 0.50$, we see that $\beta = 0.95$. For $\pi = 0.6157$, we see that $\beta = 0.50$. For $\pi = 0.70$, we calculate as follows:

$$\frac{0.70 - p^*}{\sqrt{\dfrac{(0.7) \times (0.3)}{49}}} = \frac{(0.70 - 0.6175)7}{\sqrt{0.21}} = 1.256$$

Therefore

$$\beta = 0.1046$$

TABLE 8.14.

π	β
0.50	0.95
0.6175	0.50
0.70	0.1046

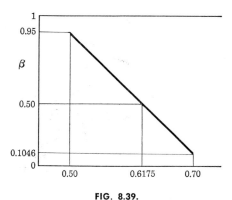

FIG. 8.39.

The results are shown in Table 8.14 and the OC curve based on these β values is sketched in Fig. 8.39. Hence we have our decision rule.

Decision rule.   Take a random sample of size $n = 49$. If

$$p \leq 61.75\% \qquad \text{take action } A_1 \text{ (use nonplastic)}$$
$$p > 61.75\% \qquad \text{take action } A_2 \text{ (use plastic)}$$

Then the α-risk is 5 percent and the β-risks for alternative hypotheses are given by the OC curve in Fig. 8.39.

Note that in this case the vertical scale of the OC curve is the probability of not using plastic.

Example 2.   Suppose in Example 1 that the company is anxious to use plastic, and unless there is evidence that 50 percent or less of purchasers prefer plastic, it will use plastic. Then the null and alternative hypotheses and the α- and β-risks are

$$H_1: \qquad \pi \geq 50\%$$
$$H_2: \qquad \pi < 50\%$$

Action	w_1, $\pi = 50\%$	w_2, $\pi < 50\%$
A_1, use plastic		$\beta = P(A_1 \mid w_2)$
A_2, use nonplastic	$\alpha = P(A_2 \mid w_1)$	

Assuming a sample of size $n = 49$ and $\alpha = 5$ percent, we find the critical value p^*, using Fig. 8.40 as a visual aid.

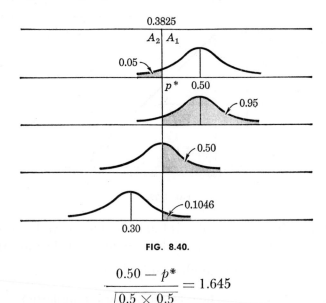

FIG. 8.40.

$$\frac{0.50 - p^*}{\sqrt{\dfrac{0.5 \times 0.5}{49}}} = 1.645$$

$$p^* = 0.3825$$

Using the $p^* = 0.3825$, let us find the β-risks for several alternative w_2's. For $\pi = 0.50$, we see from Fig. 8.40 that $\beta = 0.95$. For $\pi = 0.3825$, the $\beta = 0.50$. For $\pi = 0.30$, we calculate as follows:

$$\frac{p^* - 0.3825}{\sqrt{\dfrac{0.3 \times 0.7}{49}}} = \frac{(-0.08225)7}{0.4582} = -1.256$$

Therefore

$$\beta = 0.1046$$

TABLE 8.15.

π	β
0.50	0.95
0.3825	0.50
0.30	0.1046

The results are shown in Table 8.15 and the OC curve based on these values is sketched in Fig. 8.41. Hence, the decision rule follows.

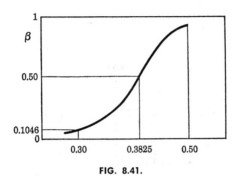

FIG. 8.41.

Decision rule.   Take a random sample of size $n = 49$. If

$$p \geqq 38.25 \qquad \text{take action } A_1 \text{ (use plastic)}$$
$$p < 38.25 \qquad \text{take action } A_2 \text{ (use nonplastic)}$$

Then $\alpha = 5$ percent and the β-risks for alternative hypotheses are given by the OC curve in Fig. 8.41.

Note that in this case the vertical scale of the OC curve is the probability of using plastic.

In Example 1 the critical value was $p^* = 61.75$ percent, and in Example 2, it was $p^* = 38.25$ percent. We can see heuristically that it is easier under the decision rule of Example 2 to switch to the use of plastic.

Example 3.   The Army has set up a criterion of acceptance of shipments of a product. It will accept the shipments if the percentage of defectives per shipment is 5 percent or less, and it will reject it if it is more than 5 percent. The null and alternative hypotheses are

$$H_1: \qquad \pi \leqq 5\%$$
$$H_2: \qquad \pi > 5\%$$

This setup implies that unless there is evidence that π is more than 5 percent, it will accept the shipments; that is, the Army is anxious to accept the shipments. The α- and β-risks are shown as follows:

Action	w_1, $\pi = 5\%$	w_2, $\pi > 5\%$
A_1, accept		$\beta = P(A_1 \mid w_2)$
A_2, reject	$\alpha = P(A_2 \mid w_1)$	

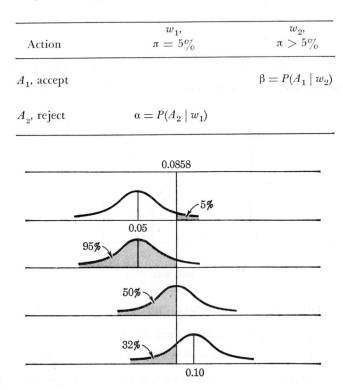

FIG. 8.42.

Let us assume that a random sample of size $n = 100$ is taken and that $\alpha = 5$ percent. Then p^* is found as follows, using Fig. 8.42 as a visual aid:

$$\frac{p^* - 0.05}{\sqrt{\dfrac{(0.05) \times (0.95)}{100}}} = 1.645$$

$$p^* = 0.0858$$

Using this $p^* = 0.0858$, we may find the β values. The results are shown in Table 8.16, and the OC curve based on these values is shown in Fig. 8.43.

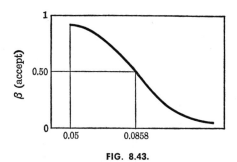

FIG. 8.43.

TABLE 8.16.

π	β
0.05	0.95
0.0858	0.50
0.10	0.32
0.15	0.036

Decision rule. Take a random sample of size $n = 100$. If

$$p \geq 8.58\% \qquad \text{take action } A_1 \text{ (accept)}$$
$$p < 8.58\% \qquad \text{take action } A_2 \text{ (reject)}$$

Then $\alpha = 5$ percent and the β-risks are shown by the OC curve in Fig. 8.43. Note that the vertical scale of the OC curve shows the probability of accepting the shipment.

Example 4. In Example 3, if the Army is not anxious to accept the shipment, it could set up the null and alternative hypotheses as follows:

$$H_1 : \qquad \pi \geq 0.05$$
$$H_2 : \qquad \pi < 0.05$$

Action	w_1, $\pi = 0.05$	w_2, $\pi < 0.05$
A_1, reject		$\beta = P(A_1 \mid w_2)$
A_2, accept	$\alpha = P(A_2 \mid w_1)$	

As this setup shows, unless there is evidence that the percentage of defects is smaller than 5 percent, the Army will reject the shipments.

Let $\alpha = 5$ percent and $n = 100$, as in Example 3. Then we can calculate the critical value p^* and the β-risks. This is left as an exercise to the students.

Note that in this case, the vertical scale of the OC curve shows the probability of *rejecting* the shipment.

8.7.   Changing the Sample Size

Up to now we assumed the sample size n as given. Let us next investigate the effect a change in n has on the decision rule, and on the β values. We shall see that as n becomes larger, β will become smaller. This simply means that as n becomes larger, the ability of the decision rule to distinguish between the null and alternative hypotheses will become better. Let us illustrate this with an example.

In Example 1 of Section 8.5, we had the results of Table 8.17 for

TABLE 8.17.

μ, lb.	β
200	0.9500
197.42	0.8413
193.42	0.5000
189.42	0.1586
185.42	0.0228

$n = 25$. The critical value was $\bar{X}^* = 193.42$ lb. Let us now increase the sample size to 100; that is, $n = 100$. Then the critical value becomes, using Fig. 8.44 as a visual aid,

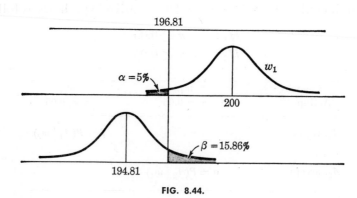

FIG. 8.44.

$$\frac{200 - \bar{X}^*}{2} = 1.645$$

$$\bar{X}^* = 196.81$$

Based on this $\bar{X}^* = 196.81$ lb., we find the β-risks as shown in Table 8.18.

TABLE 8.18.

μ, lb.	β
200	0.9500
198.81	0.8413
196.81	0.5000
194.81	0.1586
192.81	0.0228

Let us now graph the OC curve, based on $n = 25$ and $n = 100$, as shown in Fig. 8.45. We see that the OC curve for $n = 100$ is below the

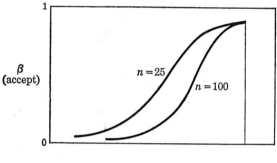

FIG. 8.45.

OC curve for $n = 25$. The probability of accepting the cables when the average strength is less than 200 lb. becomes smaller more rapidly for the OC curve ($n = 100$) than for the OC curve ($n = 25$). An increase in the sample size increases the ability of the decision rule to distinguish between the null and alternative hypotheses. Note that $\alpha = 5$ percent is fixed.

Observation of Fig. 8.45 suggests that we can draw a family of curves, each curve for a different sample size. Let the curves in Fig. 8.46 be a hypothetical illustration. Then, for example, if management requires the β-risk to be 5 percent for the alternative hypothesis μ_1, we can find from the graph the size of the sample that satisfies this requirement. In our hypothetical example in Fig. 8.46, we see that the sample size is $n = 100$.

An illustration of a family of OC curves of the one-sided normal test for a level of significance equal to 0.05 is given in Fig. 8.47. It shows

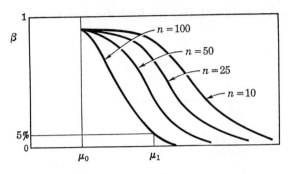

FIG. 8.46.

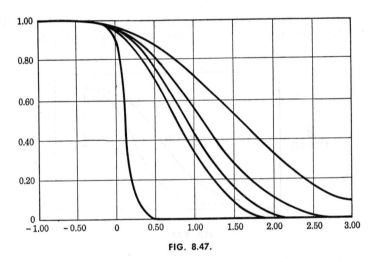

FIG. 8.47.

curves for 5 different sample sizes. The horizontal scale is in terms of standard deviations.

Other illustrations may be found in *Engineering Statistics** and graphs of *OC* curves for other two-sided and one-sided tests may be found in that book. Another source for illustrations is the previously mentioned *Military Standard Sampling Procedures and Tables* (page 199).

8.8. Calculations of the Decision Rule when β is Given

In our previous discussion, the sample size n was given and the β values were computed and an *OC* curve was drawn. If, however, a value for β is given in advance for a specific alternative hypothesis, we can

---

* A. H. Bowker and G. J. Lieberman, *Engineering Statistics,* New York: Prentice-Hall, Inc., 1959.

find the critical value and sample size that will satisfy the α- and β-risks. Let us illustrate this procedure with an illustration.

Suppose that in the TV sales company illustration, the null and alternative hypotheses are given as

$$H_1: \qquad \mu = \$400$$
$$H_2: \qquad \mu = \$370$$

where the company does not wish to start the sales campaign when the average income is as low as $370. Furthermore the α- and β-risks are given as follows:

Action	w_1, $\mu = \$400$	w_2, $\mu = \$370$
A_1, start		$\beta = 10\%$
A_2, do not start	$\alpha = 5\%$	

Using Fig. 8.48 as a visual aid, we may set up the following two equations:

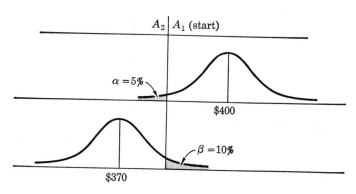

FIG. 8.48.

$$\frac{400 - \bar{X}^*}{\dfrac{50}{\sqrt{n}}} = 1.96$$

$$\frac{\bar{X}^* - 370}{\dfrac{50}{\sqrt{n}}} = 1.64$$

where $\sigma = \$50$ is assumed given. Solving these two equations for $\bar{X}^*$ and n, we find as approximate values:

$$\bar{X}^* = \$383.61$$
$$n = 36$$

Hence the decision rule is: Take a random sample of size $n = 36$. If

$\bar{X} \geqq \$383.61$	take action A_1 (start campaign)
$\bar{X} < \$383.61$	take action A_2 (do not start campaign)

Then $\alpha = 5$ percent and $\beta = 10$ percent.

Using $\bar{X}^* = \$383.61$ and $n = 36$, we may calculate the β-risks for other alternative hypotheses and find an OC curve. For this, first find the standard error:

$$\sigma_{\bar{x}} = \frac{50}{\sqrt{36}} \doteq \$8.33$$

Using this, we can find the β-risks, which are given in Table 8.19. The OC curve is given in Fig. 8.49.

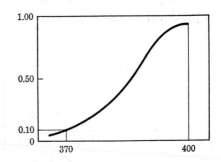

TABLE 8.19.

μ	β
400	0.95
391.94	0.84
383.61	0.50
375.28	0.15
366.95	0.02

FIG. 8.49.

DECISION THEORY

9

In Chapter 8 we discussed the testing of hypotheses, which showed how to test a null hypothesis, given a certain level of significance. We then considered a simple decision problem, which had two states of nature and two acts, and the main task was to find a decision rule that specified which act to select, given a certain outcome of an experiment.

In retrospect, we note three points:

1. The reasons why a certain level of significance (say, 5, 2.5, or 1 percent) was selected were not clear.

2. Although our main interest was the act we should ultimately select, the investigation was in terms of testing the null hypothesis.

3. The test used the objective (relative frequency) approach to probability, and the hypotheses to be tested were statistical hypotheses that assumed a frequency distribution. The conclusions we arrived at were also stated in terms of relative frequencies.

What we propose to do now is to show an alternative approach to business and economic decision problems that is based on the subjective approach to probability theory and which emphasizes the selection of acts instead of hypotheses. The main reference for this approach is Robert Schlaifer's book, *Probability and Statistics for Business Decisions* (1959), written for graduate students.* However, certain parts

---

* Robert Schlaifer, *Probability and Statistics for Business Decisions*, New York: McGraw-Hill Book Co., 1959.

of it may be read with the background that has already been acquired in Chapters 2 to 8 of this book.

A simple illustration of this alternative approach will be presented in the following section.

9.1. Introduction—Payoff Table

In the Preface to his book, Schlaifer explains this approach as follows:

"When the consequences of various possible courses of action depend on some unpredictable event, the *practical* way of choosing the 'best' act is to assign values to consequences and probabilities to events and then to select the act with the highest expected value."

This approach may be shown schematically as follows:

$$\text{Events} \longrightarrow \text{acts} \longrightarrow \text{consequences}$$

uncertainty,	values,
probabilities	profits,
	costs,
	opportunity loss

For example, suppose there is a French bakery that bakes cream cakes every morning. The cakes are such that unless sold the same day, they have to be thrown away. The number of cakes to be baked depends on the demand (number of customers) for these cakes, and the numbers of customers who buy the cakes are the *events*. These events, as we see, are *uncertain* events.

Based on this uncertain forecast, the baker decides on the number of cakes to bake (which are the *acts*) and he is faced with a decision problem of selecting an act (say, baking 3 cakes) from a number of possible acts (say, baking 0, 1, 2, 3, or 4 cakes).

We show the relation between such events and acts in Table 9.1. The cell marked X shows the relation that there is 1 customer (event)

TABLE 9.1.

Events	Acts (Number of Cakes)				
	0	1	2	3	4
0					
1		X			
2		Y			
3					
4					

and 1 cake has been baked (act). The cell marked Y shows that there are 2 customers (events) and 1 cake has been baked (act).

Note carefully that the sequence of reasoning shown by the table is: events $\longrightarrow$ acts. That is, an act is selected, *given* an event. For example, given the event that there is 1 customer, the baker will select the act of baking 1 cake.

However, the event of 1 customer is *uncertain*. It may turn out that there are 0, 2, 3, or 4 customers instead of 1 customer. The 0, 1, 2, 3, and 4 customers are the *possible events*.

Similarly, 0, 1, 2, 3, and 4 cakes are the *possible acts*.

Hence, given the event of 1 customer, the correct decision is act 1 (baking 1 cake); but since the event is uncertain, selecting act 1 may not be the best possible decision.

Let us next introduce the term *consequence*. It is the result of an act, given an event. For example, if the act is baking 1 cake, given the event of 2 customers, the consequence is the sale of 1 cake to 1 customer, the other customer being unable to buy a cake. By evaluating these consequences, we shall be able to determine the desirability of the acts.

We may *evaluate* these consequences in several ways: The first is in terms of profits; a second is in terms of cost; and a third is in terms of opportunity loss. Let us first evaluate the consequences in terms of profit.

Suppose, for simplicity, that it costs $1.00 to bake a cake which is sold for $2.00. Then, for cell X, we have the production and sale of 1 cake, and hence a profit of $2 - $1 = $1. For cell Y, we have the production of 1 cake and demand for 2 cakes. But since there is only 1 cake, the sale is still 1 cake, and 1 customer does not get a cake. Hence the profit is still $1.00. The relation between profits, sales, and cost may be shown schematically as

$$\text{Profits} = \text{sales} - \text{cost}$$

where we may also use the term *revenue* instead of sales. Let us now fill in the rest of the cells, as shown in Table 9.2.

A table, such as Table 9.2, that shows the relations between all possible events and acts and the values associated with the consequences is called a *payoff table*. This payoff table was constructed in terms of profits. The last column is to be filled in by the student as an exercise. The answers may be found in Table 9.4.

When the payoff table is constructed in terms of *cost,* we have one

TABLE 9.2. Payoff Table

Events	Acts 0	1	2	3	4
0	$0	$−1	$−2	$−3	
1	0	1	0	−1	
2	0	1	2	1	
3	0	1	2	3	
4	0	1	2	3	

like Table 9.3. For example, for the act of producing 2 cakes, the cost of production is $2.00, regardless of the event, and the costs are also fixed costs for the other acts. This payoff table is not very instructive. However, there are, of course, cases where the cost will vary according to the event; these will be more instructive in providing information for deciding which act to select. We shall give examples later.

TABLE 9.3. Payoff Table in Terms of Cost

Events	0	1	2	3	4
0	$0	$1	$2	$3	$4
1	0	1	2	3	4
2	0	1	2	3	4
3	0	1	2	3	4
4	0	1	2	3	4

A third way of constructing a payoff table is in terms of *opportunity losses,* and in this case, the payoff table is called a *loss table.* Opportunity loss of a decision is defined as: "The *difference* between the cost or profit *actually* realized under that decision and the cost or profit which *would have been* realized if the decision had been the best one possible for the event which actually occurred."*

Let us illustrate. First recall that the reasoning sequence is: event ——→ act ——→ consequences. Let us look at the payoff table (which is in terms of profits, Table 9.2), and first consider the event 1 customer. For this event, there are 5 possible acts. For act 0 (that is, baking 0 cakes), the profit is $0.00. For act 1, the profit is $1.00. In this case, only 1 cake is baked and 1 cake is sold, so there is no loss of unsold surplus cakes. For act 2, the profit is also $0.00, but only 1 of the 2 cakes were sold and the remaining 1 was thrown away. Similar inter-

---

* Robert Schlaifer, *op. cit.,* p. 117.

pretations may be applied to acts 2, 3, and 4. As the payoff table shows, given the event 1 customer, selecting act 1 is the best decision and gives the *largest* profit. Let us star this $1.00 as shown in Table 9.4.

TABLE 9.4.   Payoff Table

Events	0	1	2	3	4
0	$0*	$−1	$−2	$−3	$−4
1	0	1*	0	−1	−2
2	0	1	2*	1	0
3	0	1	2	3*	2
4	0	1	2	3	4*

TABLE 9.5.   Loss Table

Events	0	1	2	3	4
0	$0	$1	$2	$3	$4
1	1	0	1	2	3
2	2	1	0	1	2
3	3	2	1	0	1
4					

In similar manner, we have starred the *largest* profits corresponding to the other given events.

Returning to the event 1 customer, let us compare the profits of act 0 and act 1. If the baker selects act 0, he has a profit of $0.00. The greatest profit that can be made is the $1.00 profit corresponding to act 1. Hence, if the baker selects act 0, given event 1, he is missing the opportunity of making

(Profit which would have been realized) — (profit actually realized)

$$= \$1 - 0 = \$1.00$$

This $1.00 is the *opportunity loss* of the decision of selecting act 0, given event 1.

In similar manner, the opportunity loss of the decision of selecting act 2, given event 1, is

(Profit which would have been realized) — (profit actually realized)

$$= \$1 - 0 = \$1.00$$

For act 3 it is

(Profit which would have been realized) — (profit actually realized)

$$= \$1 - (-1) = \$2.00$$

and for act 4 it is
(Profit which would have been realized) — (profit actually realized)

$$= \$1 - (-2 = \$3.00$$

The opportunity losses for decisions, given events 0, 2, and 3, are shown in Table 9.5. As an exercise, compute the opportunity losses, given event 4, and complete the loss table. As is seen the largest profits of Table 9.4 correspond to the smallest opportunity losses ($0) of Table 9.5, which is what we should expect.

Let us now summarize our results. We have the simple schema:

Events ⟶ acts ⟶ consequences

A table showing the relations between all possible events, all possible acts, and the evaluation of the consequences is called a *payoff* table. The evaluation may be in terms of profits, costs, or opportunity losses. When opportunity losses are used, the table is called a *loss* table.

What we wish to do now is to select an act, *given* an event. If the event is certain, it is reasonable to select the act with the highest profit, or lowest opportunity loss. For example, when given the event 3 customers, we shall select act 3, which gives us the highest profit of $3.00 (or lowest loss of $0.00).

However, for the problems in which we are interested, the event is *uncertain*. In such cases, it is proposed that the *practical* way of choosing the best act is to select the act with the highest *expected* profits (or lowest *expected* loss). Let us investigate this problem next.

9.2. Expected Values of an Act

Suppose we have a game of tossing a 4-sided die as shown in Table 9.6. If we select act *A*, we get $1.00 when a 1 occurs, $2.00 when a 2 occurs, and so forth, as in Table 9.6. If we select act *B*, we get $3.00 when a 1 occurs, $0.00 when a 2 occurs, and so forth. Assuming a fair die, which act should we select?

As stated at the beginning of Section 9.1, the practical way of choosing the best act is to select the act with the highest expected value. The expected values of the acts have been computed in Table 9.6 and, as is seen, it is $2.5 for both acts. Hence it makes no difference which act we select.

If the die is loaded so that only even numbers appear with equal chance, the values become those given in Table 9.7.

TABLE 9.6.

Event	Probability	Act A		Act B	
		Conditional Profit	Expected Profit	Conditional Profit	Expected Profit
1	1/4	$1	$1/4	$3	$3/4
2	1/4	2	2/4	0	0
3	1/4	3	3/4	7	7/4
4	1/4	4	4/4	0	0
			$ 2.5		$ 2.5

TABLE 9.7.

Event	Probability	Act A		Act B	
		Conditional Value	Expected Value	Conditional Value	Expected Value
1	0	$1	$0	$3	$0
2	1/2	2	1	0	0
3	0	3	0	7	0
4	1/2	4	2	0	0
	1.0		$3		$0

The expected value of act A is \$3.00 and for B it is \$0.00. Hence act A is selected.

The interpretation of \$3.00 is: If the game is played a large number of times, a person will win, on the average, \$3.00 per game. Let us now give a few examples.

Example 1. In our previous example of a baker who sells cakes, let the probability of the demand for cakes be as shown in Table 9.8. This table shows that, given the probability distribution shown, the expected value of act 1 is \$1.0 and that of act 2 is \$1.8.

TABLE 9.8.

Event	Probability	Act 1		Act 2	
		Conditional Profit	Expected Profit	Conditional Profit	Expected Profit
0	0.0	$-1	$0	$-2	$0
1	0.1	1	0.1	0	0
2	0.3	1	0.3	2	0.6
3	0.4	1	0.4	2	0.8
4	0.2	1	0.2	2	0.4
			$1.0		$1.8

The $1.8, for example, means that when this situation is repeated over and over again for a large number of times, the baker will have, on the average, a profit of $1.8 per day when he selects act 2.

Table 9.9 shows the expected profits of all the acts. Act 3 has the highest expected profit of $2.0, and hence it is the act to select.

TABLE 9.9.

Acts	Expected Profits
0	$0.0
1	1.0
2	1.8
3	2.0
4	1.4

Example 2. Let us do the same problem in terms of opportunity losses. The loss table is given as Table 9.10.

TABLE 9.10. Loss Table

	Acts				
Events	0	1	2	3	4
0	$0	$1	$2	$3	$4
1	1	0	1	2	3
2	2	1	0	1	2
3	3	2	1	0	1
4	4	3	2	1	0

TABLE 9.11.

		Act 1		Act 2	
Event	Probability	Cond. Loss	Expected Loss	Cond. Loss	Expected Loss
0	0.0	$1	$0	$2	$0
1	0.1	0	0	1	0.1
2	0.3	1	0.3	0	0
3	0.4	2	0.8	1	0.4
4	0.2	3	0.6	2	0.4
			$1.7		$0.9

The expected loss of acts 1 and 2 are $1.7 and $0.9, and clearly the baker should select the act with the smaller opportunity loss, namely, act 2.

The interpretation of $0.9 is, if act 2 is selected, that the baker will have, on the average, an opportunity loss of $0.9 per day.

TABLE 9.12.

Acts	Expected Loss
0	$2.7
1	1.7
2	0.9
3	0.7
4	1.3

Table 9.12 shows the expected losses of all the acts. We see that act 3 has the lowest loss of $0.7, and hence it is the act to be selected.

Note that the difference between any two expected profits is equal to the difference between any two expected losses. For example, for acts 2 and 3, we have:

In terms of expected profits: $2.0 - 1.8 = $0.2
In terms of expected losses: $0.9 - 0.7 = $0.2

It is left as an exercise for the student to reason out why this is so.

Example 3.   A supplier of sugar wishes to have 5 grams of sugar in a bag per production run of 1000 bags. Let us assume, owing to poor adjustment, every now and then the process gets out of control. When the production process is out of control and the sugar exceeds 5 grams, he will incur an additional cost, depending on the excess amount of sugar. When the amount of sugar is less than 5 grams, he may expect the shipments to be rejected by the buyers, and he will be required to repackage the sugar in new bags. Table 9.13 shows the events and acts.

TABLE 9.13.

Event, gr.	Cost	
	Continue	Adjust
4.8	$30	$10
4.9	20	10
5.0	0	10
5.1	10	10
5.2	15	10

The events are shown as 4.8 grams, 4.9 grams, . . . , 5.2 grams. The acts are to continue the process or to adjust the process. Let us assume the cost of adjustment is $10.

Hence Table 9.13 is read as follows: For the event of 4.8 grams per bag, the supplier estimates an additional cost of $30 per shipment, and for 4.9

grams, it is $20. For events 5.1 grams and 5.2 grams, he receives no rejections from the buyer, but the additional cost of the excess sugar is $10 and $15, respectively. The cost of adjustment is $10 for all cases.

From past experience the supplier knows the probability distribution associated with the events, which is shown in Table 9.14. The 0.1 associated

TABLE 9.14.

Event, gr.	Probability	Continue		Adjust	
		Cond.	Expected	Cond.	Expected
4.8	0.1	$30	$3.0	$10	$ 1.0
4.9	0.2	20	4.0	10	2.0
5.0	0.5	0	0	10	5.0
5.1	0.1	10	1.0	10	1.0
5.2	0.1	15	1.5	10	1.0
			$9.5		$10.0

with 4.8 grams is to be interpreted to mean that when the production process is operated a number of times without adjustment, the process will be out of control, and the amount of sugar per bag will be 4.8 grams, about once in 10 times.

The expected cost of $9.5 means that when the production process is repeated many times, without adjustment, there will on the average be an additional cost of $9.5 per shipment.

Obviously it costs less to continue the process, and hence it is the act to select.

From the examples, the reader has probably already noticed that there are two main problems: Assigning correct probabilities and calculating appropriate costs or profits. The latter problem is a technical one and differs according to different situations.

As for the assessment of probabilities, we may use past experience, relative frequencies, or subjective judgment, or information from a sample. As we shall show in Chapter 16, we may have an initial probability distribution based on past experience of relative frequencies, but with a new sample drawn, we can revise the old probabilities. To explain these processes, we have to explain joint probability and Bayes theorem. These are considered in Chapter 16.

ESTIMATION

10

In Chapters 7 and 8, the population mean μ, population standard deviation σ, and population proportion π were assumed to be known or given, and the problem was to decide whether or not to accept these parameters. But in many problems, these population parameters are unknown, and the main concern may be to *estimate* them.

10.1. Introduction—Estimation and Estimators

The problem of estimating parameters can be illustrated best by examples. For instance, a department store is interested in establishing a branch in the suburbs and would like to locate it in a community that has an average income above the national average. How are they going to find the average income of a given community? It is too costly to try to find the income of each family in the community and then compute the average. A statistician may select a sample, find the sample average, and use that as an *estimator* of the average income for the whole community.

The department store may also be interested in knowing the dispersion of the incomes, to determine the price range of the goods they should sell. If the dispersion (that is, the population standard deviation σ) is unknown, it may be *estimated* from the sample standard deviation.

A chain store may be interested in the proportion π of defective fountain pens received per shipment. It is impossible, for practical reasons, to inspect all the pens. Hence, a sample is taken and the sample proportion may be used as an *estimator* of the population proportion π of defective pens.

Although we stated above that sample statistics such as the sample average, sample standard deviation, and sample proportion may be used as estimators for the corresponding population parameters, a question that naturally arises is: Why did we use these statistics as estimators? Are there other sample statistics that could be used as estimators? For example, instead of the sample mean, could we not use the sample median X_{med} as an estimator for the population mean?

The reason why we selected the sample mean $\bar{X}$ as an estimator of μ is that it is a good estimator of μ and is better than X_{med}. What, then, is a good estimator, and what do we mean when we say $\bar{X}$ is a better estimator than X_{med}?

Common sense should indicate that a good estimator is one that is near the population parameter. For instance, we should like to say that $\bar{X}$ is near the true value of μ. But can we say that $\bar{X}$ rather than X_{med} is nearer to μ?

This is tempting to say, but note that $\bar{X}$ was obtained from a particular sample. We have no way of predicating what an individual value of $\bar{X}$ will be. An individual value of $\bar{X}$ is known only after a sample has been selected. Similarly, an individual value of X_{med} is known only after a sample has been selected. Hence, we cannnot make *a general statement* that $\bar{X}$ and not X_{med} is closer to μ. For one sample, $\bar{X}$ may be closer to μ; for another sample, X_{med} may be closer to μ.

How shall we get around this impasse and be able to say that $\bar{X}$ is better than X_{med} as an estimator of μ? We shall answer this question as follows: After a large number of samples have been taken, we shall have a sampling distribution of $\bar{X}$ and a sampling distribution of X_{med}. It turns out that the sampling distribution of $\bar{X}$ rather than that of X_{med} will be more concentrated near μ.

Since the sampling distribution of $\bar{X}$ is more concentrated near μ than is the sampling distribution of X_{med} when a large number of samples are taken, $\bar{X}$ is more likely to be closer to μ than is X_{med}. It is in this sense that we say $\bar{X}$ is a better estimator than X_{med} of μ.

Our problem now is to give criteria such that when we have an estimator that satisfies these criteria, it will be a good estimator in the sense that the distribution of the estimator is concentrated near the true parameter.

What then are these criteria for a good estimator? They are:
1. Unbiasedness.
2. Consistency.
3. Efficiency.
4. Sufficiency.

In the following discussion, we shall give a nonrigorous explanation of these criteria.

After we have explained these criteria, we shall consider the problem of how to find estimators with these desirable properties. It turns out that there are a number of ways of finding estimators, and the processes are usually discussed under the topics of methods of estimation. The two main methods are the method of least squares and the method of maximum likelihood, and we shall consider only these two in this book. The method of least squares is explained in Chapter 11, and the method of maximum likelihood is a topic in this chapter.

After we have discussed the method of maximum likelihood and also have found various estimators, we shall pose and discuss the following problem: Even though $\bar{X}$ is a good estimator of μ, it is obvious that there will be a discrepancy (error) between $\bar{X}$ and μ. Thus, to have confidence in $\bar{X}$ as an estimator of μ, we should like to know the error, $e = \bar{X} - \mu$, and the risk of such an error: or we may say that we should like to find the precision of the estimator $\bar{X}$.

Up to this point, our discussion of estimators will be on *point estimators*, and the topic may be called *point estimation*. That is, when given a parameter (say, μ), it is estimated by a value $\bar{X}$. A deficiency of point estimators is that we cannot associate a probability statement with it and say how probable it is that $\bar{X}$ is equal to μ.

An alternative way of estimating μ is to say that μ is between two values, say,

$$a < \mu < b$$

and this is called *interval estimation*. For example, we may say that the average grade of the examination of the class is between 70 and 75 points;

$$70 \text{ points} < \mu < 75 \text{ points}$$

As we shall see, we shall be able to associate a probability statement with this kind of interval estimate. This topic is considered in Section 10.8. Let us now start with the criteria for a good point estimator.

10.2.   Unbiasedness

Suppose a large group of students have taken an examination and we wish to estimate the average grade point by taking a random sample. We are estimating an unknown μ, but for purposes of illustration, let us assume that:

Population mean:	$\mu = 70$ points
Standard deviation:	$\sigma = 18$ points
Size of population:	$N = 2000$

Recall that $E(\bar{X})$ was the expected value of $\bar{X}$, or in other words, the mean of all possible sample means. From the central limit theorem, we know that

$$E(\bar{X}) = \mu$$

The common sense of this is that the sampling distribution of $\bar{X}$ is evenly clustered around the value μ and not around some other value. For example, the upper part of Fig. 10.1 shows the sampling distribution of $\bar{X}$ clustered around μ.

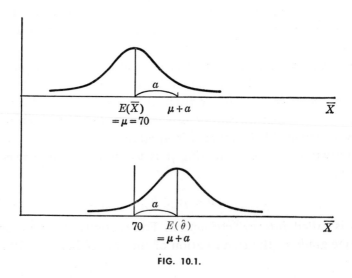

FIG. 10.1.

Now let $\hat{\theta}$ be some other sample characteristic that is used as an estimator. For example, let

$$\hat{\theta} = \bar{X} + a$$

That is, $\hat{\theta}$ is the sample mean $\bar{X}$ plus a constant a (say, $a = 5$). If the sample mean is 72 points, then $\hat{\theta} = 72 + 5 = 77$ is considered as an estimate of μ. In general, this becomes

$$\begin{aligned} E(\hat{\theta}) &= E(\bar{X} + a) \\ &= E(\bar{X}) + E(a) \\ &= \mu + a \end{aligned}$$

which implies that the sampling distribution of $\hat{\theta}$ is clustered around $\mu + a$, as shown in the lower part of Fig. 10.1.

It should be intuitively clear that it is more desirable to use $\bar{X}$ rather than $\hat{\theta}$ ($= \bar{X} + a$) as an estimator of μ. In general, when the *expected value* of the statistic used as an estimator is equal to the population parameter to be estimated, we say that the estimator is *unbiased*. In our present example, $E(\bar{X}) = \mu$; thus $\hat{\mu} = \bar{X}$ is an unbiased estimator of μ. For $\hat{\theta} = \bar{X} + a$, we had

$$E(\hat{\theta}) = \mu + a$$

and thus $\hat{\theta}$ is not an unbiased estimator of μ. We say that $\hat{\theta} = \bar{X} + a$ is a *biased* estimator of μ and a is the *bias*. If $E(\hat{\theta}) > \mu$, θ is said to be positively biased; if $E(\hat{\theta}) < \mu$, it is said to be negatively biased.

Thus the first property of a good estimator is unbiasedness, and $\hat{\mu} = \bar{X}$ is an unbiased estimator of μ.

10.3.   Consistent Estimator

Suppose a sample of size $n = 36$ is taken and $\bar{X} = 65$ points. What will happen to $\bar{X}$ if we let $n \longrightarrow N$? It should be intuitively clear that as $n \longrightarrow N$, the sample mean $\bar{X}$ will approach μ. For example, N was 2000 and $\mu = 70$. If $n = 1999$ instead of 36, we can see intuitively that the $\bar{X}$ calculated from $n = 1999$ will be very close to $\mu = 70$ (say, for example, 69.9 points).

Now let us assume that the median of the population is Med $= 73$ points. Let the sample median be denoted by X_{med} for a sample of size n. It should be clear that as $n \longrightarrow N$, the sample median, X_{med} will approach the population median Med $= 73$ points. Therefore, if X_{med} is used as an estimator of μ, as $n \longrightarrow N$, the X_{med} will *not* approach $\mu = 70$ points, but rather Med $= 73$ points.

When an estimator (such as $\bar{X}$) approaches the population parameter that is to be estimated (such as μ) as the sample size increases, the estimator is said to be a *consistent* estimator of the parameter. Thus, $\hat{\mu} = \bar{X}$ is a consistent estimator of μ, and $\hat{\mu} = X_{med}$ is not a consistent estimator of μ when we have a skewed distribution.

Thus, the second property of a good estimator is *consistency*, and $\hat{\mu} = \bar{X}$ is a consistent estimator of μ.

Let us express more rigorously the statements made above, as follows: We have seen intuitively that as n becomes larger and larger, $\bar{X}$ will approach μ. This may be shown in symbols as

$$\bar{X} \longrightarrow \mu \qquad \text{as} \quad n \longrightarrow \infty \text{ (or } N)$$

By using this formula, we can formally define consistency as follows: If

(1) $$P(\bar{X} \longrightarrow \mu) \longrightarrow 1 \qquad \text{as} \quad n \longrightarrow \infty$$

then $\bar{X}$ is called a *consistent estimator* of μ. The equation (1) is read as "the probability that $\bar{X}$ approaches μ as n becomes larger and larger is 1."

In terms of the sampling distribution of $\bar{X}$, it means that the sampling distribution of $\bar{X}$ becomes closely concentrated near μ as the sample size becomes larger. Using our example of grades, we can see intuitively that the sampling distribution of $\bar{X}$ when $n = 1999$ will be more closely concentrated near μ than when $n = 36$.

What we have said concerning the sample mean may now be stated in general terms: Let $\hat{\theta}$, which is computed from a sample $x_1, x_2, \ldots, x_n$ be an estimator of the population parameter θ. If

$$P(\hat{\theta} \longrightarrow \theta) \longrightarrow 1 \qquad \text{as} \quad n \longrightarrow \infty$$

then $\hat{\theta}$ is called a consistent estimator of θ.

10.4. Efficiency

(i) Relative efficiency

Suppose we have a population that has a normal distribution and we wish to estimate the population mean. As we have seen, we may use the sample mean $\bar{X}$, which is an unbiased and consistent estimator. We may also use the sample median (X_{med}) as an estimator, and in our present case, this is also unbiased and consistent. Which of the two is more preferable as an estimator?

We mentioned in Section 10.1 that we prefer an estimator with a sampling distribution closely concentrated around the population parameter. Which of the two, the sample mean $\bar{X}$ or the sample median

X_{med}, is more closely concentrated around μ? This may be determined by comparing the variances of both estimators; the one with the smaller variance will be the estimator that is preferable. The smaller the variance, the more concentrated the sampling distribution around the population parameter, assuming that we have consistent estimators. It turns out that the variances of $\bar{X}$ and X_{med} are for large samples,

$$\text{Var}(\bar{X}) = \frac{\sigma^2}{n}$$

$$\text{Var}(X_{med}) = \frac{\pi\sigma^2}{2n}$$

Hence, when given the same sample size,

$$\frac{\text{Var}(\bar{X})}{\text{Var}(X_{med})} = \frac{2}{\pi}$$

$$\doteq 0.64 \qquad (\pi = 3.14)$$

That is, $\text{Var}(\bar{X}) < \text{Var}(X_{med})$, and thus $\bar{X}$ is more preferable as an estimator than is X_{med}. Since, given the same sample size, the sampling distribution of $\bar{X}$ is more concentrated around μ than is X_{med}, we may say that $\bar{X}$ is more *efficient* than X_{med}.

The preceding result says

$$\text{Var}(\bar{X}) = \text{Var}(X_{med}) \times 64\%$$

That is, the variance of $\bar{X}$ is only 64 percent of the variance of the median when they both have a sample size of n.

In terms of sample size, the variance of the median from samples of size 100 is about the same as that of sample means from samples of size 64.

We summarize as follows: If we have two estimators, $\hat{\theta}_1$ and $\hat{\theta}_2$, and

$$\text{Var}(\hat{\theta}_1) < \text{Var}(\hat{\theta}_2)$$

then the efficiency of $\hat{\theta}_2$ relative to $\hat{\theta}_1$ is given by

$$E_f = \frac{\text{Var}(\hat{\theta}_1)}{\text{Var}(\hat{\theta}_2)}$$

Note that the variance of the smaller estimator is in the numerator, and thus

$$0 \leqslant E_f \leqslant 1$$

(ii) *Efficient estimators*

We have defined efficiency in relative terms and put the variance of the smaller estimator in the numerator. The efficiency was defined relative to this smaller variance estimator. But, if we could find an estimator with a variance that is smaller than the variance of any other estimator, we could use that smallest variance as the basis to measure efficiency; and, in terms of efficiency, we could say that this estimator with the smallest variance is an "efficient estimator."

Then a question arises: How small can the variance of an estimator become? If we can show that the variance cannot become smaller than a certain lower bound, and if we can find an estimator with a variance that is equal to this lower bound, then that variance will be the smallest variance. We shall use the word *minimum* instead of "smallest" and call it the *minimum variance*.

Furthermore, an estimator that has this minimum variance will be called a *minimum variance estimator*.

It turns out that there is such a lower bound, given by the Cramer-Rao inequality. A mathematical treatment of this topic is too advanced for this book, so in discussing it, let us omit derivations. We can illustrate its meaning by applying it to the problem of estimating the mean μ.

Let θ be an estimator of μ. Then the Cramer-Rao inequality tells us that the variance of $\hat{\theta}$ cannot be smaller than σ^2/n. That is

$$\mathrm{Var}(\hat{\theta}) \geq \frac{\sigma^2}{n}$$

$\hat{\theta}$ may be the sample mean $\bar{X}$, sample median X_{med}, or some other sample statistic, but no matter what it is, the variance cannot be smaller than σ^2/n. However, we know that

$$\mathrm{Var}(\bar{X}) = \frac{\sigma^2}{n}$$

This means that $\hat{\mu} = \bar{X}$ has the smallest variance an estimator can have. Thus we may conclude that $\bar{X}$ has the minimum variance, and hence is a minimum variance estimator of μ.

Combining all our previous results, we may conclude that $\bar{X}$ is an unbiased, consistent, minimum variance estimator of μ.

10.5. Sufficiency

The fourth and last property of a good estimator that we consider is sufficiency, which was developed by a famous statistician, Sir R. A.

Fisher. A *sufficient statistic* (such as $\bar{X}$) is an estimator that utilizes all the information a sample contains about the parameter to be estimated. For example, $\bar{X}$ is a sufficient estimator of the population mean μ. This means that no other estimator of μ, such as the sample median, can add any further information about the parameter μ that is being estimated.

We shall omit a mathematical discussion and merely point out that the sample mean $\bar{X}$ and sample proportion p are sufficient statistics (estimators) for μ and π.

Now that we have stated the desirable properties of a good estimator, the $64 question is: How are estimators with these desirable properties found? This leads us to the problem of methods of estimation. We shall consider the method of maximum likelihood.

10.6.   Method of Maximum Likelihood (ML)

The characteristic of the ML method is that it provides estimators with the desirable properties, such as efficiency, consistency, and sufficiency, that we have been discussing. For example, if the parameter to be estimated has a sufficient estimator, the ML estimator will be a sufficient estimator, and similarly for the other desirable properties except unbiasedness. The maximum likelihood method usually does not give unbiased estimators. We shall discuss the ideas of ML estimators, using a simple illustration.

Suppose a statistician wants to estimate the average grade μ of a large group of students. A random sample of size $n = 36$ is taken and the sample mean $\bar{X}$ is found to be $\bar{X} = 65$ points. Now, the primary assumption on which the statistician bases his reasoning is that the random sample of $n = 36$ is an image of, or representative of, the population. We have seen that this assumption is reasonable in the examples given in Chapter 7, in which sampling distributions were discussed. We saw how samples that were similar to the population had greater probability of being selected.

Let us now reverse this reasoning as follows: The statistician has before him a random sample of size $n = 36$ and $\bar{X} = 65$ points. From which population did it most probably come, a population with $\mu = 60$, 65, or 70? According to our preceding approach, the statistician would reason that it most probably came from a population with $\mu = 65$. Thus we conclude that the population mean μ is *most likely* $\mu = 65$ points.

Although we have reasoned that *the sample* most probably came from a population with $\mu = 65$, we say that the population mean μ, based on our sample, is *most likely* $\mu = 65$. This is so because the population mean μ is either 65 or not; it has only one value. Hence we use the term *likely* instead of probable.

This type of reasoning and the mathematical technique used to find the estimators were also developed by Sir R. A. Fisher in 1922, who called it the *maximum likelihood method*.

With this much background, let us consider another illustration. Suppose we have urns (states of nature) containing 4 balls that are either black or white. An urn with no black balls will be called the 0th urn; an urn with 1 black ball will be called the 1st urn; and so forth for the 2nd, 3rd, and 4th urn. We have 5 urns:

0th	1st	2nd	3rd	4th
0–b	1–b	2–b	3–b	4–b
4–w	3–w	2–w	1–w	0–w

$$\pi_0 = \frac{0}{4} \quad \pi_1 = \frac{1}{4} \quad \pi_2 = \frac{2}{4} \quad \pi_3 = \frac{3}{4} \quad \pi_4 = \frac{4}{4}$$

Let π_i be the proportions of black balls and let

$$\pi_i = \frac{i}{4} \qquad i = 0, 1, 2, 3, 4$$

Now suppose we select a random sample of 2 balls with replacement. This will generate a 2-dimensional sample space. If the 2 balls are selected from the 0th urn, the sample space will be as shown in Fig. 10.2(a). Since the probabilities of white and black balls are

$$P(\text{white} \mid \text{0th urn}) = 1$$
$$P(\text{black} \mid \text{0th urn}) = 0$$

the probabilities associated with the sample points are

$$P(\text{white, white}) = P(W)P(W) = 1 \times 1 = 1$$
$$P(\text{white, black}) = P(W)P(B) = 1 \times 0 = 0$$
$$P(\text{black, black}) = P(B)P(B) = 0 \times 0 = 0$$

and these are shown in Fig. 10.2(a).

If the 2 balls are selected from urn 1, the 2-dimensional sample space is as shown in Fig. 10.2(b) and the probability associated with the sample point (white, black) is

$$P(\text{white, black}) = P(W)P(B) = \frac{3}{4} \times \frac{1}{4} = \frac{3}{16}$$

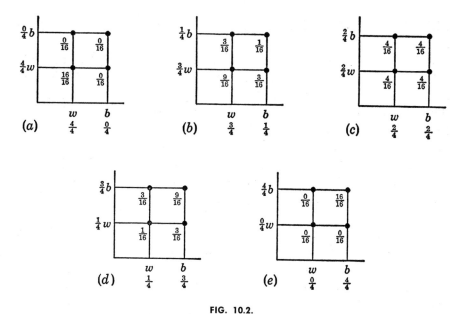

FIG. 10.2.

Since there are two such points, the probability of (white and black) is, when we disregard the order,

$$P(\text{white \& black}) = P(W)P(B) + P(B)P(W) = \frac{6}{16}$$

In similar manner, we find the sample spaces corresponding to the 3rd and 4th urn, and also calculate the probabilities of the sample points as shown in the figures.

These different sample spaces may be characterized by the different probabilities of the black ball. In the 0th space, $P(\text{black}) = 0/4 = 0$; in the 1st space it is $1/4$; in the 2nd space it is $2/4$; and so forth. That is, the sample spaces are characterized by the π_i.

Let us denote these sample spaces by

$$\Omega_0, \quad \Omega_1, \quad \Omega_2, \quad \Omega_3, \quad \Omega_4$$

Suppose the sample we have selected has 1 black and 1 white ball. The question we ask is: From which sample space did it most likely come?

Could it have come from Ω_0? Obviously not, because in Ω_0 there are no black balls. Could it have come from Ω_1 or Ω_2, or some other Ω_i? To answer this question, R. A. Fisher proposes the idea of *likelihood*.

The idea is to select the space Ω_i that will yield the given sample before us more frequently than any other space. That is, which space with which π_i will yield the observed sample most frequently, relative to the other Ω's?

Fisher explains this as follows: (Fisher uses p where we have used π):

"We must return to the actual fact that one value of p, of the frequency of which we know nothing, would yield the observed result three times as frequently as would another value of p. If we need a word to characterise this relative property of different values of p, I suggest that we may speak without confusion of the *likelihood* of one value of p being three times the likelihood of another, bearing always in mind that likelihood is not here used loosely as a synonym of probability, but simply to express the relative frequencies with which such values of the hypothetical quantity p would in fact yield the observed sample."*

Hence our problem is to decide from which sample space Ω_i, the observed sample we have before us, came. Since the sample spaces are characterized by π_i, to decide on a sample space is to select a π_i.

For our present problem, we can see from Figs. 10.2(a) through 10.2(e) that the space that yields the observed sample most frequently, relative to the other Ω's, is the space Ω_2. For Ω_2 the probability of selecting a sample (w, b), is

$$\frac{4}{16} + \frac{4}{16} = \frac{8}{16}$$

whereas it is less than $\frac{8}{16}$ for the other spaces. In other words, Ω_2 is the space in which the sample (w, b) has the largest probability.

Hence we consider the 2nd urn with $\pi = 1/2$, which generated the sample space Ω_2, to be the urn from which the sample was selected; and consider this $\pi = 1/2$ as the estimate of the parameter we seek.

In our discussion, we started from the sample, then went to the sample space and finally to the population, and found π_i. This was possible because of the simple illustration we had. However, for other problems that are not so simple, this process is difficult.

The mathematical technique of the ML method devised by R. A. Fisher enables us to find estimators that are based on the above reasoning directly from the sample. It enables us to find the space in which the probability of the sample is largest. Unfortunately, this requires a knowledge of the calculus. However, we may present the results of the ML method for several different situations as follows:

1. ML estimator of π.   We state without proof that the maximum

---

* R. A. Fisher, "On the mathematical foundations of theoretical statistics," Phil. Trans. Roy. Soc. London, Series A, Vol. 222 (1922). By permission of the author and publisher.

likelihood estimator of the population proportion π is the sample proportion p. Thus we write

(1) $$\hat{\pi} = p$$

We have seen that when the sample size n is large, the sampling distribution of p is approximately normal, with

$$E(p) = \pi$$

$$\sigma_p = \sqrt{\frac{\pi(1 - \pi)}{n}}$$

Thus p is an unbiased estimator of π. Furthermore, as $n \longrightarrow \infty$, the
standard error $\sigma_p \longrightarrow 0$. Thus p is also a consistent estimator of π.

In our illustration above, we have a sample of size $n = 2$ with 1 black
ball. Hence the ML estimator of π is

$$\hat{\pi} = p = \frac{1}{2}$$

Example 1.   To estimate the proportion of students who smoke, a random
sample of 100 students is selected and 60 students are found to be smokers.
The ML estimate of smokers for all the students is

$$\hat{\pi} = \frac{60}{100}$$

2. ML estimator of μ.   The ML estimator of μ is the sample mean $\bar{X}$.
Hence

(2) $$\hat{\mu} = \frac{\Sigma x_i}{n} = \bar{X}$$

We have already seen that $\bar{X}$ is an unbiased, consistent, minimum variance estimator of μ.

Example 2.   To estimate the average height of students, a random sample of
100 students is selected and the average is found to be 5'8". Then the ML
estimate of the height of the students is

$$\hat{\mu} = \bar{X} = 5'8''$$

3. ML estimator of σ^2.   The ML estimator of σ^2 of a normal distribution is

(3) $$\hat{\sigma}^2 = \frac{1}{n} \Sigma (x - \bar{x})^2 = s^2$$

which is the sample variance. The expected value of s^2 is

(4)
$$E(s^2) = \frac{n-1}{n} \sigma^2$$

and hence s^2 is a biased estimator of σ^2. Equation (4) may be rewritten as

$$E(s^2) = \sigma^2 - \frac{\sigma^2}{n}$$

and $-\sigma^2/n$ is the bias.

However, by making the following simple adjustment, we obtain an unbiased estimator as follows:

$$E\left(\frac{n}{n-1} s^2\right) = \sigma^2$$

The factor $n/(n-1)$ indicates that s^2 is underestimating σ^2, but as can be seen, as n becomes larger, $n/(n-1)$ approaches 1, and s^2 becomes an unbiased estimator of σ^2.

If the σ^2 of the population is unknown, we can use equation (3) for calculation purposes, but in that case, we may not be able to use the normal area table. Instead, we may have to use what is known as the t distribution, which is discussed in Chapter 18. But when the sample size n is large, the difference between s^2 and σ^2 becomes smaller, and normal distribution may be used as an approximation.

For many practical problems, the σ is taken as given, based on previous studies or other similar studies. For example, we may have a problem concerning income distribution among families. Previous studies concerning similar income distributions may have a σ of \$50. Because the dispersion of incomes does not change greatly, it is in many cases possible to use this σ in a new study. Why may we say that the dispersion of income does not change greatly? A little reflection should suggest various economic or sociological reasons, but from a statistical standpoint, we saw in Chapter 4 that $\text{Var}(X + a) = \text{Var}(X)$. We take an extreme example: If during the past 10 years, everyone's income increased by, say, \$100, then

$$\text{Var}(X) = \text{Var}(\$100 + X)$$

That is, the variance of the present income distribution will be the same as that of 10 years ago.

As another example, consider two tests, A and B, given to students.

If everyone got 15 points higher in test B than in test A, the variance would be

$$\mathrm{Var}(X) = \mathrm{Var}(X + 15)$$

where $\mathrm{Var}(X)$ is for test A and $\mathrm{Var}(X + 15)$ is for test B. Although everyone may not get exactly 15 points higher in test B, if there is no radical change in the ability of the students, it is reasonable to assume that most of the students got approximately 15 points higher. Then it follows that the variance of both distributions will also be approximately the same.

10.7.   The Relationship Between the Error, Risk, and Sample Size

(i)   The relationship between the error and the risk

The next aspect of the estimator of μ we wish to consider is the relationship between the error, risk, and sample size. We start with the relationship between the error and the risk. We have assumed that

$$\mu = 70 \text{ points}$$
$$\bar{X} = 65 \text{ points}$$

where $\mu = 70$ points is actually unknown but given for purposes of illustration.

The error of the estimator is

$$e = \bar{X} - \mu = 65 - 70 = -5 \text{ points}$$

and is shown diagrammatically in Fig. 10.3 which is a sampling distribu-

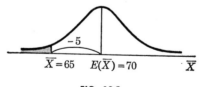

$$\bar{X} = 65 \qquad E(\bar{X}) = 70 \qquad \bar{X}$$

FIG. 10.3.

tion of $\bar{X}$. We know from the central limit theorem that

$$E(\bar{X}) = \mu = 70 \text{ points}$$

$$\sigma_{\bar{x}} = \frac{\sigma}{\sqrt{n}} = \frac{18}{\sqrt{36}} = 3 \text{ points}$$

Since the sampling distribution is normal, the area of the shaded area is found as follows:

$$z = \frac{\bar{X} - \mu}{\sigma_{\bar{x}}} = \frac{65 - 70}{3} = -1.66$$

Thus the shaded area is approximately 0.0485 or 4.85 percent. This means that there are about 4.85 chances in 100 that the sample mean will be 5 points or more *below* the population mean. Similarly, we can say that there are about 4.85 chances in 100 that the sample mean will be 5 points or more *above* the population mean.

We can now combine the two statements and say: There are about $4.85 + 4.85 = 9.7$ chances in 100 that the *error* will be equal to or greater than 5 points when a random sample of size $n = 36$ is selected.

Note carefully how we calculate the probability (risk) of a certain error occurring when the magnitude of the error ($e = 5$ points), the standard deviation ($\sigma = 18$ points), and the sample size ($n = 36$) have been specified.

Example 1. Given $n = 36$ and $\sigma = 18$ points, find the risk (probability) of having an error of $e = 3$ points or more.

$$z = \frac{\bar{X} - \mu}{\sigma_{\bar{x}}} = \frac{e}{\sigma_{\bar{x}}} = \frac{3}{3} = 1$$

where

$$\sigma_{\bar{x}} = \frac{\sigma}{\sqrt{n}} = \frac{18}{\sqrt{36}} = 3$$

Since $z = 1$, we find the probability (risk) to be

$$0.1587 + 0.1587 = 0.3174$$

This is shown in Fig. 10.4.

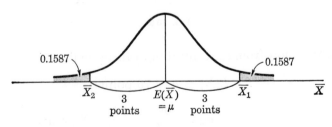

FIG. 10.4.

Example 2.   Sugar is packaged into boxes and each box is to have μ grams of sugar. The standard deviation is $\sigma = 4$ grams. A sample of size $n = 16$ is taken. What is the probability (risk) that the error will be more than 2 grams?

$$z = \frac{\bar{X} - \mu}{\sigma_{\bar{x}}} = \frac{e}{\sigma_{\bar{x}}} = \frac{2}{1} = 2$$

$$\sigma_{\bar{x}} = \frac{\sigma}{\sqrt{n}} = \frac{4}{\sqrt{16}} = 1$$

From the normal table we find, for $z = 2$,

$$0.0228 + 0.0228 = 0.0456$$

Thus the risk is about 4.56 chances in 100 of having an error of $e = 2$ grams or greater when a sample of size $n = 16$ is selected. This is shown diagrammatically in Fig. 10.5.

Note that μ and $\bar{X}$ have not been specified; only $e = \bar{X} - \mu = 2$ grams is given.

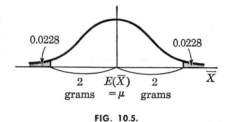

FIG. 10.5.

(ii)   *The relationship between the risk and the sample size*

In our preceding illustration, the sample size was $n = 36$, the error was $e = 5$ points, and the risk of making an error of $e = 5$ points or more was 9.7/100. What will happen to the risk if n becomes larger? It should be intuitively clear that the risk will become smaller. For example, if there is a total of 2000 students and a sample of $n = 36$ is taken to estimate the average grade point, there is a good chance of deviating as much as 5 points from μ. But, if $n = 1999$ students is taken, the chance of there being an error of 5 points or more is highly improbable; that is, the risk of there being such an error is very small. We state that, given a certain error, as the sample size increases, the risk of having such an error decreases. Let us now show how the change in the risk is calculated.

Again using our previous illustration, we have

$$n = 36, \quad e = 5 \text{ points}, \quad \sigma = 18 \text{ points}$$

$$\sigma_{\bar{x}} = \frac{\sigma}{\sqrt{n}} = \frac{18}{\sqrt{36}} = 3 \text{ points}$$

Let us increase the sample size to $n = 81$. Then the standard error becomes

$$\sigma_{\bar{x}} = \frac{\sigma}{\sqrt{n}} = \frac{18}{\sqrt{81}} = 2 \text{ points}$$

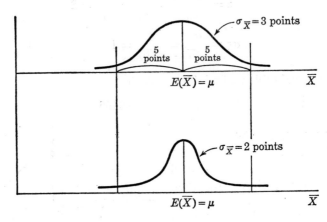

FIG. 10.6.

The sampling distribution for $n = 36$ is given in the upper part of Fig. 10.6, and for $n = 81$, it is given in the lower part. The risk of having an error of $e = 5$ points or more for $n = 81$ is found as follows:

$$z = \frac{\bar{X} - \mu}{\sigma_{\bar{x}}} = \frac{e}{\sigma_{\bar{x}}} = \frac{5}{2} = 2.5$$

and the proportion corresponding to $z = 2.5$ is 0.0062; that is, 0.62/100. Thus the risk is

$$\frac{0.62}{100} + \frac{0.62}{100} = \frac{1.24}{100}$$

As the sample size increases from $n = 36$ to 81, the risk decreases from 9.7/100 to 1.24/100.

Example 3. When $n = 36$, $\sigma = 18$, and $e = 3$ points, the risk was 0.3174. Let n become $n = 81$. Then the risk is found as follows:

$$z = \frac{e}{\sigma_{\bar{x}}} = \frac{3}{2} = 1.5$$

$$\sigma_{\bar{x}} = \frac{\sigma}{\sqrt{n}} = \frac{18}{\sqrt{81}} = 2$$

From the normal area table, the proportion is 0.0668. Thus, the risk is

$$0.0668 + 0.0668 = 0.1336$$

or 13.36/100. As the sample size increased from $n = 36$ to $n = 81$, the risk decreased from 31.74/100 to 3.36/100.

Example 4. In the sugar example, we had $n = 16$, $\sigma = 4$ grams, and $e = 2$ grams. Let $n = 64$. Then the risk is

$$z = \frac{e}{\sigma_{\bar{x}}} = \frac{2}{0.5} = 4$$

$$\sigma_{\bar{x}} = \frac{\sigma}{\sqrt{n}} = \frac{4}{\sqrt{64}} = 0.5$$

and the proportion is 0.00 (the proportion for $z = 4$ is not given in the normal area table in the Appendix); that is, the risk is zero. As the sample size increases from $n = 16$ to $n = 64$, the risk decreases from 4.56/100 to zero.

(iii) **The relationship between the error and the sample size**

The problem is to see in what way the change of the sample size will keep the error within certain limits at a certain risk. Assume that we wish to find the sample size that will keep the error within 3 points, with a risk of, say, 0.0456. The situation is shown in Fig. 10.7.

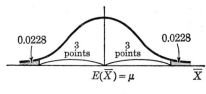

FIG. 10.7.

Since the risk is set at 0.0456, the proportion in each tail is

$$\frac{0.0456}{2} = 0.0228$$

We see from the normal area table that the z which corresponds to 0.0228 is $z = 2.0$. Thus we have, recalling that $\sigma = 18$ points,

$$z = \frac{e}{\sigma_{\bar{x}}} = \frac{3}{\frac{18}{\sqrt{n}}} = 2$$

Thus: $$\sqrt{n} = 12 \quad \text{or} \quad n = 144$$

This means that, to keep the probability (risk) of having an error of 3 points or more at 0.0456 (and the probability of having an error of less than 3 points at $1 - 0.0456 = 0.9544$), we need a sample of size $n = 144$.

We can generalize this result as follows: We have

$$z = \frac{e}{\frac{\sigma}{\sqrt{n}}}$$

$$\sqrt{n} = \frac{z\sigma}{e}$$

Therefore

(1)
$$n = \frac{z^2\sigma^2}{e^2}$$

In our present example, $z = 2$, $\sigma = 18$, and $e = 3$. Thus

$$n = \frac{(2)^2(18)^2}{(3)^2}$$

$$= 144$$

How large must the sample be to keep the probability of the error's being equal to or larger than $e = 1.5$ at 0.0456? For 0.0456 ($=2 \times$ 0.0228), the $z = 2$, and

$$n = \frac{z^2\sigma^2}{e^2}$$

$$= \frac{(2)^2(18)^2}{(1.5)^2} = 576$$

Example 5.   In the sugar example, $\sigma = 4$ grams. How large must the sample be if the probability (risk) of the error's being 1 gram or greater is 0.0456? For 0.0456, the $z = 2.0$:

$$n = \frac{z^2\sigma^2}{e^2}$$

$$= \frac{(2)^2\,(4)^2}{1} = 64$$

Note in Example 5 that the error was reduced from $e = 2$ grams to $e = 1$ gram, and the sample size has increased from $n = 16$ to $n = 64$.

That is, when the error was reduced to ½, the sample size increased four times. In general, to reduce the error to $1/k$th its size, the sample needs to be increased k^2 times. That is,

$$n = \frac{z^2\sigma^2}{\left(\dfrac{e}{k}\right)^2} = k^2 \frac{z^2\sigma^2}{e^2}$$

(iv)   The relationship between the error, risk, and sample size for proportions

Let us now show the relation between the error, risk, and the sample size for proportions. We know that the standard error of p is

$$\sigma_p = \sqrt{\frac{\pi(1-\pi)}{n}}$$

and it is necessary to know π or an estimate of it so that we can find σ_p. However, let us consider the following problem and show how a sample size may be found even though π is unknown. We wish to find the sample size that will keep the error within 3 percent with a risk of, say, 0.0456. The situation is shown in Fig. 10.8.

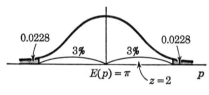

0.0228   0.0228

3%   3%

$E(p) = \pi$

$z = 2$ p

FIG. 10.8.

Since the risk is set at 0.0456, the proportion in each tail is 0.0228, and from the normal area table, the z is found to be $z = 2.0$. Thus, using the relation

$$z = \frac{e}{\sqrt{\dfrac{\pi(1-\pi)}{n}}}$$

we have, solving for n,

$$n = \frac{z^2\pi(1-\pi)}{e^2}$$

$$= \frac{(2)^2\pi(1-\pi)}{(0.03)^2}$$

We do not know the value of π. However, if we can find the value of π that will maximize $\pi(1 - \pi)$, and use it to calculate n, we can be sure that the sample size n will be large enough to satisfy the requirement that the error be within 3 percent.

To find the value of π that will maximize $\pi(1 - \pi)$, let us perform the following algebraic trick:

$$\pi(1 - \pi) = \pi - \pi^2$$

$$= \frac{1}{4} - \left(\frac{1}{4} - \pi + \pi^2\right)$$

$$= \frac{1}{4} - \left(\frac{1}{2} - \pi\right)^2$$

This shows that $\pi(1 - \pi)$ will be maximum when $\pi = \frac{1}{2}$ and the maximum value is $1/4$. Hence, the n we seek is

$$n = \frac{(2)^2 \left(\frac{1}{4}\right)}{(0.03)^2}$$

$$= \frac{1.00}{0.0009}$$

$$\doteq 1111$$

That is, when we use a sample of size $n = 1111$, the error will be less than 3 percent.

The formula may be generalized by substituting $\pi(1 - \pi) = 1/4$ in the formula for n, as follows:

(1)
$$n = \frac{(z)^2 \left(\frac{1}{4}\right)}{e^2}$$

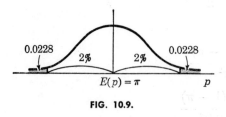

0.0228   2%   2%   0.0228

$E(p) = \pi$ p

FIG. 10.9.

Example 6. A company selling toothpaste ABC wishes to estimate the proportion of people who prefer their brand ABC. It wishes to keep the error within 2 percent, with a risk of 0.0456. How large a sample must be taken?

Since, as Fig. 10.9 shows, the $z = 2$, we find from equation (1):

$$n = \frac{(2)^2 \left(\dfrac{1}{4}\right)}{(0.02)^2}$$

$$= 1250$$

That is, if a random sample of size $n = 1250$ is taken, the error will be less than 2 percent with a risk of 0.0456.

To find an estimate of π, take a random sample of $n = 1250$. Then the maximum likelihood estimator of π is

$$\hat{\pi} = p = \frac{\Sigma x}{n}$$

where Σx is the number of people who prefer brand ABC. The $n = 1250$ in the present case. If $\Sigma x = 250$, the ML estimate of π is

$$\hat{\pi} = \frac{250}{1250} = \frac{1}{5} = 20\%$$

10.8.   Interval Estimation

(i)   Confidence interval

So far we have been concerned with estimating a parameter (say, the population mean μ) with a single value, $\bar{X} = 10$, and this is called estimation by a point or, simply, point estimation. We now wish to estimate a parameter μ by an interval:

$$a < \mu < b$$

where a and b are obtained from the sample observations. Estimating a parameter by an interval is called *interval estimation,* and it is widely used. For example, one may hear statements such as: The average grade of the students is between 70 and 74 points; or, the proportion of defective items in a shipment is between 3 and 5 percent; or, the median wage of secretaries is between $65 and $70, and so forth.

In this section we shall explain the concept of a *confidence interval,* which was proposed by Professor J. Neyman.* This approach allows the statistician to associate a probability statement with the interval. Let us

---

* Neyman, J., *Outline of a Theory of Statistical Estimation Based on the Classical Theory of Probability,* Philosophical Transactions of the Royal Society, Series A, Vol. 236, 1937.

start our discussion by using a simple illustration. Suppose we have a random sample:

$$x_1 = 1, \quad x_2 = 3, \quad x_3 = 5, \quad x_4 = 7$$

with a mean μ (unknown) and standard deviation σ. We wish to estimate μ, using this sample of four values. We know from the central limit theorem that

$$z = \frac{\bar{X} - \mu}{\sigma_{\bar{x}}}$$

is asymptotically normal with mean 0 and variance unity. From the normal area table we know that when $z = 1.96$, it corresponds to a probability of 0.95. Thus we may write

$$P\left(-1.96 < \frac{\bar{X} - \mu}{\sigma_{\bar{x}}} < 1.96\right) = 0.95$$

and this is a legitimate probability statement because z is a random variable. Let us now rewrite this equation as

$$P\left(\bar{X} - 1.96 \frac{\sigma}{\sqrt{n}} < \mu < \bar{X} + 1.96 \frac{\sigma}{\sqrt{n}}\right) = 0.95$$

Letting

$$\bar{X} - 1.96 \frac{\sigma}{\sqrt{n}} = a$$

$$\bar{X} + 1.96 \frac{\sigma}{\sqrt{n}} = b$$

we have

$$P(a < \mu < b) = 0.95$$

and this may be interpreted as follows:

From the central limit theorem we know that $\bar{X}$ is asymptotically normal, with mean μ and variance σ^2/n. This is shown diagrammatically in Fig. 10.10. The random variable $\bar{X}$ takes on various values. Let us express them by $\bar{X}_1, \bar{X}_2, \ldots$. Now, for example, let $\bar{X}_1$ take on the value as indicated in Fig. 10.10. Then the interval will be

$$\bar{X}_1 - 1.96 \frac{\sigma}{\sqrt{n}} \quad \text{to} \quad \bar{X}_1 + 1.96 \frac{\sigma}{\sqrt{n}}$$

As the graph shows, this will include μ. Similarly, for another value $\bar{X}_2$, we have

$$\bar{X}_2 - 1.96\,\frac{\sigma}{\sqrt{n}} \quad \text{to} \quad \bar{X}_2 + 1.96\,\frac{\sigma}{\sqrt{n}}$$

which also includes μ. But $\bar{X}_3$, as shown in our graph, gives us the interval

$$\bar{X}_3 - 1.96\,\frac{\sigma}{\sqrt{n}} \quad \text{to} \quad \bar{X}_3 + 1.96\,\frac{\sigma}{\sqrt{n}}$$

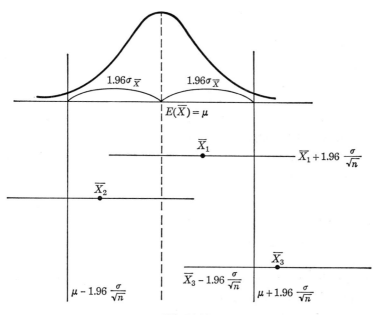

FIG. 10.10.

which does not include μ. As we can see graphically, the $\bar{X}_3$ falls outside the two limiting values of $\mu \pm 1.96\,\sigma_{\bar{x}}$.

The probability that $\bar{X}$ will be in the interval $\mu \pm 1.96\,\sigma_{\bar{x}}$ is 0.95; that is, there are 95 chances out of 100 that the $\bar{X}$ will be between $\mu - 1.96\,\sigma_{\bar{x}}$ and $\mu + 1.96\,\sigma_{\bar{x}}$, given that the μ is in fact the true value of the parameter.

Thus we can see from Fig. 10.10 that when we construct our interval

$$\bar{X} - 1.96\,\frac{\sigma}{\sqrt{n}} \quad \text{to} \quad \bar{X} + 1.96\,\frac{\sigma}{\sqrt{n}}$$

we can expect that 95 out of 100 such intervals will include μ. Thus

$$P\left(\bar{X} - 1.96\,\frac{\sigma}{\sqrt{n}} < \mu < \bar{X} + 1.96\,\frac{\sigma}{\sqrt{n}}\right) = 0.95$$

But once we select a sample and compute $\bar{X}$,

$$\bar{X} = \frac{1}{4}\,(1 + 3 + 5 + 7) = 4$$

then $\bar{X}$ is a fixed constant and is no longer a random variable. Then we have

$$P\left(4 - 1.96\,\frac{\sigma}{\sqrt{n}} < \mu < 4 + 1.96\,\frac{\sigma}{\sqrt{n}}\right) = 0.95$$

But

$$4 - 1.96\,\frac{\sigma}{\sqrt{n}} \quad \text{to} \quad 4 + 1.96\,\frac{\sigma}{\sqrt{n}}$$

is a fixed interval, so that μ is either in the interval or on its outside. Thus the probability is either 1 or 0.

Let us denote k_1 and k_2 $(k_1 < k_2)$ as the two limits obtained from a specific sample. Then

$$P(k_1 < \mu < k_2) = 0.95$$

is not a legitimate probability. J. Neyman has called the interval (k_1, k_2) a *confidence interval,* and 0.95 is called a *confidence coefficient* to distinguish it from a legitimate probability. Nevertheless, with the above explanation in mind, the 0.95 confidence interval is a meaningful measure of the reliability we place on our interval.

In general, we may write the confidence interval as

$$\bar{X} - z \cdot \sigma_{\bar{x}} < \mu < \bar{X} + z \cdot \sigma_{\bar{x}}$$

and

$$P(\bar{X} - z \cdot \sigma_{\bar{x}} < \mu < \bar{X} + z \cdot \sigma_{\bar{x}}) = \alpha$$

where $\bar{X}$ is the sample mean, α is the confidence coefficient, z is the deviation corresponding to α obtained from the normal area table, and $\sigma_{\bar{x}}$ is the standard error.

Example 1.   A restaurant wishes to estimate the average amount of money a customer spends for lunch. A random sample of size $n = 36$ is selected and the sample mean is found to be $\bar{X} = \$1.20$. Assuming $\sigma = 24\cancel{c}$ and a confidence coefficient of $a = 95$ percent, the z is obtained from the normal area table as $z = 1.96$. Hence, the confidence interval is

$$\$1.20 - (1.96)\left(\frac{0.24}{\sqrt{36}}\right) < \mu < 1.20 + (1.96)\left(\frac{0.24}{\sqrt{36}}\right)$$

$$\$1.12 < \mu < 1.28$$

The interpretation is: If 100 confidence intervals are constructed in the above manner, we expect 95 of them to contain the true parameter μ. The confidence interval that we have constructed may be considered as one of these 100 confidence intervals.

Example 2.   A school wishes to estimate the average weight of students in the sixth grade. A random sample of $n = 25$ is selected, and the sample mean is found to be $\bar{X} = 100$ lb. The standard deviation of the population is known to be 15 lb. Assuming a confidence coefficient of $a = 90$ percent, the z is $z = 1.64$. Hence, the confidence interval is

$$100 - (1.64)\left(\frac{15}{\sqrt{25}}\right) < \mu < 100 + (1.64)\left(\frac{15}{\sqrt{25}}\right)$$

$$95 < \mu < 105$$

We have assumed in our discussion that the σ is known. When σ is unknown, we may use an estimate of σ and find the confidence interval. This is discussed in Chapter 17.

(ii)   Finding the sample size for a confidence interval

Suppose in Example 2 that the school wishes to have a confidence interval of less than 3 lb. with a confidence coefficient $\alpha = 0.95$. How large must the sample size be?

Let us first draw Fig. 10.11 as a visual aid, in which, since we want

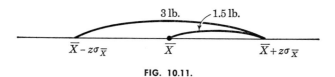

FIG. 10.11.

the interval to be less than 3 lb., we have

$$z\,\sigma_{\bar{x}} < 1.5 \text{ lb.}$$

Let us rewrite this as

$$z \cdot \frac{\sigma}{\sqrt{n}} = 1.5$$

and solve for n, which becomes

$$n = \frac{z^2\sigma^2}{1.5^2}$$

Since the confidence coefficient $\alpha = 0.95$, we have $z = 1.96$ from the normal area table; and σ was given as $\sigma = 15$ lb. Then

$$n = \frac{(1.96)^2(15)^2}{1.5^2}$$

$$= 384.16$$

Thus a sample size of approximately 384 will give us a confidence in-interval of less than 3 lb. with a confidence coefficient $\alpha = 0.95$.

In general, the sample size may be shown as

$$n = \frac{z^2\sigma^2}{e^2}$$

where e is the half-width of the interval.

We see that this is the same formula as that used in Section 10.7 to show the relation between error, risk, and sample size.

The point to note is that, when the sample mean $\bar{X}$ is given a specific value, we obtain a confidence interval and the risk (prob-ability) becomes a confidence coefficient. When we are considering only the error and are not specifying the sample mean, the risk remains a probability.

The confidence interval for proportions is discussed in Chapter 18.

INDEX NUMBERS

11

In the subsequent three chapters, index numbers and time series are discussed. By an index number we mean a ratio of two numbers. For example, an IQ quotient is the ratio of the mental age to the chronological age. However, our main concern in this chapter is indices that are used in business and economics. Some examples are the wholesale price index, cost of living index, industrial production index, business cycle index, and productivity index. The object of these indices is to *measure the changes* that have occurred in prices, production, cost of living, etc. With the help of these indices, businessmen and economists are able to describe and analyze business and economic situations quantitatively.

We shall first develop a price index and then give a brief discussion of some of the other indices.

11.1. Weighted Relative Price Index

In this section we shall first develop a simple aggregative price index based on a market basket concept. Then we shall show how its defects are corrected by a simple relative price index and finally show how weights are attached to the simple relative price index to obtain a weighted average of price relatives.

(i) Simple aggregative price index

Assume the price of bread has risen over three years as follows: 1958,

$p_0 = 10\cancel{c}$; 1959, $p_1 = 15\cancel{c}$; 1960, $p_2 = 20\cancel{c}$. To show the change in prices, we find the ratio of prices as follows:

$$1958: \quad \frac{p_0}{p_0} = \frac{10\cancel{c}}{10\cancel{c}} = 1.00 = I_0$$

$$1959: \quad \frac{p_1}{p_0} = \frac{15\cancel{c}}{10\cancel{c}} = 1.50 = I_1$$

$$1960: \quad \frac{p_2}{p_0} = \frac{20\cancel{c}}{10\cancel{c}} = 2.00 = I_2$$

$I_1 = 1.50$ shows that there has been a 50 percent increase in prices from 1958 to 1959. $I_2 = 2.00$ shows that there has been a 100 percent increase from 1958 to 1960. $I_0 = 1.00$ indicates the year from which the changes are measured and is called the *base year*.

Price indices are usually expressed on a 100 basis. Hence, in our present example, I_0, I_1, and I_2 become

$$I_0: \quad 100$$
$$I_1: \quad 150$$
$$I_2: \quad 200$$

We express this as: the price index for 1959 is 150. This means that there has been a 50 percent increase in prices from 1958 to 1959.

Note the following points:
1. The base year is indicated by the subscript 0 (zero), and the subsequent years by the numbers 1, 2, etc.
2. The p's are used to indicate the individual prices and the capital letter I's are used to denote the price indices.
3. The ratio of individual prices, such as p_1/p_0, is called a *price relative*.
4. The base year index is set at 100.

The above illustration of a price index used only one commodity, but usually we are interested in price indices for a group of commodities. For example, assume that the following *basket of commodities* is bought: a loaf of bread, a quart of milk, a dozen eggs, and a pound of beef. Let us also assume that this same amount of goods is bought in 1959 and 1960, and let their prices be as shown in the accompanying table.

The table shows that the same basket of goods cost $1.20 in 1958, $1.50 in 1959, and $1.80 in 1960. Since we are interested in finding a price index for a group of commodities, this may be accomplished

Commodity	Quantity	1958 p_0	1959 p_1	1960 p_2
Bread	Loaf	10¢	15¢	20¢
Milk	Quart	20	25	30
Eggs	Dozen	50	60	70
Beef	Pound	40	50	60
		120¢	150¢	180¢

by comparing the price of this basket of goods for the various years. Therefore, let us find the price relatives for this basket of goods. Using 1958 as the base year, we find,

$$1958: \qquad \frac{120¢}{120¢} = 1.00 \quad \text{or} \quad 100$$

$$1959: \qquad \frac{150¢}{120¢} = 1.25 \quad \text{or} \quad 125$$

$$1960: \qquad \frac{180¢}{120¢} = 1.50 \quad \text{or} \quad 150$$

There has been a 25 percent increase in the price of the basket of goods from 1958 to 1959, and a 50 percent increase from 1958 to 1960.

The price index we have obtained may be shown in symbols as follows: For 1959, it is

$$\frac{150}{120} = \frac{15 + 25 + 60 + 50}{10 + 20 + 50 + 40}$$

$$= \frac{p_{11} + p_{12} + p_{13} + p_{14}}{p_{01} + p_{02} + p_{03} + p_{04}}$$

where p_{01} shows the price of commodity 1 (bread) for the base year 0, p_{02} shows the price of commodity 2 (milk) for the base year 0, and so forth; p_{11} shows the price of commodity 1 (bread) for year 1 (which is 1959), p_{12} shows the price of commodity 2 (milk) for year 1 (1959), and so forth.

Using the summation symbol, we have, for 1959,

$$I_{59} = \frac{\sum\limits_{i=1}^{4} p_{1i}}{\sum\limits_{i=1}^{4} p_{0i}} = \frac{150}{120} = 1.25$$

This I_{59} is called the *simple price index* for 1959. In similar fashion, we find

$$I_0 = I_{58} = \frac{\Sigma \, p_{oi}}{\Sigma \, p_{oi}} = \frac{120}{120} = 1.00 \quad \text{or} \quad 100$$

$$I_1 = I_{59} = \frac{\Sigma \, p_{1i}}{\Sigma \, p_{oi}} = \frac{150}{120} = 1.25 \quad \text{or} \quad 125$$

$$I_2 = I_{60} = \frac{\Sigma \, p_{2i}}{\Sigma \, p_{oi}} = \frac{180}{120} = 1.50 \quad \text{or} \quad 150$$

In general, the simple price index for a year k is

(1)
$$I_k = \frac{\sum\limits_{i=1}^{n} p_{ki}}{\sum\limits_{i=1}^{n} p_{oi}}$$

(ii) Simple average of relatives

Two of the main defects of the simple aggregative index are:
1.   That the units of prices of the commodities will affect the price index.
2.   That no consideration is given to the relative importance of the commodities.

For example, if our basket had included a pair of shoes that cost $20 in 1958, $25 in 1959, and $30 in 1960, the price indices would have been as follows:

$$I_{58} = \frac{\$1.20 + 20}{\$1.20 + 20} = \frac{21.20}{21.20} = 1.00$$

$$I_{59} = \frac{\$1.50 + 25}{\$21.20} = \frac{26.50}{21.20} = 1.25$$

$$I_{60} = \frac{\$1.80 + 30}{\$21.20} = \frac{31.80}{21.20} = 1.50$$

Hence, the price of the shoes would have dominated the index, which is not desirable. How can we eliminate such influences due to different units?

This is achieved by constructing an index that is the average of the price relatives. First let us construct a table of the price relatives.

Commodity	p_0/p_0	p_1/p_0 (1959)	p_2/p_0 (1960)
Bread	100%	15/10 = 150%	20/10 = 200%
Milk	100	25/20 = 125	30/20 = 150
Eggs	100	60/50 = 120	70/50 = 140
Beef	100	50/40 = 125	60/40 = 150
Shoes	100	25/20 = 125	30/20 = 150
	500%	645%	790%

The average of price relatives for 1959 is

$$I_{59} = \frac{\dfrac{15}{10} + \dfrac{25}{20} + \dfrac{60}{50} + \dfrac{50}{40} + \dfrac{25}{20}}{5}$$

$$= \frac{645}{5} = 129$$

This price index, which is shown symbolically by

(2)
$$I_k = \frac{\sum_{i=1}^{n} \left(\dfrac{p_{ki}}{p_{0i}}\right)}{n}$$

is called the *simple relative price index*. For our present case, the results are

$$I_{58} = \frac{\sum \left(\dfrac{p_0}{p_0}\right)}{n} = \frac{500}{5} = 100$$

$$I_{59} = \frac{\sum \left(\dfrac{p_1}{p_0}\right)}{n} = \frac{645}{5} = 129$$

$$I_{60} = \frac{\sum \left(\dfrac{p_2}{p_0}\right)}{n} = \frac{790}{5} = 158$$

What we have actually done is to weight each item by $1/p_0$. That is, we have weighted the prices of bread by $1/10\cancel{c}$, that of milk by $1/20\cancel{c}$, and so forth. The common sense of this is that we have changed the importance of each commodity so that each has equal importance. That is, bread is just as important as milk, and shoes are just as important as beef or milk. Thus the influence due to different units has been removed.

Nevertheless, it is obvious that all goods are not of equal importance. There is a difference in the importance of the commodities, and the extent of their influence on the price index is not the same. Thus the question arises: How are we going to take into consideration their relative importance? This leads to the problem of weights.

(iii) Weighted relative price indices

What kind of weight will give us the relative importance of the commodities? For our present purpose, we consider the amount bought in terms of dollars as the weight that shows the relative importance. Let us assume for illustrative purposes that the following amounts were purchased in the base year 1958:

$$
\begin{array}{ll}
\text{Bread:} & \$\ 200 \\
\text{Milk:} & 500 \\
\text{Eggs:} & 400 \\
\text{Beef:} & 800 \\
\text{Shoes:} & \underline{\quad 100} \\
& \$2000
\end{array}
$$

Thus, we shall say that the order of importance of the commodities is

$$200 : 500 : 400 : 800 : 100 = 2 : 5 : 4 : 8 : 1$$

The amount of bread bought in 1958 was $v_1 = \$200$. This can be shown as

$$v_1 = p_{01} \cdot q_{01} = \$200$$

where p_{01} is the price and q_{01} is the quantity of bread that was purchased in 1958. Let us now weight the 1959 price relative of bread by this weight v_1. We get

$$\left(\frac{p_{11}}{p_{01}}\right) v_1 = \left(\frac{p_{11}}{p_{01}}\right) \cdot p_{01} \times q_{01} = p_{11} \cdot q_{01}$$

We find that $p_{11}q_{01}$ means: p_{11} is the price of bread in 1959; q_{01} is the amount of bread purchased in 1958. Thus $p_{11}q_{01}$ shows how much we need to spend in 1959 to buy the same amount of bread.

Therefore, by multiplying the 1959 price relatives by their corrresponding weights, we obtain the amount of expenditures necessary in 1959 to buy the same quantity of goods as we did in 1958. The results for 1958, 1959, and 1960 are shown in the accompanying table.

Commodity	Weights	1958 $(p_0/p_0)v$	1959 $(p_1/p_0)v$	1960 $(p_2/p_0)v$
Bread	$v_1 = \$\ 200$	$\$\ 200$	$15/10 \times 200 = \$\ 300$	$20/10 \times 200 = \$\ 400$
Milk	$v_2 =\ \ 500$	500	$25/20 \times 500 =\ \ 625$	$30/20 \times 500 =\ \ 750$
Eggs	$v_3 =\ \ 400$	400	480	560
Beef	$v_4 =\ \ 800$	800	1000	1200
Shoes	$v_5 =\ \ 100$	100	125	150
	$\$2000$	$\$2000$	$\$2530$	$\$3060$

The total of the 1958 column, which is $2000, shows the total amount of expenditures for a given amount of goods. The total of the 1959 column, which is $2530, shows the amount of expenditures necessary to buy the same amount of goods in 1959. Thus the ratio

$$\frac{\$2530}{\$2000} = 1.265 \quad \text{or} \quad 126.5$$

is an index that shows the change in the prices of this group of commodities. The added feature of this index is that the relative importance of the commodities has been considered.

Let us now use symbols to express what we have done. The ratio is shown as

$$\frac{\left(\dfrac{p_{11}}{p_{01}}\right)v_1 + \left(\dfrac{p_{12}}{p_{02}}\right)v_2 + \left(\dfrac{p_{13}}{p_{03}}\right)v_3 + \left(\dfrac{p_{14}}{p_{04}}\right)v_4 + \left(\dfrac{p_{15}}{p_{05}}\right)v_5}{v_1 + v_2 + v_3 + v_4 + v_5}$$

$$= \frac{300 + 625 + 480 + 1000 + 125}{200 + 500 + 400 + 800 + 100}$$

$$= \frac{2530}{2000} = 1.265 \quad \text{or} \quad 126.5$$

If we use the summation sign, this becomes

$$(3) \qquad I_1 = \frac{\displaystyle\sum_{i=1}^{5}\left(\dfrac{p_{1i}}{p_{0i}}\right)v_i}{\Sigma\, v_i}$$

This price index is called the *weighted relative price index*. The price indices for the three years are as follows:

$$I_{58} = I_0 = \frac{\Sigma \left(\dfrac{p_{0i}}{p_{0i}}\right) v_i}{\Sigma v_i} = \frac{2000}{2000}$$

$$= 1.00 \quad \text{or} \quad 100$$

$$I_{59} = I_1 = \frac{\Sigma \left(\dfrac{p_{1i}}{p_{0i}}\right) v_i}{\Sigma v_i} = \frac{2530}{2000}$$

$$= 1.265 \quad \text{or} \quad 126.5$$

$$I_{60} = I_2 = \frac{\Sigma \left(\dfrac{p_{2i}}{p_{0i}}\right) v_i}{\Sigma v_i} = \frac{3060}{2000}$$

$$= 1.53 \quad \text{or} \quad 153$$

The interpretation is as follows: The prices of 1959 have increased 26.5 percent over the 1958 price level. The prices of 1960 have increased 53 percent over the 1958 price level.

Example 1. Given the data in the accompanying table, find the weighted relative price index for 1960.

Commodity	1958 q_0	1958 p_0	$v = p_0 q_0$	1960 p_1	p_1/p_0	$(p_1/p_0)v$
Sugar	40 lb.	10¢	$ 4.00	15¢	15/10	$ 6.00
Flour	80 lb.	15¢	12.00	20¢	20/15	16.00
Milk	20 qt.	20¢	4.00	25¢	25/20	5.00
			$20.00			$27.00

From these data, we find:

$$I_{60} = \frac{\Sigma \left(\dfrac{p_1}{p_0}\right) v}{\Sigma v} = \frac{27.00}{20.00} = 1.35 \quad \text{or} \quad 135$$

The weighted relative price index for 1960 is 135. This means there has been a 35 percent increase in prices over the 1958 level.

11.2. Weighted Aggregative Price Index

(i) Laspeyres formula, base year weights

The weighted relative price index given in equation (3) of Section 11.1 may be rewritten as follows:

$$I_1 = \frac{\sum\limits_{i=1}^{5} \left(\dfrac{p_{1i}}{p_{0i}}\right) v_i}{\sum v_i}$$

$$= \frac{\left(\dfrac{p_{11}}{p_{01}}\right)(p_{01} \cdot q_{01}) + \cdots + \left(\dfrac{p_{15}}{p_{05}}\right)(p_{05} \cdot q_{05})}{p_{01} \cdot q_{01} + \cdots + p_{05}q_{05}}$$

$$= \frac{p_{11} \cdot q_{01} + p_{12} \cdot q_{02} + \cdots + p_{15} \cdot q_{05}}{p_{01} \cdot q_{01} + \cdots + p_{05}q_{05}}$$

$$= \frac{\sum\limits_{i=1}^{5} p_{1i}q_{0i}}{\sum p_{0i}q_{0i}}$$

If we abbreviate the subscript i, the result may be written in general form for the year n, as

(1)
$$I_n = \frac{\sum p_n q_0}{\sum p_0 q_0}$$

This is called the *weighted aggregative price index,* and as can be seen, p_0 and p_n are the base and given year prices. The q_0 is the base year quantity. Hence we may interpret formula (1) as follows: Given the simple aggregative price index

$$\frac{\sum p_n}{\sum p_0}$$

apply the base year quantities q_0 as weights and construct a weighted aggregative price index

$$\frac{\sum p_n q_0}{\sum p_0 q_0}$$

which is formula (1).

Our derivations show that the weighted aggregative price index (1) is the same as the weighted relative price index (3) of Section 11.1. The interpretation of (1) is also the same as (3). The denominator $\Sigma\, p_0 q_0$ shows the amount of expenditures necessary to buy a certain amount of goods in the base year. The numerator $\Sigma\, p_n q_0$ shows the amount of expenditures necessary to buy the same amount of goods in year n.

Formula (1) is sometimes called the Laspeyres formula.

Example 1.   Using the data of the preceding example in Section 11.1, find the weighted aggregative price index for 1960, with base year weights as shown in the table here.

Commodity	1958 q_0	1958 p_0	1960 p_1	$p_0 q_0$	$p_1 q_0$
Sugar	40 lb.	10¢	15¢	$ 4.00	$ 6.00
Flour	80 lb.	15¢	20¢	12.00	16.00
Milk	20 qt.	20¢	25¢	4.00	5.00
				$20.00	$27.00

We find that

$$I_{60} = \frac{\Sigma\, p_n q_0}{\Sigma\, p_0 q_0} = \frac{27.00}{20.00} = 1.35 \quad \text{or} \quad 135$$

The weighted aggregative price index for 1960 is 135. This means that there has been a 35 percent increase in prices over the 1958 level, and the results are the same as the weighted relative price index.

(ii)   Paasche formula, current year weights

The difference between the Laspeyres formula and Paasche formula is that the Paasche formula uses current year quantities q_n instead of base year quantities q_0. Thus formula (1) becomes

(2) $$I_n = \frac{\Sigma\, p_n q_n}{\Sigma\, p_0 q_n}$$

The numerator $\Sigma\, p_n q_n$ shows the amount of expenditures in the current year n for a given amount of commodities bought in the current year n. The denominator $\Sigma\, p_0 q_n$ shows the amount of expenditures necessary in the base year to buy the same amount of goods.

Note carefully that a new set of quantities q_n has to be found for each current year that is to be compared with the base year.

Example 2. Let us apply the Paasche formula to the data of Example 1.

Commodity	1958 q_0	1960 q_n	p_0	p_n	$p_0 q_n$	$p_n q_n$
Sugar	40 lb.	60 lb.	10¢	15¢	$ 6.00	$ 9.00
Flour	80 lb.	100 lb.	15¢	20¢	15.00	20.00
Milk	20 qt.	40 qt.	20¢	25¢	8.00	10.00
					$29.00	$39.00

We find:

$$I_{60} = \frac{\Sigma p_n q_n}{\Sigma p_0 q_n} = \frac{39.00}{29.00} = 1.345 \quad \text{or} \quad 134.5$$

The Laspeyres formula is also called the weighted aggregative formula using base year weights. The Paasche formula is also called the weighted aggregative formula using current year weights. We shall use these terms interchangeably.

As we mentioned before, the Paasche formula requires that new weights q_n be found for each current year. From a practical standpoint, this is a very difficult and laborious task. Furthermore, the price index of a given year can be compared only with the base year. For example, let $I_{58} = 100$, $I_{59} = 120$, and $I_{60} = 150$. Then I_{59} and I_{60} are using different weights and cannot be compared with each other. If these indices had been obtained by the Laspeyres formula, since the weights are the same base year weights (q_0), they could be compared. This is one of the reasons why the Paasche formula is usually not used.

11.3. Variations of the Weighted Price Indices

(i) Using the average quantity of several years as weights

One of the problems in the construction of indices is the selection of a *base period*. When selecting a base year or base period, it is necessary that it is not an irregular year. Or more positively, we wish to select a normal year. But what is a normal year? We generally mean a normal year in terms of economics and not in terms of psychological or political conditions of a country or region. What then is a normal economic year? This is a difficult question, and we shall simply say a normal year is one in which we have economic equilibrium. Unfortunately, this answer raises more questions than it answers, and we shall dodge this question by saying that a discussion of economic equilibrium is beyond the limits of this book. But, to develop our discussion, we shall simply state that it is a situation where the economy is not at the peak of a boom or the trough of a recession.

In many cases, there may not be a year that can be considered as normal, whereas an average of several years may be considered so. This then leads to the question: How can this idea of using the average of several years as a normal base be incorporated in the price index formulas?

The first variation to be presented will be the one that incorporates this idea by using the average of the quantities of (for example) 2 years as the weights in the Laspeyres formula. That is, instead of using q_0, we shall use

$$q' = \frac{q_0 + q_1}{2}$$

Then the price index becomes

(1)
$$I_n = \frac{\Sigma p_n \dfrac{q_0 + q_1}{2}}{\Sigma p_0 \dfrac{q_0 + q_1}{2}}$$

$$= \frac{\Sigma p_n q'}{\Sigma p_0 q'}$$

If the average is taken over 3 years, we have

(2)
$$I_n = \frac{\Sigma p_n \dfrac{q_0 + q_1 + q_2}{3}}{\Sigma p_0 \dfrac{q_0 + q_1 + q_2}{3}}$$

$$= \frac{\Sigma p_n q'}{\Sigma p_0 q'}$$

We use the data of Example 2 in Section 11.2 to illustrate.

Example 1. We use the data in the table here

Commodity	1958 q_0	1960 q_1	$q' = (q_0 + q_1)/2$	p_0	p_1	$p_0 q'$	$p_1 q'$
Sugar	40	60	50	10¢	15¢	$ 5.00	$ 7.50
Flour	80	100	90	15	20	13.50	18.00
Milk	20	40	30	20	25	6.00	7.50
						$24.50	$33.00

and find:

$$I_1 = \frac{\Sigma\, p_1 q'}{\Sigma\, p_0 q'} = \frac{33.00}{24.50} = 1.33 \quad \text{or} \quad 133$$

The prices of 1960 have increased by 33 percent over 1959.

(ii) Using the average price of several years as the base year price

Another method of adjusting the price index so as to have a normal base is to use the average price of several years as the base year price. For example, take the prices of 2 years p_0 and p_1 and find the average:

$$p' = \frac{p_0 + p_1}{2}$$

Then the price index becomes

(3)
$$I_n = \frac{\Sigma\, p_n q_0}{\Sigma\left(\dfrac{p_0 + p_1}{2}\right) q_0}$$

$$= \frac{\Sigma\, p_n q_0}{\Sigma\, p' q_0}$$

If the average of 3 years is used, we have

(4)
$$I_n = \frac{\Sigma\, p_n q_0}{\Sigma\left(\dfrac{p_0 + p_1 + p_2}{3}\right) q_0}$$

$$= \frac{\Sigma\, p_n q_0}{\Sigma\, p' q_0}$$

Example 2. Using the accompanying data and equation (3), let us find the price index.

		1958	1959	$p' = \dfrac{p_0 + p_1}{2}$		1958	1959
Commodity	q_0	p_0	p_1		$p' q_0$	$p_0 q_0$	$p_1 q_0$
Sugar	40	10¢	14¢	12¢	$ 4.80	$ 4.00	$ 5.60
Flour	80	15	21	18	14.40	12.00	16.80
Milk	20	20	28	24	4.80	4.00	5.60
					$24.00	$20.00	$28.00

From these we find:

$$I_{59} = \frac{\Sigma p_0 q_0}{\Sigma p' q_0} = \frac{20.00}{24.00} = 0.833 \quad \text{or} \quad 83.3$$

$$I_{58} = \frac{\Sigma p_1 q_0}{\Sigma p' q_0} = \frac{28.00}{24.00} = 1.166 \quad \text{or} \quad 116.6$$

Note that the base in this case is 1958 to 1959, and the price index for the base period is shown by

$$I_{58\text{-}59} = \frac{\Sigma p' q_0}{\Sigma p' q_0} = \frac{24.00}{24.00} = 1.00 \quad \text{or} \quad 100$$

The price index for such calculations are (using base 1958–1959 = 100): 1958, 83; 1959, 117. This shows that the prices of 1958 are 83 percent of the base, 1958–1959 = 100, and 1959 is 117 percent of the base.

(iii)   *Using the average price and quantity of several years as the base*

Let us now construct an index that will combine the two features discussed above. That is, let

$$q' = \frac{q_0 + q_1}{2}$$

$$p' = \frac{p_0 + p_1}{2}$$

Then the price index becomes

(5)
$$I_n = \frac{\Sigma p_n \left(\dfrac{q_0 + q_1}{2} \right)}{\Sigma \left(\dfrac{p_0 + p_1}{2} \right) \left(\dfrac{q_0 + q_1}{2} \right)}$$

$$= \frac{\Sigma p_n q'}{\Sigma p' q'}$$

If a 3-year average is used, we have

(6)
$$I_n = \frac{\Sigma p_n \left(\dfrac{q_0 + q_1 + q_2}{3} \right)}{\Sigma \left(\dfrac{p_0 + p_1 + p_2}{3} \right) \left(\dfrac{q_0 + q_1 + q_2}{3} \right)}$$

$$= \frac{\Sigma p_n q'}{\Sigma p' q'}$$

Let us illustrate with example 3.

Example 3.   We use the data in the accompanying table and find:

Com-modity	1958 q_0	1959 q_1	p_0	p_1	q'	p'	$p'q'$	p_0q'	p_1q'
Sugar	40	60	10¢	14¢	50	12¢	$ 6.00	$ 5.00	$ 7.00
Flour	80	100	15	21	90	18	16.20	13.50	18.90
Milk	20	40	20	28	30	24	7.20	6.00	8.40
							$29.40	$24.50	$34.30

$$p' = \frac{p_0 + q_1}{2}, \qquad q' = \frac{q_0 + q_1}{2}$$

$$I_{58-59} = \frac{\Sigma \, p'q'}{\Sigma \, p'q'} = \frac{29.40}{29.40} = 1.00 \quad \text{or} \quad 100$$

$$I_{58} = \frac{\Sigma \, p_0q'}{\Sigma \, p'q'} = \frac{24.50}{29.40} = 0.833 \quad \text{or} \quad 83.3$$

$$I_{59} = \frac{\Sigma \, p_1q'}{\Sigma \, p'q'} = \frac{34.30}{29.40} = 1.166 \quad \text{or} \quad 116.6$$

(iv)   Illustrations

Wholesale price index.   The wholesale price index is computed by the U.S. Bureau of Labor Statistics and may be found in the *Monthly Labor Review*. It is a price index that measures price changes in the primary markets. It dates back to the 1890s, at which time it covered about 250 commodities. After subsequent revisions, it now covers about 1900 items. The formula used is the Laspeyres formula:

$$I_n = \frac{\Sigma \, p_n q_{47}}{\Sigma \, p_{47-49} q_{47}}$$

where the base year is 1947–49 = 100 and the weights are 1947 quantity weights. The prices are monthly prices, and p_n indicates the prices in the current month.

In 1950 the Bureau of Labor Statistics adopted a chain index to calculate the wholesale price index. This will be considered after we discuss the chain index. The reason for this switch is that the chain index allows substitution of commodities.

In 1962, the base from which changes are measured, that is, the reference base, was shifted from 1947–49 = 100 to 1957–59 = 100. The term reference base is explained in Section 11.7.

Table 11.1 gives several values of the wholesale price index.

TABLE 11.1. Wholesale Price Index
(All Commodities)

Monthly Average	1947–49 = 100	1957–59 = 100
1929	61.9	
1940	51.1	
1950	103.1	
1955	110.7	93.2
1960	119.6	100.7
1961		100.3
1962		100.6

SOURCE: Business Statistics, 1961 ed., U.S.
Dept. of Commerce, p. 36. Federal Reserve
Bulletin, June, 1963, p. 850.

Prices received and paid by farmers. These two indices are published by the U.S. Department of Agriculture. The index of prices received (denote it by R) shows the change in prices that farmers receive for their products (about 50 products). The index of prices paid (denote it by P) shows the changes in prices that farmers have to pay for the purchase of family goods and production goods and equipment (about 350 items). The ratio of R to P (that is, R/P) is called the *parity ratio.*

Because agricultural prices and production fluctuate more than other goods, a relatively long period is used as a weight base, that is, a base period from which weights are selected. Furthermore, adjustments of commodities that are used as weights have been made three times over the past 50 years so that the index reflects the changes that have occurred in agriculture. The formula for the first period (from 1910 to 1934) is

$$\frac{\Sigma \, p_n q_{24\text{-}29}}{\Sigma \, p_{24\text{-}29} q_{24\text{-}29}}$$

where prices p_n are monthly. The weight base period in the formula is 1924–1929, but because of historic-economic reasons, the index is converted back to the 1910–14 = 100 reference base.

The formula for the second period (from 1935 to 1952) uses 1937–1941 as the weight base period, but this, too, is converted back to the 1910–14 = 100 reference base, so that the index is continuous.

For the first two periods, the weight base period was the same for both indices, but in the recent revision (1959), the weight base period for the index of prices received has been changed to 1953–1957 and for the index of prices paid it has been changed to 1955. Table 11.2 gives several values of these indices.

TABLE 11.2. Prices Received and Paid by
Farmers (1910–14 $= 100$)

Monthly Average	Prices Received (R)	Prices Paid (P)	Parity Ratio (R/P)
1929	148	160	92
1940	100	124	81
1950	258	256	101
1960	238	299	80
1962	243	306	79

SOURCE: *Historical Statistics of the U.S.,* 1960 ed., U.S. Dept. of Commerce, p. 283. *Business Statistics,* 1961 ed., U.S. Dept. of Commerce, pp. 33–34, 208–209.

When the parity ratio is below 100, it means that the purchasing power of the farm products is less than it was in 1910–1914.

11.4. Chain Index Numbers

Suppose we have 4 numbers:

$$a(1958) = 5, \quad b(1959) = 10, \quad c(1960) = 15, \quad d(1961) = 20$$

Letting $a = 5$ as the base, we may express these 4 numbers in index form as follows:

$$1958: \quad \frac{a}{a} = \frac{5}{5} = 1 \quad \text{or} \quad 100$$

$$1959: \quad \frac{b}{a} = \frac{10}{5} = 2 \quad \text{or} \quad 200$$

$$1960: \quad \frac{c}{a} = \frac{15}{5} = 3 \quad \text{or} \quad 300$$

$$1961: \quad \frac{d}{a} = \frac{20}{5} = 4 \quad \text{or} \quad 400$$

From a to b there is a 100 percent increase; from a to c there is a 200 percent increase; and so forth. The increases are measured from the base $a = 5$.

But now suppose that we are interested in the increases from a to b,

b to c, and c to d. Then

$$I_{58\text{-}59}: \qquad \frac{b}{a} = \frac{10}{5} = 2 \quad \text{or} \quad 200$$

$$I_{59\text{-}60}: \qquad \frac{c}{b} = \frac{15}{10} = 1.5 \quad \text{or} \quad 150$$

$$I_{60\text{-}61}: \qquad \frac{d}{c} = \frac{20}{15} = 1.33 \quad \text{or} \quad 133$$

From a to b there is a 100 percent increase; from b to c there is a 50 percent increase; and from c to d there is a 33 percent increase. This form of index, in which the base of comparison is the previous period, is called a *chain index*.

One of the defects of the weighted aggregative or relative type of index is that the quantity weights are fixed. For example, if 1947–1949 = 100 is used as a base, the weights in the Laspeyres index use quantities of that period. When this index is used to compute a cost-of-living index, it assumes that consumers in (for example) 1955 are purchasing items similar to those of the 1947–1949 period. But we know this is not true. The development of transistor radios, various kinds of instant foods, etc., change the mode of living of consumers. Thus, to maintain a market basket that is representative of what the consumer purchases, it is necessary to delete obsolete items and add new ones. A variation of the chain index allows this adjustment, and hence it is used in many types of indices, such as the consumer price index and the wholesale price index.

Furthermore, in wholesale prices where not only the changes in prices from a fixed base are of interest, but also the change from the previous period is important when analyzing turning points of business cycles, the chain index is useful.

As we shall see, the chain index is quite versatile:
1. It shows changes from the previous period by the link relatives.
2. It constructs an index with a fixed base by the product of the link relatives.
3. It allows substitution of commodities by permitting adjustments for new weights.

Point 3 is discussed in Section 11.5.

Point 1 is obvious and needs no explanation. Point 2 may be illustrated as follows: Let

$$I_{58\text{-}59} \cdot I_{59\text{-}60} = \frac{b}{a} \cdot \frac{c}{b} = \frac{c}{a}$$

This shows that the product $I_{58\text{-}59} \cdot I_{59\text{-}60}$ becomes $I_{58\text{-}60} = c/a$, which is the price index for 1960, using 1958 as the base. Similarly,

$$I_{58\text{-}59} \cdot I_{59\text{-}60} \cdot I_{60\text{-}61} = \frac{b}{a} \cdot \frac{c}{b} \cdot \frac{d}{c} = \frac{d}{a}$$

That is, the product of the 3 terms gives us $I_{58\text{-}61} = d/a$, which is the 1961 price index, using 1958 as the base. The results are summarized as follows:

$$I_{58\text{-}59} = I_{58\text{-}59}$$
$$I_{58\text{-}60} = I_{58\text{-}59} \cdot I_{59\text{-}60}$$
$$I_{58\text{-}61} = (I_{58\text{-}59} \cdot I_{59\text{-}60})I_{60\text{-}61}$$
$$I_{58\text{-}62} = (I_{58\text{-}59} \cdot I_{59\text{-}60} \cdot I_{60\text{-}61})I_{61\text{-}62}$$
$$= I_{58\text{-}61} I_{61\text{-}62}$$

.

.

.

Thus, for example, when given the regular fixed base price index $I_{58\text{-}61}$ and a link relative $I_{61\text{-}62}$, the regular fixed base price index for 1962 (that is, $I_{58\text{-}62}$), can be computed by

$$I_{58\text{-}61} \cdot I_{61\text{-}62} = I_{58\text{-}62}$$

Let us apply this chain-index technique to the Laspeyres index.

(i) The chain index applied to the Laspeyres formula

The Laspeyres formula is

(1)
$$I_{i-1,i} = \frac{\Sigma\, p_i q_a}{\Sigma\, p_{i-1} q_a} = \frac{\Sigma \left(\dfrac{p_i}{p_{i-1}}\right) p_{i-1} q_a}{\Sigma\, p_{i-1} q_a}$$

where $I_{i-1,i}$ shows the index number for period i based on the period $i - 1$; that is, the previous period. Let

(2)
$$I_{i,i+1} = \frac{\Sigma\, p_{i+1} q_a}{\Sigma\, p_i q_a}$$

be the link relative index for period $i + 1$ based on the period i. Then the Laspeyres index for the period $i + 1$, based on the period $i - 1$, is

$$I_{i-1,\,i+1} = I_{i-1,i} \cdot I_{i,i+1}$$

$$= \frac{\Sigma\, p_i q_a}{\Sigma\, p_{i-1} q_a} \cdot \frac{\Sigma\, p_{i+1} q_a}{\Sigma\, p_i q_a}$$

(3)
$$= \frac{\Sigma p_{i+1} q_a}{\Sigma\, p_{i-1} q_a}$$

Example 1. We use the data in the accompanying table

Com- modity	1958 q_0	1959 q_1	1958 p_0	1959 p_1	1960 p_2	$p_0 q_0$	$p_1 q_0$	$p_2 q_0$
Sugar	40	60	10¢	15¢	20¢	$ 4.00	$ 6.00	$ 8.00
Flour	80	100	15	20	25	12.00	16.00	20.00
Milk	20	40	20	25	30	4.00	5.00	6.00
						$20.00	$27.00	$34.00

and find:

$$I_{58\text{-}59} = \frac{\Sigma\, p_{59}\, q_{58}}{\Sigma\, p_{58}\, q_{58}} = \frac{27.00}{20.00} = 1.35$$

$$I_{59\text{-}60} = \frac{\Sigma\, p_{60}\, q_{58}}{\Sigma\, p_{59}\, q_{58}} = \frac{34.00}{27.00} = 1.259$$

$$I_{58\text{-}60} = \frac{\Sigma\, p_{60}\, q_{58}}{\Sigma\, p_{58}\, q_{58}}$$

$$= \frac{\Sigma\, p_{59}\, q_{58}}{\Sigma\, p_{58}\, q_{58}} \cdot \frac{\Sigma\, p_{60}\, q_{58}}{\Sigma\, p_{59}\, q_{58}}$$

(4)
$$= I_{58\text{-}59} \cdot I_{59\text{-}60}$$

$$= \frac{27.00}{20.00} \cdot \frac{34.00}{27.00}$$

$$= \frac{34.00}{20.00} = 1.70$$

The $I_{58\text{-}59} = 1.35$ shows that there is a 35 percent increase from 1958 to 1959; $I_{59\text{-}60} = 1.259$ shows that there is a 26 percent increase from 1959 to 1960. The $I_{58\text{-}60} = 1.70$ shows that there is an increase of 70 percent from 1958 to 1960.

Note that the quantity weights q_{58} are kept fixed. Also note that from formula (4), we have

(5) $$I_{58\text{-}60} = I_{58\text{-}59} \cdot I_{59\text{-}60}$$

Let 1958 be the base period and abbreviate it from the subscripts. Then formula (5) becomes

(6) $$I_{60} = I_{59} \cdot I_{59\text{-}60}$$

When there is only one subscript, such as I_{60}, I_{59}, etc., it means that they have a common base. When there are two subscripts, such as $I_{59\text{-}60}$, the first subscript (1959) is the base from which the change is measured. Thus (6) shows that the 1960 Laspeyres index is obtained by multiplying the 1959 Laspeyres index I_{59} by the link relative for 1959–1960, $I_{59\text{-}60}$. This may be written as

(7) $$I_{60} = I_{59} \frac{\Sigma\, p_{60} q_{58}}{\Sigma\, p_{59} q_{58}}$$

or

(8) $$I_{60} = I_{59} \frac{\Sigma \left(\dfrac{p_{60}}{p_{59}} \right) p_{59} q_{58}}{\Sigma\, p_{59} q_{58}}$$

(ii) Illustration

An illustration of the chain-index technique as shown by formula (8) is the consumer-price index. The consumer-price index is a monthly index published by the U.S. Department of Labor, Bureau of Labor Statistics. Its full name is the *Index of Change in Prices of Goods and Services Purchased by City Wage-Earner and Clerical-Worker Families to Maintain Their Level of Living,* and was previously called the *Cost of Living Index.* Our main interest in it is the formula used to compute the index. It is

(9) $$\begin{aligned} I_i &= I_{i-1} \left[\frac{\Sigma \left(\dfrac{p_i}{p_{i-1}} \right) (p_{i-1} q_a)}{\Sigma\, p_{i-1} q_a} \right] \\ &= I_{i-1} \left[\frac{\Sigma\, p_i q_a}{\Sigma\, p_{i-1} q_a} \right] \\ &= I_{i-1} \cdot I_{i-1,i} \end{aligned}$$

where I_{i-1} is the (Laspeyres) price index for the previous month, based on the base period 1947–49 = 100, and $I_{i-1,i}$ is the link relative for the month $i - 1$ and i. For example, if $i =$ April, 1961, then $i - 1$ = March, 1961; then I_{i-1} is the price index for March, 1961, and $I_{i-1,i}$ is the link relative that shows the change of prices from March to April, 1961. Note carefully that the quantity weights q_a are fixed. Furthermore, the q_a are not the quantities for 1947–1949 but the average quantities for 1952.

To calculate the price index for May, find the link relative between $i =$ April and $i + 1 =$ May:

$$I_{i,i+1} = \frac{\Sigma \left(\frac{p_{i+1}}{p_i}\right)(p_i q_a)}{\Sigma\, p_i q_a}$$

and then calculate

$$I_{i+1} = I_i \cdot I_{i,i+1}$$

This I_{i+1} is the May consumer-price index with the base 1947–49 = 100.

As an example, let $I_{i-1} = 110$ and $I_{i-1,i} = 115$. Then the price index for $i =$ April is

$$\begin{aligned} I_i &= I_{i-1} \cdot I_{i-1,i} \\ &= (1.10)(1.15) = 1.265 \text{ or } 126.5 \end{aligned}$$

Let the change from $i =$ April to $i + 1 =$ May be $I_{i,i+1} = 105$. That is, prices increased by 5 percent from April to May. Then the May price index is

$$\begin{aligned} I_{i+1} &= I_i \cdot I_{i,i+1} \\ &= (1.265)(1.05) = 1.328 \text{ or } 132.8 \end{aligned}$$

This shows that there is a 32.8 percent increase from the base period 1947–49 = 100 to May, 1961.

11.5.   Splicing and Shifting the Base of Index Numbers

(i)   Splicing two overlapping index numbers

Suppose the original data to construct two consumer-price indices, A and B, are as follows:

	A	B
1958:	$v_0 = \Sigma\, p_0 q_0 = \$5.0$	
1959:	$v_1 = \Sigma\, p_1 q_0 = \$5.5$	
1960:	$v_2 = \Sigma\, p_2 q_0 = \$6.0$	$v_3 = \Sigma\, p_2 q_1 = \$10$
1961:		$v_4 = \Sigma\, p_3 q_1 = \$13$
1962:		$v_5 = \Sigma\, p_4 q_1 = \$14$

On the bases of these original data, the (Laspeyres) price indices are as follows:

	A	B
1958:	$\dfrac{v_0}{v_0} = \dfrac{5}{5} = 1.0$	
1959:	$\dfrac{v_1}{v_0} = \dfrac{5.5}{5} = 1.1$	
1960:	$\dfrac{v_2}{v_0} = \dfrac{6.0}{5} = 1.2$	$\dfrac{v_3}{v_3} = \dfrac{10}{10} = 1.0$
1961:		$\dfrac{v_4}{v_3} = \dfrac{13}{10} = 1.3$
1962:		$\dfrac{v_5}{v_3} = \dfrac{14}{10} = 1.4$

To simplify notation, this is rewritten as:

	A	B
1958:	$I_{58} = 100$	
1959:	$I_{59} = 110$	
1960:	$I_{60} = 120$	$I'_{60} = 100$
1961:	x_1	$I'_{61} = 130$
1962:	x_2	$I'_{62} = 140$

We may suppose that weights were changed in 1961 from q_0 to q_1, and as a result, a new series B was started. However, a continuous index may be required. The problem of combining two or more such overlapping series of index numbers into one continuous series is called *splicing*.

Splicing is basically a problem of finding proportions. For example, the x_1 for 1961 is found by

$$(1) \qquad \frac{120}{x_1} = \frac{100}{130}$$

$$x_1 = \frac{120 \times 130}{100} = 156$$

Then the A-series values are as shown in the accompanying table.

Year	Index A	Index B
1960	120	100
1961	$x_1 = 156$	130
1962	$x_2 = 168$	140

The increase from 1960 to 1961 is

$$\frac{156 - 120}{120} = \frac{36}{120} = 0.3, \quad \text{or} \quad 30$$

The B series shows that the index went from $I'_{61} = 100$ to $I'_{60} = 130$; that is, a 30 percent increase, and clearly the proportionate change from 1960 to 1961 has been preserved.

The x_2 is found by

(2)
$$\frac{120}{x_2} = \frac{100}{140}$$

$$x_2 = \frac{120 \times 140}{100} = 168$$

and a check will show that the increase from 120 to 168 is 40 percent, as required by the B series.

We may combine this principle of splicing with the chain-index technique and show how weights may be changed as frequently as necessary. To illustrate this, rewrite equation (1) as

(3)
$$\frac{I_{60}}{x_1} = \frac{100}{I'_{61}}$$

Then x_1 becomes

(4)
$$x_1 = I_{60} \cdot I'_{61} \cdot \frac{1}{100}$$

$$= 120 \times 130 \times \frac{1}{100} = 156$$

Substituting the original v's for I'_{61}, (4) becomes

$$(5) \qquad x_1 = (I_{60} \cdot I'_{61}) \; \frac{1}{100}$$

$$= I_{60} \cdot \left(\frac{v_4}{v_3} \times 100 \right) \times \frac{1}{100}$$

$$= I_{60} \cdot I_{60\text{-}61} \cdot \frac{1}{100}$$

where $I_{60\text{-}61}$ is the link relative from 1960 to 1961. This shows that the 1961 price index is found by multiplying the 1960 price index I_{60} by the link relative $I_{60\text{-}61}$. This is the chain-index technique. The difference between this and what we have done previously is that the link relative $I_{60\text{-}61}$ uses quantity weights q_1 that are different from the weights of I_{60}, which are q_0.

Let us next find x_2. Since $x_1 = I_{61} = 156$ has been found, this result may be used to find x_2 as follows:

$$\frac{x_1}{x_2} = \frac{130}{140}$$

$$x_2 = x_1 \cdot \frac{140}{130}$$

$$= I_{61} \frac{\dfrac{v_5}{v_3}}{\dfrac{v_4}{v_3}}$$

$$= I_{61} \frac{v_5}{v_4}$$

But $\left(\dfrac{v_5}{v_4} \right) \times 100$ is the link relative $I'_{61\text{-}62}$. Thus

$$x_2 = I_{61} \cdot I'_{61\text{-}62} \cdot \frac{1}{100}$$

$$= (156) \left(\frac{\$14}{\$13} \right) = 168$$

This shows that the $x_2 = I_{62}$, (which is the 1962 price index) is found by multiplying the 1961 price index I_{61} by the link relative $I'_{61\text{-}62}$.

The results may now be summarized. Two overlapping indices are spliced by using the technique of proportions. A variation of this technique leads to the chain-index technique. For $I_{61} = x_1$, we find

$$I_{61} = I_{60} \cdot I'_{60\text{-}61} \times \frac{1}{100}$$

$$= (120)(130) \times \frac{1}{100} = 156$$

where I_{60} is the price index of 1960, and $I_{60\text{-}61}$ is the link relative using new quantity weights q_1. For $I_{62} = x_2$, we find

$$I_{62} = I_{61} \cdot I'_{61\text{-}62} \times \frac{1}{100}$$

$$= (156)\frac{14}{13} = 168$$

where I_{61} is the price index for 1961, and $I'_{61\text{-}62}$ is the link relative. In our example, the link relative $I'_{61\text{-}62}$ used the quantity weights q_1, but as can easily be seen, it may be a new set of weights.

By using this combination of splicing and chain-index technique, the weights may be changed as often as necessary.

Example 1. Splice the two sets of indices shown in the accompanying table.

Year	Index A	Index B
1955	100	
1956	110	
1957	130	100
1958	x_1	120
1959	x_2	125
1960	x_3	130

From the data in the table:

(6)
$$\frac{130}{x_1} = \frac{100}{120}$$

$$x_1 = \frac{130 \times 120}{100} = 156$$

(7)
$$\frac{130}{x_2} = \frac{100}{125}$$

$$x_2 = \frac{130 \times 125}{100} = 162.5$$

(8)

$$\frac{130}{x_3} = \frac{100}{130}$$

$$x_3 = \frac{130 \times 130}{100} = 169$$

Example 2. Splice the two series of Example 1, using the chain-index technique. To use the chain-index technique, we first need to find the link relatives. Since the link relatives are indices that use the preceding year as a base, they may be easily found from series B as follows:

$$I'_{57\text{-}58} = \frac{120}{100} \times 100 = 120$$

$$I'_{58\text{-}59} = \frac{125}{120} \times 100 = 104.16$$

$$I'_{59\text{-}60} = \frac{130}{125} \times 100 = 104$$

Then the price indices x_1, x_2, x_3 are obtained as follows:

(9)

$$I_{58} = x_1 = I_{57} \cdot I'_{57\text{-}58} \times \frac{1}{100}$$

$$= (130)\left(\frac{120}{100} \times 100\right) \times \frac{1}{100}$$

$$= (130)(120) \times \frac{1}{100}$$

$$= 156$$

(10)

$$I_{59} = x_2 = I_{58} \cdot I'_{58\text{-}59} \times \frac{1}{100}$$

$$= \left[(130)(120) \times \frac{1}{100}\right]\left[\frac{125}{120} \times 100\right] \times \frac{1}{100}$$

$$= (130)(125) \times \frac{1}{100}$$

$$= 162.5$$

(11)

$$I_{60} = x_3 = I_{59} \cdot I'_{59\text{-}60} \times \frac{1}{100}$$

$$= \left[(130)(125) \times \frac{1}{100} \right] \left[\frac{130}{125} \times 100 \right] \times \frac{1}{100}$$

$$= (130)(130) \times \frac{1}{100}$$

$$= 169$$

Example 3. Given the data in the accompanying table, find x_1, x_2, and x_3.

Year	Index A	Link Relatives
1955	100	
1956	110	
1957	130	
1958	x_1	$I'_{57\text{-}58} = 105$
1959	x_2	$I'_{58\text{-}59} = 90$
1960	x_3	$I'_{59\text{-}60} = 120$

1. The $I'_{57\text{-}58} = 105$ shows that there is a 5 percent increase in prices from 1957 to 1958. We may assume that new weights are used to compute $I'_{57\text{-}58}$. The x_1 is

$$I_{58} = x_1 = I_{57} \cdot I'_{57\text{-}58} \times \frac{1}{100}$$

$$= (130)(105) \times \frac{1}{100} = 136.5$$

2. $I'_{58\text{-}59} = 90$ shows that there is a 10 percent decrease from 1958 to 1959. We may assume that a different set of weights are used. Then

$$I_{59} = x_2 = I_{58} \cdot I'_{58\text{-}59}$$

$$= (136.5)(90) \times \frac{1}{100} = 122.85$$

3. $I'_{59\text{-}60} = 120$ shows that there is a 20 percent increase in prices from 1959 to 1960. We may assume that a different set of weights are used. Then

$$I_{60} = x_3 = I_{59} \cdot I'_{59\text{-}60} \times \frac{1}{100}$$

$$= (122.85)(120) \times \frac{1}{100} = 147.42$$

Example 4. Example 3 may be decomposed as shown in the table here.

Year	Index A	Index B	Index C	Index D
1955	100			
1956	110			
1957	130	100		
1958	x_1	105	100	
1959	x_2	—	90	100
1960	x_3	—	—	120

What we have done is to show the link relatives as series B, C, and D, and the problem of finding x_1, x_2, and x_3 is merely repeating the splicing technique three times. The results are, of course, the same as the chain technique of Example 3. We may assume that the weights are different for each series.

(ii) Shifting the base

The technique of shifting the base of an index number from one period (say, 1958) to another period (say, 1960) is also a problem of taking proportions. Let us shift the base of the series in the table from 1958 to 1960. All we have to do is divide each of the numbers of index A by 500:

Year	Index A	Index B
1958	100	x_1
1959	200	x_2
1960	500	100

$$x_1 = \frac{100}{500} \times 100 = 20$$

$$x_2 = \frac{200}{500} \times 100 = 40$$

If the base is to be shifted to 1959, we divide by 200. Then

$$x_1 = \frac{100}{200} \times 100 = 50$$

$$x_2 = \frac{500}{200} \times 100 = 250$$

The results are summarized in the table on page 294.

Year	Index A	Index B	Index C
1958	100	20	50
1959	200	40	100
1960	500	100	250

A check will show that the ratio between the index numbers in each series is the same, namely:

$$1 : 2 : 5$$

11.6. Deflating Prices and Income

The process of adjusting prices and income by a price index, and expressing them in terms of base-year dollars, is called *deflating* prices and income.

The first thing we need to explain is the relation between the value of a dollar and the price level. A dollar is worth what it can buy. Hence, at a time when prices are low, the dollar has more value; when prices are high, it has less value. People say "the value of a dime is only half of what it used to be; we can buy only one Coke with a dime now." This statement implies that if the general price level doubles, the real value of money falls to one-half its former value. Also, for a particular commodity such as a Coke, if its price doubles, then the value of money with respect to a Coke has fallen to one-half. If prices should triple, then the value of money will be one-third of what it was. Using this analysis, we may now distinguish the value of a dollar for different periods. For example, suppose a price index is 100 for 1950 and 200 for 1960. Since the price level has doubled from 1950 to 1960, the 1960 dollar is worth only half as much as the 1950 dollar. Or, we may say that, given a dollar bill, one could buy twice as much in 1950 as in 1960. The point to note is that the same dollar unit has been labeled as a *1950 dollar* or *1960 dollar* according to its value, which is determined by the price level.

Suppose the price of bread and Coke are as shown in the table below.

Year	Coke	Bread	Price Level
1950	5¢	10¢	100
1960	10¢	30¢	200

Since the price index of 200 indicates that the price level has been doubled, if the 1960 prices are divided by 200 percent (that is, by 2), the 1960 prices are expressed in terms of the original 1950 prices. Or we may say that the prices of Coke and bread are expressed *in terms of 1950 dollars*. We find

$$\text{Coke:} \qquad 10\text{¢} \div 200\% = 5\text{¢}$$
$$\text{Bread:} \qquad 30\text{¢} \div 200\% = 15\text{¢}$$

We show the results in table form.

				Deflated Prices	
Year	Coke	Bread	Price Level	Coke	Bread
1950	5¢	10¢	100		
1960	10¢	30¢	200	5¢	15¢

These results in the table show that the 1960 price of Coke in terms of 1950 dollars is 5¢ and is the same as its actual price of 1950. But the 1960 price of bread in terms of 1950 dollars is 15¢ and is 5¢ more than its actual price of 10¢. This shows that during 1950 to 1960, something has happened to cause the price of bread to increase more than the general rise in prices. What are these causes?

This is not a statistical question but an economic one, and we shall merely state that the increase in the price of bread beyond the increase of the general price level was due to a change in the relative demand for bread. Let us now decompose the 1960 price of bread as follows:

$$10\text{¢} \times 200\% \times 150\% = 30\text{¢}$$

change of demand

change of price level

The difference of 10¢ and 15¢ shows the increase in the "real" value of bread (or the relative value of bread in terms of other commodities) due to a change (increase) in the relative demand in 1960 for bread. This simply means that previously you demanded only 2 Cokes (1 Coke = 5¢) for 1 loaf of bread (= 10¢), but you now demand 3 Cokes (1 Coke now = 10¢) for 1 loaf of bread (1 loaf of bread now = 30¢).

The increase in the real value of bread can be measured by the difference

$$3 \text{ Cokes} - 2 \text{ Cokes} = 1 \text{ Coke}$$

We may now summarize our discussion: The process of adjusting prices or income by a price index and expressing them in terms of base-year dollars is called *deflating* prices and income. The procedure is to divide the prices by the price index.

Example 1. Given the data shown in the table for milk and a consumer-price index, deflate the milk prices.

Year	Milk Price	Price Index	Deflated Prices
1950	15¢	100	15¢
1955	22¢	110	20¢
1960	30¢	115	26¢

The deflated prices are obtained by dividing the milk prices by the corresponding price indices. For example,

$$22¢ \div 110\% = 20¢$$

The deflated price 20¢ means that the 1955 price of milk in terms of 1950 dollars is 20¢. Hence, there has been an increase in the real value of milk by

$$20¢ - 15¢ = 5¢$$

The deflated price of 26¢ means that the 1960 price of milk in terms of 1950 dollars is 26¢. There has been an increase in the real value of milk by

$$26¢ - 15¢ = 11¢$$

Example 2. Given the data in the table for wages and a consumer-price index, find whether there has been an increase in real wages.

Year	Wages	Price Index	Real Wages
1950	$0.90	100	$0.90
1955	1.20	130	0.923
1960	1.60	180	0.888

The 1955 wages of $1.20 in terms of 1950 dollars was $0.923. This means that there was an increase of $92.3 - 90 = 2.3¢$ in real wages in 1955.

The 1960 wages of $1.60 in terms of 1950 dollars was $0.888. This means there was a decrease of $90 - 88.8 = 0.12¢$ in real wages in 1960 compared with the 1955 wages.

Example 3.   The average income per person (per capita income) and a consumer-price index is given in the table. Has there been an increase in real income?

Year	Income	Price Index	Real Income
1950	$1200	100	$1200
1955	1500	110	1363
1960	1800	120	1500

The 1955 income of $1500 in terms of 1950 dollars was $1363. There was a real increase of

$$\$1363 - 1200 = \$163$$

The nominal increase was $1500 - 1200 = $300.

The 1960 income of $1800 in terms of 1950 dollars was $1500. There was a real increase of

$$\$1500 - 1200 = \$300$$

The nominal increase was $1800 - 1200 = $600.

11.7.   Comments on Price Indices

We have already briefly commented on the problem of selecting a base. Let us discuss some other problems of price indices, using the consumer-price index as an illustration.

(i)   Changes due to time

When the consumer-price index of, say, 1930 and 1960 are to be compared, the changes in the items and the quality of goods people purchase make such comparisons difficult if not meaningless. In 1930 there were no supermarkets with the vast variety of goods that was available in 1960. Instant coffee, detergents, and ready-made orange juice are only a few of the necessities of 1960 that did not exist in 1930. Furthermore, there have been vast changes in the quality of goods.

(ii)   Changes due to location

The mode of living in Montana and Southern California differ so much that an overall consumer index for the United States as a whole becomes questionable. For example, in Southern California there is probably no need for heavy winter clothes, whereas in Montana they are probably a necessity.

(iii) Problems in collection of data

The process of collecting data for the consumer-price index requires, first, the selection of a sample of cities; second, the selection of a sample of families; third, the selection of articles whose prices are to be checked; fourth, the selection of the stores; fifth, the selection of shopping days; sixth, when there are several prices, which price to use, and so forth. After families have been selected, they are requested to keep a record of the articles they buy and the prices. The Bureau of Labor Statistics collects these data and computes the consumer-price index. In the five large cities (New York, Chicago, Los Angeles, Detroit, Philadelphia) the data are collected once a month, but in small cities such as Seattle, Washington, or Madison, Wisconsin, this is done once every four months. Furthermore, it covers only clerical and urban wage earners, and excludes farmers.

Quite clearly, this procedure allows ample opportunity for various errors to creep in, and the data are not very comprehensive.

(iv) Weight base and reference base

Up to now we have used the term "base year" or "base period" from which the price changes are measured. For example, the index of prices received and paid by farmers is

$$I_n = \frac{\Sigma \, p_n q_{24\text{-}29}}{\Sigma \, p_{24\text{-}29} q_{24\text{-}29}}$$

As we said before, the base period was shifted to 1910–14 = 100 for historic-economic reasons. But, as the formula shows, the quantity weights are the average of 1924–1929, which is different from the base 1910–14 = 100. To avoid confusion, the term *weight base* is used to indicate the period from which the quantity weights (or any other kind of weight) are selected. In our present example, 1924–1929 is the weight base. The term *reference basis* is used to indicate the period from which changes are measured. In our present example, it is 1910–14 = 100.

Weights, such as quantity weights, are selected so that they will be representative of the period covered by the price index. For instance, from 1947 to 1960, the market basket of 1952 may be the appropriate market basket of goods. But for purposes of economic and business analysis, and also for convenience of comparison with other indices, 1947–49 = 100 may be the appropriate reference base.

When reading literature concerning index numbers, the term "base period" may be used to mean either the weight base or the reference base. When both refer to the same year or period, there is no confusion. But in some cases where they do differ and the single term base period is used, one should understand that the term may have two different meanings.

In 1962, various general purpose economic indices published by the Federal Government have shifted their reference base from 1947–49 = 100 to 1957–59 = 100 because it was desirable to update the reference periods. The wholesale price index mentioned earlier was an example.

The consumer price index that we mentioned on page 285 has also shifted the reference base from 1947–49 = 100 to 1957–59 = 100. However, the weight base of 1949–1950 is used to compute the indices for 1950–1952, and the weight base of 1952 is used to compute the indices from 1953 on. Since 1959, a 5-year revision program is underway to update the weights and improve the index.

(v) An alternative interpretation of the weighted aggregative price index

In Example 1 of Section 11.2, we found that

$$I_{60} = \frac{\Sigma \, p_n q_0}{\Sigma \, p_0 q_0} = \frac{\$27.00}{\$20.00} = 1.35 \quad \text{or} \quad 135$$

and we said that this meant a 35 percent increase in prices over the 1958 level. This may also be interpreted as the change in the total amount of 1960 expenditures to buy the same amount of goods. That is, there is a 35 percent increase in the total amount of 1960 expenditures to buy the same amount of goods.

The difference is merely that, in the former case, expenditures are considered on a per unit basis, and hence the term "price" is used, whereas in the latter case, expenditures are on an aggregative basis.

(vi) Criteria for a good index

The statistician I. Fisher* proposed two criteria for a good index number. One is called the *time reversal test* and the second is called the *factor reversal test*.

---

* I. Fisher, *The Making of Index Numbers*, 3rd ed., New York: Houghton Mifflin Co., 1927.

The time reversal test is explained as follows: Let I_{0n} be an index for year n based on year 0, and I_{n0} be the index for year 0 based on year n. Then, if

$$I_{0n} \cdot I_{n0} = 1$$

it satisfies the time reversal test. For example, consider the simple aggregative price index shown in the table below.

Commodity	p_0	p_1
Bread	10¢	20¢
Milk	15	25
Butter	25	35
	50¢	80¢

From the table data we find

$$I_{01} = \frac{\Sigma p_1}{\Sigma p_0} = \frac{80}{50} = 1.6 \quad \text{or} \quad 160$$

$$I_{10} = \frac{\Sigma p_0}{\Sigma p_1} = \frac{50}{80} = 0.625 \quad \text{or} \quad 62.5$$

Then

$$I_{01} \cdot I_{10} = (1.6) \times (0.625) = 1$$

and it satisfies the time reversal test.

A check will show that the Laspeyres and Paasche indices and most of the other indices do not satisfy this criterion.

The factor reversal test requires knowledge of quantity indices, which is discussed in the next section, but at this point a simple explanation will be given. Let P be a price index that shows the change of prices from year 0 to n, and let Q be a quantity index that shows the change of quantities from year 0 to n. We know that

$$(\text{Price}) \times (\text{quantity}) = \text{value}$$

The factor reversal test requires that $P \times Q$ shall show the change of values from year 0 to year n. In symbols, it requires

$$P \times Q = \frac{\Sigma p_n q_n}{\Sigma p_0 q_0}$$

where $\Sigma p_0 q_0$ shows the amount of expenditures in year 0 and $\Sigma p_n q_n$ shows the amount of expenditures in year n. Since the formula shows the changes in value, it may be called a *value index*. For example, let p be import prices and q be import quantities; assume $\Sigma \, p_0 q_0 = \$10,000,000$ and $\Sigma \, p_n q_n = \$15,000,000$. Then

$$\frac{\Sigma \, p_n q_n}{\Sigma \, p_0 q_0} = \frac{15}{10} = 1.5 \quad \text{or} \quad 150$$

shows in value terms an increase in imports of 50 percent over the base year.

Very few indices satisfy this factor reversal test, but one that does is Fisher's *ideal index number*.

(vii)   *Geometric average index number*

The ideal index number is the geometric average of the Laspeyres and Paasche index numbers. So, let us first define the geometric average index number. It is the geometric average of unweighted or weighted price (or whatever other element that is being measured) relatives. Let us consider as an example the data given in the accompanying table.

Commodity	1947–1949 p_0	8/1/60 p_1	p_1/p_0	$\log(p_1/p_0)$
Coffee (lb.)	40¢	44¢	1.10	0.0414
Cocoa (lb.)	20	24	1.20	0.0792
Sugar (lb.)	10	11	1.10	0.0414
				0.1620

The geometric average index number is

$$I_n = \sqrt[3]{\frac{p_{11}}{p_{01}} \times \frac{p_{12}}{p_{02}} \times \frac{p_{13}}{p_{03}}}$$

Logarithms are used to calculate this index:

$$\log I_n = \frac{1}{3}\left[\log \frac{p_{11}}{p_{01}} + \log \frac{p_{12}}{p_{02}} + \log \frac{p_{13}}{p_{03}}\right]$$

$$= \frac{1}{3}\,(0.1620)$$

$$= 0.0540$$

$$I_n = 1.132 \quad \text{or} \quad 113.2$$

That is, there is an increase of 13.2 percent over the 1947–1949 average. The geometric average index number satisfies the time reversal test.

In our present example, the change in prices from August, 1960, back to 1947–1949 is

$$I_0 = \sqrt[3]{\frac{p_{01}}{p_{11}} \times \frac{p_{02}}{p_{12}} \times \frac{p_{03}}{p_{13}}}$$

and a check will show that

$$I_n \cdot I_0 = 1$$

as required by the time reversal test. An advantage of this index is that price changes are symmetrical. By this we mean that if coffee prices double and sugar prices drop to a half of their former level, they will offset each other.

The *Daily Index of Spot Market Prices,* published by the U.S. Department of Labor, Bureau of Labor Statistics, is calculated by the unweighted geometric average of the price relative of the 22 basic commodities, which include (1) burlap, (2) butter, (3) cocoa beans, (4) copper scrap, (5) corn, (6) cotton seed, (7) cotton seed oil, (8) hides, (9) hogs, (10) lard, (11) lead scrap, (12) print cloth, (13) rosin, (14) rubber, (15) steel scrap, (16) steers, (17) sugar, (18) tallow, (19) tin, (20) wheat, (21) wool tops, (22) zinc. Besides the Bureau of Labor Statistics publications, data on commodity cash prices and commodity indices may be found in the *New York Times* and other papers.

Because of its sensitivity to current and future economic conditions, the *Daily Index of Spot Market Prices* is used by some economists as a lead indicator to forecast business changes.

(viii) The ideal index number

Let L be the Laspeyres index number and P be the Paasche index number. Then Fisher's ideal index number is

$$I_F = \sqrt{L \times P}$$

$$= \sqrt{\frac{\Sigma \, p_n q_0}{\Sigma \, p_0 q_0} \times \frac{\Sigma \, p_n q_n}{\Sigma \, p_0 q_n}}$$

Recall that L uses base-year quantities q_0 as weights, and P uses current year quantities q_n as weights.

Let L' be the Laspeyres index showing the change from year n back to 0 and P' be the Paasche index showing the change from year n back to 0. Then

$$I_F \cdot I_F' = \sqrt{L \times P} \, \sqrt{L' \times P'}$$

$$= \sqrt{\frac{\Sigma\, p_n q_0}{\Sigma\, p_0 q_0} \times \frac{\Sigma\, p_n q_n}{\Sigma\, p_0 q_n}} \sqrt{\frac{\Sigma\, p_0 q_n}{\Sigma\, p_n q_n} \times \frac{\Sigma\, p_0 q_0}{\Sigma\, p_n q_0}}$$

$$= 1$$

and it satisfies the time reversal test.

To check the factor reversal test, let the price index be

$$P_F = \sqrt{L \times P}$$

where P_F indicates the Fisher ideal price index. Let

$$Q_F = \sqrt{\frac{\Sigma\, q_n p_0}{\Sigma\, q_0 p_0} \times \frac{\Sigma\, q_n p_n}{\Sigma\, q_0 p_n}}$$

be the ideal quantity index that corresponds to P_F. Then

$$P_F \cdot Q_F = \sqrt{\frac{\Sigma\, p_n q_0}{\Sigma\, p_0 q_0} \times \frac{\Sigma\, p_n q_n}{\Sigma\, p_0 q_n}} \times \sqrt{\frac{\Sigma\, q_n p_0}{\Sigma\, q_0 p_0} \times \frac{\Sigma\, q_n p_n}{\Sigma\, q_0 p_n}}$$

$$= \frac{\Sigma\, p_n q_n}{\Sigma\, p_0 q_0}$$

which is the value index; hence it satisfies the factor reversal test.

The monthly *Export and Import Indexes* published by the U.S. Department of Commerce, Bureau of Foreign Commerce, uses the Fisher ideal index number to calculate the indices for quantity and unit value (prices), and from these two, calculates the value index.

The formulas are similar to those above, in which the p's are the unit values and the q's are the quantities (imported or exported). The separate price and quantity indices are necessary because of the large fluctuations in prices and quantities in imports and exports. Table 11.3 gives sample indices taken from the June, 1961, *Survey of Current Business*.

TABLE 11.3. U.S. Imports and Exports (1936–38 = 100)

	April	May
Exports	336	334
Quantity	739	733
Value	220	219
Unit value		
Imports	221	221
Quantity	610	612
Value	276	277
Unit value		

A check will show that

$$\text{(Quantity)} \times \text{(unit value)} = \text{value}$$

and, for example, using Table 11.3,

$$336 \times 220 = 739$$

where the figures are in percent terms.

11.8. Quantity Index Numbers

The quantity indices measure the changes in the quantities from a base period (reference base). Two types of quantity indices will be discussed; the weighted aggregative type and the weighted relative type. The weighted aggregative type is classified into the Laspeyres, Paasche, and other types.

(i) Laspeyres type of formula

This is the counterpart of the Laspeyres price index and is obtained by interchanging the p's and q's in the Laspeyres price index. That is,

$$\text{Price index:} \qquad \frac{\Sigma\, p_n q_0}{\Sigma\, p_0 q_0}$$

(1) $\qquad\qquad$ Quantity index: $\qquad \dfrac{\Sigma\, q_n p_0}{\Sigma\, q_0 p_0}$

The numerator shows the value of goods for year n. The denominator shows the value of goods for the base year. Since the prices p_0 are kept fixed as weights, any change is due to changes in quantities. For example, suppose

$$\frac{\Sigma\, q_n p_0}{\Sigma\, q_0 p_0} = \frac{\$20}{\$10} = 2.0 \quad \text{or} \quad 200$$

There is a 100 percent increase in the value of goods in year n over the base year. Since prices are the same for both years, the quantity of goods must have doubled.

Note carefully that when we say that the quantity of goods has doubled, we do not necessarily mean that each good has doubled in quantity. Some may have increased more than 100 percent and others less than 100 percent; the statement means only that there has been an increase, on the average, of 100 percent.

Example 1. Given the data in the table, concerning production and prices, construct a Laspeyres type of quantity index.

Commodity	1958 q_0	1959 q_1	1960 q_2	1958 p_0	$q_0 p_0$	$q_1 p_0$	$q_2 p_0$
Chair	20	30	30	$ 5	$100	$150	$150
Desk	10	20	30	8	80	160	240
Radio	30	40	50	10	300	400	500
					$480	$710	$890

From these data, then,

(2)
$$I_{58} = \frac{\Sigma\, q_0 p_0}{\Sigma\, q_0 p_0} = \frac{480}{480} = 1.0 \quad \text{or} \quad 100$$

(3)
$$I_{59} = \frac{\Sigma\, q_1 p_0}{\Sigma\, q_0 p_0} = \frac{710}{480} = 1.479 \quad \text{or} \quad 147.9$$

(4)
$$I_{60} = \frac{\Sigma\, q_2 p_0}{\Sigma\, q_0 p_0} = \frac{890}{480} = 1.854 \quad \text{or} \quad 185.4$$

The $I_{59} = 1.479$ indicates that the amount of 1959 expenditures for the goods is 47.9 percent greater than the 1958 level. But, since the prices are the same, the change is due to the change in the quantity of the goods. That is, there is a 47.9 percent increase in the quantity of goods over the 1958 level.

(ii) Paasche type of formula

This is obtained by interchanging the p's and q's in the Paasche price index. That is,

$$\text{Price index:} \quad \frac{\Sigma\, p_n q_n}{\Sigma\, p_0 q_n}$$

(5)
$$\text{Quantity index:} \quad \frac{\Sigma\, q_n p_n}{\Sigma\, q_0 p_n}$$

Example 2. Given the data in the table, concerning production and prices, construct a Paasche type of quantity index.

Commodity	1958 q_0	1959 q_1	1960 q_2	1959 p_1	1960 p_2	$q_0 p_1$	$q_1 p_1$	$q_0 p_2$	$q_2 p_2$
Chair	20	30	30	$ 6	$ 8	$120	$180	$160	$ 240
Desk	10	20	30	10	12	100	200	120	360
Radio	30	40	50	12	15	360	480	450	750
						$580	$860	$730	$1350

From these data we have

(6)
$$I_{58} = \frac{\Sigma q_0 p_0}{\Sigma q_0 p_0} = 1.0 \quad \text{or} \quad 100$$

(7)
$$I_{59} = \frac{\Sigma q_1 p_1}{\Sigma q_0 p_1} = \frac{860}{580} = 1.482 \quad \text{or} \quad 148.2$$

(8)
$$I_{60} = \frac{\Sigma q_2 p_2}{\Sigma q_0 p_2} = \frac{1350}{730} = 1.849 \quad \text{or} \quad 184.9$$

$I_{59} = 1.482$ shows that there is a 48.2 percent increase in quantity from 1958 to 1959. Note carefully that $I_{59} = 1.482$ is not being compared with $I_{58} = 1.0$. Since the weights of 1958 are p_0 and those of 1959 are p_1, I_{58} and I_{59} cannot be compared. What is being compared is the amount of expenditures $\Sigma q_0 p_1 = \$580$ and $\Sigma q_1 p_1 = \$860$; and $I_{59} = 1.482$ shows that there has been a 48.2 percent increase. But, since p_1 is kept fixed, the change is due to quantity changes. Hence, we conclude that there is a 48.2 percent increase in quantities.

$I_{60} = 1.849$ is interpreted in a similar manner. Note that $I_{59} = 1.482$ and $I_{60} = 1.849$ may not be compared because different price weights have been used.

(iii) *Variations of the weighted aggregative type of quantity index*

In a manner similar to that for the variations of the weighted aggregative price indices, variations of the quantity indices are obtained by using average prices and average base-year quantities. An illustration is the *Federal Reserve Monthly Index of Industrial Production* (abbreviated IIP): It is

$$\frac{\Sigma q_n p_{47}}{\Sigma q_{47\text{-}49} p_{47}}$$

where the base-year quantities are the average over 1947–1949.

The construction of other variations are left to the reader.

(iv) *Weighted relative quantity index*

The weighted relative quantity index is

(9)
$$I_n = \frac{\Sigma \left(\dfrac{q_n}{q_0} \right) w}{\Sigma w}$$

where q_n / q_0 are the quantity relatives and the w's are the weights. The interpretation is analogous to that for the weighted relative price index.

The quantity relatives q_n/q_0 show the proportionate increase in quantity from the base year, and each good is given equal weight. The index formula (9) is a weighted average of these quantity relatives.

As can be easily seen, the main problem is the selection of weights. The rationale we follow is that the weights w should indicate the relative importance of the quantities. This in turn implies that the weights will depend on the kind of quantity changes we wish to measure. For example, if we are interested in changes in industrial output, the appropriate weights may be the value added. If we are interested in changes in freight car loadings, the weights may be the tonnages. If we are interested in changes in egg production, the weights may be the number of boxes.

This flexibility in the selection of weights gives the weighted relative quantity index a wider range of applicability than that of the weighted aggregative quantity index. In fact the Laspeyres and Paasche types of formulas are special cases of formula (9), where the weights are $w = \Sigma\, q_0 p_0$ for the Laspeyres type and $w = \Sigma\, q_0 p_n$ for the Paasche type.

Let us first give an example of how formula (9) is used, and then discuss some of the problems in determining weights.

Example 3. Given the data in the accompanying table, find the weighted relative quantity index.

Com- modity	1958 q_0	1959 q_1	1960 q_2	p_0	$q_0 p_0$	q_1/q_0	q_2/q_0
Chair	20	30	30	$ 5	$100	30/20	30/20
Desk	10	20	30	8	80	20/10	30/10
Radio	30	40	50	10	300	40/30	50/30
					$480		

The index for 1959 is obtained from

$$I_{59} = \frac{\Sigma\left(\dfrac{q_1}{q_0}\right) w}{\Sigma\, w}$$

To show the relative importance, let us use the proportion of total value of the base year. For chairs, we have

$$w_1 = \frac{q_0 p_0}{\Sigma\, q_0 p_0} = \frac{\$100}{\$480}$$

For desks, we have

$$w_2 = \frac{q_0 p_0}{\Sigma\, q_0 p_0} = \frac{\$80}{\$480}$$

For radios, we have

$$w_3 = \frac{q_0 p_0}{\Sigma\, q_0 p_0} = \frac{\$300}{\$480}$$

Then the sum of the weights is

$$\Sigma w = w_1 + w_2 + w_3$$

$$= \frac{\$100}{\$480} + \frac{\$80}{\$480} + \frac{\$300}{\$480} = 1$$

as we expect. By substituting these values into the quantity index formula, we find

$$I_{59} = \frac{\Sigma \left(\dfrac{q_1}{q_0}\right) w}{\Sigma\, w}$$

$$= \frac{\Sigma \left(\dfrac{q_1}{q_0}\right)\left(\dfrac{q_0 p_0}{\Sigma\, q_0 p_0}\right)}{\Sigma \left(\dfrac{q_0 p_0}{\Sigma\, q_0 p_0}\right)}$$

$$= \frac{\left(\dfrac{30}{20}\right)\left(\dfrac{100}{480}\right) + \left(\dfrac{20}{10}\right)\left(\dfrac{80}{480}\right) + \left(\dfrac{40}{30}\right)\left(\dfrac{300}{480}\right)}{\dfrac{100}{480} + \dfrac{80}{480} + \dfrac{300}{480}}$$

$$= \frac{71}{48} = 1.479 \quad \text{or} \quad 147.9$$

Therefore, the result is the same as that obtained by the Laspeyres type of quantity index in Example 1, and this occurs because of the way the weights were selected. The relationship can be shown algebraically as follows:

$$I_{59} = \frac{\Sigma \left(\dfrac{q_1}{q_0}\right) w}{\Sigma\, w}$$

$$= \frac{\Sigma \left(\dfrac{q_1}{q_0}\right)\left(\dfrac{q_0 p_0}{\Sigma\, q_0 p_0}\right)}{\Sigma \left(\dfrac{q_0 p_0}{\Sigma\, q_0 p_0}\right)}$$

$$= \frac{\Sigma\, q_1 p_0}{\Sigma\, q_0 p_0}$$

The result for I_{60}, using the weighted relative formula, is $I_{60} =$ 1.854, or 184.5, which is the same as the result in Example 3 of Section 11.6 when using the Laspeyres type of formula. The reader should work this out for himself.

(v) Index of industrial production

As an illustration of some of the problems involved in determining weights, the IIP is briefly discussed. The IIP measures the changes in the output of manufacturing and mining industries. The most recent revision of the index, in 1959, extended its coverage to include utility output. The overall index is subdivided into 207 individual monthly series. The weight base is 1957. The reference base which was 1947–49 $= 100$ was shifted to 1957 $= 100$, but in 1962 it was again shifted to 1957–59 $= 100$ to keep it uniform with other Federal Government general purpose economic indices.

Our main interest here is to see how the weights have been determined. The index in schematic form is

$$I = \frac{\Sigma\left(\dfrac{q_n}{q_0}\right) w}{\Sigma\, w}$$

and measures changes of output. The weights w, then, should indicate the relative importance of the individual outputs. This is accomplished by contrasting the relative share of the output of a commodity (for example, a chair) against the total output. To find this relative share, we first have to decide what is meant by total output.

At first glance, it may seem that all we have to do is add up the various outputs. But what happens, for example, when we add lumber output, chair output, desk output, etc., in value terms? Part of the lumber is used for chairs, part is used for desks, etc. Hence, a simple summation of these outputs will involve double counting. That is, the lumber will be counted twice, once as lumber output and again as part of desks and chairs. To avoid this, the concept of *value added* has been developed. Let us illustrate this in Table 11.4 with the production of chairs.

A firm producing chairs purchases lumber (called intermediate goods), and by employing factors of production (labor, land, capital, and entrepreneur), produces chairs. A breakdown of this allocation of

TABLE 11.4.   Firm Producing Chairs

Allocations		Sources	
Lumber	$ 5	Sale of chair	$10
Wages	2		
Rent	1		
Interest	1		
Profit	1		
Total allocation of value production	$10	Total value of production	$10

value of production is shown on the left side of Table 11.4. The chair is sold and the firm realizes the total value of production. Hence, the net value that this firm adds to lumber to produce a chair is the difference between the total value of production and the value of the intermediate products. This is shown in Table 11.5.

TABLE 11.5.   Statement of Value Added

Allocations		Sources	
Labor	$2	Sale of chair	$10
Land	1		
Capital	1		
Profit	1	Minus: Lumber	5
Total allocation of value added	$5	Total value added	$ 5

The total output, then, is the sum of the value added of all the goods. Roughly speaking, it is the sum of the factor payments, that is, wages, rent, interest, and profits.

What we wish to do now is to use this concept of value added to determine the relative shares of an individual output versus total output. For this, let us assume that the value added for chairs, desks, and radios in our example are as given in the table on page 311.

The $q_0 p_0$ shows the value added for the base year 1958. For chairs, for example,

$$q_0 p_0 = \$40$$

But $q_0 = 20$ chairs. Thus

$$p_0 = \frac{\$40}{20} = \$2.00 \text{ per chair}$$

Commodity	1958 q_0	1959 q_1	1960 q_2	Value Added $q_0 p_0$	q_1/q_0	q_2/q_0
Chairs	20	30	30	$ 40	30/20	30/20
Desks	10	20	30	30	20/10	30/10
Radios	30	40	50	120	40/30	50/30
				$190		

This shows that the value added per chair is $2.00. Note carefully that the p_0 is *not* the price of the chairs. In similar manner the value added per desk and radio are obtained as

$$p_0 = \frac{\$30}{10} = \$3.00 \text{ per desk}$$

$$p_0 = \frac{\$120}{30} = \$4.00 \text{ per radio}$$

The total value added is $190, as the table shows.

Hence, the relative shares of the chairs, desks, and radios are

$$w_1 = \frac{q_{01} p_{01}}{\Sigma \, q_0 p_0} = \frac{40}{190}$$

$$w_2 = \frac{q_{02} p_{02}}{\Sigma \, q_0 p_0} = \frac{30}{190}$$

$$w_3 = \frac{q_{03} p_{03}}{\Sigma \, q_0 p_0} = \frac{120}{190}$$

$$\Sigma \, w = w_1 + w_2 + w_3 = \frac{40}{190} + \frac{30}{190} + \frac{120}{190} = 1.00$$

By using these weights, the quantity index can be constructed as follows:

$$I_{59} = \frac{\Sigma \left(\frac{q_1}{q_0}\right)\left(\frac{q_0 p_0}{\Sigma \, q_0 p_0}\right)}{\Sigma \left(\frac{q_0 p_0}{\Sigma \, q_0 p_0}\right)}$$

$$= \left(\frac{30}{20}\right)\left(\frac{40}{190}\right) + \left(\frac{20}{10}\right)\left(\frac{30}{190}\right) + \left(\frac{40}{30}\right)\left(\frac{120}{190}\right)$$

$$= 1.473 \quad \text{or} \quad 147.3$$

$$I_{60} = \frac{\Sigma\left(\dfrac{q_2}{q_0}\right)\left(\dfrac{q_0 p_0}{\Sigma\, q_0 p_0}\right)}{\Sigma\left(\dfrac{q_0 p_0}{\Sigma\, q_0 p_0}\right)}$$

$$= \left(\frac{30}{20}\right)\left(\frac{40}{190}\right) + \left(\frac{30}{10}\right)\left(\frac{30}{190}\right) + \left(\frac{50}{30}\right)\left(\frac{120}{190}\right)$$

$$= 1.842 \quad \text{or} \quad 184.2$$

The two main points to understand are:

1. p_0 are not prices but value added per unit.
2. The reason why value added was used instead of prices.

The IIP is given as

(10)
$$\frac{\Sigma\left(\dfrac{q_n}{q_{57}}\right)\left(\dfrac{q_{57} p_{57}}{\Sigma\, q_{57} p_{57}}\right)}{\Sigma\left(\dfrac{q_{57} p_{57}}{\Sigma\, q_{57} p_{57}}\right)}$$

The denominator is 1.00. Thus the index may be rewritten as follows:

(11)
$$\Sigma\left(\frac{q_n}{q_{57}}\right)\left(\frac{q_{57} p_{57}}{\Sigma\, q_{57} p_{57}}\right) = \frac{\Sigma\, q_n p_{57}}{\Sigma\, q_{57} p_{57}}$$

The form of (11) is the same as the Laspeyres quantity index (6), but the difference is that in (11) the p_0 show value added and not price.

The IIP was used to illustrate how weights are determined for this specific index. The *Consumer Durables Output Index,* published by the Federal Reserve System, uses gross factory value of production for the weights; the *Agricultural Marketings and Production Indices,* published by the U.S. Department of Agriculture, uses fixed prices as weights; the *Freight-Carloadings Index,* published by the Federal Reserve System, uses revenues to calculate weights, and so forth. The weights to be used for any specific quantity index are usually determined as a compromise between an analysis of what is to be measured and the availability of data.

GOVERNMENT PRICE STATISTICS

TUESDAY, MAY 2, 1961

CONGRESS OF THE UNITED STATES,
SUBCOMMITTEE ON ECONOMIC STATISTICS OF THE
JOINT ECONOMIC COMMITTEE,
Washington, D.C.

The subcommittee met at 10:10 a.m., pursuant to recess, in room G–308, New Senate Office Building, Senator Paul H. Douglas presiding.

Present: Senator Douglas.

Also present: John W. Lehman, deputy executive director and clerk; and James W. Knowles, economist.

Senator DOUGLAS. Gentlemen, will you come forward?

While I was not able to be present during the complete testimony of the Committee on Price Statistics yesterday, I did have the chance to go over their recommendations, and I think I am going to ask Dr. Clague to lead off this morning and I am going to ask him, if he would, to comment especially about the recommendations for measuring to a greater degree the qualitative changes which take place in the goods whose prices are studied, and, second, the recommendation that more frequent budgetary studies be made to develop a better weighting system.

Mr. Clague, if you will lead off.

I am going to ask also the Department of Commerce to comment on the recommendation that the export and import prices be segregated so that we may get comparative indexes of those.

Mr. Clague.

STATEMENT OF EWAN CLAGUE, COMMISSIONER OF LABOR STATISTICS, U.S. DEPARTMENT OF LABOR; ACCOMPANIED BY ARNOLD E. CHASE AND SIDNEY A. JAFFE

Mr. CLAGUE. Mr. Chairman, I have a brief statement here I would like to read, if I may, before taking up your questions.

Senator DOUGLAS. Yes, do.

Mr. CLAGUE. Each of the Government's major price indexes involves many complex concepts, many intricate statistical procedures, and many difficulties in meeting the particular needs of various users of the indexes.

For example, the well-known Consumer Price Index is based on prices for about 300 items which must be selected to represent the movement of prices for all of the many thousands of items that urban families buy.

Next, the items in the index are priced monthly or quarterly by about 160 full-time or part-time employees in stores and service establishments which must be so selected that they will represent the movement of prices in the hundreds of thousands of retail establishments throughout the country.

Many complications arise to add to the magnitude of the job. New items constantly appear on the market, some old items disappear, and others take new forms. Models, sizes, and packaging change frequently. New stores come into business; old stores expand, relocate, or go out of business.

A price decrease for a small item, such as a dozen aspirin tablets, must be properly balanced in an index with a price increase for a large item, such as a new house.

Other complications arise in trying to meet, in one price index, the needs of many different users, such as the Government for economic policy determination, business and labor for wage negotiations, business for market analysis and forecasting, academic economists and statisticians for economic analysis, State and local organizations for adjustments in public assistance, and the general public for understanding price stability, inflation, or deflation. The concepts and procedures most appropriate for one of these important uses are not always the best for others.

Having in mind all of these factors, together with the normal operating problems of obtaining the required information accurately from reporting establishments, it is easy to see that the compilation of a price index to be published each month is, indeed, a complex undertaking.

This complexity is reflected in the report of the Price Statistics Review Committee, and especially in the staff papers which accompany it.

Many of the problems involved are highly technical, and adequate treatment of just one of them would require more time than is available for this hearing.

With the committee's permission, I propose, therefore, to discuss briefly only the major policy questions raised by the report and to submit a more detailed, technical statement to be appended to my testimony.

I would ask, Mr. Chairman, if you would put that detailed statement in the record.

Senator DOUGLAS. That will be printed at the conclusion of your testimony and discussion which may follow it.

Mr. CLAGUE. I would like to say, first, that there are many recommendations in the report which we, in the Bureau of Labor Statistics, have found to have merit. Insofar as possible, they are being taken into account in our program planning, especially in the revision of the Consumer Price Index which is now in progress. Among the recommendations which we believe should be considered favorably, with certain modifications as indicated briefly below and amplified in the statement which I have submitted, are those recommendations with respect to the following:

(1) Probability sampling and replication of samples. That is, multiplication of samples, division of samples into parts so we can check one with the other. We agree with that, although the Bureau's

efforts to use probability sampling techniques in recent years have shown that there are practical difficulties not fully recognized in the report which may prevent their application at some sampling stages.

(2) Weight revisions on a regular periodic basis. The Bureau would prefer 10-year intervals, subject to change only if economic conditions change drastically between regularly scheduled revisions.

(3) Earlier introduction of new products—provided that objective criteria on timing and method of introduction can be established and that some apparent inconsistencies with the sampling recommendations can be resolved.

(4) Specification pricing—which the Bureau adopted many years ago. But the part of the recommendation which calls for broadening the specifications could be accepted only with respect to certain items. Moreover, it is necessary in our judgment to maintain a considerable degree of centralized control over the price collection process in order to maintain the quality of the price data.

(5) Actual transactions prices for the Wholesale Price Index. However, the Bureau wants to profit from its earlier experience in this field. It would place emphasis first on more intensive efforts to obtain actual transactions prices from sellers, resorting to obtaining prices from buyers only where absolutely necessary, because of the great difficulty and expense involved in the latter method.

(6) Extending the scope of the price indexes. We have already reached a decision to cover single-person families and are considering further extensions which may eventually expand the index to represent all nonfarm families.

(7) Collection of price data outside the scope of the official indexes. This would be useful, especially with respect to new products.

(8) More extensive documentation of the indexes.

(9) More research, especially on the quality measurement problem, on sampling methods, and on the types of indexes best suited for various major uses—but the Bureau cannot accept the thesis, which is emphasized in the report, that the procedures which it has used to adjust for quality changes have resulted in any substantial or systematic bias in its indexes.

(10) Organization of wholesale and other nonretail price data within a sector framework, or input-output framework. But it must be recognized that this would entail a substantial expansion of the coverage of nonretail price statistics, that the weighting factors needed for this purpose are not now available, and that an index based on commodity groupings probably would have to be continued indefinitely, since the new form of index would not replace it for many important uses.

Those are the recommendations then which we endorse with the modifications we have suggested.

It is only fair to say that full implementation of the recommendations listed above would require a considerable increase in the funds devoted to price work in the Bureau of Labor Statistics. Also, some of them would require research on the development of proper techniques prior to their adoption.

Certain recommendations, which the report characterizes as cost saving (as, for example, the broadening of specifications), would increase rather than decrease costs, in our judgment.

Some other recommendations probably would produce better results with the same resources, but we cannot find in any of the recommendations significant savings which would permit us to carry on the additional work suggested by the report within our present resources.

There is one very important recommendation with which the Bureau of Labor Statistics cannot agree, even with modifications. This is the recommendation that the Consumer Price Index be reoriented gradually toward a "welfare" or "constant utility" index. We would see some value in having a "true cost-of-living" or constant utility index if techniques can be developed for defining such an index unambiguously, and then for compiling it objectively.

We must emphasize, however, that this is a long-range goal that is now unattainable, may always be unattainable, and at best could be fully attained only after considerable further theoretical and statistical exploration.

We believe that a pure price index, such as the CPI, is needed for many of the important purposes which it now serves, and that it most definitely should not be hybridized toward a welfare index.

The Bureau also questions the soundness of the following recommendations:

(1) Publishing seasonally adjusted indexes. Seasonal fluctuations in the all-items CPI are relatively minor, and many laymen who rely on the index would be confused as to whether they should use the adjusted or unadjusted index.

(2) Retroactive correction of minor errors in the Consumer Price Index—because such corrections go beyond the requirements of statistical purity and might cause disruption of good contractual relations between users of the index merely for the sake of overrefinement.

(3) Use of Census unit value data in the Wholesale Price Index—because tests which we have made show that real price changes cannot be separated from changes in product mix which are reflected in unit values.

From this very brief summary, it is apparent that we have found many good points in the report of the Price Statistics Review Committee. Except for a few major issues, such as the "welfare" index, our disagreements with the recommendations in the report are mainly based on practical considerations.

Senator DOUGLAS. Mr. Clague, if you will turn to your memorandum, you seem to accept the recommendation of the Committee that the weights be revised every 10 years.

Mr. CLAGUE. Yes, sir, I agree with this suggestion which we have included there. If economic conditions change very markedly in between, it might be done more frequently.

Senator DOUGLAS. Now, may I ask about the dates of the weighting systems adopted in the Consumer Price Index and the cost-of-living index which preceded it? As I understand, the weights were originally based on budget studies for the years 1947, 1918, and 1919.

Mr. CLAGUE. That is correct.

Senator DOUGLAS. And for how long did that weighting system prevail?

Mr. CLAGUE. That continued until the new consumer price studies were undertaken in 1934–36, and the final revision of the index was accomplished in 1939. So it lasted nearly 20 years.

Senator DOUGLAS. That covered the period roughly from 1914 to 1939?

Mr. CLAGUE. Well, yes, that is right. But remember that the weights were based on 1917–19.

Senator DOUGLAS. Then the new weights were used from 1939 on?

Mr. CLAGUE. That is right.

Senator DOUGLAS. And when were they revised again?

Mr. CLAGUE. They were revised again in—well, there were some revisions made during the war. I have that included in my longer statement.

At the time of the 1939 CPI revision, the BLS not only recomputed the index back to March 1935 using the 1934–36 expenditure data as the weights, but it also reweighted the price indexes for major groups with the same set of revised weights to introduce a new CPI series for the period June 1930 through March 1935.

Then for the period 1925 to 1929 the CPI was recomputed in the same manner using an average of the old 1917–19 weights and the revised 1934–36 weights.

Senator DOUGLAS. When was the final budgetary study made?

Mr. CLAGUE. The last one? You mean down to date?

Senator DOUGLAS. Yes.

Mr. CLAGUE. We made, Mr. Chairman, several partial studies during the war, I believe in 1941 and 1944, to meet wartime conditions. And then following the war, in 1946, 1947, and 1948, we had a system of doing a few cities each year, three cities each year.

Then we started the big revision in 1949 to 1952. Well, the year 1950 really was the year for which the expenditures data were taken.

We had the advantage of those several preceding years on a few cities that gave us a little backward look.

We carried our weights forward as best we could to 1952, when we shifted to the new index we now have beginning January 1953.

Now we are 10 years, as you can see, 11 years, away from that in making this survey.

I would like to add, Mr. Chairman——

Senator DOUGLAS. So, if I may interject——

Mr. CLAGUE. Yes.

Senator DOUGLAS. Your first system of weights lasted for about 17 years?

Mr. CLAGUE. Yes.

Senator DOUGLAS. Your second system of weights for about 17 years, with some modifications?

Mr. CLAGUE. Yes.

Senator DOUGLAS. And the final system for 9 years? It has been in effect for 9 years?

Mr. CLAGUE. Well, Mr. Chairman, you really ought to count till we make the new revision, which will be 1964, so that you see it will be 11 years.

Senator DOUGLAS. Eleven years?

Mr. CLAGUE. Yes.

Senator DOUGLAS. Has that been authorized?

Mr. CLAGUE. Yes—this program.

Senator DOUGLAS. And money is appropriated?

Mr. CLAGUE. It is appropriated each year as we go. So far the committee has given us substantially—and the Budget Bureau—the funds we require, so that——

Senator DOUGLAS. Have you ever published a bulletin describing each of these and summarizing the whole index from 1914 on and the methods which have been used in construction?

Mr. CLAGUE. Not in any single bulletin do we have this.

Senator DOUGLAS. How many bulletins has your Bureau published? I think I used to be the only man in the country who read all the statistical bulletins the Bureau published.

Mr. CLAGUE. In 1934–36 there was, of course, a great number of bulletins published on those consumer expenditure studies.

Senator DOUGLAS. Is it not true you have published over a thousand bulletins?

Mr. CLAGUE. On prices? Or all?

Senator DOUGLAS. In all.

Mr. CLAGUE. In all, yes indeed.

Senator DOUGLAS. Several thousand? Is that not true?

Mr. CLAGUE. I think we are up approaching two thousand as our latest number.

Senator DOUGLAS. I lost track some years back, but——

Mr. CLAGUE. I think we are around 2,000.

Senator DOUGLAS. Do you not think that one bulletin or a couple of bulletins could be used to summarize the whole index from 1914 on and describe the different methods used at these different times so that we might get a connected picture of 47 years of I would say the cost of living for urban families?

Mr. CLAGUE. The answer is "Yes."

Senator DOUGLAS. The answer is "Yes?"

Mr. CLAGUE. We could do that. I want to emphasize we did in Bulletin 699 back in 1941 publish quite a comprehensive review back at that period.

Senator DOUGLAS. I hope you will take this injunction very seriously, because I think this is extremely important.

I know one gets absorbed in the current tasks and current pressures, but if you could assign a couple or two or three of your people to work on this, I think it would be extremely valuable.

Mr. CLAGUE. Yes, sir; I agree and I would only emphasize that one of the recommendations of this price committee has been a little more money for research.

I would say to you that is one of our great problems—that the current pressure on timing and dates and getting material out——

Senator DOUGLAS. I know.

Mr. CLAGUE. Has overwhelmed us, and we sometimes do not take these longer range views.

Senator DOUGLAS. I understand.

Now, if I may ask a technical question. My memory has slipped on this matter. In computing your countrywide index of the cost of living, do you first take an average of the commodities based on the cities and then weight them by national weights, or do you get an index for each city based on the weights for that city and then combine the index of the cities into a national index?

Mr. CLAGUE. We use the second method you have described.

Senator DOUGLAS. You use the second method?

Mr. CLAGUE. That is right.

Senator DOUGLAS. And what importance do you give to the various cities? Do you use simple weighting or weighting according to population?

Mr. CLAGUE. I think I will ask Mr. Chase to answer that since he is the one who prepares the index. Mr. Chase, do you want to answer that?

Mr. CHASE. These are basically population weights.

Senator DOUGLAS. Well, I am very glad you say that, because I used population weights in computing the nationwide index but I was severely taken to task by many critics who said that it gave excessive importance to the indexes of the huge metropolitan cities such as New York and Chicago and Philadelphia and that it obscured the importance of the smaller cities.

And, as a matter of fact, as the years have gone by I have rather been inclined to think that my critics were perhaps closer to the truth than I was.

Mr. CHASE. Mr. Chairman, there are smaller cities represented in the index.

Senator DOUGLAS. Oh, I understand that. But if the cities are weighted according to their population, you naturally have a much greater sample from the big cities. You have all the big cities but you cannot have all the small cities. There is New York with 9 million, and Chicago with 3½ million, and Detroit with 2¼ million, and I do not know what the population of Los Angeles was this morning, but it has been growing very rapidly. You get those cities in. But then cities like, say, South Bend, Ind., and Springfield, Ill., or Peoria, Ill., or Sioux City, Iowa, and so forth, some of those may be included, but a great many of them are not.

If you merely weight the cities, say, in the 50,000 to 100,000 class by the number of cities so covered or cities from 100,000 to 250,000 where the number is so covered, you give them relatively small weights, whereas the group may be extremely important.

Mr. CHASE. I was just going to say, Mr. Chairman, that some of the larger cities represent only themselves in the index.

Senator DOUGLAS. I understand.

Mr. CHASE. But those of a smaller size on down to the very smallest represent all cities in those size classes.

Senator DOUGLAS. Oh.

Mr. CLAGUE. They are weighted.

Senator DOUGLAS. Well, that is very good.

What are the classes that you use?

Mr. CHASE. The smallest class is up to 30,000 population. The next class is up to 240,000, I believe is the figure. And then there is a third class of 240,000 to 1 million. The fourth class is 1 million and over in the present index.

Senator DOUGLAS. I think that is fine.

Mr. CLAGUE. May I say, Mr. Chairman, that is one of our problems. Our representation of these small cities is not very large when you consider the enormous number of them.

Senator DOUGLAS. Yes.

Mr. CLAGUE. We have only 9 in one of those classes, and we have 16 small ones in the under 30,000 that represent several thousand small cities.

Senator DOUGLAS. Yes.

Mr. CLAGUE. We are not too happy about that. And, by the way, that weight which they have had in the past represented a fifth of the total U.S. population. There is a question of whether our sample is large enough.

Senator DOUGLAS. Now, what do you think of this recommendation which I was very dubious about, as a matter of fact, that price indexes measure qualitative changes to a much greater degree than now?

I asked the committee yesterday as to whether you could measure qualitative changes by quantitative methods. I was not fully satisfied with their reply. But I inferred that they thought they could take the changes in the nature of a commodity on a number of specific points, such as a house, and get an appraisal of the changing quality of a house in terms of different improvements put in.

What do you think of that?

Mr. CLAGUE. Well, we have reservations on that, as you notice from our statement. There is no consumer index in the world, no matter what name they call it, that has ever attained anything resembling this constant utility or this cost of living in this psychological sense. We do not say it cannot be done. In fact, we would like to do some work to see if there are ways and means of doing it. But I would say this: It is not done now anywhere, and we do not see the way to do it in any significant proportion of items.

We now have a price index, which does represent the effect of price changes on the cost of living. Now, admittedly, there are many elements in cost of living other than price changes. It seems to us that the exploration of alternative kinds of indexes is good. We still insist you need a price index of the kind we have, even if you tried to get this constant utility index. But at the moment we would say that we cannot do anything more than try to do some research work and see if there are ways of doing this. We do not know how to do it now.

Senator DOUGLAS. Now, if I may revert again to these past studies, did the use of the 1934–36 family budgets appreciably change the movement of the cost-of-living index as compared to the 1918 weights?

In other words, did the system of changing weights produce a different movement during the periods in which the two indexes overlapped?

Mr. CLAGUE. Well, again, this is covered in my longer manuscript.

Senator DOUGLAS. Well, I have not had time to read that.

Mr. CLAGUE. I know you have not, but I just indicate that the full story can be read there.

I would say here that both the old and the new indexes—this is from March 1935 to December 1939, the new basis—the old and the new indexes showed the same pattern of change with the maximum discrepancy at any time being approximately an index point over that period. The total increase over this 5-year period was 1.8 percent for the new index series as compared to 1.9 percent for the old index series.

So the difference is not very great.

Senator DOUGLAS. Wait a minute. What about the change in the 1950's? You had an overlapping period in the 1950's.

Mr. CLAGUE. We did not have an overlapping period there. Whether we have some unpublished studies that went back over several years or not I do not know. Did we have any?

Mr. JAFFE. The sample of cities was completely changed in the 1952 revision, and there were a considerable number of conceptual changes in the structure of the index. The sample of items was completely revamped so it was not possible to reconstruct the index backward for any length of time.

So we do not have any real comparison for an overlap period for the 1952 revision.

In the 1939 revision there were less serious changes. The sample of cities remained approximately the same. I think one city changed. The structure of the index was pretty much the same. The only important change was the sample of items so that you have a more realistic comparison for the overlap periods.

Senator DOUGLAS. So that if you were to go back and recompute you would be in difficulty because you would have to recompute for each city——

Mr. CLAGUE. Yes.

Senator DOUGLAS. With new weights?

Mr. CLAGUE. And you would have the problem of trying to collect past prices on the new cities. It is very hard to make any comparison.

However, we have always maintained, Senator, that there is not a great deal of difference in these weights from time to time. They must not be ignored, but they are not such a tremendously important factor.

Senator DOUGLAS. Have you experimented with using the different population weights as applied to the cities? That is, I suppose for the 1917–19 system we used the census of 1900. Probably for the weights in the 1930 period the census of 1930. And for the period of the 1950's, for the 1950 weights, the census of 1950? Is that not true?

Mr. CLAGUE. Yes.

Mr. CHASE. Yes.

Senator DOUGLAS. Of course, what we have had during this period has been a great drift of people not only into the cities but into the larger metropolitan areas, and I should not think it would be too difficult in these cases to take your end-year weightings and carry them back and see what the difference is as compared with the base-year weightings.

Mr. CLAGUE. Mr. Chairman, this was the reason we shifted the cities in 1952. You see, as long as we were staying with those same cities, even though they did not all grow equally, we were dealing with cities larger than a hundred thousand and, therefore, the changes would not be so important.

Now, when we reached out and took in the smaller cities, shifted the list, then of course we got quite a different type of index.

It would be possible now to take the current population weights of these same cities that are still in the index and work it backward to 1952, of course.

Senator DOUGLAS. I should not think that would be too difficult either, because you would only be dealing with how many cities?

Mr. CLAGUE. Forty-six.

Senator DOUGLAS. Forty-six? I should not think that would be too difficult.

I think you could compare, therefore, the results under the Paasche formula and the Laspeyres formula.

Mr. CLAGUE. Yes.

Senator DOUGLAS. Then I would like to see you experiment with the Irving Fisher formula which, as I remember, is the geometric average of the product of the Paasche and the Laspeyres formulas. Is that not true?

Mr. CLAGUE. That is right.

By the way, I think we have done some work not exactly on what you are saying but have we not done some work on the comparison of the Laspeyres and the Paasche indexes and the effect of it on certain changes?

Mr. JAFFE. We have been able to do that in a more realistic manner in connection with our Wholesale Price Index, because there we have a program of quinquennial weight revisions because there is a census of industries available. The changes in the structure of that index in recent years have not been as drastic as in the CPI.

The last time we made a weight revision we recomputed, in effect, the index with Paasche weights as well as with Laspeyres weights, and we intend to do it again in the current weight revision as we are incorporating 1958 weights.

We have cited in this longer document some comparisons of the movement of the index over a number of years using the Laspeyres formula and the movement using the Paasche formula, and it is not too significant, if I can find it here.

Mr. CLAGUE. I would say, Mr. Chairman, we would be glad to do it on the CPI for the period back to 1952, because that could be done readily.

Senator DOUGLAS. Well, hitherto we have been discussing the cost-of-living index. Now the Wholesale Price Index has been interjected into the discussion. What are the weights you used on prices in the Wholesale Price Index?

Mr. JAFFE. The weights for the Wholesale Price Index are the shipments data which are derived from the census of manufacturers.

Senator DOUGLAS. Is this value added?

Mr. JAFFE. This is the value of shipments which includes the value added.

In other words, I think the point you are trying to make is that they are duplicated weights.

Senator DOUGLAS. No; I was not originally making this point. I was just trying to find out. You mean that they are total value?

Mr. JAFFE. They are total value of shipments as they leave the establishment which reports to the Census Bureau.

Senator DOUGLAS. Now we will come to this point that you anticipated. Your total values consist of prices and quantities? So you weight prices by prices and quantities? The next question is whether this gives a dual weight to prices.

Mr. JAFFE. Shall I answer?

Mr. CLAGUE. Yes.

Mr. JAFFE. As you aggregate the Wholesale Price Index data to summary levels, you are correct; this does give a dual weight to various commodities which have been processed at different stages and shipped out from one plant to another.

Senator DOUGLAS. Now, the alternative would be to use simple quantities. Can you do that or is that impractical?

Mr. JAFFE. It is really impractical. I do not think we have the data, and I am not too sure what the interpretation of that kind of an index would be.

The recommendation of the Price Statistics Review Committee takes a middle ground, as I recall. They would use real prices corresponding to, say, shipments, but the weights would be net weights, so that as you aggregated shipments the interplant or interestablishment transactions within a category would be washed out, so that you would not build up this duplication of values in your weighting structure.

Senator DOUGLAS. Well, similarly, I suppose in your price index you weight those not merely by quantities consumed by families but by amounts of money spent? Is that not true?

Mr. CLAGUE. Yes, that is right.

Mr. JAFFE. Yes.

Senator DOUGLAS. So you weight consumer prices by prices times quantities on a consumption level, and your wholesale index is similarly prices weighted by price times quantity? Is that true?

Mr. JAFFE. That is true.

Mr. CLAGUE. That is right.

(The following was later received for the record:)

Upon reading the transcript of the May 2 hearings on price statistics, it became apparent that the BLS representatives missed the point of Senator Douglas' question with regard to the weighting of prices by prices and quantities. When value weights (that is, products of prices and quantities) are used in either the Consumer Price Index or the Wholesale Price Index they are multiplied against price relatives and not against prices. Thus there is no double weighting in the sense that Senator Douglas was discussing.

Senator DOUGLAS. Now, do we have a representative of the Federal Reserve Board to testify on the index of production here?

(No response.)

They get an index of production. How do they weight their quantities? Does anyone know in the guild of Government statisticians? Do they weight their quantities by prices or by values which in turn are pq's?

Mr. JAFFE. As I recall—I am not an expert on this subject, Mr. Chairman—I think within industry categories they weight by shipments data. But as they combine the data across industries they use net value added weights.

Senator DOUGLAS. Which in turn are pq's?

Mr. JASZI. Yes.

Senator DOUGLAS. So the pq's are used for weights both for prices and for quantities?

Mr. JAFFE. It is a little different kind of pq as you aggregate across industries.

Senator DOUGLAS. I understand.

Did you ever try taking the geometric average of the end-year weights on your wholesale prices? Or, what difference is there by end-year weights as compared to base-year weights?

Mr. JAFFE. Well, I have some figures that I can cite from this appendix in Mr. Clague's testimony.

We had several major weight revisions in the Wholesale Price Index. There was a completely comprehensive revision in 1947 when the weights of the WPI were revised on the basis of the 1947 census of industries. Actually this was done in 1952, but the census was for 1957.

And at the same time the structure of the index was extended to cover the entire nonretail commodity sector.

Then in 1957 there was another revision of weights incorporating the data for the more recent census.

Now, the all-commodities Wholesale Price Index based on 1947 weights rose 14.4 percent, while the reweighted index based on 1954 weights increased 11.1 percent.

Now, this is as close as you can get to a true Laspeyres-Paasche comparison, because there were no major expansions or changes in the structure of the Wholesale Price Index over this period. There wer. a few changes introduced at the same time the 1954 weights were introduced, but we washed them out in making this comparison, so this is as close to a Laspeyres-Paasche comparison as we could get.

Senator DOUGLAS. I used to think a good deal on this question. I have not had much opportunity to think about it in recent years. But if you will forgive me, I would like to think about it for a moment now.

Such experimentation as I did with indexes of production in Great Britain and the United States and certain other countries made me tentatively form the conclusion that the commodities which increased most in quantity decreased most in price.

Mr. JAFFE. The next few sentences of this paragraph go into that in connection with this same 1947–54 comparison. Taking the 15 major commodity groups, they showed a generally similar pattern with the 1947 weighted series increasing more (or decreasing less) than the 1954 weighted series in 13 of the 15 cases. Only the group indexes for hides, skins, and leather and leather products, and for lumber and wood products showed the reweighted index increasing more than the official series.

Now, this is in accord with the conclusions that you were expressing I think.

Senator DOUGLAS. Now, I don't know if you use proportionate net values or proportionate consumption figures. I do not know whether this gives a systematic bias in the price index or not, because I think it depends upon the relative elasticity of demand. If you have a commodity which has an appreciable decrease in price and an appreciable increase in production, the question as to whether it forms a greater weight depends upon whether historically its elasticity of demand is greater than unity, so in comparison with other products, it comes to comprise a larger share of the total net value that you are studying.

But this is a very interesting field for research. And the experiments that I had made indicated that, as your comparison does, the use of end-year weights tended to result in a lower index than base-year weights.

Mr. JAFFE. Mr. Chairman, as——

Senator Douglas. But it is not as simple as merely saying that the commodities which have the greatest decrease in "p" have the greatest increase in "q," because you must also get the product of the two, "pq," and in turn the share which "pq" forms of the sum of the "pq's."

Mr. Jaffe. Yes.

Mr. Clague. That is right.

Mr. Jaffe. Mr. Chairman, in the 1947–54 period it embraces some rather important periods of economic change, so that you have to look at that factor in relation to the 3.3-percent discrepancy in the price movement.

If you were to make this same comparison from 1954 to 1957, the WPI recomputed with 1954 weights increased 7.3 percent, whereas the official WPI as originally computed increased 7.4 percent.

So it depends really on what is happening in the economy, how volatile the changes are.

Senator Douglas. This is a prelude to saying that Congress is generous to such institutions as the GeologicalSurvey and the Smithsonian Institution in making appropriations for theoretical research, pieces of which have no practical significance. We have been very utilitarian in the appropriations which we make to Government departments, including the Bureau of Labor Statistics, and the refinement, the statistical refinement, of series has been thrown upon private scholars and private foundations.

This may be a fairly good division of labor provided you get the private resources to carry this out. It suffers from the difficulty that the people on the outside may not know the full intricacies of the figures from the inside and may at times misinterpret the data.

Also at times they make impossible demands, as I think in this case they did, in some instances, upon the Government agencies.

What I am leading up to is this: I am not on the Appropriations Committee, but I think that provision in your budget for some theoretical work on just these issues would be helpful, and somebody at least should try to see that those were approved.

If I know Government agencies, they are always expert in concealing purposes within their budget estimates which hide their true design, and while I do not wish to encourage deception I would say that if there is a practice of deception I do not see any greater ethical wrong in practicing it in this case than in other cases.

Mr. Clague. Mr. Chairman, all I can say is we are very poor at it.

The only time we get any money to do any analytical work at all is when we have an enlarged project of some sort in which we scrape a few people to one side. There is not a recognized field of research such as there is in many other agencies.

Senator Douglas. In that connection, Mr. Curtis, who is a leading minority member, has expressed his regrets that he is not able to be here this morning but wishes to say that he is for an expanded statistical program.

I know Mr. Bolling feels very much in this way.

In the past I have been somewhat skeptical, but I am getting more mellow. Some of my earlier interests are returning to me.

Mr. Clague. Mr. Chairman, you did raise one point that I would like to say just a word on.

Senator DOUGLAS. I wish you would.

Mr. CLAGUE. That is this qualitative matter.

Senator DOUGLAS. Yes.

Mr. CLAGUE. Because I think it has gotten into the testimony so far, the question of quality improvement——

Senator DOUGLAS. Yes.

Mr. CLAGUE. As though it were tied in with a welfare-type index rather than a price index. That is simply not true. We have a problem of taking care of quality improvement, and it must be taken care of, in a price index, and we do try to take care of it.

Senator DOUGLAS. I wish you would address yourself to that question, because you said there was not a systematic bias in the price index, and we have had testimony that with the apparent continuous improvement in the quality of many goods, perhaps in most goods, although there is a degeneration in the quality of others, it is said that therefore there is a hidden factor that for the same commodity you are getting a better product and that therefore this present index exaggerates the real increase in the cost of living.

I wish you would reply to that.

Mr. CLAGUE. Well, first of all, I would like to emphasize that some of this confusion that has arisen on the outside is perhaps due to a lack of knowledge of the way we actually carry on the index.

I would like to make two points.

One is that when there is a change of any kind and a new product comes in, or if instead of the old basket of tomatoes there are tomatoes in cellophane packages, we do it by linking. We do not just show a price increase—the fact that the cellophane packages cost more. We run them both.

The effect of linking is sometimes to produce a downward bias to the index, as you can see.

There may be a real price change involved here, but it does not show up because we have put both items in, and we carry them both from month to month.

Senator DOUGLAS. You mean as a new product comes on the market its original price is higher than it was later?

Mr. CLAGUE. Yes.

Senator DOUGLAS. Although it may come in at a higher level than the old product, you are saying that the cellophane tomatoes start off at a higher price than the plain tomatoes but may become cheaper with the passage of time?

Mr. CLAGUE. Yes; I think I should change my illustration—I used packaged tomatoes. In this case we did make the direct comparison.

But let me take the frozen foods which are a better illustration and have a substantially higher cost in them. But the same thing applies. By linking we may work a downward bias in the index.

Now, secondly, another point——

Senator DOUGLAS. This is very important testimony.

Mr. CLAGUE. Secondly—and, by the way—we make these decisions on linking, and we use it very, very freely, because it is the safest for us. If both items are on the market, we prefer it that way. We would rather let the weights gradually shift and we can make changes in the weights within limits.

For example, we shifted on our initiative from time to time the weights between butter and oleomargarine, keeping the group weight the same, but as the consumption of one went down and the other went up during the war we were able to make those shifts, and we carired both prices along.

Senator DOUGLAS. Now, reversing the statement in the Old Testament, may I say: Tell it, publish it, in the streets of Absalom.

Mr. CLAGUE. The second point I would like to make in connection with quality improvement is that our most difficult situation arises in the durable goods where we have a change of model and then we do not have this overlapping that we can use freely. And it is on that ground that many people think, "Well, the quality changes are the major factor."

But we factor out all of the quality changes that we can detect. For example, in an automobile when the manufacturers put in the automatic transmission, we took the price of that transmission and factored it out of the increase.

Since 1939 we factored out $650 or $700 of the price rise in a car.

Now, somebody can criticize us and say, "You did not take out enough." We did not take out the grillework. We have not taken out the foam-rubber cushions. Anything that is simply appearance or mere comfort was not taken out if that was higher priced.

Senator DOUGLAS. You did not take out chrome?

Mr. CLAGUE. No, we did not take out chrome. And to a certain——

Senator DOUGLAS. What about length?

Mr. CLAGUE. No, we did not take out length.

Senator DOUGLAS. Or breadth?

Mr. CLAGUE. Or breadth. But we took out such things as a hill holder or a radio in the car or types of things that seemed to have some connection with the operation of the car.

So that we have factored out a great deal of it. And one answer to the criticism is that if we had funds to do a little more work on it perhaps we could factor out some more.

But I want to say for the record here to the people who think there is an enormous rise in this index because of our failure to measure quality improvement, it is just not so.

The balance of some of our downward biases and the efforts we make to factor out quality improvements indicate to us that this upward bias is relatively small, if any. I think I would not even want to concede there is any rise at all. But I would be foolish to argue that there isn't any, because I do not know enough to do so.

But we know that we try to take out all the quality improvement we can in every way that we can.

Senator DOUGLAS. Now, did this committee come down to you and go over these facts with you?

Mr. CLAGUE. Our business committee and our labor committee go over these facts so intensively that we spend hours and meetings and days going over them.

Senator DOUGLAS. I mean this committee which testified yesterday. Did they go over these?

Mr. CLAGUE. Oh. The Price Research Committee; yes, they went over these.

Senator DOUGLAS. They knew of the method of linking?

Mr. CLAGUE. Yes, we told them about the method of linking. I think they have the impression, however—you see, they are thinking in terms of this welfare-index concept. They are thinking of the notion of utility that they believe would not be shown by these physical changes in the items.

The question of consumer satisfaction in riding around in a car might be unrelated to any physical changes, but I do not know how to get at that.

Senator DOUGLAS. Well, neither do I.

Mr. CLAGUE. Oh, by the way——

Senator DOUGLAS. When you speak, I remember those lines of Browning, "All the world's coarse thumb and finger fail to plumb." I always thought that there was always a large part of satisfaction that could not be plumbed by figures.

Mr. CLAGUE. One can always say it is worth exploring to see. And I would not reject this concept. But I would certainly say the exploration must precede any effort to incorporate it into this index.

I would like to add one more point. Mr. Jaffe here has published a paper which appeared in the American Statistical Association's 1959 proceedings. It is exactly on this point. "The Consumer Price Index—Technical Questions and Practical Answers."

In that, he takes up this question of quality improvement and how we handle it. I would like to submit this paper for the record as part of the appendix.

Our problem, Mr. Chairman, is that not always do people read what we say. It is hard to get this across to many diverse audiences. And our voices are limited.

Senator DOUGLAS. Well, I think this strengthens the case for a couple of statisticians and economists who, without being attorneys for the defense, can go into these matters and present a somewhat different, perhaps a better point of view than mere outsiders sometimes do.

Mr. CLAGUE. Mr. Chairman, just yesterday, to get down to practical things, the chief of publications in the Bureau was discussing with me how we could get somebody to write some articles for the Monthly Labor Review on some of these questions.

He was asking if we could comb the Bureau for somebody or how we could find somebody who would be willing to come in and do this kind of writing for us.

It is tough in an operating bureau with the deadlines we have, and we must bring our indexes out on time. That has such a priority in our work that unless we have a special unit set aside to do this analytical work, it just does not get done in the degree about which we are talking.

Senator DOUGLAS. Well, the State Department some years ago decided that it had to have a brain trust, and if you can get the gentlemen of the State Department to admit that they need a brain trust, it ought not to be too difficult to get a brain trust for the Bureau of Labor Statistics.

Mr. CLAGUE. We are going to try.

I might say, Mr. Chairman, we are acting on this for the 1963 budget. I do have some budget proposals ready to go in. I do not know the exact amounts yet, but we are going to ask for some funds to implement these recommendations which we like and which we think would be beneficial.

Senator DOUGLAS. Very good. Thank you very much, Mr. Clague.

TIME SERIES—TREND LINE

12

In this chapter we shall be using equations and graphs to describe straight lines. So, let us first review some elementary algebraic properties of straight lines.

For those who are already familiar with these topics, the review may be skipped.

12.1. Review

(i) Graphing a straight line

The general formula for a straight line is

$$Y = a + bX$$

For example,

$$Y = 1 + 2X$$

where X is called the *independent variable,* and Y is called the *dependent variable.* Fill in the values of Y that correspond to the values of X in the table on page 331. Then plot the points on the graph.

In the figure, the straight line cuts across the Y-axis at the point $Y = 1$. This is called the *Y-intercept,* and the $a = 1$ in the equation shows this intercept. The $b = 2$ in the equation shows the *slope* of the curve. This means, when X increases by 1 unit, that Y will *increase* by 2 units. If $b = -2$, then it means that Y will *decrease* by 2 units when X increases by 1 unit, and the curve will slope downward.

X	−2	−1	0	1	2
Y					

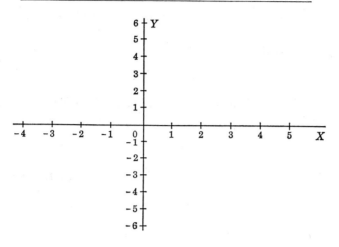

(ii) *Solving simultaneous equations*

Solve the following equations:

(1) $$12 = 5a + 13b$$

(2) $$74 = 15a + 58b$$

$(Eq. 2) − (Eq. 1) \times 3$

$$74 = 15a + 58b$$
$$-36 = 15a + 39b$$
$$\overline{38 = 0 + 19b}$$
$$b = 2$$
$$a = -2.8$$

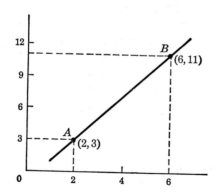

(iii)   Fitting a straight line

Assume we have two points A and B on a graph, on page 331. We wish to find the equation of the straight line going through these two points.

The equation of the straight line is

$$Y = a + bX$$

According to the graph above, when $X = 2$, then $Y = 3$ for point A. Substituting these values into the equation, we find

$$3 = a + 2b$$

Likewise, for point B we see that, when $X = 6$, then $Y = 11$. Then

$$11 = a + 6b$$

Solve the two equations simultaneously for the coefficients a and b.

$$
\begin{aligned}
11 &= a + 6b \\
- \quad 3 &= a + 2b \\
\hline
8 &= 0 + 4b \\
b &= 2 \\
a &= -1
\end{aligned}
$$

Thus the equation for the straight line going through points A and B is

$$Y = -1 + 2X$$

12.2.   Introduction

Whenever one looks at an economic situation, whether it be of a firm, industry, or economic conditions of the United States as a whole, he will observe an incessant flow of economic activity. The economic statistician would like to describe this in "figures," and to do this, he obtains a set of observations (concerning economic activity, etc.) made at different periods of time. This is called a *time series*.

Statisticians have classified these economic activities into four elements:

1.   The trend (T).
2.   Cyclical fluctuations (C).

3. Seasonal variations (S).
4. Irregular variations (I).

What we propose to do in Chapters 13 and 14 is first to give a cookbook type of explanation of various methods of finding the T, S, C, and I. And after this technical background has been obtained, we shall discuss various problematic aspects of time series in Section 13.7. The student is requested to grind patiently through these various techniques and to reserve judgment on the merits and demerits of these techniques until he reaches Section 13.7. In this chapter we shall discuss the various techniques of finding a trend line.

The trend is the long-term movement of a time series. For example, the trend of the growth of national income is its long-term movement, say, over a period of 10 to 20 years or more. For the United States, this long-term movement shows a gradual rise of about 3 percent per year. Other examples with which the student is probably familiar are the growth of population, industrial production, energy, and so forth.

There are various types of trend lines to express the different modes of growth. For example, the growth of productivity of labor in the United States approximates a straight line that slopes upward, and thus a straight line may be used. When fruit flies are put in a small container, the population of flies grows geometrically at first, and as it becomes crowded in the container, it gradually tapers off. The growth of an industry in a certain region or the growth of the TV industry shows similar characteristics of growing rapidly at first and then tapering off. This type of trend is shown by the Pearl-Reed curve. Other types of trend lines are the parabolic, logarithmic, Gompertz, and some types of lesser importance. In the present chapter, we shall discuss only the straight line trend line. The other types of trend lines are discussed in Chapter 23.

We are interested in finding and expressing a trend in terms of an equation, and also in showing it graphically. With given data, a graph is plotted, and the problem becomes one of fitting a straight line to the data so as to show the long-run gradual growth of the time series. There are various methods of fitting a straight line, such as the freehand method, the method of semiaverages, the method of moving averages, and the method of least squares. In this chapter our main interest is in developing the method of least squares. The freehand method, the method of semiaverages, and the method of moving averages will serve as preliminaries to this method. The method of moving averages is discussed again in more detail in Chapter 23.

12.3.   The Freehand Method

The simplest method of finding a trend line when given a set of time series data is the freehand method. The procedure is to plot the time series on a graph and then, by observation, fit a straight line through the plotted points in a way such that the straight line shows the trend of the time series. Let us illustrate with the hypothetical data in the accompanying table.

Year	X	Y (Millions of Pounds)
1950	0	5
1951	1	8
1952	2	12
1953	3	15
1954	4	20
1955	5	23

Let Y show the annual production of some commodity in millions of pounds. The points are plotted in Fig. 12.1. We draw in a line by

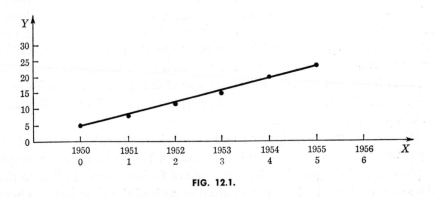

FIG. 12.1.

observation. Obviously, this is not an accurate way of fitting a straight line or a curve to the data, but in some instances we may be interested first in getting a rough idea as to whether a straight line or some other kind of a curve should be fitted before using refined methods. In such cases, the line may prove helpful.

Let us assume that the trend line goes through the points for 1950 and 1955. Then the problem of finding the trend line becomes one of finding the equation for the straight line going through the two points 1950 and 1955.

If the line that is drawn does not go through any of the plotted points, the procedure is to select two points on the straight line, determine their coordinates graphically, and then calculate the equation.

A characteristic of time series is that the data are given in order of time. In our example, it starts from 1950 and goes up to 1955 in one-year time intervals. This allows us to assign a sequence of numbers to the data. Let us start at 1950, and call it the *origin,* and designate it as zero. Then 1951 is 1, 1952 is 2, and so forth, as shown in the table and also Fig. 12.1. Mathematically, we are simply shifting the origin from 0 to 1950 and letting 1950 become the new origin. It is evident that the origin may be placed at any year. If we let 1951 be the origin, then 1950 is -1, 1951 is 0, 1952 is 1, 1953 is 2, and so forth.

The coordinates of the two points selected now become (0, 5) and (5, 23). Substituting the values of these coordinates into the equation for a straight line as shown in Section 12.1, we find

$$5 = a + 0b$$
$$23 = a + 5b$$

Solving these two equations gives $a = 5$, $b = 3.6$. Thus the equation for the trend line is

$$Y_c = 5 + 3.6X$$
$$\text{Origin:} \quad 7/1/50$$
$$X: \quad \text{1-year units}$$

Note that Y_c has a subscript c, which indicates that the Y values obtained from the equation are not the actual values, but that they are computed or estimated values. Also note that the equation has meaning only when the origin and the units of X are specified. It is customary to take the middle of the year, that is, July 1, as the point to represent the data for that year. For example, when the $Y = 5{,}000{,}000$ lb. is plotted at $X = 0$ (1950), this point indicates $7/1/50$.

The interpretation of the equation is, when $X = 0$ (1950),

$$Y_c = 5 + (3.6)(0) = 5$$

which indicates that the estimated production by the trend line is 5,000,000 lb. In this case, the estimated production $Y_c = 5{,}000{,}000$ lb.

is equal to the actual production of $Y_{50} = 5,000,000$ lb. When $X = 3$ (1953),

$$Y_c = 5 + (3.6)(3) = 15.8$$

The actual production for $Y_{53} = 15$, and there is a discrepancy of

$$Y_c - Y_{53} = 15.8 - 15 = 0.8$$

The $b = 3.6$ shows that the estimated annual increase of production is 3,600,000 lb.

12.4. Method of Semiaverages

The method of semiaverages divides the time series into two parts, finds the average of each part, and then fits a trend line through these averages. Using the hypothetical data of Section 12.3, let us illustrate this method.

Year	X	Y		
1950	0	5	$\dfrac{25}{3}$	$= 8.3$
1951	1	8		
1952	2	12		
1953	3	15	$\dfrac{58}{3}$	$= 19.3$
1954	4	20		
1955	5	23		

The averages of each part are 8,300,000 and 19,300,000 lb. Since 8,300,000 lb. is the average of 1950, 1951, and 1952, the 8,300,000 is plotted at 1951. (See Fig. 12.2.) Likewise the 19,300,000 lb. is plotted at 1954. The straight line going through these two points (1, 8.3) and

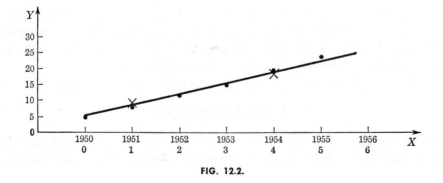

FIG. 12.2.

(4, 19.3) is the semiaverage trend line we seek. We find

$$8.3 = a + b$$
$$19.3 = a + 4b$$

Solving for a and b gives us $a = 4.63$ and $b = 3.6$. Thus the equation for the trend line is

$$Y_c = 4.63 + 3.6X$$
$$\text{Origin:} \quad 7/1/50$$
$$X: \quad \text{1-year units}$$

The estimated production for $X = 0$ (that is, for 1950) is

$$Y_c = 4.63 + (3.6)(0) = 4.63$$

The actual production is $Y_{50} = 5$, and thus the discrepancy between actual and estimated production is

$$Y_c - Y_{50} = 4.63 - 5 = -0.37$$

The $b = 3.6$ shows that the estimated annual increase of production is 3,600,000 lb.

When there is an odd number of years, the series cannot be divided evenly, and hence the middle year may be left out or the series may be split unevenly.

One extreme value of the series may influence one of the semi-averages and throw the whole trend line off, in which case it may be omitted. For example, when fitting a trend line for steel production, there may be a year with a prolonged strike, causing the output of that year to be extremely low. In such a case, it may be omitted.

This is a crude and simple way of fitting a trend line, but its simplicity is its advantage.

12.5.   The Method of Moving Averages

A brief explanation of the moving average is presented here and a more detailed explanation is given in Chapter 23. It is used to smooth out fluctuations in time series and is applied not only to trend lines but also to seasonal and cyclical variations. Let us illustrate the procedure by using simplified hypothetical data in the table on page 338. Suppose the given data concern the sales of a commodity.

First find the 3-year *moving totals*. For example, for 1947, 1948, and 1949, we have

$$3 + 4 + 8 = 15$$

This $15,000,000 is entered so that it corresponds to the middle year, 1948. The next total is for 1948, 1949, and 1950. This will be

$$4 + 8 + 6 = 18$$

Year	Sales, Millions of Dollars	Three-Year Moving Total	Three-Year Moving Average
1947	3		
1948	4	15	5
1949	8	18	6
1950	6	21	7
1951	7	24	8
1952	11	27	9
1953	9	30	10
1954	10	33	11
1955	14	36	12
1956	12		

and this corresponds to the middle year, 1949. This process is continued, and we find the column of 3-year moving totals. We do not have a total for 1947 or for 1956.

Next find the 3-year *moving averages* by dividing the moving totals by 3. This gives us the 3-year moving average column.

The graph shows that the sales have a regular 3-year cycle. For example, from a peak at 1949 to the next peak of 1952, we have 3 years. Then the next peak comes 3 years later at 1955.

When the 3-year moving averages are plotted on the graph as in Fig. 12.3, they fall on a straight line, and the cyclical fluctuations have been *smoothed out*. The straight line is the trend line we seek. The hypothetical data have been adjusted so that the trend line is a straight line; however, in general, we shall have a smooth curve.

After the 3-year moving average points have been plotted, we have a problem of fitting a trend line to these points. The freehand method, semiaverage method, method of least squares, or some of the other methods explained in Chapter 23 may be used to fit a trend line to these moving average points.

Why have we obtained a smooth curve? This results because the data have within them a regular cycle with the same duration and amplitude. Noticing that the cycle was of a 3-year duration, we selected a 3-year moving average. If the duration was 4 years, we should have selected a 4-year moving average. The rationale is that in the course of

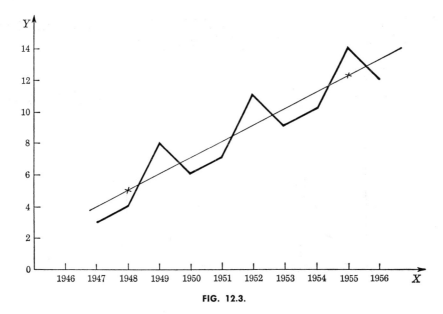

FIG. 12.3.

one cycle, we expect half of it to be above the midpoint of the cycle and half of it below. Thus, when an average is taken, there will be a canceling-out effect, and if the half that is above the midpoint of the cycle is larger than the lower half, as in our example, the moving average will show a rising trend.

Thus, if a moving average is to be applied effectively, it becomes necessary to determine first whether a regular, periodic cycle exists. In practical cases where cycles do exist, the duration of the cycles are usually not very regular, but in many cases there is enough regularity to allow the use of the moving average method.

Also notice that the trend line obtained was a straight line. If the basic nature of the time series is linear, then we shall get a straight line; if it is curvilinear, then the trend will appear as a curve.

This moving average method is applicable not only to trend lines but also to all kinds of data that show regular periodic fluctuations. We shall use it later to eliminate seasonal fluctuations.

Notice that we have merely smoothed out the series. We have not obtained a mathematical equation for the moving average trend line.

12.6. The Method of Least Squares

The method of least squares is the most widely used method of fitting a straight line to a series of data. We shall discuss the simple case in which only one independent variable is involved, and extensions and refinements will be taken up in later chapters.

(i) Principle

In Fig. 12.4, Y_c is the computed trend line, and α, β, and γ are

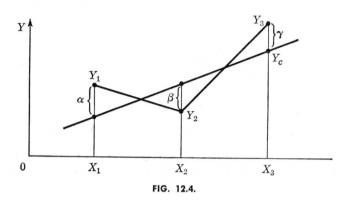

FIG. 12.4.

the deviations of the observed points (actual data) from the trend line (computed values). The method of least squares is a method by which we can fit the computed trend line Y_c to the observed data so that the sum of the squares of the deviations are at a minimum; that is,

$$\alpha^2 + \beta^2 + \gamma^2 = \text{minimum}$$

Let us say that the computed equation is

$$Y_c = a + bX$$

We want to find a and b. This can be accomplished by solving the following set of equations:

(1)
$$\Sigma Y = na + b\Sigma X$$
$$\Sigma XY = a\Sigma X + b\Sigma X^2$$

These are called the *normal equations*. We shall now illustrate how they are used.

(ii) Odd number of years

Suppose we have been given the data in the accompanying work-sheet, concerning the production of petroleum in millions of barrels produced annually. We wish to fit a straightline trend line by the method of least squares. The a and b parameters are found from formula (1). We see that we need ΣY, ΣX, ΣXY, and ΣX^2 to solve

Worksheet

Year	X	Y	XY	X^2
1950	-2	5	-10	4
1951	-1	8	-8	1
1952	0	12	0	0
1953	1	15	15	1
1954	2	20	40	4
	0	60	37	10

(1) for a and b. These values are found from the table (worksheet) we have constructed. As the table shows, the X's have been designated such that $\Sigma X = 0$. The reason for this is that it simplifies the solution of (1) for a and b. Once the numbering of the X's has been determined, we may find the other quantities. They are

$$\Sigma Y = 60, \quad \Sigma XY = 37, \quad \Sigma X^2 = 10$$

The n is the number of years, that is, $n = 5$. Substituting these into formula (1), we find

$$60 = (5)(a) + b(0)$$
$$37 = a(0) + b(10)$$

and a and b are

$$a = \frac{60}{5} = 12$$

$$b = \frac{37}{10} = 3.7$$

Thus the equation for the trend line is

(2)
$$Y_c = 12 + 3.7X$$
$$\text{Origin:} \quad 7/1/52$$
$$X: \quad \text{1-year units}$$

The simplification brought about by numbering the X's so that $\Sigma X = 0$ is shown as follows: The normal equations are

$$\Sigma Y = na + b\Sigma X$$
$$\Sigma XY = a\Sigma X + b\Sigma X^2$$

Since $\Sigma X = 0$, this becomes

$$\Sigma Y = na$$
$$\Sigma XY = b\Sigma X^2$$

Thus the a and b may be found immediately by

(3)
$$a = \frac{\Sigma Y}{n}$$

$$b = \frac{\Sigma XY}{\Sigma X^2}$$

Using these formulas (3) for our example, we may find a and b directly as

$$a = \frac{\Sigma Y}{n} = \frac{60}{5} = 12$$

$$b = \frac{\Sigma XY}{\Sigma X^2} = \frac{37}{10} = 3.7$$

In the subsequent discussion, we shall use this formula (3).

Let us now plot the data and the trend line as shown in Fig. 12.5.

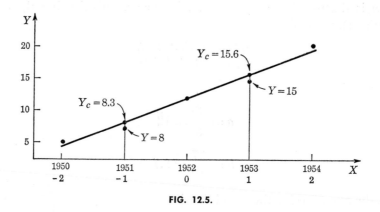

FIG. 12.5.

The markings on the horizontal axis of 1950, 1951, etc., indicate 7/1/50, 7/1/51, etc. There is no problem in plotting the observed Y values.

To plot the trend line formula (2), any two values of Y_c are found and a straight line is drawn through them. For example:

$$X = -1: \qquad Y_c = 12 + (3.7)(-1) = 8.3$$
$$X = +1: \qquad Y_c = 12 + (3.7)(1) = 15.7$$

Then plot the two points $(-1, 8.3)$ and $(1, 15.7)$ and draw a straight line. This will be the trend line we seek.

Since Y gives us *annual totals,* the interpretation of the equation is as follows: $b = 3.7$ is the estimated annual change in the production of petroleum, in millions of barrels. The estimated production of 1954 is

$$Y_c = 12 + (3.7)(2) = 19.4$$

(iii)   Even number of years

The difference between the application of the method of least squares to a time series of odd and even number of years is the numbering system applied to the X's so that $\Sigma X = 0$. Suppose we have the following data on the production of petroleum, where we now have 6 years.

Year	X	Y	XY	X²
1950	−5	5	− 25	25
1951	−3	8	− 24	9
1952	−1	12	− 12	1
1953	1	15	15	1
1954	3	20	60	9
1955	5	25	125	25
	0	85	139	70

There are several ways of numbering the X's so that $\Sigma X = 0$. One is to designate them as 1, 3, 5, as shown in the table. We cannot use $-3, -2, -1, 1, 2, 3$ because between -1 and 1 there are 2 units (that is, $-1, 0, 1$), whereas 1, 2, 3 differ by 1 unit each. The $\Sigma X = 0$, and this enables us to use formula (3).

From the table we find

$$\Sigma XY = 139 \qquad \Sigma X^2 = 70$$

The $n = 6$. Substituting these into (3), we find

$$a = \frac{\Sigma Y}{n} = \frac{85}{6} = 14.2$$

$$b = \frac{\Sigma XY}{\Sigma X^2} = \frac{139}{70} = 1.99$$

Thus the trend line is

$$Y_c = 14.2 + 1.99X$$
$$\text{Origin:} \qquad 1/1/53$$
$$X: \qquad \text{half-year units}$$

Notice the following two changes: First, the origin is between 7/1/52 and 7/1/53. Thus it is 1/1/53. Second, the X's are in half-year units. This is so because the X's are labeled 1, 3, 5, etc., and each year differs by 2 units. In other words, to go from 7/1/53 to 7/1/54, X has to go from 1 to 3 (not to 2). When X goes from 1 to 2, it only goes a half-year from 7/1/53 to 1/1/54. This also means that

$$b = 1.99$$

shows the estimated increase per half-year (in millions of barrels). The estimated production of petroleum for 1954 is

$$Y_c = 14.2 + (1.99)(3) = 20.17$$

For 1955 it is

$$Y_c = 14.2 + (1.99)(5) = 24.15$$

The trend line is graphed in Fig. 12.6.

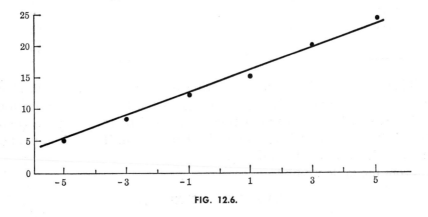

FIG. 12.6.

Other ways of numbering the X's are by multiplying the present numbering system 1, 3, 5, etc., by any arbitrary number. But usually the only other system that is used is obtained by multiplying the present numbers by $\frac{1}{2}$. Thus the two numbering systems are

| −5 | −3 | −1 | 1 | 3 | 5 |
| −2.5 | −1.5 | −0.5 | 0.5 | 1.5 | 2.5 |

When this second system is used, the unit of X becomes 1 year instead of a half-year. Some prefer to use this system because it avoids half-year units.

12.7.   Changing the Unit Value and Shifting the Origin

(i)   Changing the unit value

So far the data of the time series and the equations were annual totals. But in many cases the data are given as *annual monthly averages* and *monthly data*. An illustration will show the distinction between the annual total, annual monthly average and monthly data, and the corresponding trend line equations.

Suppose a person was hired as a statistician in 1955 with an annual salary of $6000. Let us further assume that his salary was increased to $7200 in 1956 and then to $8400 in 1957.

Then the *annual monthly average* salary for 1955 is $500; for 1956 it is $600; and for 1957 it is $700. Thus the *annual* increase of the annual monthly average salary is $100.

The *monthly* increase of the monthly average salary is $100/12 = $8.33. From these data we may construct three equations:

The annual total equation:

(1)
$$Y_c = \$6000 + 1200X$$
$$X = 0 \qquad \text{at July 1, 1955}$$

where X is in 1-year units.

The annual monthly average equation:

(2)
$$Y_c = \frac{6000}{12} + \frac{1200}{12} X$$

$$Y_c = 500 + 100X$$

$$X = 0 \qquad \text{at July 1, 1955}$$

where X is in 1-year units.

The monthly equation:

(3)
$$Y_c = \frac{6000}{12} + \frac{1200}{12 \times 12} X$$

$$Y_c = 500 + 8.33X$$

$$X = 0 \qquad \text{at July 1, 1955}$$

where X is in 1-month units.

The b coefficient in equation (2) is $1200/12 = \$100$ and shows the annual increase of the monthly average salary. The b coefficient of equation (3) is $1200/(12 \times 12) = 8.33$ and shows the monthly increase of the monthly average salary.

Thus, when given an equation expressing a trend, one must consider which of the three types of equations it is.

It should be noticed that in equation (3) we have left the origin at July 1. To be consistent with our rule of using the middle of the year or month to represent the data, it should be moved to the middle of the month, that is, to July 15, since it is a monthly equation. Carry this out and write out the new equation.

Many time series are presented as monthly average data. For example, data for production of paper are given in Table 12.1.

TABLE 12.1. Production of Paper

Year Monthly Average	Production (1000, Short Tons)
1950	887
1952	908
1954	971
1956	1166
1958	1127

Source: *Business Statistics,* U.S. Dept. of Commerce, 1959, p. 181.

The 887 means that the monthly average production of paper for 1950 was 887 thousands of short tons.

Example 1. The annual total equation for the production of radios by a firm is as follows (in hundreds of sets).

$$Y_c = 144 + 72X$$
$$\text{Origin:} \quad 7/1/58$$
$$X: \quad \text{1-year units}$$

This means that in 1958 the estimated total was 144×100 sets. In 1959 the estimated total is

$$144 + (72)(1) = 216$$

that is, 216×100 sets. The $b = 72$ shows that there was an estimated annual increase of 72×100 sets.

The annual monthly average equation is found as follows:

$$Y_c = \frac{144}{12} + \frac{72}{12}X$$
$$Y_c = 12 + 6X$$

$$\begin{aligned} &\text{Origin:} &&7/1/58 \\ &X: &&\text{1-year units} \end{aligned}$$

This means that in 1958 the estimated monthly average was 12×100 sets. That is, on the average, 12×100 sets were made every month during 1958. For 1959 we find

$$Y_c = 12 + (6)(1) = 18$$

That is, on the average, 18×100 sets were made every month during 1959.

The $b = 6$ means that, for every year, the estimated increase of the monthly average has been 6×100 sets.

The monthly equation is

$$Y_c = 12 + \frac{6}{12}\, X$$

$$Y_c = 12 + 0.5X$$

$$\begin{aligned} &\text{Origin:} &&7/1/58 \\ &X: &&\text{1-month units} \end{aligned}$$

This shows that the production on a monthly basis for $7/1/58$ was

$$Y_c = 12 + (0.5)(0) = 12$$

Let us shift the origin to $7/15/58$, that is, half a month ahead. For $7/15/58$ the production was

$$Y_c = 12 + (0.5)\,\frac{1}{2} = 12.25$$

Thus the monthly equation for $7/15/58$ is

$$Y_c = 12.25 + 0.5X$$

$$\begin{aligned} &\text{Origin:} &&7/15/58 \\ &X: &&\text{1-month units} \end{aligned}$$

This means that the estimated production for July, 1958, was

$$Y_c = 12.25 + (0.5)(0) = 12.25$$

that is, 12.25×100 sets for the month of July. For August, production was

$$Y_c = 12.25 + (0.5)(1) = 12.75$$

and for June,

$$Y_c = 12.25 + (0.5)(-1) = 11.75$$

Example 2.   Given the table data on the production of wallets for a firm, find the monthly average trend-line equation by the method of least squares.

Year	X	Monthly Average, (1000) Y	XY	X²
1953	−2	4	− 8	4
1954	−1	7	− 7	1
1955	0	8	0	0
1956	1	10	10	1
1957	2	15	30	4
	0	44	25	10

From these data we find

$$a = \frac{\Sigma Y}{n} = \frac{44}{5} = 8.8$$

$$b = \frac{\Sigma XY}{\Sigma X^2} = \frac{25}{10} = 2.5$$

$$Y_c = 8.8 + 2.5X \qquad (7/1/55)$$
$$X: \quad \text{1-year units}$$

The estimated monthly average production for the year 1956 was

$$Y_c = 8.8 + (2.5)(1) = 11.3$$

that is, 11.3×1000 wallets per month during 1956.

The estimated annual total production for 1956 was

$$(11.3 \times 12) \times 1000 = 135.6 \times 1000$$

that is, 135.6×1000 wallets for 1956.

(ii) *Shifting the origin*

The monthly average equation concerning salaries used in (i) is

$$Y_c = 500 + 100X \qquad (7/1/55)$$
$$X: \qquad \text{1-year units}$$

Suppose we want to shift the origin to 7/1/59. The problem of shifting the origin to 1959 in terms of Fig. 12.7 is to find the new Y-intercept a_{59}. This is

$$a_{59} = 500 + (100 \times 4) = 900$$

Thus the equation becomes

$$Y_c = 900 + 100X \qquad (7/1/59)$$

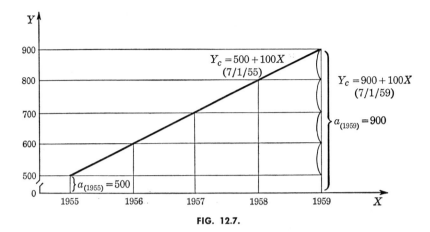

FIG. 12.7.

This can be carried out in one step as follows:

$$Y_c = 500 + 100(X + 4) = 900 + 100X$$

SEASONAL
AND CYCLICAL MOVEMENT

<table>
<tr><td>

13

</td><td>

The second component of economic time series we shall consider is the seasonal movement. But first let us define several new terms which we shall be using in subsequent discussion.

</td></tr>
</table>

13.1. Definitions of Terms

The economic time series was classified into four components, trend (T), seasonal variation (S), business cycle (C), and irregular variations (I). These four components are related to the original series denoted by O as follows:

$$(1) \qquad\qquad O = T \times S \times C \times I$$

For example, let $O = 1{,}890{,}000$ barrels of petroleum for May. Then this is decomposed as follows: Let $T = 2{,}000{,}000$ barrels; $S = 105$, which means that the amount of petroleum has a $+5$ percent seasonal variation in May; $C = 100$, which means that there is no business cycle effect; and $I = 90$, which means that, because of some irregular forces, the amount of petroleum has a -10 percent irregular variation in May. Then

$$O = T \times S \times C \times I$$
$$= 2.0 \times 105 \times 100 \times 90$$
$$= 1.89$$

Note that the S, C, and I are expressed as percentages and are indices. A second way of expressing the decomposition of O is

(2) $$O = T \times S \times I$$

where T is called the *trend-cycle component* and is a combination of the $T \times C$ of equation (1). The Bureau of Labor Statistics uses this approach.

A third way of decomposing O is

(3) $$O = T + S + C + I$$

Examples of this approach may be found in the writings of mathematical statisticians. In this case the S, C, and I are not indices, but are quantitative deviations due to seasonal, cyclical, and irregular forces.

For purposes of explanation we shall use equations (1) and (3).

When the trend T is removed from the original data O, we have a trendless, or detrended, time series that is called a *stationary time series*. Figure 13.1 shows schematically the idea of a stationary time

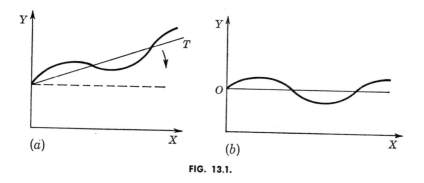

FIG. 13.1.

series. Figure 13.1(a) shows the original series O and a freehand trend T. Removing the trend may be thought of as rotating T to a horizontal position, as shown in Fig. 13.1(b). Since in (b) we are interested only in the deviations, we may set the horizontal axis at zero and express the deviations in terms of $+$ and $-$ quantities. An alternative way is to show them as proportions, which requires finding the various corresponding T values.

What we wish to do now is to define a few terms for the stationary time series. Figure 13.2 is a series that repeats itself every 2 (time) intervals; that is, from 1 to 3, from 3 to 5, etc. The number of time intervals (minutes, hours, days, weeks, months, or years) is the *period* of the series. In our example, 2 time intervals (say, 2 months) is the period. The variation of the Y value shown by r is called the *amplitude* of this series.

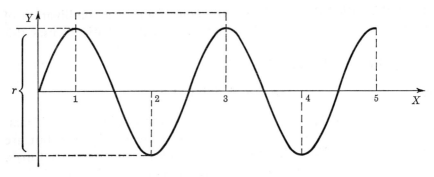

FIG. 13.2.

A series that repeats itself regularly every period is called a *periodic series*. A series that repeats itself, but which does not have a fixed period, is called an *oscillatory series*. As is seen, we have made no requirements about the amplitude.

A periodic series exists only theoretically, but the seasonal variations we are considering are close enough to the requirement of having a fixed period to be classified as a periodic series. An example of the oscillatory series is the business cycle that varies in duration.

The underlying assumption of the periodic series (seasonal variations) and oscillatory series (business cycles) is that there are systematic causes that generate these fluctuations. When there are no systematic causes generating the fluctuations and they are purely random fluctuations, the series is called a *random series*. The irregular fluctuations I is an example.

We shall use the term *cyclical fluctuations* (cyclical variations, or cyclical movements) to denote the oscillatory fluctuations of business cycles. The term *cyclical series* is sometimes used to denote periodic series, but in this text, to avoid confusion, the term cyclical series will not be used. We shall use the term *periodic series*.

With this much background let us now consider seasonal fluctuations. We shall first explain what it is; then give a brief discussion of the technical computational aspects; and then show how it is applied. After that we shall briefly discuss cyclical fluctuations.

13.2. Seasonal Variation

Seasonal variation was classified as a periodic series and our main concern will be with periodic series that have a period of one year. Some examples are the production of soft drinks, which is high during the summer and low during the winter; department store sales, which are high during Christmas season and Easter and low at other times; the production of cars and eggs, collection of taxes, etc. But aside from these seasonal variations that take place over the period of a year, we may extend the coverage to include the fluctuation of temperature during a day; the sales at a supermarket during a week; the collection of credit accounts of a department store during a month, and so forth.

In each of these examples, note that there are systematic causes of these fluctuations, such as the weather (which is an external cause), holidays and government accounting procedures (which are man-made institutional causes) and so forth. These systematic causes occur regularly, although over a long period there may be changes such as the date (fall or spring) when new cars are introduced to the consumer. Another example of a small shift is the different day on which Easter or Thanksgiving may occur; this affects the sales of a department store. Nevertheless there is a certain amount of regularity year after year. The seasonal variations that we observe in the economic time series are indices of these real underlying causes. Our first problem is to find a way of measuring and expressing this seasonal varation.

Let us consider the consumption of soft drinks. We know from experience that consumption is high in the summer and low in the winter, and this pattern repeats itself every year. This is shown schematically in Fig. 13.3, which plots the fluctuations of soft drink consumption over 3 years. Depending on seasonal conditions (particularly weather in this case), the peak and trough of consumption will vary slightly from year to year, and this may be thought to be due to random disturbances.

The random disturbances of the different years are assumed to be independent of each other. For example, if there is a random disturbance in July of the first year, it is assumed to be independent of the random disturbance in July of the second or any other year. This assumption implies that if we sum the values of Julys for a number of

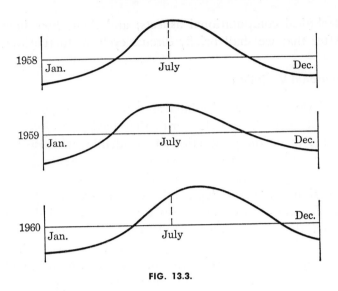

FIG. 13.3.

years, the irregular variations due to the random disturbances will cancel each other.

This assumption suggests that if a number of years are summed and an average year is found, it will be devoid of irregular variations (I). If we can also eliminate the trend (T) and cycle (C), we shall be left with the seasonal variation (S), and when this is expressed as an index, we shall have the seasonal index.

Our problem now is to translate this idea into a mathematical procedure so that we can find the S. There are several methods: One is the method of simple averages, a second is the method of medians, and a third is the ratio-to-moving average method. We shall first discuss the method of simple averages because it explains the principal ideas in an elementary manner, although it is generally not used in practice. Then we shall discuss the ratio-to-moving average method, which is the preferable method.

13.3. The Method of Simple Averages

Let us illustrate this method by using the hypothetical figures (Table 13.1) of stocks of frozen vegetables in cold storage, in millions of pounds. For simplicity, only 2 years are considered, but the procedure can easily be extended to as many years as necessary. As was mentioned, we assume the series to be expressed by

$$O = T + S + C + I$$

TABLE 13.1.   Frozen Vegetables in Cold Storage

Month	(1) 1956	(2) 1957	(3) (1) + (2)	(4) AM	(5) T	(6) A AM	(7) S
Jan.	560	780	1340	670	0	670	97.4
Feb.	500	720	1220	610	5	605	88.0
Mar.	450	670	1120	560	10	550	80.0
Apr.	420	660	1080	540	15	525	76.3
May	420	630	1050	525	20	505	73.5
June	480	660	1140	570	25	545	79.3
July	590	730	1320	660	30	630	91.6
Aug.	750	860	1610	805	35	770	112.0
Sept.	860	970	1830	915	40	875	127.3
Oct.	900	980	1880	940	45	895	130.2
Nov.	900	950	1850	925	50	875	127.3
Dec.	850	870	1720	860	55	805	117.1
Total	7680	9480				8250	1200.0
Average	640	790				687.5	100.0

(4) AM: Arithmetic Mean   (6) A AM: Adjusted Arithmetic Mean
(5) T: Trend   (7) S: Seasonal index

Column 3 is the sum of the 2 years and column 4 is the arithmetic mean. This column 4 may be interpreted in two ways. One is that it is the original time series without the I because of the averaging process. The second is that when a sufficient number of years are taken to cover the period of cycles, not only I but also the C is eliminated. We shall adopt the second view. It assumes that the upswing and downswing of a cycle are fairly even, so that if the number of years covers one cycle, the averaging process will cancel out the cyclical effects. This is a rather drastic assumption because it assumes that the upswing and downswing are about the same in duration and amplitude, and also that the shape of the upswing and downswing are not sharp (peaked). It further assumes that we have been able to identify the period of a business cycle or cycles.

Let us conclude that all this is possible and that for practical purposes, the shapes of the business cycles satisfy our assumptions. Then the average in column 4 is the original series without the I and C; that is, column 4 is T and S. If we remove the T, we shall be left with the S. To do this column 5 (which is the effect of the trend) is subtracted from column 4, and the result S is given in 6.

Let us explain this last point as follows: Data of the stock of frozen vegetables show there is a gradual increase in the stock, which will have the effect of pulling up the seasonal variations. This is shown graphically in Fig. 13.4. If there were no trend, the S would fluctuate around the horizontal axis, as shown by the dotted lines, and the horizontal axis would be at the level of the annual monthly averages. For example, point A is the sum of the seasonal variation AB and the trend BD. To remove the trend is to remove BD and rotate point A to point C, where $AB = CD$ shows the seasonal variation S. To obtain these trend corrections, we have to find the monthly increases in stocks, and for this, we first have to find the equation for the trend line. We proceed to do this.

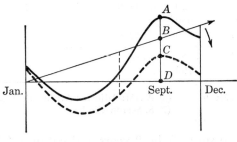

FIG. 13.4.

The data for stocks of frozen vegetables are given in Table 13.2 in annual monthly averages (millions of pounds).

TABLE 13.2. Frozen Vegetables in Cold Storage (Monthly Average)

Year	X	Y	XY	X²
1953	−2	520	−1040	4
1954	−1	580	− 580	1
1955	0	540	0	0
1956	1	640	640	1
1957	2	790	1580	4
		3070	600	10

From these data we find

$$a = \frac{\Sigma Y}{n} = \frac{3070}{5} = 614$$

$$b = \frac{\Sigma XY}{\Sigma X^2} = \frac{600}{10} = 60$$

$$Y_c = 614 + 60X$$

$$\text{Origin:} \quad 7/1/55$$
$$X: \quad \text{1-year units}$$

This is an annual monthly average equation and the $b = 60$ shows the annual increase of the monthly average. The increase per month is thus

$$\frac{b}{12} = \frac{60}{12} = 5$$

That is, there is an increase of 5,000,000 lb. per month. As Fig. 13.3 shows, the correction for January is 0; for February, 5; for March, $5 \times 2 = 10$; for April, $5 \times 3 = 15$; and so forth. These corrections are entered into column 5 of Table 13.1 and then subtracted from column 4. The result is column 6.

Column 6 is the S we seek, but it is customary to express the seasonal index with a base of 100. This is done by finding the average of column 6, which is 687.5, and dividing each number in column 6 by 687.5. The result, on a 100 basis, is given in column 7.

The meaning of the seasonal index will be discussed later.

13.4.   Ratio-to-Moving Average Method

The rationale of this method uses the basic relationship

(1) $$O = T \times S \times C \times I$$

or

(2) $$O = T \times S \times I$$

where the T in the second relationship is the trend cycle, which is a combination of $T \times C$ of (1).

We make the basic assumption that the seasonal variation S has a 12-month period and that the shape of the variation is the same each year. We also assume that the irregular variations I are independent for different periods (years). Then, when a 12-month moving average is applied to (1) or (2), it will smooth out the $S \times I$, and we shall have as a remainder the $T \times C$. That is, the moving average is $T \times C$.

By using this moving average $T \times C$, we can find the $S \times I$ as follows:

$$\frac{\text{Original data}}{\text{Moving average}} = \frac{T \times S \times C \times I}{T \times C} = S \times I$$

This computational process is shown in the accompanying Worksheet.

Worksheet. Beer Production in Millions of Barrels

(1) Year	Month	(2) Original Data	(3) 12-Month Moving Total	(4) 12-Month Moving Average	(5) 2-Month Moving Total	(6) Centered 12-Month Moving Average	(7) (2) ÷ (6)
		TSCI				*TC*	*SI*
1955	July	8.9					
	Aug.	9.2					
	Sept.	7.3					
	Oct.	6.4					
	Nov.	5.8					
	Dec.	6.2	90.7	7.57			
1956	Jan.	6.4	91.4	7.62	15.19	7.60	84
	Feb.	6.6	90.9	7.58	15.20	7.60	87
	Mar.	7.9	90.1				105
	Apr.	7.9	90.2				105
	May	8.7	90.3				116
	June	9.4	90.2				125
	July	9.6	90.7				127
	Aug.	8.7	90.0				116
	Sept.	6.5	89.7				86
	Oct.	6.5	89.9				87
	Nov.	5.9	90.2				79
	Dec.	6.1	89.8				81
1957	Jan.	6.9	90.0				92
	Feb.	5.9	89.7				79
	Mar.	7.6	90.0				102
	Apr.	8.1	90.3				108
	May	9.0	89.6				120
	June	9.0	89.5				121
	July	9.8	89.4				131
	Aug.	8.4	89.8				112
	Sept.	6.8					91
	Oct.	6.8					91
	Nov.	5.2					70
	Dec.	6.0					81

SOURCE: *Business Statistics*, U.S. Dept. of Commerce, 1959, p. 131; *ibid.*, 1961, p. 129.

For example, in column 3, the first 12-month moving total, 90.7 (which is the total from July, 1955, to June, 1956) is entered *on* the line between December, 1955, and January, 1956. The second moving total, 91.4, is entered *on* the line between January and February of 1956, and likewise for the others.

The 12-month moving average of column 4 is obtained by dividing the moving totals by 12. This moving average is the $T \times C$, which has been obtained by smoothing out the $S \times I$.

But, as is seen from the Worksheet below, these figures are entered *between* the months. To adjust them so that they correspond directly to the months, add the first two moving averages, and enter the total in column 5 so that it corresponds to January. Since this is the total for

Worksheet

Year	(1) Month	(2) TSCI	(3) 12-Month Moving Total	(4) 12-Month Moving Average	(5) 2-Month Moving Total	(6) Centered (5) ÷ (2)	(7) (2) ÷ (6) %
	Nov.	5.8					
1955	Dec.	6.2					
1956	Jan.	6.4	90.7	7.57	15.19	7.60	84
	Feb.	6.6	91.4	7.62			

two months, divide by 2 and enter the result in column 6. What we have in column 4 and column 6 are the same thing, namely, TC, except that we have shifted the values by a half-month in column 6 so that it corresponds directly to the months.

The last step is to find SI. This is obtained by dividing column 2 ($TSCI$) by column 6 (TC). The result is column 7, which is expressed in percentage terms.

Once the SI has been obtained, we should like to remove as much as possible of the I from SI. This is done by taking the average of the SI's. We set up the Worksheet.

The SI figures are obtained from the previous worksheet, and the average for each month for the years are calculated. This removes the I, and we have the S, which is then adjusted so that the base is 100. This is shown in the Adj-M row. The 89 of January is the S of January, and so forth.

One of the basic assumptions of this method was that the 12-month

Worksheet. Seasonal Index

Year	Jan.	Feb.	Mar.	Apr.	May	June	July	Aug.	Sept.	Oct.	Nov.	Dec.	Total
1956	84	87	105	105	116	125	127	116	86	87	79	81	1198
1957	92	79	102	108	120	121	131	112	91	91	70	81	1198
1958	92	86	100	102	118	130	131	105	97	91	78	92	1222
Total	268	252	307	315	354	376	389	333	274	269	227	264	3618
AM	89	84	102	105	118	125	130	111	91	90	76	85	1206
Adj-M	89	84	101	104	117	124	129	110	91	90	76	85	1200

ever, when the business cycles are not very long (2 or 3 years) and have sharp turning points, the 12-month moving average may remove not only the $S \times I$ from the $O = T \times S \times C \times I$ but also part of the C. Then the result $T \times C$ may be T with only part of C. If this should be the case,

$$\frac{\text{Original data}}{\text{Moving average}} = \frac{TSCI}{TC} = SI$$

may give SI with a certain amount of C left in it.

To cope with this problem as well as other problems such as gradual shifts in seasonal patterns, the Bureau of Labor Statistics, Federal Reserve Board, and the Census Bureau have developed techniques of finding S that use ideas similar to the ratio-to-moving average method. Since we are interested in understanding the basic principles of seasonal indices, we shall not discuss these specialized techniques. Explanations of these techniques may be found in the references at the end of the chapter.

13.5. Seasonally Adjusted Data

When the S is removed from the original time series, it is called *seasonally adjusted data,* or deseasonalized data. This may be shown schematically as

$$\frac{T \times S \times C \times I}{S} = T \times C \times I$$

Deseasonalized data show the average value of the data. Let us illustrate this.

The *Survey of Current Business* gives data concerning retail trade, as shown in Table 13.3.

TABLE 13.3.

1947–49 = 100	1959
	Jan. Feb. Mar. Apr. May June July Aug. Sept. Oct. Nov. Dec.
Sales, Unadjusted, Total U.S.	106 107 125 130 141 137 121 132 145 100 176 261
Sales, Seasonally Adj., Total U.S.	138 140 138 141 144 144 150 149 143 144 145 149

SOURCE: *Survey of Current Business*, U.S. Dept. of Commerce, February, 1960.

As can be seen from the unadjusted totals, sales during Christmas season are high but drop drastically in January. This seasonal pattern repeats itself annually, and the seasonally adjusted figures remove these seasonal variations.

The economic phenomena "sales" is decomposed into T, S, C, and I, which are then divided into two parts, $T \times C \times I$ and S. The interpretation is that the $T \times C \times I$ shows an average (for example, average sales, average rate of growth, average value, average output) over the year. But, because of seasonal influences, the actual rate of sales (or value, or output, or growth, etc.), which is shown by $O = T \times S \times C \times I$, deviates from this average rate of sales $T \times C \times I$. We are not saying that $T \times C \times I$ is what the sales would be if there were no seasonal variations.

Seasonally adjusted data are also used to state results as annual rates. Let us illustrate. The seasonally adjusted quarterly totals of national income at annual rates for 1959 are:

Month	Billions of Dollars
Mar.	389.4
June	403.9
Sept.	398.2
Dec.	402.8

Economic quantities such as national income and total sales are usually measured in terms of 1-year totals. For example, the national income in 1958 was $366,200,000,000; in 1959, it was $398,500,000,000, and so forth. Comparisons of the national income are easier when the data are in terms of annual totals.

For instance, the quarterly national income total of January, February, and March is obtained and then deseasonalized. This seasonally adjusted quarterly total gives us an average quarterly total. Thus, if this average quarterly total is multiplied by 4, it will give us the national income of the first quarter on an annual basis. The figures cited above show these annual rates, and because they are expressed as annual rates, comparison is facilitated.

13.6.   Cyclical Fluctuations

So far we have discussed ways of finding the trend T and the seasonal variation S. Of the two remaining components, C and I, the main interest in I is to find adequate ways of removing it from the series. We have used the process of averaging a number of years to eliminate the I from the series.

There are also methods of finding a cyclical index, but each business cycle has its own characteristics and is in contrast to the seasonal variations that occur with regularity and are due mainly to the same causes. Business cycles differ in length and can be as short as $2\frac{1}{2}$ years or as long as 8 years.

For these reasons, most studies of cycles do not rely exclusively on statistics, but use a great deal of economic analysis. We shall therefore make no attempt to present a simple statistical solution to this problem. The National Bureau of Economic Research (NBER) has done a great deal of work in this field and its methods of measuring business cycles are described in a book issued by this institution.[*]

Econometricians associated with the Cowles Foundation have also contributed greatly to this study.[**] Students interested in statistical analysis of business cycles are referred to publications by these two institutions, but it is recommended that students take advanced work in statistics and economics before trying to read the various works cited here. Other publications that may be of value include:

1. Bureau of Census Method Reference:
    J. Shiskin and H. Eisenpress, "Seasonal Adjustments by Electronic Computer Methods," J.A. Statistical Assoc., 1957, pp. 415–449.
2. Bureau of Labor Statistics Reference:
    A. Rothman, "The BLS Seasonal Factor Method," The American

---

[*] A. F. Burns and Wesley C. Mitchell, *Measuring Business Cycles*, National Bureau of Economic Research, New York, 1946.
[**] L. R. Klein, *Economic Fluctuations in the U.S., 1921–1942*, New York: John Wiley & Sons, 1950.

Statistical Assoc., *1960 Proceedings* of the Business and Economic Statistics Section, pp. 2–12.
3. Federal Reserve Board Reference:
   H. C. Barton, "Adjustment for Seasonal Variation," Federal Reserve Bulletin, 1941, pp. 518–528.

13.7. Comments on Time Series

(i) A basic point of view

Our discussion of time series was mainly descriptive and no explicit explanation was given of the basic ideas upon which our discussion was based. But with the background we have acquired, let us now investigate some of these basic assumptions. In approaching the subject of time series, we are basically assuming a population from which a sample is taken; then, using the ideas of probability, statistical inference, and estimation, we wish to make statements about the population. For example, when we have an annual series of data on the production of beer (say, y millions of barrels), we may consider a value of y for a given year to be one of the many possible values of y for that year. The annual series of data is a sample, and using this sample, we wish to make statements about the production of beer.

To apply various statistical techniques, we usually assume that the observations are independent of each other. However, it is easy to see that the assumption of independence of observations is rarely fulfilled. If there is overproduction of steel this year, it will clearly affect the production of steel next year.

The relation between successive values of variables is also dependent on the time interval used. If the time interval is short (say, one month), it is more probable that two successive values will be correlated with each other than when the time interval is long (say, one year).

An investigation of economic time series that does not assume independence of observations leads to the topic of serial correlation, which is a very difficult topic. A brief explanation of this is given in Chapter 23.

(ii) Basic models

Given the basic point of view, usually two basic models are assumed:

1. $O = T + S + C + I.$

2. $O = T \times S \times C \times I.$

There are, however, various other possibilities, such as $O = S + T \times C \times I$, but we shall confine our attention to the first two models.

The first model assumes that the economic time series is additive and is made up of the four components T, S, C, and I. This assumption of additivity in turn is assuming that the components are independent of each other. This means, for example, that no matter how high the trend value may be, it will have no effect on the seasonal variation. It also means that the 4 components are the outcomes of four independent causes. As a concrete example, the production of beer has been increasing over the past 50 years. This additivity assumption implies that this steady increase in the production of beer has no effect on the seasonal variation of the production of beer. It also implies that the causes for the increase in the production of beer are different from the causes of the seasonal variation of beer. Although the causes for the increase in the production of beer may be different from the causes of the seasonal variation, it is probably safe to say that the increase in the production has an effect on the seasonal variation of the production of beer.

The second model is the one we have been using, and it assumes that the four components are related to each other. The reason for using this model is that it allows convenient isolation of the components. This in turn assumes that the four components are due to different causes. Although they are due to different causes, we are assuming that they affect each other.

However, one may argue that the components are not due to different causes and cannot be isolated. In particular, one may argue that many factors (such as population and changes in taste) affect both the trend and cycle.

(iii)   Isolation of trend (T)

The first component isolated was the trend. We are assuming that a trend exists, and it may be rising, falling, or constant.

The first thing we have to do is to decide whether the trend is a straightline or curvilinear trend. We have dealt only with the straight-line trend case. This assumes that the annual (or per period) change in the economic time series is constant.

Now that we have decided to use a straightline trend, the next problem is to decide how to fit the straight line to the data. In our previous discussion, we fitted the straight line by the freehand method, method of semiaverages, method of moving averages, and method of least squares. Of these various methods, the method of least squares is more widely used. The question that naturally arises is: Why is this method favored over the other methods?

The reason is that it is the best method. Then the question becomes: What do we mean by best method? When fitting a straight line to a set of data, we wish to have a close fit. By a close fit, we mean a fit such that the deviations d_i are small. There are several ways of making the d_i small. One is to minimize the sum of the absolute values of d_i. A second is to minimize the sum of the squares of d_i, which leads to the method of least squares. (See Fig. 13.5.)

From our discussion above where the observations were regarded as a sample from a population, we may consider this process of fitting a straight line as one of estimating the parameters a and b of a linear trend line:

FIG. 13.5.

$$Y_c = a + bX$$

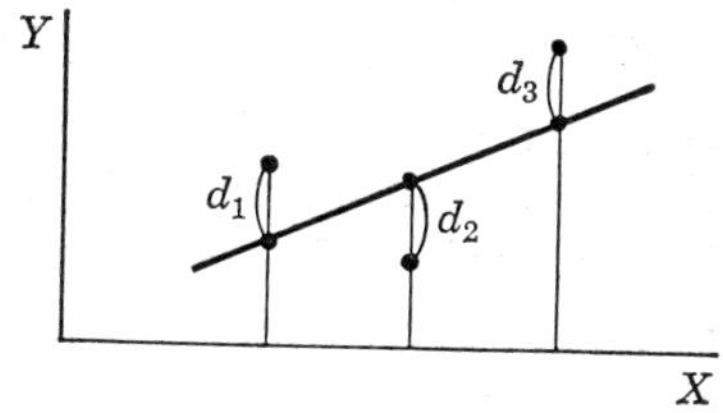

If the values of Y are random and the values of X are fixed, then the Markoff theorem tells us that this method of least squares will give us a linear unbiased estimate of Y. Furthermore, the variance of this estimate will be smaller than any other estimate of Y.

If, in addition, Y is *normally* distributed, the a and b estimated by the least squares method will be the same as those obtained by the maximum likelihood method. We have discussed the method of maximum likelihood in Chapter 10, where we stated without proof that this method gives us desirable estimators.

However, the Y's are usually not independent, and in many cases, they cannot be assumed to be normally distributed. Hence, the results of the Markoff theorem or the method of maximum likelihood do not hold. In spite of this, the method of least squares is used because of its convenience.

The method of least squares is a technique of estimating the parameters and may be applied to curvilinear as well as linear equations. We shall discuss the application of this technique to the curvilinear cases in Chapter 23.

As can be seen, once the shape of the trend line and the method of estimation have been determined, fitting a trend becomes a simple mechanical computational problem.

(iv) Caution on using the moving average

The moving average was used to find a trend line and also the seasonal variation. When applying the moving average technique to find the trend line, we are assuming that the economic time series is made up of two main components: One is the trend that represents a systematic growth (rising, constant, or falling), and the other components are those that may be considered divergences from the trend, which are the C, S, and I.

The moving average method of finding the trend is based on the idea of "averaging out" these divergences from the trend.

We have seen that if we have periodic fluctuations with a period of (say) 3 years, and use a 3-year moving average, these periodic fluctuations will cancel each other. Hence, if the C or S are fluctuations that have a period of 3 years or multiples of 3 years, they will be averaged out. However, C and I usually do not have systematic period fluctuations, and hence the application of the moving average technique will only partially cancel out these effects. The S component is usually of a shorter period (say, 12 months, 1 week, etc.) and is relatively regular.

When the three components C, S, and I are combined and treated as divergences from the trend, there is probably no period common to all three. When applying the moving average to eliminate the combined divergence of the C, S, and I from T, we shall probably be only partially successful.

In spite of these criticisms, the moving average techniques give us results that are useful in practical applications of business and economics. The point to bear in mind is that the trend is based on a number of assumptions, and care must be taken when interpreting the results.

The moving average technique was also used to find the seasonal variation. In this case, the basic model assumed is that the S component diverges from the relatively stable T and C component; by using the moving average technique, we average out these divergences due to S.

The causes of the seasonal variation are usually natural (weather) or institutional (Christmas, Easter, fall sale of new cars, etc.) and have a relatively regular period. Hence, when applying a (say) 12-month moving average to an economic time series, we may expect an effective averaging-out process.

Another characteristic of the moving average is that it may generate an oscillatory series when applied to a random series. This is known as the Slutzky-Yule effect. This Slutzky-Yule effect raises the following problem when the moving average technique is applied to fitting a trend: An economic time series usually contains a random component. Hence, when taking the moving average of the time series to find the trend, we are also taking the moving average of the random component. Because of the Slutzky-Yule effect, this will generate an oscillatory series, which may become a part of the trend we seek.

This also leads to the observation that if the moving average technique is used to remove the trend from an economic time series, the remaining components of the time series may, as a result of the Slutzky-Yule effect, show an oscillatory trend.

Because of these effects, care must be exercised when using the moving average on economic time series.

(v) Caution on forecasting

When economic time series are used for forecasting, the first thing that needs to be done is to decide what is being forecast. We may broadly divide this into two aspects: One is forecasting the trend and the other is forecasting business cycles.

To forecast trends, the usual procedure is to project the trend into the future, such as projecting the trend of population, production of steel, sales of a company, or national income.

One of the basic assumptions we made about our time series model was that the components T, S, C, and I were due to different sets of causes. The idea of projecting a trend implies that we are assuming that the set of causes of the trend will continue or change only gradually in the future.

Whether or not this assumption of slow change is acceptable should be considered in connection with the individual situations. For example, population changes slowly. The consumption of silk, on the other hand, showed a sudden change due to the appearance of nylon.

Forecasting of business cycles, as mentioned earlier, is too difficult to discuss in this book.

LINEAR REGRESSION ANALYSIS

14

One of the most frequently used techniques in economics and business research, to find a relation between two or more variables that are related causally, is regression analysis. In this chapter we shall consider the simplest case where there are only two variables, such as the yield of wheat and the amount of fertilizer. This will give us the basic ideas of regression analysis. In Chapter 22, we shall extend this to the general case of more than two variables, such as the relation between yield of wheat and the amount of fertilizer, rainfall, temperature, etc. Let us now introduce the problem.

14.1. Introduction

Generally we observe that the taller a person, the heavier he is, and hence we know that there is a relation between height and weight. What kind of a relationship is it? Is it proportional, or is there some other kind of a relationship?

We may also wish to know the closeness of this relationship. If it is very close, then given the height of a student, we may be able to estimate (predict) with accuracy his weight.

As another example, consider income and consumption expenditures. We know that as one's income increases, there is a tendency to spend more. What kind of a relationship is there between income and consumption expenditures? Is it proportional, or is there some other kind of a relationship? Secondly, how close is this relationship between income and consumption expenditures?

In this chapter we shall study the question about the relationship between two variables X and Y. Thus, for example, we are considering the relationship between height (X) and weight (Y), or between the horsepower (X) and speed (Y) of a car, or between the amount of fertilizer (X) and the yield of wheat (Y), or between advertising (X) and sales (Y).

This introduction of a second variable is in contrast to our previous studies in which we dealt with only one variable, such as the IQ of a student, or his height, or weight. We now deal with two variables and later on we shall deal with cases in which there are more than two variables.

In Chapter 15 we shall discuss correlation analysis, which is a study of the degree of closeness of the relationship between X and Y.

Let us now set up a hypothetical situation and discuss the basic ideas of regression analysis.

14.2. The Regression Problem

Suppose we have a group of children who are grouped according to their height (X), as shown in Table 14.1. We see that there are 25

TABLE 14.1.

X, inches	Y, pounds					E(Y)
50	40	41	42	43	44	42
51	41	43	44	46	46	44
52	41	44	45	48	52	46
53	43	46	47	49	55	48
54	44	46	49	51	60	50

pairs of observations such as (50 in., 40 lb.), (50 in., 41 lb.), . . . , (54 in., 60 lb.). These 25 pairs of observations comprise the *population,* and Fig. 14.1 is a graph of these observations.

Note that the groupings are according to fixed heights, such as 50 in. and 51 in., and each group has 5 pairs of observations. Each group is called a *subpopulation,* and there are 5 subpopulations corresponding to the fixed variable height (X). We shall say that we have a *collection* or *family* of subpopulations.

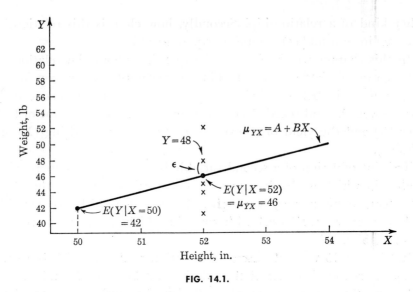

FIG. 14.1.

The average of the Y's in each subpopulation is called the *expected values* of Y for given heights (X), and is written $E(Y|X)$. For example,

$$E(Y|X = 50 \text{ in.}) = \frac{40 + 41 + 42 + 43 + 44}{5} = 42 \text{ lb.}$$

The data have been doctored up so that the averages will fall on a straight line, which has been drawn in on Fig. 14.1.

Let us now focus our attention on the subpopulation corresponding to $X = 52$ in. Then

$$E(Y|X = 52) = \frac{41 + 44 + 45 + 48 + 52}{5} = 46$$

The $Y = 48$ lb. in this subpopulation deviates from $E(Y|X)$ by

$$Y - E(Y|X = 52) = 48 - 46 = 2 \text{ lb.}$$

and these deviations will be expressed by ϵ. Then the $Y = 48$ lb. can be expressed as

$$Y = E(Y|X = 52) + \epsilon$$

This is a general expression for the individual Y values of the $X = 52$ subpopulation. That is, when $\epsilon = -4$,

$$Y = E(Y|X = 52) + \epsilon = 46 - 4 = 42$$

When $\epsilon = -3$, then $Y = 43$; when $\epsilon = -1$, then $Y = 45$; when $\epsilon = 3$, then $Y = 48$; and when $\epsilon = 6$, then $Y = 52$.

The individual Y values in each of the subpopulations may be expressed in similar manner. That is,

$$Y = E(Y|X = 50) + \epsilon = 42 + \epsilon$$
$$Y = E(Y|X = 51) + \epsilon = 44 + \epsilon$$

$$\cdots\cdots$$

$$Y = E(Y|X = 54) + \epsilon = 50 + \epsilon$$

In general, an individual Y is expressed as

(1) $$Y = E(Y|X) + \epsilon$$

Since $E(Y|X)$ gives us a straight line, as shown in Fig. 14.1, we may express $E(Y|X)$ as

$$E(Y|X) = A + BX$$

For brevity, let us write

$$E(Y|X) = \mu_{YX}$$

Then

(2) $$\mu_{YX} = A + BX$$

and this is the straight line going through the average weights $E(Y|X)$. The parameters A and B are easily determined by observation as

$$\mu_{YX} = 42 + 2X$$
$$\text{Origin: } X = 0 \qquad \text{for 50 in.}$$

This may be summarized in worksheet form as shown below.

Worksheet

Height	X	$E(Y|X) = \mu_{YX}$
50 inches	0	42 lb.
51	1	44
52	2	46
53	3	48
54	4	50

Equations (1) and (2) were

(1) $$Y = E(Y|X) + \epsilon$$
(2) $$\mu_{YX} = A + BX$$

By combining these two equations, an individual value Y may be expressed as

$$(3) \qquad\qquad Y = A + BX + \epsilon$$

These three equations summarize all the data in the population and will be called the *model* (or regression model). The equation (2) is called the *regression curve of* Y *on* X and shows the relation between the expected values of Y and the independent values X. It is also simply called the *regression function*. The coefficients A and B are called *population regression coefficients*.

As an illustration of the meaning of the model, let X be income and Y be consumption expenditures. Then equation (2) tells us that when we have a certain given income X, the expected consumption expenditures will be μ_{YX}.

Another illustration is: Let X be the amount of advertising and Y be the amount of sales. Then equation (2) tells us when, given a certain amount of advertising, the expected amount of sales is μ_{YX}.

Let us now generalize our *model. First,* instead of having only five pairs of observations per fixed height, let us have a large number of cases, many of which we may not observe but which we know exist. Thus, each subpopulation becomes very large.

Second, we shall *assume* that each subpopulation has a normal distribution. This assumption holds in a great many practical cases.

Third, we shall *assume,* for simplicity, that the standard deviation (variance) of all the subpopulations is equal. The variance of Y by definition is

$$(4) \qquad\qquad \sigma^2 = E[Y - E(Y|X)]^2$$

Fourth, we shall *assume* that the deviation (or error) ϵ has a normal distribution, with

$$(5) \qquad\qquad E(\epsilon) = 0$$

The variance of ϵ is

$$\begin{aligned}
\text{Var}(\epsilon) &= E[\epsilon - E(\epsilon)]^2 \\
&= E(\epsilon)^2 \\
&= E[Y - E(Y|X)]^2
\end{aligned}$$

But, from (4), this is the variance σ^2 of the population; thus,

$$(6) \qquad\qquad \text{Var}(\epsilon) = \sigma^2$$

To illustrate the meaning of this generalization, consider the height and weight relation. For a given height (say, $X = 50$ in.), there are many possible weights, Y. We assume that most of the weights will be around $E(Y|X = 50) = 42$ lb. and the remainder will taper off in the form of a normal distribution, as shown in Fig. 14.2. That the

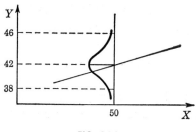

FIG. 14.2.

deviation of the individual Y values from $E(Y|X = 50)$ (that is, ϵ) will have a variance σ^2 should also be clear from Fig. 14.2.

Let us now summarize our discussion. We have been given a family of subpopulations of Y's (say, weights) corresponding to fixed X's (say, heights). The distribution of the Y's in each subpopulation is assumed to be normal, with mean $E(Y|X)$ and variance σ^2. Then the regression function of Y on X is defined as

(7) $$E(Y|X) = A + BX$$

where A and B are the population regression parameters (or coefficients). The individual Y values are shown by

(8) $$Y = A + BX + \epsilon$$

where ϵ is normally distributed, with

$$E(\epsilon) = 0, \qquad \text{Var}(\epsilon) = \sigma^2$$

Note that we defined (7) simply as a straight line, but it can be shown theoretically that, when given the assumptions we stated, the regression function will be a straight line. This is discussed again in Chapter 22. This explains why it is called a *linear* regression function.

Evidently, if we can determine the population regression coefficients A and B, we can find the expected value of Y for given X values. For example, if A and B are known for the height and weight regression function, we can find the expected weight when given the height. In our simplified height and weight illustration, the A and B were found by finding the $E(Y|X)$ for each X and fitting a straight line to the points $E(Y|X)$. This was possible because there were only five X's and five Y values for each X. But, in our generalized model, we have many X's and many (theoretically an infinite number) Y values. What shall we do?

As one can easily see by now, we take a *sample* of these observations and *estimate* the A and B. Since this is the statistical problem in which we are now interested, let us consider it next.

14.3. Estimation of Population Regression Coefficients A and B

Using our hypothetical population, let us discuss the estimation procedure. Table 14.1 is reproduced here for convenience as Table 14.2.

TABLE 14.2.

X, inches	Y, pounds					$E(Y|X) = \mu_{YX}$
50	40	41	42	43	44	42
51	41	43	44	46	46	44
52	41	44	45	48	52	46
53	43	46	47	49	55	48
54	44	46	49	51	60	50

A random sample is selected from this population and the parameters A and B are estimated. Let the estimates be denoted by a and b and identified as *sample regression coefficients*. Then the estimated regression line becomes

(1) $$Y_c = a + bX$$

where Y_c is an estimate of μ_{YX}. Note carefully that Y_c is not an estimate of the individual values, but an estimate of the expected value of Y.

What method shall we use to estimate A and B? In Chapter 10, two methods were mentioned, the method of least squares and the method of maximum likelihood. We shall use the method of least squares, which we already know, but when given the assumptions on which we base our discussion, the method of maximum likelihood will give us the same results. This is discussed in Chapter 22.

The first thing we have to do is to select a random sample, and for simplicity we select one pair from each subpopulation. The sample is given in Table 14.3. Figure 14.3 is a graph of these observations and is called a *scatter diagram*. We can estimate the A and B without any

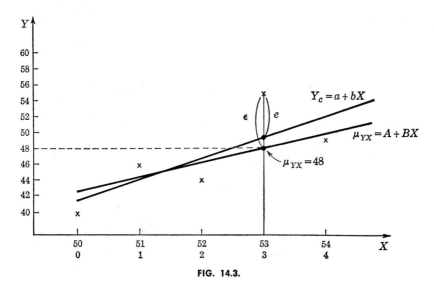

FIG. 14.3.

TABLE 14.3.

Observation	X	Y
50 in.	0	40
51	1	46
52	2	44
53	3	55
54	4	49

diagrams, but this scatter diagram serves to give a preliminary idea of the shape of the regression function. Although there are only 5 observations, we observe from the scatter diagram that the relationship is linear.

Let Y be the individual sample values and Y_c be the estimate of $E(Y|X)$. We know that

$$\epsilon = Y - E(Y|X)$$

In similar manner we define the deviations of Y from the Y_c as e; that is,

$$e = Y - Y_c$$
$$= Y - a - bX$$

Clearly, the smaller the e's, the closer the Y_c to the actual Y values. That is, the smaller the e's, the better the fit of the regression line to the observations of Y by Y_c. This is obviously a desirable property, and hence we wish to find an a and b that will make e as small as possible.

This is accomplished by setting

$$\sum_{i=1}^{5} e_i^2 = \sum_{i=1}^{5} (Y_i - a - bX_i)^2 = \text{minimum}$$

That is, we find the a and b such that the sum of the squared deviations Σe^2, taken over the sample values, is at a minimum. The a and b, as we know, are found by the *normal equations:*

(2)
$$\Sigma Y = na + b\Sigma X$$
$$\Sigma XY = a\Sigma X + b\Sigma X^2$$

Using the data of Table 14.4, let us find a and b as follows:

TABLE 14.4.

Height, inches	X	Y	XY	X²
50	0	40	0	0
51	1	46	46	1
52	2	44	88	4
53	3	55	165	9
54	4	49	196	16
	10	234	495	30

$$234 = 5a + 10b$$
$$495 = 10a + 30b$$

$$a = 41.4 \text{ lb.} \qquad b = 2.7 \text{ lb.}$$

(3)
$$Y_c = 41.4 + 2.7X$$
$$X = 0 \quad \text{at 50 in.}$$
$$X: \quad \text{1-in. units}$$

The estimates of A and B are

$$\hat{A} = a = 41.4 \text{ lb.}$$
$$\hat{B} = b = 2.7 \text{ lb.}$$

Then, for example, for 53 in., the $X = 3$ and the Y_c becomes

$$Y_c = 41.4 + (2.7)(3) = 49.5 \text{ lb.}$$

The interpretation is as follows: Equation (3) is an estimate of the population regression function. It tells us that, for example, given a

child of $X = 53$ in., the estimated expected (average) weight is 49.5 lb.
Let us next check the errors. Since $Y = 55$ lb.,

$$e = Y - Y_c = 55 - 49.5 = 5.5 \text{ lb.}$$

We also know from the hypothetical population that $E(Y|X = 53) = 48$ lb. Thus

$$\epsilon = Y - E(Y|X) = 55 - 48 = 7 \text{ lb.}$$

The justification for using the method of least squares to estimate A, B, and μ_{YX} was that the sum of the squared deviations is at a minimum. The student may have noticed that this does not agree with the reasons given in Chapter 10 for using a specific method of estimation. In Chapter 10 it was explained that the reason for using the method of maximum likelihood was because it was based on the idea of likelihood; furthermore, it gave estimators that had desirable properties, such as unbiasedness, consistency, and efficiency. It can be shown that the method of least squares, which is based on the idea of giving the best fit, will give us the same results as the maximum likelihood method and that the estimators have the desirable properties.

Computational procedures

The illustration above was simple and thus there were no difficulties in the computations. Furthermore, the X's were evenly spaced, and as a result we could have renumbered them so that $\Sigma X = 0$, which would have simplified computations. But generally the samples are much larger and the X's are not evenly spaced; therefore, renumbering them so that $\Sigma X = 0$ is usually not feasible. Nevertheless there are several formulas that simplify computations considerably, especially for calculating machines. Let us explain these formulas.

The normal equations are

(4)
$$\Sigma Y = na + b\Sigma X$$
$$\Sigma XY = a\Sigma X + b\Sigma X^2$$

The a and b become

(5)
$$b = \frac{\Sigma (X - \bar{X})(Y - \bar{Y})}{\Sigma (X - \bar{X})^2}$$

(6)
$$a = \bar{Y} - b\bar{X}$$

Formula (5) involves deviations from the mean, which make computations tedious. Fortunately, (5) and (6) may be modified as follows:

(7) $$b = \frac{n\Sigma\, XY - \Sigma\, X\, \Sigma\, Y}{n\Sigma\, X^2 - (\Sigma\, X)^2}$$

(8) $$a = \frac{\Sigma\, Y}{n} - b\,\frac{\Sigma\, X}{n}$$

Using the values of Table 14.3 as an example, we find

$$b = \frac{5(495) - (10)(234)}{5(30) - (10)^2} = \frac{27}{10} = 2.7$$

$$a = \frac{234}{5} - 2.7 \times \frac{10}{5} = 41.4$$

These results are the same as those we obtained previously.

14.4. Finding a Regression Function

A few examples will illustrate the mechanical procedures of finding a regression function.

Example 1. Consider a random sample of pairs of heights and weights as in Table 14.5.

TABLE 14.5.

Height	X	Y, pounds	XY	X²	Y_c
5′3″	0	130	0	0	
4″	1	145	145	1	
5″	2	150	300	4	152
6″	3	165	495	9	
7″	4	170	680	16	
	10	760	1620	30	

The first step is to find the regression function of weight (Y) on height (X) and we therefore plot the scatter diagram, as in Fig. 14.4. Observation of the scatter diagram shows that a straight line will adequately fit these points.

The second step is to fit a sample regression line by method of least squares. Using the formulas for the sample regression coefficients, we find

$$b = \frac{5(1620) - (10)(760)}{5(30) - (10)^2} = 10$$

$$a = \frac{760}{5} - 10 \times \frac{10}{5} = 152 - 20 = 132$$

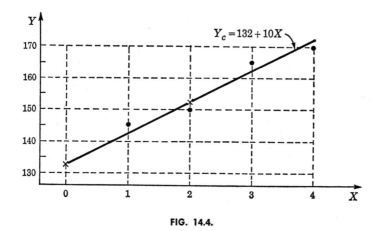

FIG. 14.4.

Thus, the sample regression line of Y on X is

$$Y_c = 132 + 10X$$

$X = 0$ at 5 ft. 3 in. and X is in 1-in. units. For example, for $X = 2$ (that is, 5′5″), the estimate of the average (expected) weight is

$$Y_c = 132 + 10 \times 2 = 152 \text{ lb.}$$

This means: If the height of a student is 5′5″, the *estimated expected value* of his weight is $Y_c = 152$ lb. Calculate the other Y_c values and complete Table 14.5.

Example 2. In Example 1 the heights (X) were evenly spaced so that 0, 1, 2, 3, 4 were used instead of the original values, but in general the independent variable X is not evenly spaced, in which case the X values have to be used as given. Let us examine a hypothetical example.

Suppose we have a random sample of pairs of hours studied and grade points, as shown in Table 14.6. We wish to find the regression of grade points (Y) on hours studied (X).

TABLE 14.6.

X, Hours	Y, Grade	XY	X²
4	40	160	16
6	60	360	36
7	50	350	49
10	70	700	100
13	90	1170	169
40	310	2740	370

$$b = \frac{5(2740) - 40(310)}{5(370) - (40)^2} = \frac{26}{5} = 5.2$$

$$a = \frac{310}{5} - 5.2 \times \frac{40}{5} = 62 - 41.6 = 20.4$$

The first step is to draw a scatter diagram and to find whether the regression relationship is linear. A check will show that the scatter diagram satisfies this linear requirement.

The sample regression coefficients are then found by the method of least squares, which we used above. Thus, the sample regression line is

$$Y_c = 20.4 + 5.2X$$

The origin is $X = 0$ hours, and X is in 1-hr. units. For example, if the student studies $X = 5$ hr., then

$$Y_c = 20.4 + (5.2)(5) = 46.4 \text{ points}$$

That is, the estimated expected average grade is 46.4 points.

Example 3.   From Example 2 we can see that if the values of X and Y are large, a considerable amount of calculation will be involved in the calculation of the slope b. This may be avoided by subtracting a constant from each of the X values (say, $k = 8$), and a constant from each of the Y values (say,

X' = X − 8, Hours	Y' = Y − 60, Grade	$X'Y'$ = (X − 8)(Y − 60)	X'^2 = (X − 8)²
−4	−20	80	16
−2	0	0	4
−1	−10	10	1
2	10	20	4
5	30	150	25
0	10	260	50

$m = 60$). Graphically, we are merely shifting the origin from $(0, 0)$ to a new origin $(8, 60)$, as shown schematically in Fig. 14.5. The slope of the regres-

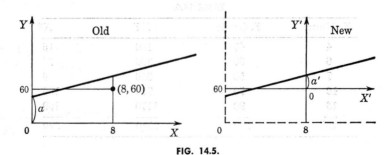

FIG. 14.5.

sion function b remains the same and is found as follows:

$$b = \frac{n \Sigma X'Y' - \Sigma X' \Sigma Y'}{n \Sigma X'^2 - (\Sigma X')^2}$$

$$= \frac{(5)(260) - (0)(10)}{5(50) - 0}$$

$$= \frac{260}{50} = \frac{26}{5} = 5.2$$

The $b = 5.2$ is the same as that found in Example 2, as expected. The a has been already found as $a = 20.4$. Thus, we obtain the same regression function

$$Y_c = 20.4 + 5.2X$$

where the origin is at $X = 0$ hours.

The a may also be found as follows:

$$a = \frac{\Sigma Y}{n} - b \frac{\Sigma X}{n}$$

$$= \frac{\Sigma (Y' + 60)}{n} - b \frac{\Sigma (X' + 8)}{n}$$

and (since $X' = X - 8$, $Y' = Y - 60$),

$$a = \left(\frac{\Sigma Y'}{n} + 60\right) - b \left(\frac{\Sigma X'}{n} + 8\right)$$

$$= \frac{\Sigma Y'}{n} - b \frac{\Sigma X'}{n} + (60 - b \cdot 8)$$

$$= \frac{10}{5} - (5.2)\left(\frac{0}{5}\right) + (60 - 5.2 \times 8)$$

$$= 20.4$$

Example 4. Given the data in the accompanying table, concerning income and consumption, find the regression of consumption on income.

X Income	Y Consumption	Y_c
$ 200	$ 180	185.6
300	270	258.6
400	320	331.6
600	480	477.6
900	700	696.6
$2400	$1950	

To simplify computations, let us divide both X and Y values by 100 (or 10, or any other number), as shown in the table below. Graphically, we are re-

X' Income	Y'	$X'Y'$	X'^2
2	1.8	3.6	4
3	2.7	8.1	9
4	3.2	12.8	16
6	4.8	28.8	36
9	7.0	63.0	81
$\overline{24}$	$\overline{19.5}$	$\overline{116.3}$	$\overline{146}$

ducing the *scale* of the diagram to $1/100$ (or $1/10$), and hence it has no effect on the slope b of the regression function. This is similar to taking a photo of the scatter diagram whose measurements were $1/100$ of the original diagram. Then the values become:

$$b = \frac{n \Sigma X'Y' - (\Sigma X')(\Sigma Y')}{n \Sigma X'^2 - (\Sigma X')^2}$$

$$= \frac{(5)(116.3) - (24)(19.5)}{(5)(146) - (24)^2}$$

$$= \frac{581.5 - 468}{730 - 576}$$

$$= \frac{113.5}{154} = 0.73$$

$$a = \frac{\Sigma Y'}{n} - b \frac{\Sigma X'}{n}$$

$$= \frac{19.5}{5} - (0.73)\left(\frac{24}{5}\right)$$

$$= 3.9 - 3.504 = 0.396$$

Since the scale was reduced to $1/100$, the a is $0.396 \times 100 = 39.6$. Thus the regression line is

$$Y_c = 39.6 + 0.73X$$

where the origin is at zero dollar and X is in $1.00 units.

The estimated expected value of consumption when income is $200 is

$$Y_c = 39.6 + (0.73)(200) = \$185.6$$

The other Y_c values are given in the right-hand column of the first table above.

14.5.   Sample Standard Deviation of Regression (Standard Error of Estimate)

A measure that shows the degree of concentration (dispersion) of the observations around the regression line is the standard deviation of the regression line. Figure 14.6(a) shows a case where the observations

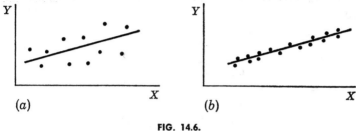

(a)   *(b)*

FIG. 14.6.

are loosely scattered around the regression line, whereas in Fig. 14.6(b), they are concentrated near it. The standard deviation for Fig. 14.6(a) is large, whereas for Fig. 14.6(b) it is small. Let us now show how this standard deviation is found.

In Section 14.2 we assumed that the variance of each subpopulation was equal and denoted it by

(1) $\sigma^2 = E[Y - E(Y|X)]^2$

Figure 14.7 shows 3 subpopulations and the corresponding distributions of the Y values. The dotted lines show the distance of 1 standard devia-

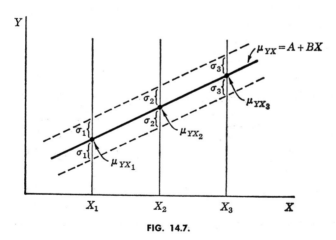

FIG. 14.7.

tion from the regression line. Formula (1) in computational form is as follows:

$$\sigma^2 = \frac{\Sigma (Y - \mu_{YX})^2}{N}$$

where the sum is taken over the subpopulation and N is the size of the subpopulation. For example, if the subpopulations corresponding to X_1, X_2, and X_3 have N_1, N_2, and N_3 observations of Y values, the variances are

$$\sigma_1{}^2 = \frac{\overset{N_1}{\Sigma} (Y - \mu_{YX_1})^2}{N_1}$$

$$\sigma_2{}^2 = \frac{\overset{N_2}{\Sigma} (Y - \mu_{YX_2})^2}{N_2}$$

$$\sigma_3{}^2 = \frac{\overset{N_3}{\Sigma} (Y - \mu_{YX_3})^2}{N_3}$$

where $\sigma_1{}^2$, $\sigma_2{}^2$, and $\sigma_3{}^2$ are the variances of the first, second, and third subpopulations. Our assumption is that

$$\sigma_1{}^2 = \sigma_2{}^2 = \sigma_3{}^2$$

and the common variance is denoted by σ^2.

To show that it is the standard deviation of the Y values around the regression line for given values of X, it is usually denoted as

(2)
$$\sigma_{YX}^2 = \frac{\Sigma (Y - \mu_{YX})^2}{N}$$

and is called the *population variance of regression*. The square root of σ_{YX}^2 is called the *population standard deviation of regression*.

But, as we have discussed previously, only sample data are usually available, and we have to estimate the population parameters. Thus, the problem is, how are we going to estimate σ_{YX}^2?

We may use the method of maximum likelihood to estimate the σ_{YX}^2, but the deviation is mathematically too advanced for this book. We shall present only the results. The maximum likelihood estimate is

(3)
$$\hat{\sigma}_{XY}^2 = \frac{\overset{n}{\Sigma} (Y - Y_c)^2}{n}$$

where the sum is over the sample values and n is the sample size. Formula (3) is similar to formula (2) except that μ_{YX} is replaced by its estimate Y_c, N by n, and the sum is over the sample instead of the subpopulation. We shall, however, use $n - 2$ instead of n because when $n - 2$ is used, $\hat{\sigma}_{YX}$ becomes an unbiased estimate of σ_{YX}. This $n - 2$ is called *degrees of freedom* and is discussed in Chapter 17. The estimate $\hat{\sigma}_{YX}$ is called the *standard error of estimate*, or the *sample standard deviation of regression*. We shall use the latter term.

Formula (3) shows that when Y is close to Y_c, that is, when the sample observations are concentrated near the regression line, $\hat{\sigma}_{Y_c}$ is small. When all the points lie on the sample regression line, σ_{YX} becomes zero, which means that there is no distribution of the Y values. That is, when given a value of X, we get a specific value of Y and we have a (mathematical) functional relation between X and Y, and not a stochastic relation.

Example 1. Using Example 1 of Section 14.4, let us illustrate the computational procedures:

Worksheet

Height	X	Y	Y_c	$Y - Y_c$	$e^2 = (Y - Y_c)^2$
5'3"	0	130	132	-2	4
4"	1	145	142	3	9
5"	2	150	152	-2	4
6"	3	165	162	3	9
7"	4	170	172	-2	4
					30

$$\hat{\sigma}_{YX}^2 = \frac{\Sigma (Y - Y_c)^2}{n - 2} = \frac{30}{5 - 2} = 10$$

$$\hat{\sigma}_{YX} = \sqrt{10} = 3.16 \text{ lb.}$$

Example 2. The procedure in Example 1 required calculation of Y_c, but this can be avoided by using the following relation:

$$\Sigma (Y - Y_c)^2 = \frac{\Sigma (X - \bar{X})^2 \, \Sigma (Y - \bar{Y})^2 - [\Sigma (X - \bar{X}) (Y - \bar{Y})]^2}{\Sigma (X - \bar{X})^2}$$

where

$$\Sigma (X - \bar{X})^2 = \Sigma X^2 - \frac{1}{n} (\Sigma X)^2$$

$$\Sigma(Y - \bar{Y})^2 = \Sigma Y^2 - \frac{1}{n}(\Sigma Y)^2$$

$$\Sigma(X - \bar{X})(Y - \bar{Y}) = \Sigma XY - \frac{1}{n}\Sigma X \Sigma Y$$

Furthermore, note that

$$Y - \bar{Y} = (Y - C) - (\bar{Y} - C) = Y' - \bar{Y}'$$

where C is an arbitrary constant. Hence, we may use Y' and $\bar{Y}'$ instead of Y and $\bar{Y}$ in the formulas above. Using the relations above, we set up the worksheet.

Worksheet

X	Y	$Y - C = Y'$	X^2	Y'^2	XY'
0	130	$130 - 150 = -20$	0	400	0
1	145	-5	1	25	-5
2	150	0	4	0	0
3	165	15	9	225	45
4	170	20	16	400	80
10		10	30	1050	120

Substituting the results of the worksheet into the formulas gives

$$\Sigma(X - \bar{X})^2 = \Sigma X^2 - \frac{1}{n}(\Sigma X)^2$$

$$= 30 - \frac{1}{5}(10)^2 = 10$$

$$\Sigma(Y - \bar{Y})^2 = \Sigma Y'^2 - \frac{1}{n}(\Sigma Y')^2$$

$$= 1050 - \frac{1}{5}(10)^2 = 1030$$

$$\Sigma(X - \bar{X})(Y - \bar{Y}) = \Sigma XY' - \frac{1}{n}\Sigma X \Sigma Y'$$

$$= 120 - \frac{1}{5}(10)(10) = 100$$

$$\Sigma(Y - Y_c)^2 = \frac{(10)(1030) - (100)^2}{10} = 30$$

Thus the sample standard deviation of regression is

$$\hat{\sigma}_{YX} = \sqrt{\frac{\Sigma (Y - Y_c)^2}{n - 2}} = \sqrt{\frac{30}{5 - 2}} = \sqrt{10} = 3.16$$

Although at first glance this procedure may seem more complicated, after experience has been gained and computational procedures of correlation coefficients have been studied, it will be easier to handle because it can be adapted to various other situations.

The interpretation of $\hat{\sigma}_{YX} = 3.16$ lb. is that approximately $2/3$ of the sample observations are expected to fall within ± 3.16 lb. of the sample regression line. This is shown in Fig. 14.8. Since the sample regression

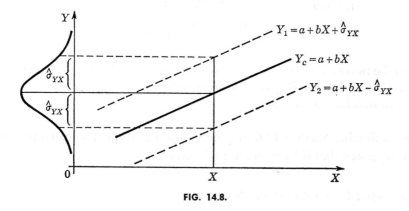

FIG. 14.8.

line is

$$Y_c = a + bX$$

the two dotted lines that constitute the band within which about $2/3$ of the points are expected to fall are shown by

$$Y_1 = a + bX + \hat{\sigma}_{YX}$$
$$Y_2 = a + bX - \hat{\sigma}_{YX}$$

In terms of Example 2, they are

$$Y_1 = 132 + 10X + 3.16$$
$$Y_2 = 132 + 10X - 3.16$$

The band that contains 95 percent of the points is

$$Y_1 = a + bX + 1.96\hat{\sigma}_{YX}$$
$$Y_2 = a + bX - 1.96\hat{\sigma}_{YX}$$

Example 3. As an illustration of how the sample standard deviation of regression may be used, consider the following problem: Given the data of Example 1, concerning heights and weights, find the probability of selecting a student weighing more than 158 lb.

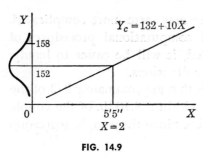

who is 5 ft. 5 in. tall. Figure 14.9 shows the situation diagrammatically. From the regression line we know that for 5 ft. 5 in. ($X = 2$), the $Y_c = 152$ lb. The probability of finding a student who weighs more than 158 lb. is shown by the shaded area under the normal curve. Since $\hat{\sigma}_{YX} = 3.16$ lb., this shaded area is found as follows:

FIG. 14.9

$$z = \frac{158 - 152}{3.16} = 1.898$$

From the normal area table we find the proportion to be 0.0287, or 2.87 percent. Thus the probability of finding a student weighing more than 158 lb. who is 5 ft. 5 in. is about 0.0287.

[The following Section 14.6 may be skipped without loss of continuity. It is suggested that it be read after Chapter 21.]

14.6.   Tests Concerning *a* and *b*

Since the sample regression coefficients *a* and *b* are estimates of *A* and *B* (just as $\bar{X}$ is an estimate of μ), they will have sampling distributions (just as $\bar{X}$ has a sampling distribution). It turns out that these sampling distributions of *a* and *b* have the following characteristics, which are stated without derivation:

1.   *a* and *b* are unbiased estimates of *A* and *B*; that is,

$$E(a) = A, \qquad E(b) = B$$

2.   The sampling distributions of *a* and *b* are normal with variances

$$\sigma_a{}^2 = \frac{(\sigma_{YX}^2)(\Sigma\, X^2)}{n\Sigma\, (X - \bar{X})^2}$$

$$\sigma_b{}^2 = \frac{\sigma_{YX}^2}{\Sigma\, (X - \bar{X})^2}$$

Since σ_{YX}^2 is unknown, the estimate $\hat{\sigma}_{YX}^2$ is used. Then

$$\hat{\sigma}_a{}^2 = \frac{(\hat{\sigma}_{YX}^2)(\Sigma\, X^2)}{n\Sigma\, (X - \bar{X})^2}$$

$$\hat{\sigma}_b{}^2 = \frac{\hat{\sigma}_{YX}^2}{\Sigma\, (X - \bar{X})^2}$$

(i) Tests of hypotheses concerning **B**

The *B* coefficient is usually the parameter that is of interest to economic statisticians. For example, let the population regression function be

$$\mu_{YX} = A + BX$$

where μ_{YX} is consumption and X is income. Then B shows the increase in consumption when there is a unit increase (a one dollar increase) in income. It is usually called the *marginal propensity to consume*. As another example, let μ_{YX} be the expected yield of wheat and X be the amount of fertilizer. Then B shows the increase in the yield of wheat when there is a unit increase of fertilizer.

But what if $B = 0$? This means, graphically, that the population regression line is horizontal, which implies that X and Y are independent of each other. It means that no matter what the increase in income, there is no change in consumption; or, a change in the amount of fertilizer has no effect on the yield of wheat. As can be seen, it is of interest to the investigator to check whether or not $B = 0$, and the sampling distribution of b enables him to do this. Let us illustrate with our example of heights and weights.

The null hypothesis H_1 is that $B = 0$, and the alternative hypothesis H_2 is that $B \neq 0$:

$$H_1: \quad B = 0$$
$$H_2: \quad B \neq 0$$

Since b is normally distributed with mean $E(b) = B$ and variance σ_b^2 as given above, we may graph the sampling distribution as shown in Fig. 14.10. Let $B = 0$. From our calculations we know that

$$Y_c = 132 + 10X$$

and the $b = 10$ lb. If $E(b) = B = 0$, how probable is it that we shall have a b greater than 10 lb.? For this we find

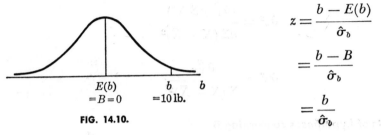

$$z = \frac{b - E(b)}{\hat{\sigma}_b}$$

$$= \frac{b - B}{\hat{\sigma}_b}$$

$$= \frac{b}{\hat{\sigma}_b}$$

FIG. 14.10.

The $\hat{\sigma}_b$ is

$$\hat{\sigma}_b^{\,2} = \frac{\hat{\sigma}_{YX}^{\,2}}{\Sigma\,(X - \bar{X})^2}$$

$$= \frac{10}{10} \qquad \text{(from previous calculations)}$$

$$= 1$$

Then the z becomes

$$z = \frac{10}{1} = 10$$

which shows that $b = 10$ lb. is 10 standard deviations away from $E(b) = 0$. Thus we conclude that it is highly improbable that $b = 10$ lb. came from a population with $B = 0$, and we *reject* H_1. That is, we accept H_2, which is $B \neq 0$.

It should be noted that when sample sizes are small, we should use the t distribution rather than the normal distribution because we are using $\hat{\sigma}_{YX}$. But we shall assume that all samples are large, and the difference between the t distribution and normal distribution for large samples is small enough to allow us to use the normal distribution. The t distribution is discussed in Chapter 17.

We may also test the hypothesis that $B \neq 0$. The procedure is the same as above, namely, let

$$t = \frac{b - B}{\hat{\sigma}_b}$$

where the statistic t has a t distribution with $n - 2$ degrees of freedom. Using the t table (Table 3 in Appendix), we can find the probability of selecting a sample with a sample regression coefficient greater than *b* from a population with a regression coefficient *B*. If the probability is very small (say, smaller than $\alpha = 5$ percent), then we reject the hypothesis. If the probability is larger than α, we accept the hypothesis.

(ii)   Confidence interval for B

By applying the method of least squares, we have estimated *B* by the sample regression coefficient *b* and have found it to be $b = 10$ lb. This is point estimation, and a deficiency of this is that we do not have a means of measuring the reliability of *b* as an estimate of *B*. But, by using interval estimation, we can find a measure of reliability. Let us explain this, using our illustration of heights and weights.

The sample regression line is

(1) $$Y_c = 132 + 10X$$

and $b = 10$ lb. Since the distribution of

$$t = \frac{b - B}{\hat{\sigma}_b}$$

has a *t* distribution with $n - 2$ degrees of freedom,

(2) $$P[-t_{0.05} < \frac{b - B}{\hat{\sigma}_b} < t_{0.05}] = 0.95$$

where $t_{0.05}$ corresponds to $\alpha = 5$ percent and is obtained from the *t* table. Equation (2) becomes

(3) $$P[b - t_{0.05}\hat{\sigma}_b < B < b + t_{0.05}\hat{\sigma}_b] = 0.95$$

In our present case, we know that $b = 10$ lb., $\hat{\sigma}_b = 1$ lb., and $t_{0.05}$ (for $n - 2 = 5 - 2 = 3$ degrees of freedom) is 3.18; we find the 95 percent confidence interval as

$$10 - (3.18)(1) < B < 10 + (3.18)(1)$$

(4) $$6.82 < B < 13.18$$

That is, *B* is between 6.82 lb. and 13.18 lb. with a 95 percent confidence coefficient. This means that if 100 samples of size 5 are selected, and 100 confidence intervals

(5) $$b - t_{0.05}\hat{\sigma}_b < B < b + t_{0.05}\hat{\sigma}_b$$

are constructed, we expect 95 of them to contain the true population parameter *B*.

Note that as the sample size *n* becomes larger, $t_{0.05}$ and $\hat{\sigma}_b$ become smaller, and thus the interval (5) will become smaller.

Procedures for testing hypotheses and finding confidence intervals A are similar to B and thus are omitted.

[The following Section 14.7 may be skipped without loss of continuity. It is suggested that it be read after Chapter 21.]

14.7.   Confidence Interval for μ_{YX}

The Y_c is an estimate of $\mu_{YX} = E(Y|X)$, and hence it is desirable to know how reliable it is as an estimate of μ_{YX}. This is shown by constructing a confidence interval using Y_c. The construction of a confidence interval requires that we know the distribution, the mean, and the variance of Y_c. Let us explain how these elements are found, and construct a confidence interval using our illustration.

The sample regression line

(1) $$Y_c = 132 + 10X$$

gives a value of Y_c for a given X. For example, for $X = 2$ (5 ft. 2 in.), the $Y_c = 152$. If a second sample is selected, we shall find another sample regression line, and for $X = 2$ the value of Y_c will be different from the $Y_c = 152$ we found in (1). That is, for each sample selected, there is a different (some may be equal) value of Y_c corresponding to a given X (say, $X = 2$). In other words, there is a distribution of Y_c's for a given X. It is important to note that there is a distribution of Y_c for each given X.

We state without proof that the distribution of the Y_c's is a t distribution with $n - 2$ degrees of freedom.

The mean (expected value) of this distribution of Y_c's is

$$\begin{aligned} E(Y_c) &= E(a + bX) \\ &= E(a) + E(b)X \\ &= A + BX = \mu_{YX} \end{aligned}$$

That is, the expected value of Y_c is μ_{YX}:

(2) $$E(Y_c) = \mu_{YX} = E(Y|X)$$

The variance of this distribution may be classified into two cases.

(i)   Case 1 ($X = \bar{X}$)

The sample regression equation is

(3) $$Y_c = a + bX$$

where we know that

(4) $$a = \bar{Y} - b\bar{X}$$

Substituting (4) into (3) gives us

(5) $$Y_c = \bar{Y} + b(X - \bar{X})$$

As we mentioned above, the distribution of the Y_c is for a given X.

Now let us first consider the distribution of Y_c for the case where X is equal to $\bar{X}$; that is, $X = \bar{X}$ (Fig. 14.11). Then (5) becomes, for this

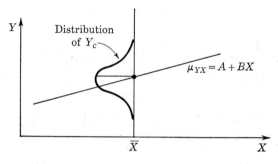

FIG. 14.11.

special case,

(6) $$Y_c = \bar{Y}$$

Using (6) we can easily find the variance of Y_c as follows:

$$\text{Var}(Y_c) = \text{Var}(\bar{Y})$$

$$= \text{Var}\left(\frac{\Sigma Y}{n}\right)$$

$$= \frac{1}{n^2} \text{Var}(Y_1 + \cdots + Y_n)$$

$$= \frac{1}{n^2} [\text{Var}(Y_1) + \cdots + \text{Var}(Y_n)]$$

$$= \frac{1}{n^2} [\sigma_{YX}^2 + \cdots + \sigma_{YX}^2]$$

$$= \frac{\sigma_{YX}^2}{n}$$

where σ^2_{YX} is the population variance of regression. Let the $\mathrm{Var}(Y_c)$ be denoted by $\sigma^2(Y_c)$, and for our special case where $Y_c = \bar{Y}$, the $\sigma^2(Y_c) = \sigma^2(\bar{Y})$. Since the estimate $\hat{\sigma}_{YX}$ is used instead of σ_{YX}, the estimate of $\sigma^2(Y_c)$ becomes

(7)
$$\hat{\sigma}^2(Y_c) = \hat{\sigma}^2(\bar{Y}) = \frac{\hat{\sigma}^2_{YX}}{n}$$

For our present illustration, we know that $\hat{\sigma}^2_{YX} = 10$. Thus

$$\hat{\sigma}^2(\bar{Y}) = \frac{10}{5} = 2$$

Now that we have found the distribution, mean, and variance of Y_c for the case where $X = \bar{X}$, we can construct the confidence interval as follows: Since the Y_c has a t distribution, the 95 percent confidence interval is

(8)
$$Y_c - t_{0.05}\,\hat{\sigma}(Y_c) < \mu_{YX} < Y_c + t_{0.05}\,\hat{\sigma}(Y_c)$$

or, since $Y_c = \bar{Y}$ in this particular case,

$$\bar{Y} - t_{0.05}\hat{\sigma}(\bar{Y}) < \mu_{YX} < \bar{Y} + t_{0.05}\hat{\sigma}(\bar{Y})$$

Since $Y_c = \bar{Y} = 152$, $t_{0.05} = 3.18$, and $\hat{\sigma}(\bar{Y}) = \sqrt{2}$, the 95 percent confidence interval is

$$152 - (3.18)\,(\sqrt{2}) < \mu_{YX} < 152 + (3.18)\,(\sqrt{2})$$
(9)
$$147.52 < \mu_{YX} < 156.48$$

The interpretation is: If 100 samples are selected and the 95 percent confidence intervals (8) are constructed, we should expect 95 of them to contain $\mu_{YX} = E(Y|X = 2)$. The confidence interval (9) is one of the 100 such intervals.

Figure 14.12 shows the confidence interval as AB. Note that the points A and B are measured from Y_c; that is,

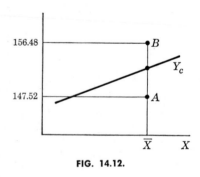

FIG. 14.12.

$$A = Y_c - t_{0.05}\,\hat{\sigma}(Y_c)$$
$$= 152 - (3.18)\,(\sqrt{2})$$
$$= 147.52$$

$$B = Y_c + t_{0.05}\,\hat{\sigma}(Y_c)$$
$$= 152 + (3.18)\,(\sqrt{2})$$
$$= 156.48$$

(ii)   Case 2 ($X \neq \bar{X}$)

We are now considering subpopulations other than the one corresponding to $X = \bar{X}$. Let us consider the subpopulation corresponding to 5 ft. 3 in. ($X = 3$).

The distribution of Y_c for a given $X \neq \bar{X}$ (say, $X = 3$) has a t distribution, and the mean $E(Y_c)$ is equal to μ_{YX}, as in Case 1. But the variance of Y_c (that is, $\sigma^2(Y_c)$) differs from the one in Case 1 as follows: The sample regression line is

$$Y_c = \bar{Y} + b(X - \bar{X})$$

Thus the variance Y_c is

$$\mathrm{Var}(Y_c) = \mathrm{Var}[\bar{Y} + b(X - \bar{X})]$$
$$= \mathrm{Var}(\bar{Y}) + \mathrm{Var}[b(X - \bar{X})]$$
$$= \frac{\sigma_{YX}^2}{n} + (X - \bar{X})^2 \mathrm{Var}(b)$$
$$= \frac{\sigma_{YX}^2}{n} + (X - \bar{X})^2 \frac{\sigma_{YX}^2}{\Sigma\,(X - \bar{X})^2}$$

That is,

$$(10) \qquad \sigma^2(Y_c) = \frac{\sigma_{YX}^2}{n} + (X - \bar{X})^2 \frac{\sigma_{YX}^2}{\Sigma\,(X - \bar{X})^2}$$

This shows that the $\sigma^2(Y_c)$ is affected by the variance of $\bar{Y}$, b, and also by the quantity $(X - \bar{X})^2$.

Since we use the estimate $\hat{\sigma}_{YX}^2$ for σ_{YX}^2, the estimate of $\sigma^2(Y_c)$ becomes

$$(10') \qquad \hat{\sigma}^2(Y_c) = \frac{\hat{\sigma}_{YX}^2}{n} + (X - \bar{X})^2 \frac{\hat{\sigma}_{YX}^2}{\Sigma\,(X - \bar{X})^2}$$

From our previous calculations (Example 2, Section 14.5) we know that

$$\hat{\sigma}_{YX}^2 = 10, \qquad n = 5, \qquad \Sigma\,(X - \bar{X})^2 = 10$$

Thus the estimate $\hat{\sigma}^2(Y_c)$ is for $X = 3$:

$$\hat{\sigma}^2(Y_c) = \frac{10}{5} + (3 - 2)^2 \frac{10}{10}$$

$$= 3$$

Using this estimated variance, the 95 percent confidence interval is

$$\text{(11)} \qquad Y_c - t_{0.05}\,\hat{\sigma}(Y_c) < \mu_{YX} < Y_c + t_{0.05}\,\hat{\sigma}(Y_c)$$

In our present case, where $X = 3$, the Y_c is

$$Y_c = 132 + 10X = 162$$

Thus the confidence interval is, since $n - 2 = 5 - 2 = 3$ degrees of freedom,

$$\text{(12)} \qquad \begin{aligned} 162 - (3.18)\,(\sqrt{3}) &< \mu_{YX} < 162 + (3.18)\,(\sqrt{3}) \\ 156.5 &< \mu_{YX} < 167.5 \end{aligned}$$

The interpretation is: If 100 samples of size 5 are selected and confidence intervals (11) are constructed, which correspond to $X = 3$, we should expect that 95 of them contain the true mean $\mu_{YX} = E(Y\,|\,X = 3)$. The interval (12) is one of the 100 such intervals.

Example 1.　Let us find the confidence intervals that correspond to the other X's and show the confidence intervals diagrammatically.

Worksheet

Height	X	Y	Y_c	$\hat{\sigma}^2_{YX}$	$\hat{\sigma}^2(\bar{Y})$	$\hat{\sigma}^2(Y_c)$
5'3"	0	130	132	10	2	6
5'4"	1	145	142	10	2	3
5'5"	2	150	152	10	2	2
5'6"	3	165	162	10	2	3
5'7"	4	170	172	10	2	6
	10	760				

(i) $X = 0$

$$Y_c = 132 + 10X = 132 + (10)(0) = 132$$

$$\hat{\sigma}^2(Y_c) = \frac{\hat{\sigma}^2_{YX}}{n} + (X - \bar{X})^2 \frac{\hat{\sigma}^2_{YX}}{\Sigma\,(X - \bar{X})^2}$$

$$= \frac{10}{5} + (0 - 2)^2 \cdot \frac{10}{10} = 6$$

The 95 percent confidence interval is

$$Y_c - t_{0.05}\hat{\sigma}(Y_c) < \mu_{YX} < Y_c + t_{0.05}\,\hat{\sigma}(Y_c)$$

$$132 - (3.18)(\sqrt{6}\,) < \mu_{YX} < 132 + (3.18)(\sqrt{6}\,)$$

$$124.21 < \mu_{YX} < 139.79$$

(ii) $X = 1$

$$Y_c = 132 + (10)(1) = 142$$

$$\hat{\sigma}^2(Y_c) = \frac{10}{5} + (1 - 2)^2\,\frac{10}{10} = 3$$

$$142 - (3.18)(\sqrt{3}\,) < \mu_{XY} < 142 + (3.18)(\sqrt{3}\,)$$

$$136.5 < \mu_{YX} < 147.5$$

(iii) $X = 2$. This is the case where $X = \bar{X}$.

$$Y_c = 132 + (10)(2) = 152 = \bar{Y}$$

$$\hat{\sigma}^2(Y_c) = \hat{\sigma}^2(\bar{Y})$$

$$= \frac{10}{5} + (2 - 2)^2\,\frac{10}{10} = 2$$

$$152 - (3.18)(\sqrt{2}\,) < \mu_{YX} < 152 + (3.18)(\sqrt{2}\,)$$

$$147.52 < \mu_{YX} < 156.48$$

(iv) $X = 3$

$$Y_c = 132 + (10)(3) = 162$$

$$\sigma^2(Y_c) = \frac{10}{5} + (3 - 2)^2\,\frac{10}{10} = 3$$

$$162 - (3.18)(\sqrt{3}\,) < \mu_{YX} < 162 + (3.18)(\sqrt{3}\,)$$

$$156.5 < \mu_{YX} < 167.5$$

(v) $X = 4$

$$Y_c = 132 + (10)(4) = 172$$

$$\hat{\sigma}^2(Y_c) = \frac{10}{5} + (4 - 2)^2\,\frac{10}{10} = 6$$

$$172 - (3.18)(\sqrt{6}\,) < \mu_{YX} < 172 + (3.18)(\sqrt{6}\,)$$

$$164.21 < \mu_{YX} < 179.79$$

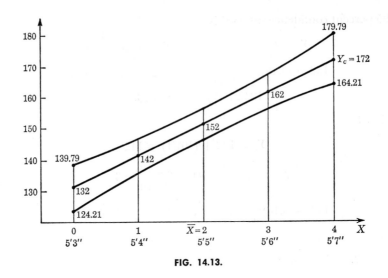

FIG. 14.13.

The confidence intervals are plotted in Fig. 14.13. As can be seen when the points are linked, we get a *confidence belt* that is symmetric in width around the value of $X = \bar{X}$. Note carefully that this confidence belt was constructed from a single sample. Each time a new sample is selected, there will be a new confidence belt.

The interpretation of the confidence belt is the same as that for the confidence interval. That is, if 100 samples are selected and 100 such confidence belts are calculated, we expect that about 95 of them will contain the population regression line. The confidence belt we have drawn is one of the 100 such confidence belts.

Also note how the confidence belt widens as it goes farther away from $X = \bar{X}$. This is due to the quantity $(X - \bar{X})^2$ in the variance formula (10).

[The following Section 14.8 may be skipped without loss of continuity. It is suggested that it be read after Chapter 21.]

14.8.   Confidence Interval for Y

In some cases, one may wish to make predictions about individual Y values. For instance, given a student who is 5 ft. 3 in. ($X = 1$); what is his predicted weight? We are not inquiring about the average weight of all students who are 5 ft. 3 in.; we are asking about the weight of an individual student. This question is answered by finding the confidence interval for Y.

The process of finding this confidence interval is as follows: Consider the distribution of the difference $Y_c - Y$. Then the mean is, for a given X,

(1)
$$E(Y_c - Y) = E(Y_c) - E(Y)$$
$$= \mu_{YX} - \mu_{YX}$$
$$= 0$$

The variance is, for a given X,

(2)
$$\text{Var}(Y_c - Y) = \text{Var}(Y_c) + \text{Var}(Y)$$

From previous calculations we know that

$$\text{Var}(Y_c) = \text{Var}(Y) + \text{Var}(b(X - \bar{X}))$$
$$= \frac{\sigma_{YX}^2}{n} + (X - \bar{X})^2 \frac{\sigma_{YX}^2}{\Sigma(X - \bar{X})^2}$$

and the variance for Y is

$$\text{Var}(Y) = \sigma_{YX}^2$$

Thus Var $(Y_c - Y)$ becomes

(3)
$$\text{Var}(Y_c - Y) = \sigma_{YX}^2 + \frac{\sigma_{YX}^2}{n} + (X - \bar{X})^2 \frac{\sigma_{YX}^2}{\Sigma(X - \bar{X})^2}$$

Since we use the estimate $\hat{\sigma}_{YX}^2$ for σ_{YX}^2, the estimate of $\text{Var}(Y_c - Y)$ is

(4)
$$\text{Var}(Y_c - Y) = \hat{\sigma}^2_{YX} \left[1 + \frac{1}{n} + \frac{(X - \bar{X})^2}{\Sigma(X - \bar{X})^2} \right]$$

Let us now construct the statistic

(5)
$$t = \frac{(Y_c - Y) - E(Y_c - Y)}{\hat{\sigma}_{YX} \sqrt{1 + \frac{1}{n} + \frac{(X - \bar{X})^2}{\Sigma(X - \bar{X})^2}}}$$
$$= \frac{Y_c - Y}{\hat{\sigma}_{YX} \sqrt{1 + \frac{1}{n} + \frac{(X - \bar{\bar{X}})^2}{\Sigma(X - \bar{X})^2}}}$$

We state without proof that this t has a t distribution with $n-2$ degrees of freedom. Thus

$$P[-t_{0.05} < t < t_{0.05}] = 0.95$$

which becomes

(6) $\quad P[-t_{0.05} < \dfrac{Y_c - Y}{\hat{\sigma}_{YX}\sqrt{1 + \dfrac{1}{n} + \dfrac{(X - \bar{X})^2}{\Sigma(X - \bar{X})^2}}} < t_{0.05}] = 0.95$

From (6) we can easily find the confidence interval of Y as

(7) $\qquad Y_c - t_{0.05}\hat{\sigma}_{YX}\sqrt{1 + \dfrac{1}{n} + \dfrac{(X - \bar{X})^2}{\Sigma(X - \bar{X})^2}}$

$$< Y < Y_c + t_{0.05}\,\hat{\sigma}_{YX}\sqrt{1 + \dfrac{1}{n} + \dfrac{(X - \bar{X})^2}{\Sigma(X - \bar{X})^2}}$$

The interpretation of (7) is: If we select 100 samples and construct 100 confidence intervals for a given X, as given by (7), we should expect 95 of them to include a Y corresponding to the given X. The confidence interval (7) is one of 100 such confidence intervals. We are not saying that the probability of Y in the confidence interval is 0.95. The probability of Y's being in the interval is either 0 or 1.

In our present illustration, where $X = 3$, the $Y_c = 162$ and

$$\hat{\sigma}_{YX}^2\left[1 + \dfrac{1}{n} + \dfrac{(X - \bar{X})^2}{\Sigma(X - \bar{X})^2}\right] = 10\left[1 + \dfrac{1}{5} + \dfrac{1}{10}\right]$$

$$= 13$$

Since there are $n - 2 = 5 - 2 = 3$ degrees of freedom, the $t_{0.05} = 3.18$. Thus the confidence interval is, for $X = 3$,

$$162 - (3.18)(\sqrt{13}) < Y < 162 + (3.18)(\sqrt{13})$$

$$150.55 < Y < 173.45$$

In similar manner, the confidence intervals for Y corresponding to $X = 0, 1, 2,$ and 4 can be calculated. The results are as follows:

$$X = 0 : \qquad 119.28 < Y < 144.72$$
$$X = 1 : \qquad 130.55 < Y < 153.55$$

$$X = 2 : \quad 140.87 < Y < 163.13$$
$$X = 3 : \quad 150.55 < Y < 173.45$$
$$X = 4 : \quad 159.28 < Y < 184.72$$

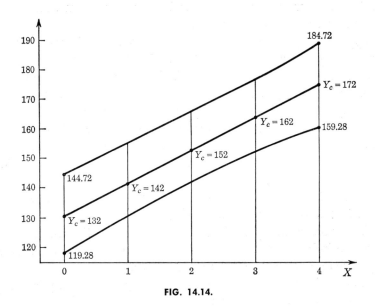

FIG. 14.14.

Figure 14.14 is a graph of these confidence intervals which, when linked together, make a confidence belt. The interpretation is as follows: If we select 100 samples and construct 100 confidence belts, we should expect 95 of them to include the Y values corresponding to given X's. The confidence belt we drew in Fig. 14.14 is one of 100 such confidence belts.

Note carefully that these Y values are values computed from the regression line and not from the sample observations.

14.9. Comments on Regression Analysis

1. *The idea of regression.* Assume that tall people tend to marry tall people and tall parents have tall or taller children, and that the converse holds for short people. Then, after a number of generations, the people will be divided up into two groups: a group of people like giants and a group like midgets.

Fortunately, or unfortunately, this has not happened. Instead, studies have shown that tall parents have tall children but, in many cases, not so tall as their parents. There is a tendency for the children to regress toward the average height of the population. Likewise, short parents tend to have short children but not so short as the parents. There is a tendency for the children to regress toward the average height of the population. This tendency to regress toward an average from both extremes led to the idea of regression analysis.

2. *Type of population.* The population we had was a family of subpopulations corresponding to fixed X values, and the subpopulations were each normally distributed. Another type of population is where X and Y vary jointly; this is called a bivariate normal distribution. This type of distribution is explained in Chapter 15.

3. *The regression function shows a stochastic relationship.* The dependent variable Y is related to the independent variable X stochastically. By this we mean that, when given a value of X, we do not get a unique value of Y, but the expected (average) value of Y. When the standard deviation of regression is zero, the relation becomes a mathematical (as opposed to stochastic) relationship.

4. *Extension to many variables.* Our present discussion was confined to one independent variable X, but as explained in Chapter 22, we may have more than one independent variable.

5. *Assumptions.* When applying the regression analysis, keep in mind the following assumptions:

(a). The relation is linear. For nonlinear regression see the reference on page 640.

(b). The X values are fixed and do not have a distribution. The cases where the X values also have a distribution are discussed in Chapters 15 and 22.

(c). The Y values of each subpopulation have a normal distribution.

(d). The variance of Y for each subpopulation σ_{YX}^2 which is called the variance of regression, is equal for all subpopulations.

(e). The error $\epsilon = Y - \mu_{YX}$ is independent and normally distributed with mean $E(\epsilon) = 0$ and variance $\mathrm{Var}(\epsilon) = \sigma_{YX}^2$

6. *Applications.* Regression analysis is very widely used in business and economics. Let us first discuss the rationale and then give some illustrations.

The rationale is very simple. Suppose there is a phenomena Y that is related to another phenomenon X. It is easy to measure and predict X, but difficult to measure and predict Y. Then, to measure and predict Y, find the regression of Y on X, and by using the values of X, we can find Y.

As a hypothetical example, let Y be the length of wire on a spool and X be the weight; find the regression of Y (length) on X (weight). Instead of unwinding the wire to measure its length, it is weighed, and the length is estimated by the regression line.

Example 1.   A machine tool company wishes to forecast its sales one year in advance so that it can decide on the scale of operation it should plan for. A statistical analysis of past data shows that there is a close relationship between the volume of its sales and index of the Federal Reserve Board's *Index of Industrial Production*. Thus the company finds the regression of sales (Y) on IIP(X), and by using the predicted values of IIP(X) for the coming year, predicts its sales (Y) volume.

7.   *When the subpopulations are not normally distributed.*   When the Y of the subpopulations are simply defined as independent random variables with an unknown distribution, but with equal (unknown) variances σ^2, we cannot use the method of maximum likelihood to estimate the A, B, and σ^2. We may, however, use the method of least squares to estimate the A and B. It turns out that the estimators $\hat{A} = a$ and $\hat{B} = b$ are the same as those obtained by the maximum likelihood method of Section 14.3.

We cannot obtain an estimator for σ^2 by the method of least squares. We can, however, provide an estimator by using the estimators $\hat{A} = a$ and $\hat{B} = b$ obtained by the method of least squares. It is

$$(1) \qquad \hat{\sigma}_{YX}^2 = \frac{1}{n-2} \Sigma (Y - Y_c)^2 = \frac{1}{n-2} \Sigma (Y - a - bX)^2$$

and this is an unbiased estimator of σ^2.

A theorem called the Gauss Markoff theorem states that the $\hat{A} = a$ and $\hat{B} = b$ are unbiased estimators with minimum variance.

Hence, we can find a regression function of Y on X when Y is not normal by the method of least squares with regression coefficients that have the above properties, and an estimate of σ^2 given by (1).

But note carefully that we cannot test hypotheses or construct confidence intervals as we have done in Sections 14.6–14.8 using the t-distribution. (We also cannot use the F distribution for tests of significance. See page 678.)

CORRELATION ANALYSIS

15	Correlation analysis is a discussion of the degree of closeness of the relationship between two variables. We shall first discuss the kind of population we are assuming, show how this is related to regression analysis, and then derive the correlation coefficient.

15.1. The Bivariate Distribution

In Chapter 13 the population was a collection of normally distributed subpopulations of Y's that corresponded to fixed X's. In correlation analysis, we assume a population where both X and Y vary jointly. It is called a *joint distribution of two variables* or a bivariate distribution. The hypothetical bivariate distribution in Table 15.1 is an illustration.

Let us explain this bivariate distribution. Consider the following 4 heights: 47, 48, 49, and 50 in. and let the frequencies of occurrence be as shown in the accompanying table.

X Height, Inches	Frequency
47	1
48	2
49	3
50	2
	8

TABLE 15.1.

Height X Inches

	46	47	48	49	50	51	52	53	54	55	f_Y
40	1										1
41		1	1	1							3
42		2	2	2	1						7
43			3	3	2						8
44			2	4	2	1					9
45			1	3	5	2	1				12
46				3	4	3	2				12
47				2	4	2	1	1			10
48					2	1	2	1	1		7
49							1	1	1	1	4
f_X	1	3	9	18	20	9	7	3	2	1	73

(Weight, Y pounds — row labels at left)

The distribution of the heights (X) may be shown by a histogram, as in Fig. 15.1. There are 8 persons, and to each person is associated 1 variable, namely, height (X).

Let us now associate 2 variables to each person, height (X) and weight (Y), and assume the 4 pairs of values of X and Y in the accompanying table, which shows the fre-

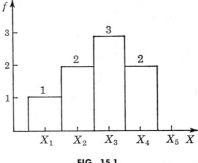

FIG. 15.1.

X Height, Inches	Y Weight, Pounds	Frequency
$X_1 = 47$	$Y_1 = 41$	1
$X_2 = 48$	$Y_2 = 42$	2
$X_3 = 49$	$Y_3 = 43$	3
$X_4 = 50$	$Y_4 = 44$	2
		8

quencies of occurrence of each pair of values of X and Y. Now that there are 2 variables instead of 1, the frequency distribution is shown as a 3-dimensional histogram, as in Fig. 15.2. (Note that we should have columns with the bars we have drawn in the middle of Fig. 15.2,

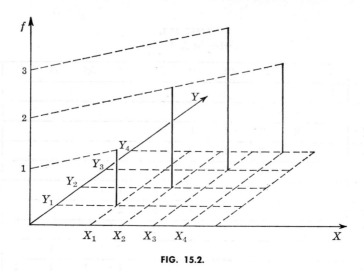

FIG. 15.2.

but for brevity, we shall just show the bars. The student is requested to visualize the missing columns.)

Instead of merely having an X-axis, we now have an X–Y plane, and the height of the bars shows the frequencies of each event, which is made up of a pair (X, Y). A point on the plane indicates an event.

The joint distribution of X and Y was shown graphically in Fig. 15.2 by only 4 events (pairs of X and Y) and 8 occurrences (observed values). But as one can readily see, there are many possible events (pairs of X and Y) and also many possible occurrences (observed values). In Table 15.1 we have 73 observed values. Figure 15.3 is a generalized illustration of a joint distribution of two variables, where we now have a *frequency surface* instead of a frequency curve.

Let us slice this population at some height X (say, $X = 49$ in.). As Fig. 15.3 shows, we have a frequency curve giving the frequencies of Y for the given X. That is, we have a subpopulation of Y's corresponding to a given $X = 49$ in., and this subpopulation is shown by the column corresponding to $X = 49$ in. in Table 15.1. So far, this is similar to the population we assumed in regression analysis.

But now let us slice the population at some weight Y (say, $Y = 42$ lb.). Then we have a corresponding subpopulation of heights X, which is given by the row corresponding to $Y = 42$ lb. in Table 15.1. We thus have a family of subpopulations of X's corresponding to given Y's.

When both subpopulations corresponding to the X's and Y's have normal distributions, we shall call this bivariate distribution a *bivariate normal distribution*.

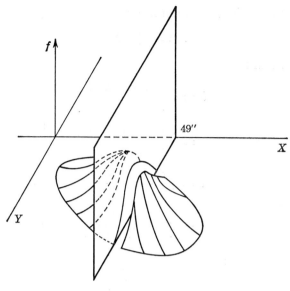

FIG. 15.3.

Thus we have two types of populations, one with fixed X and variable Y and a second with both X and Y variable. Correlation analysis was originally concerned with the second type of population, but it is now applied to both types, as we shall see. We shall first be concerned with the bivariate distribution.

15.2.   The Bivariate Distribution and Regression Analysis

Before starting the discussion of correlation analysis, a question that naturally arises is whether regression analysis can be applied to bivariate distributions. The answer is "yes," and we shall illustrate with a simple hypothetical distribution.

Assume that a random sample of size $n = 3$ is selected from a bivariate distribution of hours of study (X) and grade point (Y), which is on a 10-point basis. Since both X and Y vary, we can find the regression of Y (grade) on X (hours), where we assume that X is held fixed, or X on Y, where we assume that Y is held fixed.

X, Hours	Y, Grade	XY	X^2	Y^2
2	5	10	4	25
4	3	12	16	9
6	7	42	36	49
12	15	64	56	83

For the first case, the regression line is

(1) $$Y_c = a + bX$$

and the a and b are

$$b = \frac{n\Sigma XY - \Sigma X \Sigma Y}{n\Sigma X^2 - (\Sigma X)^2}$$

$$= \frac{3(64) - (12)(15)}{3(56) - (12)^2} = \frac{1}{2}$$

$$a = \frac{\Sigma Y}{n} - b\frac{\Sigma X}{n}$$

$$= \frac{15}{3} - \left(\frac{1}{2}\right)\left(\frac{12}{3}\right) = 3$$

Thus the regression line (1) becomes

(2) $$Y_c = 3 + \frac{1}{2} X$$

For the second case, the regression line is

(3) $$X_c = a' + b'Y$$

and the a' and b' are found to be

$$b' = \frac{1}{2}, \qquad a' = \frac{3}{2}$$

Thus the regression line (3) becomes

(4) $$X_c = \frac{3}{2} + \frac{1}{2} Y$$

The regression line (1) is shown in Fig. 15.4(a); (2) is shown in Fig. 15.4(b), and both are shown together in Fig. 15.4(c). As Fig. 15.4(c) shows, the two regression lines intersect at $\bar{X} = 4$, $\bar{Y} = 5$. This is easily seen by

$$Y_c = 3 + \frac{1}{2} (4) = 5 = \bar{Y}$$

and

$$X_c = \frac{3}{2} + \frac{1}{2} (5) = 4 = \bar{X}$$

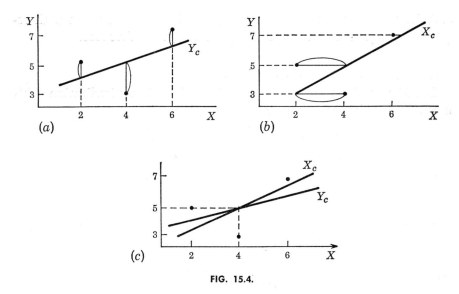

FIG. 15.4.

The difference of the two regression lines can be seen graphically. The regression line of Y on X is fitted so that the sum of the squared deviations taken in the vertical direction is minimized. For X on Y, the sum of the squared deviations in the horizontal direction is minimized.

The regression analysis of Y on X implied that Y is dependent on X. As we shall see when we are dealing with bivariate distributions and applying correlation analysis, the data are treated as if there were a two-way relation. For example, if we have a bivariate distribution of heights of brothers and sisters, we can see that they vary together to some extent, but there is no cause and effect relation. When we have a bivariate distribution of heights of father (X) and son (Y), the son's height (Y) is to some extent dependent on the father's height (X). But correlation analysis as applied to these data treats the data as if there were a two-way relationship. When applying correlation analysis, and a dependency relation between X and Y is assumed, it is not based on ideas due to correlation analysis, but on other nonstatistical considerations such as heredity. Correlation analysis treats the data symmetrically and is neutral concerning the *direction* of dependency.

15.3.   The Correlation Coefficient: Case I

The population correlation coefficient is defined in two ways: the *first* as the covariance between two variables in a bivariate distribution and the *second* as a measure of closeness of fit in connection with regression analysis. In this section we shall discuss the first case.

(i) Population correlation coefficient

Let X and Y be two variables with a bivariate distribution with means and variances as follows:

$$E(X) = \mu_X, \qquad E(Y) = \mu_Y$$
$$\mathrm{Var}(X) = \sigma_X{}^2, \qquad \mathrm{Var}(Y) = \sigma_Y{}^2$$

Then the covariance (cov) between X and Y is defined as

(1) $$\mathrm{Cov}(X, Y) = E(X - \mu_X)(Y - \mu_Y)$$

The population correlation coefficient, which is denoted by ρ, is defined as

(2) $$\rho = \frac{\mathrm{Cov}(X, Y)}{\sigma_X \sigma_Y}$$

$$= \frac{E(X - \mu_X)(Y - \mu_Y)}{\sqrt{E(X - \mu_X)^2}\sqrt{E(Y - \mu_Y)^2}}$$

Note three things in connection with (2). The first is that the formula is symmetric with respect to X and Y. The second is that by dividing by σ_X and σ_Y the ρ becomes independent of the units of measurements. Third, the process of subtracting μ_X and μ_Y indicates that the origin has been shifted to μ_X and μ_Y. Hence, ρ may be considered as the covariance of two standardized variables. Therefore, to understand ρ, we need to understand what is meant by a covariance.

Let us explain this heuristically by a hypothetical example. Consider the following function

(3) $$Y = 2X$$

When $X = 1, 2, 3,$ and 4, the Y values are as shown in the table below. The equation (3) gives perfect covariability between X and Y.

X	Y	$X - \mu_X$	$Y - \mu_Y$	$(X - \mu_X)(Y - \mu_Y)$	X^2	Y^2
1	2	−1.5	−3	4.5	1	4
2	4	−0.5	−1	0.5	4	16
3	6	0.5	1	0.5	9	36
4	8	1.5	3	4.5	16	64
10	20	0	0	10.0	30	120

Let us now find ρ for this case. We first calculate the covariance, which is

$$E(X - \mu_X)(Y - \mu_Y) = \frac{1}{N} \Sigma (X - \mu_X)(Y - \mu_Y)$$

$$= \frac{1}{4} (10) = 2.5$$

The characteristic of the covariance we computed is that it is positive, and this is because each of the cross products is positive. When the covariability between X and Y is not as perfect as the covariability between X and Y in equation (3), but nevertheless they move together in the same direction, most of the cross products will be positive. Hence, the covariance that is the average of these cross products will be positive.

As the degree of covariability lessens and the direction of variability becomes random, the number of positive and negative cross products becomes equal and the cross products tend to cancel each other out. The table below is an example of a case where there is no covariability

X	Y	$X - \mu_X$	$Y - \mu_Y$	$(X - \mu_X)(Y - \mu_Y)$
1	4	−1.5	−1	1.5
2	8	−0.5	3	−1.5
3	2	0.5	−3	−1.5
4	6	1.5	1	1.5
				0

and as a result the covariance is

$$E(X - \mu_X)(Y - \mu_Y) = \frac{1}{4} (0) = 0$$

Thus we may conclude that when there is a high degree of covariability between X and Y and both vary in the same direction, the covariance $\text{Cov}(X, Y)$ is large and positive. If X and Y vary in opposite directions, the covariance is large and negative.

When there is only a small degree of covariability between X and Y, which implies that the direction in which they vary is random, the covariability is close to zero.

To present this covariability as an index, we divide the covariance by σ_X and σ_Y and make it independent of the units of measurements.

We find for the perfect covariability case:

$$\sigma_X{}^2 = \frac{1}{N} \Sigma (X - \mu_X)^2$$

$$= \frac{1}{N} \Sigma X^2 - \left(\frac{\Sigma X}{N}\right)^2$$

$$= \frac{1}{4} (30) - (2.5)^2$$

$$= 1.25$$

$$\sigma_Y{}^2 = \frac{1}{N} \Sigma Y^2 - \left(\frac{\Sigma Y}{N}\right)^2$$

$$= \frac{1}{4} (120) - 5^2$$

$$= 5$$

Thus the ρ becomes

$$\rho = \frac{2.5}{\sqrt{1.25} \sqrt{5}} = \frac{2.5}{\sqrt{6.25}}$$

$$= \frac{2.5}{2.5} = 1$$

This shows that when there is perfect covariability between X and Y and both vary in the same direction, the $\rho = 1$.

It can also be shown that when there is perfect covariability, but X and Y vary in opposite directions, then $\rho = -1$.

For the case where there was no covariability, the covariance was zero, and thus $\rho = 0$.

(ii) Comments

1. The correlation coefficient ρ as explained above which is based on the idea of covariance was used by biostatisticians in biological research. For example, we know that tall brothers tend to have tall sisters, and vice versa. Neither is the cause of the other, but of the various factors that affect stature, the brothers and sisters seem to have certain characteristics in common that cause the covariability. The corre-

lation coefficient is an index of the degree of this covariability, but does not explain the reasons.

2. This ρ also assumes a bivariate distribution, and both X and Y vary. A population with fixed X's, such as we discussed in Chapter 14, will not give us a ρ based on this covariation type of interpretation.

3. Another situation in which there is no covariability is where one of the variables is a constant. For example, let $Y = 5$. Then we may have values of X and Y as in the table below. In this case the covariance

X	Y	$X - \mu_X$	$Y - \mu_Y$	$(X - \mu_X)(Y - \mu_Y)$
1	5	−1.5	0	0
2	5	−0.5	0	0
3	5	0.5	0	0
4	5	1.5	0	0
				0

becomes

$$\text{Cov}(X, Y) = \frac{1}{N} \Sigma (X - \mu_X)(Y - \mu_Y)$$

$$= \frac{1}{4} (0) = 0$$

Thus it would seem that the $\rho = 0$. However, if we calculate σ_Y^2, we find

$$\sigma_Y^2 = \frac{1}{N} \Sigma (Y - \mu_Y)^2 = \frac{1}{4} (0) = 0$$

Thus

$$\rho = \frac{\text{Cov}(X, Y)}{\sigma_X \sigma_Y}$$

becomes meaningless.

The implication of this example is that both X and Y must vary, and when X and Y are independent of each other, there is no covariation between X and Y; hence, $\rho = 0$.

But note that $\rho = 0$ does not necessarily mean that X and Y are statistically independent. For example, when the relation between X and Y are as shown by Fig. 15.5(a) and (b), we can see intuitively that

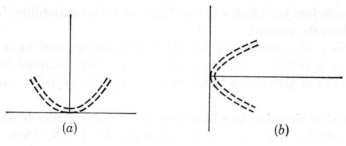

FIG. 15.5.

the average of the cross products will be zero because the positive and negative elements will cancel out; thus the covariance will be zero although clearly X and Y are not independent.

(iii) Sample correlation coefficient

The bivariate population we have assumed has only 4 observations, but in general, the size of the population is large, and hence it is necessary to estimate ρ. When we have a bivariate *normal* distribution, the procedure is to apply the method of maximum likelihood and estimate ρ. Without derivation we present the result:

(4)
$$r = \frac{\dfrac{1}{n-1} \Sigma (X - \bar{X})(Y - \bar{Y})}{\sqrt{\dfrac{1}{n-1} \Sigma (X - \bar{X})^2} \sqrt{\dfrac{1}{n-1} \Sigma (Y - \bar{Y})^2}}$$

$$= \frac{\Sigma (X - \bar{X})(Y - \bar{Y})}{\sqrt{\Sigma (X - \bar{X})^2} \sqrt{\Sigma (Y - \bar{Y})^2}}$$

where r is the sample correlation coefficient. The interpretation is the same as that for ρ.

For purpose of calculation, formula (4) is usually rewritten as follows:

(5)
$$r = \frac{\Sigma XY - n\bar{X}\bar{Y}}{\sqrt{[\Sigma X^2 - n\bar{X}^2][\Sigma Y^2 - n\bar{Y}^2]}}$$

$$= \frac{n\Sigma XY - (\Sigma X)(\Sigma Y)}{\sqrt{[n\Sigma X^2 - (\Sigma X)^2][n\Sigma Y^2 - (\Sigma Y)^2]}}$$

Example 1. Suppose a random sample of 5 students is selected and their English and mathematics grades (on a 10-point basis) are as shown in the table. Find the correlation coefficient r.

X English	Y Math	XY	X²	Y²
2	3	6	4	9
5	4	20	25	16
3	4	12	9	16
7	8	56	49	64
8	9	72	64	81
25	28	166	151	186

Using formula (5), we find

$$r = \frac{(5)(166) - (25)(28)}{\sqrt{[(5)(151) - (25)^2][(5)(186) - (28)^2]}}$$

$$= \frac{130}{\sqrt{(130)(146)}}$$

$$= \frac{130}{137.77} = 0.95$$

The sample correlation coefficient is $r = 0.95$, and the data show a high degree of covariability.

Example 2. Suppose the grades in Example 1 are on a 100 basis as shown in the table.

X English	Y Math
20	30
50	40
30	40
70	80
80	90

Then, as one can readily see, the cross products, squares, and the sums will become very large numbers, making the calculations tedious. To avoid this, we may divide both X and Y by 10, which will make it the same as Example 1. There will be no effect on r.

We may also divide only the X or the Y by 10 or some other number, and there will be no effect on r. A check of these results will be left to the student.

Example 3. Suppose the grades in English and mathematics of the 5 randomly selected students are as in the table below.

X English	Y Math	X' $= X - 70$	Y' $= Y - 80$
72	83	2	3
75	84	5	4
73	84	3	4
77	88	7	8
78	89	8	9

In this case, dividing by 10 or some other number will not simplify calculations. But, as observations show, if we let

$$X' = X - 70$$

$$Y' = Y - 80$$

as shown in the table, the data are simplified and calculations become easier. A check will show that the r calculated by X' and Y' (or X and Y', or X' and Y) will give the same results as use of X and Y. The verification is left to the student.

Example 4. Let X be the number of pounds of items in a handbag and Y be the sizes of the handbags women carry. A random sample of 15 women produced the data in the accompanying table, where there are 2 women who

		X, Pounds				f_Y	Yf_Y	Y^2	Y^2f_Y	XY
		2	3	4	5					
Y,	4	1	1	–	–	2	8	16	32	20
Bag	5	1	2	1	–	4	20	25	100	60
Size	6	–	1	3	2	6	36	36	216	150
	7	–	–	2	1	3	21	49	147	91
	fx	2	4	6	3	15	85		495	321
	Xf_X	4	12	24	15	55				
	X^2	4	9	16	25					
	X^2f_X	8	36	96	75	215				
	XY	18	60	148	95	321				

have size 5 handbags and 3 lb. of items. There are altogether 15 observations. The difference between this sample and the previous one is that in the previous one there was only 1 observation for each pair of X, Y, but in our present sample, there may be more than 1 observation.

The introduction of frequencies (number of observations) requires a few changes in the sample correlation formula as follows:

(6)
$$r = \frac{\frac{1}{n-1} \Sigma (X - \bar{X})(Y - \bar{Y})}{\sqrt{\frac{1}{n-1} \Sigma (X - \bar{X})^2 f_X} \sqrt{\frac{1}{n-1} \Sigma (Y - \bar{Y})^2 f_Y}}$$

where

$$\bar{X} = \frac{1}{n} \Sigma X f_X$$

$$\bar{Y} = \frac{1}{n} \Sigma Y f_Y$$

The $1/(n-1)$ cancels out and (6) becomes

(7)
$$r = \frac{\Sigma (X - \bar{X})(Y - \bar{Y})}{\sqrt{\Sigma (X - \bar{X})^2 f_X} \sqrt{\Sigma (Y - \bar{Y})^2 f_Y}}$$

The numerator may be rewritten as

$$\Sigma (X - \bar{X})(Y - \bar{Y}) = \Sigma XY - n\bar{X}\bar{Y}$$

The denominator becomes

$$\Sigma (X - \bar{X})^2 f_X = \Sigma (X^2 - 2X\bar{X} + \bar{X}^2) f_X$$
$$= \Sigma X^2 f_X - 2\bar{X} \Sigma X f_X + \bar{X}^2 \Sigma f_X$$
$$= \Sigma X^2 f_X - 2n\bar{X}^2 + n\bar{X}^2$$
$$= \Sigma X^2 f_X - n\bar{X}^2$$
$$\Sigma (Y - \bar{Y})^2 f_Y = \Sigma Y^2 f_Y - n\bar{Y}^2$$

Substituting these results into (7) gives us

(8)
$$r = \frac{\Sigma XY - n\bar{X}\bar{Y}}{\sqrt{[\Sigma X^2 f_X - n\bar{X}^2][\Sigma Y^2 f_Y - n\bar{Y}^2]}}$$
$$= \frac{n \Sigma XY - (\Sigma X f_X)(\Sigma Y f_Y)}{\sqrt{[n \Sigma X^2 f_X - (\Sigma X f_X)^2][n \Sigma Y^2 f_Y - (\Sigma Y f_Y)^2]}}$$

Using (8) and the calculations shown in the table, the r becomes

$$r = \frac{(15)(321) - (55)(85)}{\sqrt{[(15)(215) - (55)^2][(15)(495) - (85)^2]}}$$
$$= \frac{28}{40} = 0.70$$

Note that the summation in ΣXY extends over all sample values. Hence, in the last column showing XY in the table, we have

$$(4 \times 2) \times 1 + (4 \times 3) \times 1 = 20$$
$$(5 \times 2) \times 1 + (5 \times 3) \times 2 + (5 \times 4) \times 1 = 60$$
$$(6 \times 3) \times 1 + (6 \times 4) \times 3 + (6 \times 5) \times 2 = 150$$
$$(7 \times 4) \times 2 + (7 \times 5) \times 1 = 91$$

and the total is

$$\Sigma XY = 20 + 60 + 150 + 91 = 321$$

The XY in the last row of the table is calculated in the same manner and the total is also 321.

REFERENCE

(i) Shifting the origin and changing the scale of the unit does not affect ρ

$$\rho = \frac{E(X - \bar{X})(Y - \bar{Y})}{\sqrt{E(X - \bar{X})^2}\sqrt{E(Y - \bar{Y})^2}}$$

Let

$$X' = a + bX$$
$$Y' = c + dY$$

Then

$$\bar{X}' = E(X') = a + bE(X) = a + b\bar{X}$$
$$\bar{Y}' = E(Y') = c + dE(Y) = c + d\bar{Y}$$

The correlation coefficient of X' and Y' is

$$\rho' = \frac{E(X' - \bar{X}')(Y' - \bar{Y}')}{\sqrt{E(X' - \bar{X}')^2}\sqrt{E(Y' - \bar{Y}')^2}}$$

The numerator becomes

$$E(\bar{X}' - \bar{X}')(Y' - \bar{Y}') = E[a + bX - (a + b\bar{X})][c + dY - (c + d\bar{Y})]$$
$$= E[bX - b\bar{X}][dY - d\bar{Y}]$$
$$= bdE[X - \bar{X}][Y - \bar{Y}]$$

The denominator becomes

$$E(X' - \bar{X}')^2 = E[a + bX - (a + b\bar{X})]^2$$
$$= b^2 E[X - \bar{X}]^2$$

$$E(Y' - \bar{Y}')^2 = d^2 E[Y - \bar{Y}]^2$$

$$\sqrt{E(X' - \bar{X}')^2 \, E(Y' - \bar{Y}')^2}$$

$$= bd \sqrt{E(X - \bar{X})^2 \, E(Y - \bar{Y})^2}$$

Substituting these results into ρ', we find

$$\rho' = \frac{bd E(X - \bar{X})(Y - \bar{Y})}{bd \sqrt{E(X - \bar{X})^2 \, E(Y - \bar{Y})^2}}$$

$$= \frac{E(X - \bar{X})(Y - \bar{Y})}{\sqrt{E(X - \bar{X})^2 \, E(Y - \bar{Y})^2}}$$

$$= \rho$$

In similar manner, the correlation coefficient between X and X', or X' and Y, are all equal to ρ.

(ii)   When there is perfect covariability, $\rho = 1$. Consider the function

$$Y = a + bX$$

Then X and Y have perfect covariability. The ρ for X and Y is

$$\rho = \frac{E(X - \mu_X)(Y - \mu_Y)^2}{\sqrt{E(X - \mu_X)^2} \sqrt{E(Y - \mu_Y)^2}}$$

$$= \frac{E(X - \mu_X)(a + bX - a - b\mu_X)}{\sqrt{E(X - \mu_X)^2} \sqrt{E(a + bX - a - b\mu_X)^2}}$$

$$= \frac{b E(X - \mu_X)^2}{b \sqrt{E(X - \mu_X)^2} \sqrt{E(X - \mu_X)^2}}$$

$$= 1$$

(iii)   When X and Y are independent, $\rho = 0$.

$$E(X - \mu_X)(Y - \mu_Y) = E(X - \mu_X)E(Y - \mu_Y)$$

$$= 0 \times 0 = 0$$

Thus, $\rho = 0$ when X and Y are independent.

15.4.   The Correlation Coefficient: Case II

The second approach to correlation is related to regression analysis and shows the closeness of fit of the regression line to the distribution of observations. Let us first show the idea schematically and then work out the details.

(i) Population correlation coefficient

Regression analysis was applicable to two types of populations. One was a collection of subpopulations of Y's corresponding to given X values, and a second was a bivariate distribution. Up to now we have assumed a bivariate normal distribution and estimated ρ by the maximum likelihood method. However, many of the results of correlation analysis may be applied to the first type of population. We shall first discuss the problem in terms of the general bivariate type of population and then show how the results also hold true for the first type, except with a different interpretation. Let Fig. 15.6 show a population regression line and let Y be an individual value; then

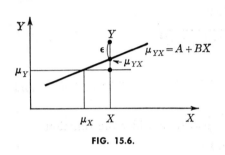

FIG. 15.6.

$$\mu_{YX} = A + BX$$
$$Y = \mu_{YX} + \epsilon$$

Let μ_Y be the average of Y values. Then, as the diagram shows,

$$(1) \qquad \underset{\text{Total error}}{Y - \mu_Y} = \underset{\text{Unexplained error}}{(Y - \mu_{YX})} + \underset{\text{Explained error}}{(\mu_{YX} - \mu_Y)}$$

The interpretation of equation (1) is as follows: The $(Y - \mu_Y)$ is called the *total error* and is the deviation between Y and the arithmetic mean of Y. The $(\mu_{YX} - \mu_Y)$ is called the *explained error*, and it may be thought of as the amount of error removed when the regression line is fitted to the points. The $(Y - \mu_{YX})$ is called the *unexplained error* and is the error that still remains (unexplained) after the regression line has been fitted. Each point may be decomposed in the manner explained above.

We state without proof that the following relation holds among the errors in equation (1):

$$(2) \qquad \Sigma\,(Y - \mu_Y)^2 = \Sigma\,(Y - \mu_{YX})^2 + \Sigma\,(\mu_{YX} - \mu_Y)^2$$

where the sum is taken over the population. The $\Sigma\,(Y - \mu_Y)^2$ is called the *total sum of squares*. Equation (2) shows how it can be split up (partitioned) into two parts: the $\Sigma\,(Y - \mu_{YX})^2$, which is called the *unexplained sum of squares;* and $\Sigma\,(\mu_{YX} - \mu_Y)^2$, which is called the *explained sum of squares.*

If we divide both sides by the population size N, we find

(3) $$\frac{1}{N} \Sigma (Y - \mu_Y)^2 = \frac{1}{N} \Sigma (Y - \mu_{YX})^2 + \frac{1}{N} \Sigma (\mu_{YX} - \mu_Y)^2$$

The first term, $(1/N) \Sigma (Y - \mu_Y)^2$, is the variance of Y, that is, $\text{Var}(Y)$. The second term is the variance of Y around the regression line, that is, σ_{YX}^2. The third term is the variance of μ_{YX} around μ_Y. Thus, (3) shows how the total variance, $\text{Var}(Y)$, is split (partitioned) into two parts by a regression line. Therefore we may say that the regression line has reduced the total variance, $\text{Var}(Y)$, by $(1/N) \Sigma (\mu_{YX} - \mu_Y)^2$.

With this much background, let us now define the population correlation coefficient. It is

(4) $$\rho^2 = \frac{\Sigma (\mu_{YX} - \mu_Y)^2}{\Sigma (Y - \mu_Y)^2}$$

$$= \frac{\text{explained sum of squares}}{\text{total sum of squares}}$$

where ρ^2, sometimes called the *coefficient of determination*, is the square of the population correlation coefficient. If, for example, $\rho^2 = 0.90$, it means that 90 percent of the variability has been explained by the regression line. Or we may say that 90 percent of the total variance has been explained by the regression line.

Formula (4) looks quite different from our previous population correlation coefficient formula, which was defined as the covariance of standardized variables X and Y. However, a small amount of algebraic manipulation will show that both definitions are the same. Let us show this as follows: The regression line may be shown as

(5) $$\mu_{YX} = \mu_Y + B(X - \mu_X)$$
$$A = \mu_Y - B\mu_X$$

(5′) $$B = \frac{\Sigma (X - \mu_X)(Y - \mu_Y)}{\Sigma (X - \mu_X)^2}$$

where the regression line has been fitted to the points by the method of least squares. From (5) we get

(6) $$\mu_{YX} - \mu_Y = B(X - \mu_X)$$

Substituting (6) and (5′) into (4) gives us

(7)
$$\rho^2 = \frac{B^2 \, \Sigma \, (X - \mu_X)^2}{\Sigma \, (Y - \mu_Y)^2}$$

$$= \left[\frac{\Sigma \, (X - \mu_X)(Y - \mu_Y)}{\Sigma \, (X - \mu_X)^2} \right]^2 \left[\frac{\Sigma \, (X - \mu_X)^2}{\Sigma \, (Y - \mu_Y)^2} \right]$$

$$= \frac{[\Sigma \, (X - \mu_X)(Y - \mu_Y)]^2}{\Sigma \, (X - \mu_X)^2 \, \Sigma \, (Y - \mu_Y)^2}$$

$$= \frac{\left[\dfrac{1}{N} \, \Sigma \, (X - \mu_X)(Y - \mu_Y) \right]^2}{\dfrac{1}{N} \, \Sigma \, (X - \mu_X)^2 \, \dfrac{1}{N} \, \Sigma \, (Y - \mu_X)^2}$$

$$= \left[\frac{\mathrm{Cov}(X, \, Y)}{\sigma_X \sigma_Y} \right]^2$$

which shows that both definitions are equivalent. What differs, though, is the interpretation, since in our present case the ρ^2 is showing the amount of variability (variance) that has been removed.

Before going on any farther, let us point out that, in practice, we find the estimate of ρ and not ρ itself; that is, we find the sample correlation coefficient r. Since the properties we shall work out for r are the same as those for ρ, let us next discuss r.

(ii) Sample correlation coefficient

The sample regression line is obtained from the sample data by applying the *method of least squares* and is

(8)
$$Y_c = a + bX$$
$$a = \bar{Y} - b\bar{X}$$

(8′)
$$b = \frac{\Sigma \, (X - \bar{X})(Y - \bar{Y})}{\Sigma \, (X - \bar{X})^2}$$

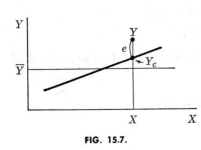

FIG. 15.7.

Similar to the relation of equation (1) found in the previous discussion, we find for the sample regression line (see Fig. 15.7)

(9)
$$Y - \bar{Y} = (Y - Y_c) + (Y_c - \bar{Y})$$

| Total error | Unexplained error | Explained error |

and the relation between these error terms is similar to that of equation (2), that is,

$$(10) \qquad \underset{\text{Total}}{\Sigma (Y - \bar{Y})^2} = \underset{\text{Unexplained}}{\Sigma (Y - Y_c)^2} + \underset{\text{Explained}}{\Sigma (Y_c - \bar{Y})^2}$$

where the sum is taken over the sample. It shows how the total sum of squares (total variance) is split (partitioned) into two parts, the unexplained and explained sum of squares.

The sample correlation coefficient r is defined as

$$(11) \qquad r^2 = \frac{\Sigma (Y_c - \bar{Y})^2}{\Sigma (Y - \bar{Y})^2}$$

where r^2 is the square of the sample correlation coefficient and is called the sample coefficient of determination. The r is the estimate of ρ.

The connection between (11) and the previous sample correlation coefficient that was defined in terms of covariances is shown as follows: From (8) we have

$$(12) \qquad \begin{aligned} Y_c &= \bar{Y} + b(X - \bar{X}) \\ Y_c - \bar{Y} &= b(X - \bar{X}) \end{aligned}$$

By substituting this (12) and (8′) into (11), we get

$$r^2 = \frac{b^2 \Sigma (X - \bar{X})^2}{\Sigma (Y - \bar{Y})^2}$$

$$= \left[\frac{\Sigma (X - \bar{X})(Y - \bar{Y})}{\Sigma (X - \bar{X})^2} \right]^2 \left[\frac{\Sigma (X - \bar{X})^2}{\Sigma (Y - \bar{Y})^2} \right]$$

$$= \frac{[\Sigma (X - \bar{X})(Y - \bar{X})]^2}{\Sigma (X - \bar{X})^2 \Sigma (Y - \bar{Y})^2}$$

or

$$(13) \qquad r = \frac{\Sigma (X - \bar{X})(Y - \bar{Y})}{\sqrt{\Sigma (X - \bar{X})^2 \Sigma (Y - \bar{Y})^2}}$$

which is the same as we found in Section 15.3. For calculation purposes, (13) is rewritten as

$$(14) \qquad r = \frac{n \Sigma XY - (\Sigma X)(\Sigma Y)}{\sqrt{[n \Sigma X^2 - (\Sigma X)^2][n \Sigma Y^2 - (\Sigma Y)^2]}}$$

Let us illustrate these various relations with a hypothetical illustration. Let X be hours of study and Y be grades as given in the table below. The regression line of Y on X and X on Y are found by the

X, Hours	Y, Grades	XY	X^2	Y^2	Y_c
2	5	10	4	25	4
4	3	12	16	9	5
6	7	42	36	49	6
12	15	64	56	83	15

method of least squares and the results are as follows:

$$(15) \qquad Y_c = 3 + \frac{1}{2} X$$

$$(16) \qquad X_c = \frac{3}{2} + \frac{1}{2} Y$$

$$\bar{X} = 4, \qquad \bar{Y} = 5$$

Figure 15.8 shows the regression line (15) and the relation

$$(Y - \bar{Y}) = (Y - Y_c) + (Y_c - \bar{Y})$$

$$(7 - 5) = (7 - 6) + (6 - 5)$$

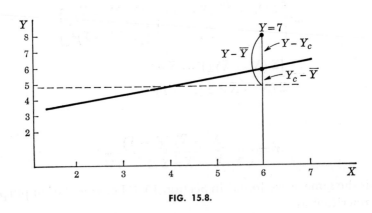

FIG. 15.8.

Let us next check the relation between the sum of squares given by (10). For this we construct a worksheet.

$Y - \bar{Y}$	$(Y - \bar{Y})^2$	$Y - Y_c$	$(Y - Y_c)^2$	$Y_c - \bar{Y}$	$(Y_c - \bar{Y})^2$
0	0	1	1	−1	1
−2	4	−2	4	0	0
2	4	1	1	1	1
	$\overline{8}$		$\overline{6}$		$\overline{2}$

$$\Sigma (Y - \bar{Y})^2 = \Sigma (Y - Y_c)^2 + \Sigma (Y_c - \bar{Y})^2$$
$$8 \qquad = \qquad 6 \qquad + \qquad 2$$

The coefficient of determination is

$$r^2 = \frac{\Sigma (Y_c - \bar{Y})^2}{\Sigma (Y - \bar{Y})^2}$$

$$= \frac{2}{8} = 0.25$$

This shows that 25 percent of the variability has been explained (removed) by the regression line. The correlation coefficient is

$$r = \pm \sqrt{0.25} = \pm 0.5$$

and observation of the data and the scatter diagram show that

$$r = +0.5$$

When the computational formula (14) is used, the sign of r is automatically determined. For the present case,

$$r = \frac{(3)\,(64) - (12)\,(15)}{\sqrt{[(3)\,(56) - (12)^2]\,[(3)\,(83) - (15)^2]}}$$

$$= \frac{4}{8} = 0.5$$

(iii)   Closeness of fit

The coefficient of determination, r^2, is a measure of the closeness of fit of the regression line to the points. We explain this as follows: From equation (10) we have, by dividing through by $\Sigma (Y - \bar{Y})^2$,

(17) $$1 = \frac{\Sigma (Y - Y_c)^2}{\Sigma (Y - \bar{Y})^2} + \frac{\Sigma (Y_c - \bar{Y})^2}{\Sigma (Y - \bar{Y})^2}$$

(17′) $$1 = \frac{\Sigma (Y - Y_c)^2}{\Sigma (Y - \bar{Y})^2} + r^2$$

When the points all fall on the regression line and the fit is perfect, the Y_c is equal to Y; that is, $Y_c = Y$. Then

$$r^2 = \frac{\Sigma (Y_c - \bar{Y})^2}{\Sigma (Y - \bar{Y})^2}$$

$$= \frac{\Sigma (Y - \bar{Y})^2}{\Sigma (Y - \bar{Y})^2} = 1$$

and

$$\frac{\Sigma (Y - Y_c)^2}{\Sigma (Y - \bar{Y})^2} = \frac{\Sigma (Y_c - Y_c)^2}{\Sigma (Y - \bar{Y})^2}$$

$$= \frac{0}{\Sigma (Y - \bar{Y})^2}$$

$$= 0$$

This relation (perfect fit) is shown in Fig. 15.9(a).

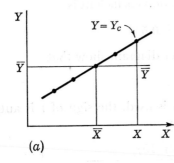 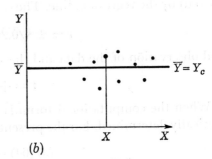

(a)   (b)

FIG. 15.9.

On the other hand, when the points are scattered in such a way that the regression line is parallel to the horizontal axis, then Y_c is equal to $\bar{Y}$. This happens when the regression line is horizontal and the slope is $b = 0$. But we know that

$$Y_c = \bar{Y} + b(X - \bar{X})$$

and when $b = 0$, then $Y_c = \bar{Y}$. When $Y_c = \bar{Y}$, the r^2 is

$$r^2 = \frac{\Sigma (Y_c - \bar{Y})^2}{\Sigma (Y - \bar{Y})^2}$$

$$= \frac{0}{\Sigma (Y - \bar{Y})^2}$$

$$= 0$$

and

$$\frac{\Sigma (Y - Y_c)^2}{\Sigma (Y - \bar{Y})^2} = \frac{\Sigma (Y - \bar{Y})^2}{\Sigma (Y - \bar{Y})^2} = 1$$

We summarize: When the points Y all fall on the regression line, then $r^2 = 1$. When the points Y are scattered, such that the regression line becomes horizontal, then $r^2 = 0$. The closer the fit of the regression line to the points, the closer r^2 is to 1.

We may now reverse the preceding statement and say that the closer r^2 is to 1, the closer will be the fit of the regression line to the points.

One important point to keep in mind is that the Y's need to be scattered, that is, have a distribution. Consider the case where Y is equal to a constant m, that is, $Y = m$. Then, for each value of X, $Y = m$ and the arithmetic mean of Y is also $\bar{Y} = m$. Thus, as Fig. 15.10 shows,

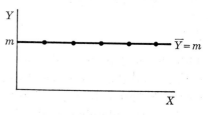

FIG. 15.10.

the Y values corresponding to the X's will fall on the line given by $\bar{Y} = m$, which is horizontal. Since it is a perfect fit, it may seem that $r^2 = 1$. On the other hand, since it is horizontal, it may seem that $r^2 = 0$. The difficulty here is that the Y's do not have a distribution and

$$\Sigma (Y - \bar{Y})^2 = 0$$

which makes the denominator of our formulas zero, and hence meaningless. We do not have a regression problem in this case. The main point is that the Y's need to have a distribution, or to put it another way, they have to be scattered.

We have seen that the coefficient of determination is between

$$0 \leqslant r^2 \leqslant 1$$

Thus the correlation coefficient r is between

$$-1 \leqslant r \leqslant 1$$

For example, when $r^2 = 0.81$, we can say immediately that 81 percent of the variability of Y has been removed (or explained) by the regression line. But we cannot tell from $r^2 = 0.81$ alone whether the variables move in the same direction or in opposite directions.

However, when given $r = -0.9$, we know that X and Y vary in opposite directions. By squaring r (that is, $r^2 = (-0.9)^2 = 0.81$), we find that 81 percent of the variability is explained by the regression line.

This idea of closeness of fit may be summarized in a compact manner as follows: From equation (17′) we find that

$$\frac{\Sigma\,(Y - Y_c)^2}{\Sigma\,(Y - \bar{Y})^2} = 1 - r^2$$

or

$$\Sigma\,(Y - Y_c)^2 = (1 - r^2)\,\Sigma\,(Y - \bar{Y})^2$$

Dividing through by $n - 1$ gives us

(18) $$\hat{\sigma}_{YX}^2 = (1 - r^2)\hat{\sigma}_Y^2$$

This shows that the variance of Y, $\hat{\sigma}_Y^2$, has been reduced by $r^2 \times 100$ percent and that there is a $(1 - r^2) \times 100$ percent residual unexplained part of $\hat{\sigma}_Y^2$ after the regression line has been fitted. When $r^2 = 1$, the $\hat{\sigma}_Y$ has been completely explained (removed or reduced), and when $r^2 = 0$, nothing has been explained (removed or reduced) by fitting the regression line.

(iv) The relation between r and b

The correlation coefficient r is the geometric mean of b and b', which are the slopes of the two regression lines. That is,

$$r = \sqrt{b \cdot b'}$$

We explain this as follows: Given a random sample, we may find the regression of X on Y or Y on X; the two regression lines are

$$Y_c = a + bX$$
$$X_c = a' + b'Y$$

where

$$b = \frac{\Sigma\,(X - \bar{X})(Y - \bar{Y})}{\Sigma\,(X - \bar{X})^2}$$

$$b' = \frac{\Sigma\,(X - \bar{X})(Y - \bar{Y})}{\Sigma\,(Y - \bar{Y})^2}$$

When b and b' are multiplied, we find that

$$(19) \qquad bb' = \frac{[\Sigma (X - \bar{X})(Y - \bar{Y})]^2}{\Sigma (X - \bar{X})^2 \, \Sigma (Y - \bar{Y})^2}$$

But from equation (13) we know that

$$(20) \qquad r = \frac{\Sigma (X - \bar{X})(Y - \bar{Y})}{\sqrt{\Sigma (X - \bar{X})^2 (Y - \bar{Y})^2}}$$

Thus, from (19) and (20), we see that the relation between r and b is

$$(21) \qquad bb' = r^2$$

or

$$(22) \qquad r = \sqrt{bb'}$$

This relation assumes that regression analysis has been applied to a bivariate distribution, and hence finding X on Y and Y on X is possible although it may not be meaningful. For example, suppose we have a bivariate distribution of heights of brothers (X) and sisters (Y). We can find the regressions of X on Y and Y on X although it is not meaningful; that is, the heights of brothers (X) do not depend on the heights of sisters (Y), and vice versa. Nevertheless, we may find the regression lines and find the b and b'. Then r is the geometric average of b and b'; $r = \sqrt{bb'}$.

The implication of this is that the r does not indicate whether X is dependent on Y, or vice versa.

This also shows that for problems where X and Y may have covariance but do not have a dependency relation, the correlation coefficient is the appropriate measure to use.

(v) Computation procedures

The basic computational formula is

$$(23) \qquad r = \frac{n\Sigma XY - (\Sigma X)(\Sigma Y)}{\sqrt{[n\Sigma X^2 - (\Sigma X)^2][n\Sigma Y^2 - (\Sigma Y)^2]}}$$

as given previously. To avoid tedious computational procedures, we may divide the variables by any number or shift the origin, or do both, as was discussed in the preceding chapter. Since the technique is the same, the discussion is omitted here.

Example.   Using our previous hypothetical example of hours of study and grade point, let us illustrate how shifting the origin may simplify computations.

X Hours	Y Grade	X' = X − 3	Y' = Y − 3	X'Y'	(X')²	(Y')²
2	5	−1	2	−2	1	4
4	3	1	0	0	1	0
6	7	3	4	12	9	16
12	15	3	6	10	11	20

Let us shift the origin to (3, 3). That is, let

$$X' = X - 3, \qquad Y' = Y - 3$$

Then the r becomes

$$r = \frac{n \Sigma X'Y' - (\Sigma X')(\Sigma Y')}{\sqrt{[n \Sigma X'^2 - (\Sigma X')^2][n \Sigma Y'^2 - (\Sigma Y')^2]}}$$

$$= \frac{(3)(10) - (3)(6)}{\sqrt{[(3)(11) - (3)^2][(3)(20) - (6)^2]}}$$

$$= \frac{4}{8} = 0.5$$

In some cases, it is advantageous to shift the origin to $(\bar{X}, \bar{Y})$, since then

$$\Sigma X' = 0, \qquad \Sigma Y' = 0$$

and r becomes

$$r = \frac{n \Sigma X'Y'}{\sqrt{(n \Sigma X'^2)(n \Sigma Y'^2)}}$$

In our present example, we have

$$\bar{X} = \frac{12}{3} = 4, \qquad \bar{Y} = \frac{15}{3} = 5$$

Thus we set

$$X' = X - 4, \qquad Y' = Y - 5$$

Then the table becomes as shown below.

X	Y	X'	Y'	X'Y'	(X')²	(Y')²
2	5	−2	0	0	4	0
4	3	0	−2	0	0	4
6	7	2	2	4	4	4
		0	0	4	8	8

We find

$$r = \frac{n \Sigma X'Y' - (\Sigma X')(\Sigma Y')}{\sqrt{[n \Sigma X'^2 - (\Sigma X')^2][n \Sigma Y'^2 - (\Sigma Y')^2]}}$$

$$= \frac{(3)(4) \quad - 0}{\sqrt{[(3)(8) - 0][(3)(8) - 0]}}$$

$$= \frac{4}{8} = 0.5$$

(vi) The r² as applied to the first type of population

Up to now we have assumed a bivariate distribution, with a population correlation coefficient ρ. By taking a random sample and applying the method of maximum likelihood or method of least squares, we were able to find the sample correlation coefficient r, which was an estimate of ρ; that is,

$$\hat{\rho} = r$$

We also found the various relations between regression analysis and r. For example,

$$r = \sqrt{bb'}$$
$$\Sigma (Y_c - \bar{Y})^2 = (1 - r^2) \Sigma (Y - \bar{Y})^2$$

or

$$\hat{\sigma}_{YX}^2 = (1 - r^2)\hat{\sigma}_Y{}^2$$

But when we have a population that is made up of a collection of subpopulations of Y's corresponding to fixed X's, such as we assumed in regression analysis, it has no ρ as a measure of covariation.

Nevertheless, when a sample is selected and a sample regression line

$$Y_c = a + bX$$

is estimated by the method of least squares, the basic relationships

$$Y - \bar{Y} = (Y - Y_c) + (Y_c - \bar{Y})$$
$$\text{Total} \quad \text{Unexplained} \quad \text{Explained}$$
$$\text{error} \qquad \text{error} \qquad \text{error}$$

and

$$\Sigma (Y - \bar{Y})^2 = \Sigma (Y - Y_c)^2 + \Sigma (Y_c - \bar{Y})^2$$

hold. When we divide through by $\Sigma (Y - \bar{Y})^2$, we find that

$$1 = \frac{\Sigma (Y - Y_c)^2}{\Sigma (Y - \bar{Y})^2} + \frac{\Sigma (Y_c - \bar{Y})^2}{\Sigma (Y - \bar{Y})^2}$$

Now we define ρ_o^2 and r^2 as

$$\rho_o^2 = \frac{\Sigma (\mu_{YX} - \mu_Y)^2}{\Sigma (Y - \mu_Y)^2} \quad \text{and} \quad r^2 \equiv \frac{\Sigma (Y_c - Y)^2}{\Sigma (Y - Y)^2}$$

Then we have for r^2

$$1 = \frac{\Sigma (Y - Y_c)^2}{\Sigma (Y - \bar{Y})^2} + r^2$$

which leads to

$$\Sigma (Y - Y_c)^2 = (1 - r^2) \Sigma (Y - \bar{Y})^2$$

All the preceding relations are identical to those we derived for the bivariate distribution case, except for a very important difference, namely, that r as defined is not an estimate of ρ which measures co-variation but an estimate of ρ_o. The ρ_o and r we have defined above are merely parameters showing the amount of reduction of the total sum of squares (or total variance) due to regression.

Hence, it is not proper to call r a correlation coefficient in this case, but since many writers use this term to mean two different things (as stated above), the student should take care to distinguish the two meanings by the context of the discussion.

15.5. Comments and Summary

1. The population correlation coefficient ρ assumes a bivariate distribution. When the population is not a bivariate distribution, but is a population that is a collection of subpopulations of Y's corresponding to fixed X's, we have ρ_o. Another type of population to which a nonparametric statistic called *rank correlation* is applied is discussed in Section 15.7.

2. The method of selecting a sample. In regression problems, samples may be selected by first fixing the X values and then pairs of X and Y. For example, students may be grouped according to fixed heights (X), and then students may be selected from these groups at random and their heights (X) and weights (Y) may be recorded. But in correlation analysis, the pairs of observations should be selected at random without predetermining either X or Y. For example, pairs of

brothers and sisters should be selected at random without designating beforehand the height of the brother or sister. However, we may also apply regression analysis to this second type of sample and find the regression lines.

3. Size of sample and sampling distribution of r. In our hypothetical distributions, samples of size $n = 3$ were used, but this was to avoid obscuring in any way the derivations and principles by the burden of large and tedious computations. In practice, such small samples should not be used.

When samples are small, the r is frequently very different from ρ. However, there are methods of checking the reliability of r. For this it is necessary to discuss the sampling distribution of r, but since this becomes quite involved if a reasonable attempt is made to discuss it, it is omitted here. The student is referred to works by R. A. Fisher* and G. W. Snedecor.**

4. Regression analysis is usually applied to cases where there is a direction of dependency, whereas correlation analysis is more suitable for cases where there is no direction of dependency. For example, if we have yield of wheat and fertilizer, there is a direction of dependency, whereas in the case of heavy smoking and indigestion, there is no direction of dependency or it is not clear. Both may be due to emotional disturbances. Other examples are the covariability of stature or IQ between brothers and sisters, which may be due to hereditary factors.

5. The correlation coefficient shows the degree of covariability between two variables, but may also be interpreted as a measure of the closeness of fit of the regression line, as we have discussed.

6. However, the correlation coefficient squared, that is, r^2, is also used to show the proportion of the total sum of squares that has been removed (or reduced) by the regression line. In this case r^2 is merely an algebraic parameter, and r is not an estimate of ρ.

7. When the correlation coefficient is interpreted as a measure of covariability between X and Y, it should be considered in connection with the idea of statistical independence. This is because the correlation coefficient is the covariance of two normalized variables and the covariance in turn is related to the idea of dependent and independent variables. When X and Y are independent, $\text{Cov}(X, Y) = 0$, and the $\rho = 0$. When the relation between X and Y is linear, and X and Y are not independent, $\text{Cov}(X, Y) \neq 0$ and the $\rho \neq 0$.

---

* Fisher, R. A., *Statistical Methods for Research Workers,* 12th ed., New York: Hafner Publishing Co., 1954.

** Snedecor, G. W., *Statistical Methods,* 5th ed., Ames: Iowa State University Press, 1956.

8. However, as we saw, we may have $\text{Cov}(X, Y) = 0$ even when X and Y are not independent. The examples we gave were shown diagrammatically, and the relations of X and Y were not linear. But we may also have a case where two baseball teams play a series of games against each other and the scores X and Y of both teams are such that $r = 0$. In this case, it is clear that X and Y are dependent on each other.

9. Regression and correlation are stochastic processes. By this is meant that both X and Y have to vary, and in the regression case, Y has a distribution; in the correlation case, both X and Y have a joint distribution. When $r = \pm 1$, the situation degenerates into a case of complete functional dependence between X and Y. That is, X gives a unique value of Y, or we may say that X and Y are the same thing.

10. Causation and correlation. It is possible to correlate the temperature of the sidewalks of New York City with the birth rate of a foreign country. It is possible also that a high, positive correlation may be found to show that when the sidewalk temperature is high, the birth rate is high, and when the temperature is low, the birth rate is low. There is no meaning to such a correlation, and there is no causal relationship between the two phenomena. This example merely illustrates that you can correlate anything, and there are chances that you may obtain a high correlation even if it has no significant meaning.

Assume that we want to find the relation between the number of hours of outside work (X) and the grade point (Y) a student makes in school, and we set up a hypothesis: the more hours of outside work (X), the lower the grade point (Y).

Suppose the $r = -0.9$. Can we conclude that "therefore, the more hours of outside work, the lower the grade point"?

The answer is: $r = -0.9$ is not enough evidence to verify the statement. It simply tells us that the data we have collected are *consistent* with the hypothesis we set up. That is, it supports our hypothesis. We may have the following situations that brought about $r = -0.9$:

(a). X is the cause of Y.
(b). Y is the cause of X.
(c). There is a third factor, Z, that affects X and Y such that they show a close relation.
(d). The correlation of X and Y may be due to chance.

Only by more thorough investigation, which may be economic, sociological, etc., can we come to some conclusion as to whether or not X is the cause of Y.

15.6. Rank Correlation

There are many cases where a dependency between two variables X and Y can be observed but where the distribution is unknown. In such cases, the previous methods of finding r cannot be applied. A statistic to measure the degree of association between variables X and Y when their distribution is unknown was developed by a statistician, C. Spearman, in 1904 and called the *rank correlation coefficient*.* It is based on the ranks (or order) of the observations and does not depend on a specific distribution of X and Y. Such a statistic that does not depend on a specific distribution of the variables is called a *nonparametric* or *distribution-free* statistic. We explain by illustration.

A random sample of 5 college students is selected and their grades in a high school mathematics course and college algebra course are found to be as follows as shown in the table here.

High School Grade X	College Grade Y	Rank of X	Rank of Y	$d = X - Y$	d^2
85	93	2	1	1	1
60	75	4	3	1	1
73	65	3	4	-1	1
40	50	5	5	0	0
90	80	1	2	-1	1
					$\overline{4}$

Spearman's rank correlation coefficient is defined as

(1)
$$r_s = 1 - \frac{6 \, \Sigma \, d^2}{n(n^2 - 1)}$$

where d denotes the differences between the ranks of X and Y. In our present example,

$$r_s = 1 - \frac{6\,(4)}{5\,(25 - 1)}$$
$$= 1 - 0.2$$
$$= 0.8$$

---

* C. Spearman, "The Proof and Measurement of Association Between Two Things," *American Journal of Psychology*, Vol. 15, 1904, pp. 72–101.

For formula (1) to correspond to our previous correlation coefficients, it should range between $+1$ and -1 for the cases where there is complete agreement in the order of the ranks and in the same direction in the first case and opposite directions in the second case. Let us check this.

X	Y	$d = X - Y$	d^2
1	1	0	0
2	2	0	0
3	3	0	0
			0

X	Y	$d = X - Y$	d^2
1	3	-2	4
2	2	$\cdot0$	0
3	1	2	4
			8

$$r_s = 1 - \frac{6\,\Sigma\,d^2}{n(n^2 - 1)}$$

$$= 1 - 0$$

$$= 1$$

$$r_s = 1 - \frac{6\,(8)}{3\,(9 - 1)}$$

$$= 1 - \frac{6}{3}$$

$$= -1$$

This may be generalized to more than 3 numbers. Thus, the results satisfy the requirements

$$-1 \leqq r_s \leqq 1$$

The sampling distribution of r_s needs to be known in order to check the reliability of r_s. The distribution of r_s is symmetrical around the value 0, approaches the normal curve as n becomes large, and is truncated at -1 and $+1$, as shown schematically in Fig. 15.11. It shows the distribution of r_s, assuming that the population $\rho_s = 0$.

In our present example, $n = 5$ and $r_s = 0.7$. Is $r_s = 0.7$ significant? Stated in a different way, we are testing the null hypothesis that the rank correlation coefficient in the population is zero, or we may say that the observations in the population are independent.

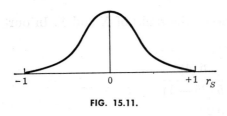

FIG. 15.11.

When $n > 20$, the sampling distribution is close enough to normality so that the normal area table may be used to find the probabilities. The variance of r_s is

$$(2) \qquad \mathrm{Var}(r_s) = \sigma_r^2 = \frac{1}{n - 1}$$

Thus, for example, if $n = 26$ and $r_s = 0.7$,

$$\sigma_r{}^2 = \frac{1}{26 - 1} = \frac{1}{25}$$

and the standard error is

$$\sigma_r = \frac{1}{5}$$

Then the test is

$$z = \frac{r_s}{\sigma_r} = \frac{0.7}{\dfrac{1}{5}} = 3.5$$

This means that r_s is 3.5 standard deviations away from 0 in the sampling distribution, and hence we conclude that there is a significant difference between 0 and $r_s = 0.7$. That is, we reject the null hypothesis that $\rho_s = 0$, and accept the alternative hypothesis that the observations are not independent.

When $n < 20$, we may use tables prepared by E. G. Olds, which are found in the *Annals of Mathematical Statistics* (1938 and 1939).* Several values close to the $\alpha = 5$ percent level of significance have been reproduced in Table 15.2 below. The table shows the values of $\Sigma \, d^2$ instead of the r_s which saves the trouble of computing the r_s when the test is not significant. A few values of r_s have been included for reference.

The table up to $n = 7$ is computed from exact frequencies of r_s; from $n = 8$ to 10, it is computed from curves; and from $n = 11$ to 20, it is computed from normal curves.

Let us illustrate the use of Table 15.2 by examples.

For the case where $n = 4$ and $\Sigma \, d^2 = 0$, the r_s may be found as

$$r = 1 - \frac{6 \, \Sigma \, d^2}{n(n^2 - 1)} = 1 - \frac{6 \times 0}{4(16 - 1)}$$

$$= 1$$

And the table shows that the probability of $r_s \geq 1$, when $\rho_s = 0$ is 0.0417.

---

* E. G. Olds, "Distribution of Sums of Squares of Rank Differences for Small Numbers of Individuals," *Annals of Mathematical Statistics*, **9**, 1938, pp. 133–148.

E. G. Olds, "The 5% Significance Levels for Sums of Squares of Rank Differences and a Correction," *Annals of Mathematical Statistics*, **20**, 1949, pp. 117–118.

TABLE 15.2.

n	$\Sigma\, d^2$	r_s	Σ_M	P_r
4	0 (20)	1 (−1)	10	.0417
5	2 (38)	.9 (−.9)	20	.0417
5	4 (36)	.8 (−.8)	20	.0667
6	6 (64)		35	.0292
6	8 (62)		35	.0514
7	16 (96)		56	.0440
7	18 (94)		56	.0548
8	30 (138)		84	.0469
8	32 (136)		84	.0550
9	48 (192)		120	.0470
9	50 (190)		120	.0528
10	72 (258)		165	.0472
10	74 (256)		165	.0515
11	83.6 (356.4)			.050
12	117.0 (455.0)			.050
13	158.0 (570.0)			.050
14	207.7 (702.3)			.050
15	266.7 (853.3)			.050
16	335.9 (1024.1)			.050
17	416.2 (1215.8)			.050
18	508.4 (1429.6)			.050
19	613.3 (1666.7)			.050
20	732.0 (1928.0)			.050

SOURCE: E. G. Olds, *op. cit.* By permission of author and publisher.

The term 20 in parentheses shows that when $\Sigma\, d^2 = 20$ we get $r_s = -1$, and the probability of $r_s \leqq -1$ is also 0.0417. The $r_s = -1$ is obtained from

$$r_s = 1 - \frac{6 \times 20}{4(16 - 1)} = -1$$

and is shown in parentheses next to $r_s = 1$.

The distribution of r_s is symmetrical around 0, and the Σ_M is the $\Sigma\, d^2$ at which $r_s = 0$. For example, for $n = 4$ we have $\Sigma_M = \Sigma\, d^2 = 10$. Hence

$$r = 1 - \frac{6 \times 10}{4 \times 15} = 0$$

For the $n = 5$, and $\Sigma\, d^2 = 2$ case,

$$r_s = 1 - \frac{6 \times 2}{5 \times 24}$$

$$= 1 - \frac{1}{10} = 0.9$$

and the probability of $r_s \geqq 0.9$ is 0.0417. For the $n = 5$ and $\Sigma\, d^2 = 38$ case,

$$r_s = 1 - \frac{6 \times 38}{5 \times 24} = -.9$$

and this gives the results for the left tail. Let us show this diagrammatically in Fig. 15.12.

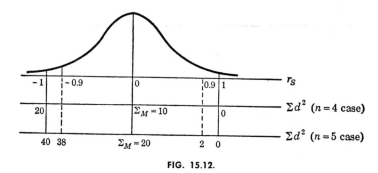

FIG. 15.12.

Example. The ranking of 6 students in English and mathematics are as follows.

English	Mathematics	d	d^2
1	2	-1	1
2	1	1	1
3	3	0	0
4	5	-1	1
5	4	1	1
6	6	0	0
			4

Is there a correlation between the English and mathematics grades?
  The null and alternative hypotheses are:

$$H_1: \qquad \rho_s = 0$$
$$H_2: \qquad \rho_s \neq 0$$

From Table 15.2 we find that when $\Sigma d^2 \leq 6$, the probability of such an r_s occurring is less than 0.0291. Our calculations show that $\Sigma d^2 = 4$. Thus, since we are using the $\alpha = 5\%$ level of significance, we reject the null hypothesis. The r_s corresponding to $\Sigma d^2 = 4$ is

$$r_s = 1 - \frac{6 \times 4}{6 \times 35} = .885$$

The results may be shown diagrammatically as in Fig. 15.13.

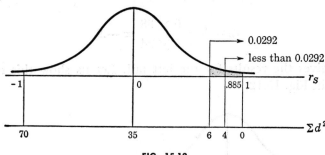

FIG. 15.13.

RANDOM VARIABLES AND PROBABILITY DISTRIBUTIONS

16

In Chapter 5 probability theory was discussed on an elementary level. In this chapter we shall discuss probability theory on a slightly more advanced level by introducing the idea of set theory and explaining the concepts of sample space, random variable, postulates of probability theory, and probability distributions. Following this, we shall consider conditional probabilities again and give a brief discussion of Bayes' theorem.

16.1. Sets

Set theory, which was developed by Georg Cantor (1845–1918) between 1874–1895, is a basic mathematical tool that is used by the various branches of mathematics, such as probability theory, calculus, and geometry. Cantor was born in Russia in 1845, but moved to Germany in 1856. In 1863 he entered the University of Berlin, where he studied under K. Weierstrass (1815–1897), L. Kronecker (1823–1891), and E. E. Kummer (1810–1893), all of whom are famous mathematicians, and received his Ph.D. in 1867. One of the subsequent main works in set theory is by F. Hausdorff,* which was first published in 1914. A transla-

---
* F. Hausdorff, *Set Theory*, 4th ed., trans. by J. R. Auman, New York: Chelsea Publishing Co., 1957.

tion of the fourth edition (1957) is available in English. An elementary text of set theory by J. Breuer* is available in an English translation.

(i) A set

A set is a collection into a whole of definite and well-distinguished objects: for example, a group of students, a deck of cards, and beads in a box are examples of sets.

Let a set be denoted by S, and call the objects *elements*. Then an element a is related to the set as:

$$a \text{ is an element of } S : \quad a \in S$$
$$a \text{ is not an element of } S : \quad a \notin S$$

For example, the set S may be 3 numbers: 1, 2, and 3, which are the elements of the set. To show that this comprises a set, we use braces $\{1, 2, 3\}$. Then, for the element 2, we write

$$2 \in \{1, 2, 3\}$$

The elements must be distinct. Thus, 1, 2, 3, 3, is a set $\{1, 2, 3\}$, where the repeated elements are deleted. The order of the elements does not matter for the present.

We say that $\{2\}$ is a set of 1 element: 2. A set with no element is called the *null set,* or *empty set,* and is denoted by 0.

If every element in S_1 is an element of S, then we say that S_1 is a *subset* of S. For example, let $S = \{1, 2, 3\}$. Then the subsets will be

$$0, \quad \{1\} \quad \{2\} \quad \{3\} \quad \{1, 2\} \quad \{1, 3\} \quad \{2, 3\} \quad \{1, 2, 3\}$$

A subset is denoted by

$$S_1 \subseteq S$$

When $S_1 \subset S$, that is, when S contains at least 1 element not in S_1, S_1 is called a *proper subset* of S.

There are $2^3 = 8$ subsets from a set of 3 elements. There will be 2^n subsets from a set of n elements. (See Section 16.3 for proof.)

(ii) Set operations

Let $S_1 = \{a, b, c, 2\}$ and $S_2 = \{1, 2, 3\}$. Then the *union* of S_1 and S_2 is the set S:

$$S = S_1 \cup S_2 = \{a, b, c, 1, 2, 3\}$$

---

* J. Breuer, *Introduction to the Theory of Sets,* trans. by H. F. Fehr, Englewood Cliffs, N.J.: Prentice-Hall, Inc., 1958.

It is the set that consists of all the elements that belong to either S_1 or S_2, or both [Fig. 16.1(a)].

The *intersection* of S_1 and S_2 is the set S:

$$S = S_1 \cap S_2 = \{2\}$$

It is the set of elements that belong to both S_1 and S_2 [Fig. 16.1(b)]. If the set S_3 is $\{a, b, c\}$, then

$$S_1 \cap S_3 = 0$$

That is, the intersection of nonoverlapping, or *disjoint,* sets is the null set. In this case, instead of using the

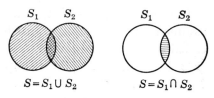

$$S = S_1 \cup S_2 \qquad S = S_1 \cap S_2$$

FIG. 16.1.

symbol $\cup$, we sometimes use the symbol $+$ for the union of disjoint sets and also use the word "sum" instead of "union." Let

$$S = S_1 \cup S_2 = \{a, b, c, 1, 2, 3\}$$

In general, the set S of all points under discussion is called the *universal set* for the given discussion, or simply the *universe.* Frequently, the universe is not explicitly specified.

Let $S_4 = \{a, b, 1, 2\}$ be a subset of S. The *complement* of S_4 with respect to the universe S is the set

$$\bar{S}_4 = \{c, 3\}$$

That is, it is those elements of the universe $\{a, b, c, 1, 2, 3\}$ that are not elements of $S = \{a, b, 1, 2\}$. See Fig. 16.2(a).

Next, the *difference* of sets S_1 and S_2 is the set S:

$$S = S_1 - S_2 = \{a, b, c, 2\} - \{1, 2, 3\} = \{a, b, c\}$$

Thus, a, b, c are elements of S_1, but are not elements of S_2, whereas 2 is

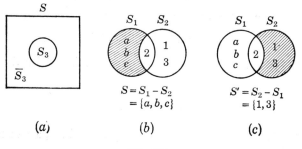

$$S = S_1 - S_2 \qquad\qquad S' = S_2 - S_1$$
$$= \{a, b, c\} \qquad\qquad = \{1, 3\}$$

(a) $\qquad\qquad\qquad$ (b) $\qquad\qquad\qquad$ (c)

FIG. 16.2.

an element of S_1 and S_2 [Fig. 16.2(b)]. For $S_2 - S_1$, we have

$$S' = S_2 - S_1 = \{1, 2, 3\} - \{a, b, c, 2\} = \{1, 3\}$$

16.2. Sample Space

In discussing probability and statistics, a basic concept that is always assumed is a sample space. In Chapter 5, the 6 outcomes of a die were called simple events and were shown graphically by 6 points on a line (Fig. 16.3). As we see, these simple events may be shown as points in a 1-dimensional space. If 2 dice are tossed, there are 36 simple events, and these simple events may be shown as 36 points in a 2-dimensional space (Fig. 16.4).

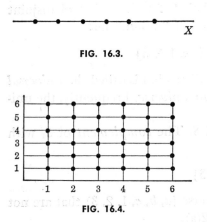

FIG. 16.3.

FIG. 16.4.

With this geometrical interpretation in mind, simple events will be called *sample points*. The set of all sample points will be called the *sample space*. Hence, the 6 points in Fig. 16.3 are each a sample point, and the aggregate of the 6 points is the sample space. Similarly, each of the 36 points in Fig. 16.4 are sample points, and the aggregate of these 36 points is the sample space.

Our previous and subsequent discussion of probability and statistics always assumed and will assume these notions of sample points and sample space.

Simple events are represented by sample points. Hence, a compound event that is a combination of simple events will be a combination of sample points. A combination of sample points, in terms of set theory, is a subset of the sample space. For example, let the sample space be

$$S = \{1, 2, \ldots, 6\}$$

which shows the 6 possible outcomes of a die. Let A be the compound event

$$A = E_1 \cup E_2$$

where $E_1 = 1$, $E_2 = 2$. That is, A is the event of either a 1 or 2 occurring. Then A may be shown by the subset:

$$A = E_1 \cup E_2 = \{1\} \cup \{2\} = \{1, 2\}$$

and $A \subset S$.

How many simple and compound events may be generated from the sample space S? In terms of set theory, this question may be restated as: How many subsets may be generated from the set S? These subsets are

$$0, \quad \{1\}, \quad \{2\}, \quad \{3\}, \quad \ldots, \quad \{1, 2\},$$
$$\{1, 3\}, \quad \ldots, \quad \{1, 2, 3, 4, 5, 6\}$$

By using the ideas of all possible samples explained in Chapter 7, the number of subsets may be shown as follows: There are $\binom{6}{0}$ ways of selecting a subset 0 from S. There are $\binom{6}{1}$ ways of selecting a subset with 1 element from S, etc. Thus the total number of subsets is

(1) $$\binom{6}{0} + \binom{6}{1} + \binom{6}{2} + \binom{6}{3} + \binom{6}{4} + \binom{6}{5} + \binom{6}{6}$$

But from the binomial theorem, we have

(2) $$(a + b)^6 = \binom{6}{0} a^6 + \binom{6}{1} a^5 b + \binom{6}{2} a^4 b^2 + \binom{6}{3} a^3 b^3 + \binom{6}{4} a^2 b^4$$
$$+ \binom{6}{5} ab^5 + \binom{6}{6} b^6$$

If we let $a = 1$ and $b = 1$, equation (2) becomes equation (1). Hence, the number of subsets generated from (1) will be

$$(1 + 1)^6 = 2^6 = 64$$

That is, we may generate 64 simple and compound events from S, where $\{ \ \} = 0$ is included as an event. The number of compound events is

$$64 - \left[\binom{6}{0} + \binom{6}{1} \right] = 64 - 7 = 57$$

We may conclude that we have a *collection* of 64 subsets taken from S. Instead of using the term *collection*, we may use the term *class* of subsets.

In general, given a set of n elements, we may generate 2^n subsets.

It is possible to qualify the subsets by some characteristic. For example, we can select subsets such that the sum of the numbers will be even; or such that the sum of numbers will be odd; or such that the sum of numbers will exceed 10; and so forth. We say that we have different classes of subsets.

The characteristics of the 64 subsets selected are:

1. The *union* of any number of these subsets will produce a subset that is a member of this class of subsets.
2. The *intersection* of any number of these subsets will produce a subset that is a member of this class of subsets.
3. The *difference* of any two subsets is a member of this class of subsets.
4. The *complement* of any subset is a member of this class of subsets.

Let us call these 64 subsets a *field* and denote it by F. Thus we may say that a field shows all the possible combinations of events that can be generated from the basic sample space.

16.3. Axioms

Now that we have translated an experiment in terms of sets, we shall state the basic axioms of probability theory, using set terminology. The advantage of this procedure is that when the probability axioms are stated in terms of set theory, we can apply the various rules of set operations of these axioms and derive various theorems concerning probability theory.

Let R be a sample space made up of sample points (simple events) and F be a field that has been generated from R. The elements of F are simple and compound events. Let the sample points in R be denoted by $E_1, E_2, \ldots E_n$. Then we state the following axioms:

1. To each sample point E_i we associate a nonnegative real number and call it the *probability* of the event E_i. This will be denoted by $P(E_i) \geq 0$.
2. $P(R) = 1$.
3. If two events A and B of the field F have no elements (sample points) in common, then

$$P(A \cup B) = P(A) + P(B)$$

From this we can see immediately that, since

$$R = E_1 \cup E_2 \cup \cdots \cup E_n$$

we get

$$P(E_1) + P(E_2) + \cdots + P(E_n) = 1$$

The third part of the axiom gives us a *rule of addition* of probabilities.

Let us illustrate. When a die is tossed, we have a sample space of 6 sample points, which we denote by $E_1, E_2, \ldots, E_6$. Let us assign non-negative numbers $1/6$ to each of these points. This is written

$$P(E_i) = \frac{1}{6}$$

Then

$$P(R) = P(E_1) + P(E_2) + \cdots + P(E_6)$$

$$= \frac{1}{6} + \cdots + \frac{1}{6} = 1$$

We may now apply the rules of set operation and obtain the following results: Let A be the event that 1 or 2 or both occur. Then

$$A = E_1 \cup E_2$$

But since 1 and 2 cannot both occur at the same time, $E_1 \cap E_2 = 0$. Thus

$$A = E_1 + E_2$$

That is, either 1 or 2 occurs. Let B be the event that either E_3 or E_4 occurs. Then we have

$$P(A) = P(E_1) + P(E_2) = \frac{1}{6} + \frac{1}{6} = \frac{2}{6}$$

$$P(B) = P(E_3) + P(E_4) = \frac{2}{6}$$

The probability that either A or B occurs is

$$P(A \cup B) = P(A) + P(B) = \frac{2}{6} + \frac{2}{6} = \frac{4}{6}$$

In common terminology, we are saying that when a die is tossed, the probability of a 1, 2, 3, or 4 occurring is $4/6$.

16.4. Random Variable

In Chapter 5 a random variable X was defined nonrigorously as a variable with probabilities associated with it. With our discussion of sets and space, we may now give a more rigorous definition. *A random variable is a real valued function defined on a sample space.*

The first point to note in this definition is that the random variable X is a function. In standard mathematical notation, a function is shown as

$$y = f(x)$$

where x is called the independent variable and y is the dependent variable. y is also called the value of the function $f(x)$. As an example we may have

$$y = x + 1$$

To correspond to this type of expression, we may write the random variable X as

$$x = X(w)$$

where w is the independent variable and x is the individual value that the random variable $X(w)$ takes; or simply, it is the value of the function $X(w)$.

The question that immediately arises is: What is the w? Our definition answers this question and tells us that w is the set of sample points in the sample space. This is what we mean when we say that $X(w)$ is defined on a sample space. We shall illustrate this with a simple example.

Suppose a die is tossed twice. Then we have a 2-dimensional sample space with 36 sample points E_1, E_2, ..., E_{36}, as shown in Fig. 16.5(a). Let $X(w)$ be a random variable (function) that is defined on this sample space. That is, each of the 36 sample points is an independent variable of $X(w)$.

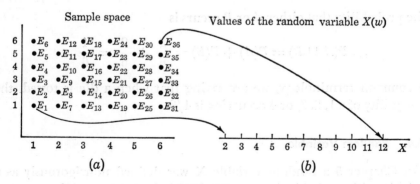

FIG. 16.5.

A function may be thought of as a rule that shows how the independent variable and the value of the function are related. Suppose in our present case that $X(w)$ is a rule, and tells us that the value of the function x is the sum of the numbers of the 1st and 2nd toss of the die. For example, the sample point E_1 is (1, 1), which shows that a 1 has occurred on the 1st and 2nd toss. Then

$$X(E_1) = 1 + 1 = 2$$

For the sample point E_9, we have (2, 3), which shows that a 2 has occurred on the 1st toss and a 3 has occurred on the 2nd toss. Then

$$X(E_9) = 2 + 3 = 5$$

But note that we also have $X = 5$ for the sample points $E_4 = (1, 4)$, $E_9 = (2, 3)$, $E_{14} = (3, 2)$, and $E_{19} = (4, 1)$. That is, when we have

$$X(w) = 5$$

the independent variable w is the subset

$$\{E_4,\ E_9,\ E_{14},\ E_{19}\}$$

and each of these 4 sample points satisfies the function (random variable) $X(w) = x$ for $x = 5$.

We can see that the possible values $X(w)$ can take are 2, 3, . . . , 12 because the smallest number of a die is 1 and the largest number is 6. For $X(w) = 2$, the w is E_1; and for $X(w) = 12$, the w is E_{36}.

Let us now consider an experiment of tossing 1 die. Then the sample space is made up of the 6 sample points:

$$E_1 = 1, \quad E_2 = 2, \quad E_3 = 3, \quad E_4 = 4, \quad E_5 = 5, \quad E_6 = 6$$

Let $X(w)$ be the random variable defined on this sample space, and let the rule (that is, the function) be that the values of the function (that is, the random variable) x are the numbers that occur. This relation is shown in Fig. 16.6(a) and (b), where Fig. 16.6(a) is the sample space and Fig. 16.6(b) shows the value x of the function $X(w)$.

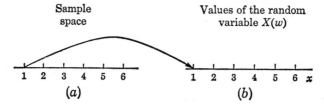

FIG. 16.6.

Obviously, the sample space and the space showing the values of $X(w)$ are the same.

We summarize: A random variable is a real valued function defined on a sample space. The sample points are the independent variables.

Example 1. In Chapter 2 we had a random variable X which denoted the grades of students who took an economics test. The random variable $X(w)$ took on 101 values (0, 1, 2, . . . , 100). In terms of our new definition, the 101 possible outcomes are the sample points in a 1-dimensional sample space. These 101 sample points are the independent variables for the random variable. The rule (that is, the function) tells us that the values x of the random variable $X(w)$ are also the 101 possible grades.

Example 2. Let X be a random variable that shows the number of misprints on a page of a book. The maximum number of letters on a page is 500. Thus, the possible values of X are 0, 1, . . . , 500. These possible values are the sample points in a 1-dimensional sample space and are the independent variables. They are also the values x of the random variable $X(w)$.

In the preceding examples, the space of the independent variables [that is, the sample space of $X(w)$] and the space of the values of $X(w)$ were the same. We shall now give some examples where the spaces are different.

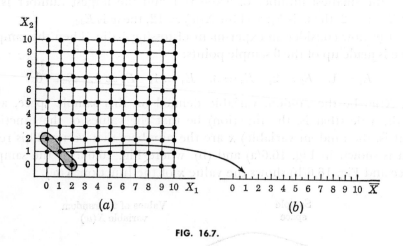

FIG. 16.7.

Example 3. Suppose a group of students have taken an exam where the possible values are 0, 1, 2, . . . , 10. A sample of 2 students is selected, and the sample mean $\bar{X}$ is calculated. Then this $\bar{X}$ is a random variable.

The sample space on which X is defined is the 2-dimensional sample space

generated from the sample of size 2, as shown in Fig. 16.7(a). There are 121
sample points.

The random variable $\bar{X}$ tells us that the values of $\bar{X}$ are the mean of the
grades of the 1st and 2nd students. Thus the possible values of $\bar{X}$ are

$$0, \quad 0.5, \quad 1, \quad 1.5, \quad \cdots, \quad 9.5, \quad 10$$

This is shown in Fig. 16.7(b).

When $\bar{X}$ takes the value of 1 (that is, $\bar{X} = 1$), the sample points that
satisfy this relation are $E_3 = (0, 2)$, $E_{13} = (1, 1)$, $E_{23} = (2, 0)$.

Example 4.   Suppose a sample of 3 students had been selected in Example 3.
Then we should have a 3-dimensional sample space with $11 \times 11 \times 11 =$
1321 sample points. Let the sample mean $\bar{X}$ be the random variable defined
on this sample space. Then the possible values of the random variable $\bar{X}$ (Fig.
16.8) are

$$0, \quad \frac{1}{3}, \quad \frac{2}{3}, \quad 1, \quad \cdots, \quad 10$$

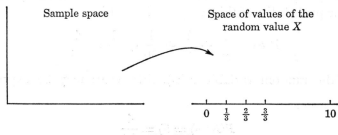

FIG. 16.8.

When $\bar{X} = 1$, the sample points that satisfy this relation are the following
10 points:

$$(0, 0, 3), \quad (0, 3, 0), \quad (3, 0, 0)$$
$$(0, 1, 2), \quad (1, 0, 2), \quad (1, 2, 0)$$
$$(0, 2, 1), \quad (2, 0, 1), \quad (2, 1, 0)$$
$$(1, 1, 1)$$

Now that the concept of a random variable has been defined, let us
explain what is meant by *the probability distribution of the random
variable* X. Figure 16.9 is the sample space generated by 2 tosses of a
die. Assuming a fair die, we shall assign a probability of 1/36 to each
sample point. Let $X(w)$ be a random variable that gives the rule: The
value of $X(w)$ is the sum of the numbers that occur on the 1st and 2nd
toss. Then when

$$X(w) = 5$$

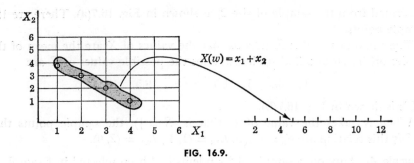

FIG. 16.9.

the sample points that satisfy this relation are the points in the subset E:

$$E = \{(1, 4), \quad (2, 3), \quad (3, 2), \quad (4, 1)\}$$

which is the shaded part in Fig. 16.9(a). This subset is, according to our previous discussion, a compound event.

The sample points in this compound event are mutually exclusive. Hence, the probability of this compound event is

$$P(E) = \frac{1}{36} + \frac{1}{36} + \frac{1}{36} + \frac{1}{36} = \frac{4}{36}$$

Using the random variable $X(w)$, this result may be expressed as follows:

$$P(X(w) = 5) = \frac{4}{36}$$

Or, in general,

(1) $$P(X = x_i) = f(x_i)$$

where in our present case, $i = 1, 2, \ldots, 11$:

$$P(X = x_1 = 2) = f(x_1) = \frac{1}{36}$$

$$P(X = x_2 = 3) = f(x_2) = \frac{2}{36}$$

$$P(X = x_3 = 4) = f(x_3) = \frac{3}{36}$$

$$P(X = x_4 = 5) = f(x_4) = \frac{4}{36}$$

$$P(X = x_5 = 6) = f(x_5) = \frac{5}{36}$$

$$P(X = x_6 = 7) = f(x_6) = \frac{6}{36}$$

$$P(X = x_7 = 8) = f(x_7) = \frac{5}{36}$$

$$P(X = x_8 = 9) = f(x_8) = \frac{4}{36}$$

$$P(X = x_9 = 10) = f(x_9) = \frac{3}{36}$$

$$P(X = x_{10} = 11) = f(x_{10}) = \frac{2}{36}$$

$$P(X = x_{11} = 12) = f(x_{11}) = \frac{1}{36}$$

Obviously,

$$f(x_1) + f(x_2) + \cdots + f(x_{11}) = \Sigma f(x_i) = 1$$

The function given in equation (1) is called the *probability distribution of the random variable* X.

The probability distribution is shown as a histogram in Fig. 16.10.

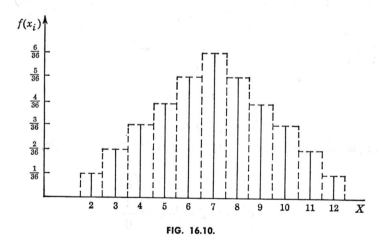

FIG. 16.10.

We see that $f(x_i)$ is the height of the bars and is what we have been calling the frequency density.

We may also say that when we have a discrete random variable, as above, the $f(x_i)$ shows the probability of the event x_i.

Example 5. Suppose a die is tossed once. Then the sample space is 1-dimensional, as in Fig. 16.11(a). If the random variable X is defined as the number

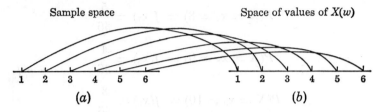

Sample space   Space of values of $X(w)$

(a) (b)

FIG. 16.11.

that occurs, the space of the values of X is the same as the sample space. Then the probability distribution is

$$P(X = x_i) = f(x_i), \qquad i = 1, 2, \cdots, 6$$

and

$$f(x_i) = \frac{1}{6}, \qquad i = 1, 2, \cdots, 6$$

Example 6. If, in Example 5, the random variable is defined as either an odd or an even number, the sample space and space of values of X are as shown in Figs. 16.12(a) and (b). The probability distribution is

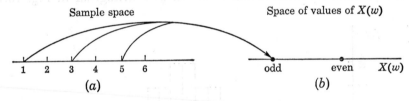

Sample space   Space of values of $X(w)$

odd   even $X(w)$

(a) (b)

FIG. 16.12.

$$P(X = x_i) = f(x_i), \qquad i = 1, 2$$

where $x_1 =$ odd number, $x_2 =$ even number. Assuming a fair die,

$$P(X = x_1) = f(x_1) = \frac{3}{6}$$

$$P(X = x_2) = f(x_2) = \frac{3}{6}$$

and

$$f(x_1) + f(x_2) = 1$$

Using the concept of a probability distribution of X, we may now define the *distribution function* $F(x)$ of X as follows:

(2) $$F(x) = P(X \leqslant x)$$

The $X \leqslant x$ gives us the compound event, which consists of all sample points that satisfy the values of X equal to or less than x.

This may be illustrated with our example of tossing a die twice and defining X to be the sum of the 1st and 2nd toss. Let $x = 4$. Then $X \leqslant x$ becomes

$$X \leqslant 4$$

and the values of X that satisfy this inequality are

$$x_1 = 2, \quad x_2 = 3, \quad x_3 = 4$$

The sample points that satisfy these values of X are

$$E = \{(1, 1), \quad (1, 2), \quad (2, 1), \quad (1, 3), \quad (2, 2), (3, 1)\}$$

Hence, E is the compound event that satisfies (2).

Equation (2) may be written for $x = 4$ as

$$F(x) = P(X \leqslant x) = f(x_1) + f(x_2) + f(x_3)$$

$$= \frac{1}{36} + \frac{2}{36} + \frac{3}{36} = \frac{6}{36}$$

Or, in general,

(3) $$F(x) = P(X \leqslant x) = \Sigma f(x)$$

where the sum is over all x_i such that $x_i \leqslant x$.

In terms of the previous histogram, which is reproduced below as Fig. 16.13, it is the sum of the area of the first three shaded bars.

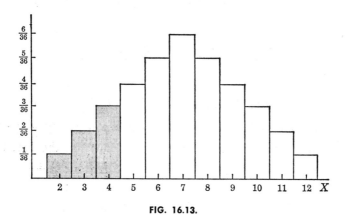

FIG. 16.13.

We may, as in Chapter 2, show this in terms of a less than cumulative frequency curve (Fig. 16.14), which is the usual way of expressing $F(x)$.

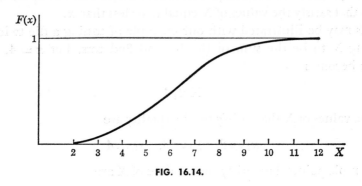

FIG. 16.14.

16.5. Conditional Probability

(i) Theorem on total probability

In Chapter 5 we found that the conditional probability formula is

$$(1) \qquad P(A \mid H) = \frac{P(A \cap H)}{P(H)}$$

where $P(H) > 0$. From this, a rule of multiplication

$$(2) \qquad P(A \cap H) = P(A \mid H) \cdot P(H)$$

was found. This may be generalized by letting H be the event $B \cap C$, which leads to

$$(3) \qquad P(A \cap B \cap C) = P(A \mid B \cap C) \cdot P(B \cap C)$$
$$= P(A \mid B \cap C) \cdot P(B \mid C) \cdot P(C)$$

Since

$$P(C \cap B \cap A) = P(A \cap B \cap C)$$

we may write

$$(4) \qquad P(C \cap B \cap A) = P(C) \cdot P(B \mid C) \cdot P(A \mid B \cap C)$$

Equation (4) was used in Chapter 7 to find the probability of selecting a 4 on the 3rd draw, given that it was not drawn on the first 2 draws from a box with 6 slips of paper numbered 1 to 6. We had

$$P(C \cap B \cap A) = \frac{5}{6} \times \frac{4}{5} \times \frac{1}{4} = \frac{1}{6}$$

where

C: a 4 is not selected on the 1st draw
B: a 4 is not selected on the 2nd draw
A: a 4 is selected on the 3rd draw

Let us now denote H_1 to be the event of selecting a slip with the number 1; H_2 to be the event of selecting a slip with the number 2; and so forth, up to H_6. Then $H_1, H_2, \ldots, H_6$ are mutually exclusive and exhaustive events.

Let A be the event of an odd number occurring. Then

$$A \cap H_1 = \{1, 3, 5\} \cap \{1\} = \{1\}$$
$$A \cap H_2 = \{1, 3, 5\} \cap \{2\} = \{\ \}$$
$$A \cap H_3 = \{1, 3, 5\} \cap \{3\} = \{3\}$$
$$A \cap H_4 = \{1, 3, 5\} \cap \{4\} = \{\ \}$$
$$A \cap H_5 = \{1, 3, 5\} \cap \{5\} = \{5\}$$
$$A \cap H_6 = \{1, 3, 5\} \cap \{6\} = \{\ \}$$

Hence,

$$A = AH_1 \cup AH_2 \cup AH_3 \cup AH_4 \cup AH_5 \cup AH_6$$
$$= \{1, 3, 5\}$$

The probabilities may be shown as

$$P(A) = P\{AH_1 \cup AH_2 \cup \cdots \cup AH_6\}$$

But, since AH_i are mutually exclusive events, we may add the probabilities. Thus we get

(5) $$P(A) = P(AH_1) + P(AH_2) + \cdots + P(AH_6)$$
$$= \Sigma\, P(AH_i)$$

In our present case,

$$P(A) = \frac{1}{6} + 0 + \frac{1}{6} + 0 + \frac{1}{6} + 0 = \frac{3}{6}$$

But, from equation (2), we have $P(AH_i) = P(A \mid H_i) \cdot P(H_i)$. Thus (5) becomes

(6) $$P(A) = \Sigma\, P(A \mid H_i) \cdot P(H_i)$$

In terms of our example, $P(A \mid H_1)$ is the probability of getting an odd number, given that a 1 has been drawn, which is

$$P(A \mid H_1) = 1$$

Similarly, we find

$$P(A \mid H_2) = 0, \qquad P(A \mid H_3) = 1$$
$$P(A \mid H_4) = 0, \qquad P(A \mid H_5) = 1$$
$$P(A \mid H_6) = 0$$
$$P(H_i) = \frac{1}{6}, \qquad i = 1, 2, \cdots, 6$$

Hence, from (6), we find

$$P(A) = 1 \times \frac{1}{6} + 0 + 1 \times \frac{1}{6} + 0 + 1 \times \frac{1}{6} + 0 = \frac{3}{6}$$

Formula (6) is sometimes called the *theorem on total probability.* We may state this formally as follows: Let $H_1 + H_2 + \ldots + H_n = E$, where $H_1, H_2, \ldots, H_n$ are mutually exclusive and exhaustive events, and E is the sample space. Let A be an arbitrary event generated from E. Then

$$P(A) = P(A \mid H_1) \cdot P(H_1) + \cdots + P(A \mid H_n) \cdot P(H_n)$$
$$= \Sigma \, P(A \mid H_i) \, P(H_i)$$

Example 1. Suppose we have two machines, I and II, that produce shoes. Let H_1 be the event of shoes produced by machine I, and H_2 be the event that they are produced by machine II. Let A be the event that a shoe is nondefective. Then

$$A = AH_1 + AH_2$$

since AH_1 and AH_2 are mutually exclusive. Thus

$$P(A) = P(AH_1) + P(AH_2)$$
$$= P(A \mid H_1) \cdot P(H_1) + P(A \mid H_2) \cdot P(H_2)$$

If machine I makes 60 percent of the shoes, then

$$P(H_1) = 60\%, \qquad P(H_2) = 40\%$$

Furthermore, if 10 percent of the shoes made on machine I are defective, and 20 percent of the shoes from machine II are defective, we have

$$P(A \mid H_1) = 90\%, \qquad P(A \mid H_2) = 80\%$$

Thus the probability of producing a nondefective shoe is

$$P(A) = (0.9)(0.6) + (0.8)(0.4) = 0.86$$

Example 2. Let H_1, H_2, H_3, and H_4 be college freshmen, sophomores, juniors, and seniors. Let p_i ($i = 1, 2, 3, 4$) be the probability that a student selected at random belongs to H_i. Obviously

$$p_1 + p_2 + p_3 + p_4 = 1$$

Let A be the event that a student wears glasses. Then the probability of selecting a student who wears glasses is

$$P(A) = P(AH_1) + P(AH_2) + P(AH_3) + P(AH_4)$$
$$= P(A \mid H_1) P(H_1) + \cdots + P(A \mid H_4) P(H_4)$$

where

$$P(H_i) = p_i$$

and $P(A \mid H_i)$ is the probability of selecting a student with glasses, given H_i.

(ii) Bayes' theorem

In Example 1, where two machines were producing shoes, suppose a person is interested in the following question: What is the probability that a nondefective shoe will be manufactured by machine I? Since A was the event of a nondefective shoe and H_1 was the event of the shoe being produced by machine I, our question in symbols is

(7) $$P(H_1 \mid A)$$

That is, given a nondefective shoe, what is the probability that it was manufactured by machine I?

In our previous discussion of conditional probabilities, the problem was the other way around, namely,

(8) $$P(A \mid H_1)$$

That is, given machine I, what is the probability of manufacturing a nondefective shoe?

If H_1 is considered as a hypothesis and A as an event based on this hypothesis, $P(H_1 \mid A)$ is the probability of the hypothesis H_1, given the occurrence of the event A. The $P(A \mid H_1)$ is the probability of the event A, given the occurrence of the hypothesis H_1.

From our conditional probability formula, the probability $P(H_1 \mid A)$ is

(9) $$P(H_1 \mid A) = \frac{P(H_1 \cap A)}{P(A)}$$

But from the theorem on total probabilities, the $P(A)$ becomes

(10) $\quad\quad P(A) = P(AH_1) + P(AH_2)$

$\quad\quad\quad\quad = P(A \mid H_1) P(H_1) + P(A \mid H_2) P(H_2)$

$\quad\quad\quad\quad = \Sigma P(A \mid H_i) P(H_i)$

Substituting this result in (9), we get

(11) $\quad\quad\quad\quad P(H_1 \mid A) = \dfrac{P(H_1 \cap A)}{\Sigma P(A \mid H_i) P(H_i)}$

which may also be written as

(12) $\quad\quad\quad\quad P(H_1 \mid A) = \dfrac{P(A \mid H_1) P(H_1)}{\Sigma P(A \mid H_i) P(H_i)}$

Formula (12) is called *Bayes' theorem.*

Note that $P(H_1)$ is the probability of a shoe being produced by machine I, whereas $P(H_1 \mid A)$ is the probability of a shoe being produced by machine I, given that it is a nondefective shoe. The probability $P(H_1)$ is called *prior probability* and $P(H_1 \mid A)$ is called *posterior probability.* The $P(A \mid H_1)$ is called the *likelihood.*

Example 3. Using Example 1, let us calculate the probability that a nondefective shoe was manufactured by machine I.

TABLE 16.1.

Event	Prior $P(H_i)$	Likelihood $P(A \mid H_i)$	Joint $P(H_i \cap A)$	Posterior $P(H_i \mid A)$
Machine I(H_1)	0.6	0.9	0.54	$0.54/0.86 = 0.63$
Machine II(H_2)	0.4	0.8	0.32	$0.32/0.86 = 0.37$
	1.0		0.86	1.00

$P(H_i)$ gives the prior probabilities of a shoe being produced by machine H_i. $P(A \mid H_i)$ is the probability of producing a nondefective shoe, given event H_i. $P(H_i \cap A)$ is the probability of the joint event H_i and A. For example, $H_1 \cap A$ is the event of machine I producing a nondefective shoe.

Then the posterior probability $P(H_i \mid A)$ is, by Bayes' theorem,

$$P(H_i \mid A) = \frac{P(H_i \cap A)}{P(H_1 \cap A) + P(H_2 \cap A)}$$

As Table 16.1 shows, $P(H_1 \mid A) = 0.63$ and $P(H_2 \mid A) = 0.37$.

The result may be interpreted as follows: Given a nondefective shoe, the probability that it was produced by machine I is 0.63 and the probability that it was produced by machine II is 0.37.

Example 4. Suppose urn I has 10 red balls and urn II has 5 red and 5 green balls. A ball has been selected and found to be red. From which urn was the ball drawn?

TABLE 16.2.

Event	Prior $P(H_i)$	Likelihood $P(A \mid H_i)$	Joint $P(H_i \cap A)$	Posterior $P(H_i \mid A)$
Urn I(H_1)	0.5	1	0.5	$0.5/0.75 = 2/3$
Urn II(H_2)	0.5	0.5	0.25	$0.25/0.75 = 1/3$
	1.0		0.75	1.0

In Table 16.2, $P(H_i)$ shows the prior probabilities of selecting an urn. The $P(A \mid H_i)$ shows the probability (likelihood) of selecting a red ball, given H_i. We know that

$$P(H_i \cap A) = P(H_i) \, P(A \mid H_i)$$

and this gives us the fourth column. The fifth column is obtained from Bayes' formula:

$$P(H_i \mid A) = \frac{P(H_i \cap A)}{\Sigma \, P(H_i \cap A)}$$

$$= \frac{P(A \mid H_i) \, P(H_i)}{\Sigma \, P(A \mid H_i) \, P(H_i)}$$

The last column in Table 16.2 shows that the probability of the ball being drawn from urn I, when it is a red ball, is 2/3, whereas it is 1/3 from urn II. We shall agree to choose the urn (that is, hypothesis H_i) with the largest probability. In our present case, it is H_1; that is, we decide that the ball came from urn I.

Note that in Example 4, we have set $P(H_i) = \frac{1}{2}$. Why did we do this? The assumption behind this is that when there is no reason to doubt one hypothesis more than another, both should be held in equal doubt. This is the principle of insufficient reason.

Hence, when there is no concrete information concerning the probability distribution of the hypothesis $H_1, H_2, \ldots , H_n$, equal probabilities are assigned. That is, the prior probabilities are

$$P(H_i) = \frac{1}{n}, \qquad i = 1, 2, \cdots , n$$

A question that naturally arises is: Is this distribution of prior proba-bilities meaningful? The probabilities have been assigned on the basis of the statistician's subjective confidence or lack of it. Hence, those who support the objective relative frequency theory approach question the meaningfulness of the subjective approach, whereas those who support the subjective approach consider it meaningful.

Example 5. Suppose there are 4 urns that contain red and green balls, as shown in Fig. 16.15. A ball selected from one of the urns turns out to be red. From which urn was it selected?

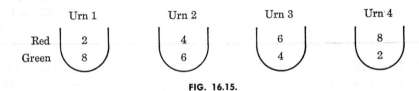

FIG. 16.15.

TABLE 16.3.

Event	Prior $P(H_i)$	Likelihood $P(A \mid H_i)$	Joint $P(A \cap H_i)$	Posterior $P(H_i \mid A)$
Urn 1(H_1)	0.25	0.2	0.05	$0.05/0.50 = 0.10$
Urn 2(H_2)	0.25	0.4	0.10	$0.10/0.50 = 0.20$
Urn 3(H_3)	0.25	0.6	0.15	$0.15/0.50 = 0.30$
Urn 4(H_4)	0.25	0.8	0.20	$0.20/0.50 = 0.40$
	1.00		0.50	1.00

$P(H_i)$ show the prior probabilities obtained by using the principle of in-sufficient reason. The largest posterior probability is

$$P(H_4 \mid A) = \frac{P(H_4 \cap A)}{\Sigma P(H_i \cap A)} = 0.40$$

Hence we choose urn 4 as the urn from which the red ball was selected.

Bayes' theorem gives us a criterion for choosing a hypothesis H_i. The hypothesis with the largest posterior probability is chosen. An alterna-tive method of choosing hypotheses, called the *maximum likelihood method,* was given in Chapter 10.

(iii) Application of Bayes' theorem*

Let us summarize Bayes' theorem as follows: We are given a set of hypotheses, $H_1, H_2, \ldots, H_n$, which are mutually exclusive and ex-

---

* For further discussion of Bayesian statistics, see R. Schlaifer, *Introduction to Statistics for Business Decisions,* New York: McGraw-Hill Book Company, Inc., 1961.

haustive. It is assumed that the probabilities $P(H_i)$ are known, and these are called prior probabilities. Let A be an event and assume that $P(A \mid H_i)$ is known. Then

$$P(H_i \mid A) = \frac{P(H_i \cap A)}{P(A)}$$

$$= \frac{P(A \mid H_i)\, P(H_i)}{\Sigma\, P(A \mid H_i)\, P(H_i)}$$

As pointed out previously, the assumption that the prior probabilities $P(H_i)$ are known has been questioned by the objectivists.

In many cases where we have a probability distribution for the H_i, we may wish to revise it in view of the additional information that has been obtained from an event A (which may, for example, be a sample). For instance, one may have a probability distribution concerning the effectiveness of a birth control pill that will be reformulated after experimentation. Or, one may have a probability distribution concerning the number of defects in a certain product which, after checking, needs to be redesigned. Or, one may have a distribution of demand for a product from various sources which, after actual receipt of orders, needs to be revised.

Let us investigate in a little more detail how experimental evidence can be used to revise the original (prior) probability distribution. We shall use Example 4 again. Table 16.2 is reproduced as Table 16.4 for convenience.

TABLE 16.4.

Event	Prior $P(H_i)$	Likelihood $P(A \mid H_i)$	Joint $P(H_i \cap A)$	Posterior $P(H_i \mid A)$
Urn I(H_1)	0.5	1	0.5	$0.5/0.75 = 2/3$
Urn II(H_2)	0.5	0.5	0.25	$0.25/0.75 = 1/3$
	1.0		0.75	1.0

Suppose a second ball is drawn and is found to be red. Using this information, we wish to revise the probabilities associated with H_1. For this, we use the posterior probabilities as the prior probabilities, as shown in Table 16.5.

Obviously, the probability associated with H_1 becomes larger.

Instead of calculating posterior probabilities for each draw, we may

TABLE 16.5.

Event	Prior $P(H_i)$	Likelihood $P(A \mid H_i)$	Joint $P(H_i \cap A)$	Posterior $P(H_i \mid A)$
Urn I(H_1)	2/3	1	2/3	$2/3 \div 5/6 = 4/5$
Urn II(H_2)	1/3	0.5	1/6	$1/6 \div 5/6 = 1/5$
	1.0		5/6	1

consider the 2 draws of a red ball as a random sample of size 2. Then the probabilities $P(A \mid H_2)$ will be

$$P(A \mid H_1) = 1 \times 1 = 1$$

$$P(A \mid H_2) = 0.5 \times 0.5 = 0.25$$

Using these results, Table 16.5 becomes Table 16.6.

TABLE 16.6.

Event	Prior $P(H_i)$	Likelihood $P(A \mid H_i)$	Joint $P(H_i \cap A)$	Posterior $P(H_i \mid A)$
Urn I(H_1)	0.5	1	0.5	$0.5/0.625 = 4/5$
Urn II(H_2)	0.5	0.25	0.125	$0.125/0.625 = 1/5$
	1.0		0.625	1

We see that we obtain the same results. But, if we had taken a random sample of size 3 and all 3 balls had been red, we should have had

$$P(A \mid H_1) = 1 \times 1 \times 1 = 1$$

$$P(A \mid H_2) = 0.5 \times 0.5 \times 0.5 = 0.125$$

and using these probabilities, we may compute the new posterior probabilities.

The point to note is how the sample information may be used in the form of $P(A \mid H_i)$. We shall give several more examples.

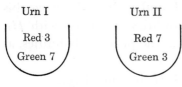

FIG. 16.16.

Example 6.   Suppose we have 2 urns with red and green balls, as shown in Fig. 16.16. An urn is presented to us and a ball is drawn and found to be red. From which urn did it come?

Our analysis is presented in Table 16.7.

TABLE 16.7.

Event	Prior $P(H_i)$	Likelihood $P(A \mid H_i)$	Joint $P(H_i \cap A)$	Posterior $P(H_i \mid A)$
Urn I(H_1)	0.5	0.3	0.15	$0.15/0.50 = 3/10$
Urn II(H_2)	0.5	0.7	0.35	$0.35/0.50 = 7/10$
	1.0		0.50	1

$P(H_i)$ gives the prior probabilities and was based on the principle of insufficient reason. A is the event of selecting a red ball. The posterior probabilities are $3/10$ and $7/10$, and hence we shall conclude that the red ball came from urn II.

Let us now draw a random sample of 2 balls from an urn and find them to be red and green. From which urn did this sample come?

TABLE 16.8.

Event	Prior $P(H_i)$	Likelihood $P(A \mid H_i)$	Joint $P(H_i \cap A)$	Posterior $P(H_i \mid A)$
Urn I(H_1)	0.5	p_1	$0.5p_1$	$p_1/(p_1 + p_2) = 0.5$
Urn II(H_2)	0.5	p_2	$0.5p_2$	$p_2/(p_1 + p_2) = 0.5$
	1.0		$0.5(p_1 + p_2)$	1

The prior probabilities $P(H_i)$ are 0.5. The event A is now a sample of red and green. Hence,

$$P(A \mid H_1) = \binom{2}{1}(0.3)(0.7) = p_1$$

$$P(A \mid H_2) = \binom{2}{1}(0.7)(0.3) = p_2$$

The posterior probabilities we seek are

$$P(H_1 \mid A) = \frac{(0.5)\binom{2}{1}(0.3)(0.7)}{(0.5)\binom{2}{1}(0.3)(0.7) + (0.5)\binom{2}{1}(0.7)(0.3)} = 0.5$$

$$P(H_2 \mid A) = 0.5$$

That is, the posterior probability that the sample came from urn I is 0.5.

Let us next select a random sample of size 3 which has 2 red balls and 1 green ball and call this event A. What is the probability that this sample came from urn I? The probabilities $P(A \mid H_i)$ of the sample become

$$P(A \mid H_1) = \binom{3}{2} (0.3)^2 (1 - 0.3)$$

$$P(A \mid H_2) = \binom{3}{2} (0.7)^2 (1 - 0.7)$$

Hence, the posterior probability we seek is

$$P(H_1 \mid A) = \frac{(0.5) \binom{3}{2} (0.3)^2 (1 - 0.3)}{(0.5) \binom{3}{2} (0.3)^2 (1 - 0.3) + (0.5) \binom{3}{2} (0.7)^2 (1 - 0.7)}$$

$$= 0.3$$

$$P(H_2 \mid A) = 0.7$$

Thus, the probability of selecting a sample of size 3 with 2 red balls and 1 green ball from urn I is 0.3.

Example 7. Using the data of Example 3, let us ask the following question: Given a sample size of 3 shoes, where 2 are nondefective and 1 is defective, what is the probability that these shoes were produced by machine I?

The event A is the selection of a sample of 2 nondefective shoes and 1 defective shoe. The $P(A \mid H_1)$ and $P(A \mid H_2)$ are

$$P(A \mid H_1) = \binom{3}{2} (0.9)^2 (1 - 0.9) = p_1$$

$$P(A \mid H_2) = \binom{3}{2} (0.8)^2 (1 - 0.8) = p_2$$

Hence, our calculation of posterior probabilities becomes as shown in Table 16.9.

TABLE 16.9.

Event	Prior $P(H_i)$	Likelihood $P(A \mid H_i)$	Joint $P(A \cap H_i)$	Posterior $P(H_i \mid A)$
Machine I(H_1)	0.6	p_1	$0.6p_1$	$0.6p_1(0.6p_1 + 0.4p_2) = 0.49$
Machine II(H_2)	0.4	p_2	$0.4p_2$	$0.4p_2(0.6p_1 + 0.4p_2) = 0.51$
	1.0		$(.6p_1 + .4p_2)$	1.00

We find

$$p'_1 = \frac{P(A \cap H_1)}{P(A \cap H_1) + P(A \cap H_2)}$$

$$= \frac{(0.6)\binom{3}{2}(0.9)^2\,(0.1)}{(0.6)\binom{3}{2}(0.9)^2\,(0.1)\ +\ (0.4)\binom{3}{2}(0.8)^2\,(0.2)}$$

$$= 0.49$$

$$p_2' = 0.51$$

The posterior probabilities we seek are

$$P(H_1 \mid A) = 0.49, \quad P(H_2 \mid A) = 0.51$$

Examples 6 and 7 show that as the sample size becomes larger, the present method of calculating the probabilities $P(A \mid H_i)$ of the samples becomes very difficult. A question that naturally arises is: Is there any way of simplifying this process of calculating the probabilities of selecting a certain sample?

We have seen in Chapter 7 that simplification is possible by using the central limit theorem. That is, we used the sample mean to represent the sample and found the sampling distribution of sample mean to be approximately normal. This enabled us to calculate the probabilities of selecting a sample. Let us consider this problem in the next section.

The main point to be learned in this section is the meaning and use of Bayes' theorem to compute posterior probabilities.

(iv)   Calculation of the likelihood of a sample

In this section we shall first show how the likelihood of a sample is calculated and then calculate the posterior probabilities of a random variable. We shall explain the process with an illustration.

Suppose the demand for shirts is estimated as shown in the accompanying table. These relative frequencies estimate the prior proba-

Shirt Size	Relative Frequency
13	0.20
14	0.50
15	0.30
	1.00

bilities $P(H_i)$, where H_i indicate the shirt sizes.

Suppose a sample of 16 men is selected, the sample mean is size 13, and the standard deviation is estimated as $\sigma = 2$. How probable is it that we shall select such a sample, given a population with mean size 14?

A sample size of 16 is rather small, but for purposes of illustration let us assume it to be large enough to assume that the sampling distribution of the sample mean will be approximately normal. The situation is shown graphically in Figs. 16.17(a) and (b).

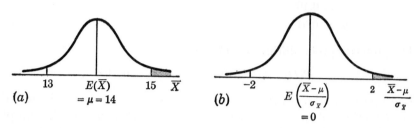

FIG. 16.17.

What we wish to do is to calculate the probability of a sample mean of size 13, given $E(\bar{X}) = 14$ and $\sigma = 2$. For this, we first transform the sampling distribution of $\bar{X}$ into a unit distribution so that we can use the normal area and ordinate tables. Let us set

$$z = \frac{\bar{X} - \mu}{\sigma_{\bar{x}}}$$

Then Fig. 16.17(b) shows the distribution of z, where the mean is zero and $\sigma = 1$. For our present problem,

$$z = \frac{\bar{X} - \mu}{\sigma_{\bar{x}}} = \frac{13 - 14}{\dfrac{2}{\sqrt{16}}} = -2$$

That is, 13 is 2 standard deviations away from $E(\bar{X}) = 14$.

According to the normal ordinate table, the height of the ordinate at $z = 2$ is 0.0540.

Let $d\bar{x}$ be the width of the bar at $z = 2$ in the sampling distribution of $\bar{X}$ [Fig. 16.17(a)]. Then, in the unit distribution [Fig. 16.17(b)], this is reduced to $d\bar{x}/\sigma_{\bar{x}} = d\bar{x}/0.5$.

Hence, the *area* of the bar at $z = 2$ is

$$0.0540 \times \frac{d\bar{x}}{0.5}$$

Since the area shows the probabilities, this is the likelihood of a sample mean $\bar{X} = 13$, given a population mean of $\mu = 14$.

In similar manner we may compute the likelihood for $\mu = 13$ and $\mu = 15$. The calculations are shown in Table 16.10.

TABLE 16.10.

Shirt	$z = (\bar{X} - \mu)/\sigma_{\bar{x}}$	Height	Width	Area
13	0	0.3989	$d\bar{x}/0.5$	$0.3989 d\bar{x}/0.5$
14	-2	0.0540	$d\bar{x}/0.5$	$0.0540 d\bar{x}/0.5$
15	-4	0.000	$d\bar{x}/0.5$	$0.000\ d\bar{x}/0.5$

Using these likelihoods, we calculate the posterior probabilities, as shown in Table 16.11.

TABLE 16.11.

Event	Prior $P(H_i)$	Likelihood $P(A \mid H_i)$	Joint $P(A \cap H_i)$	Posterior $P(H_i \mid A)$
13	0.2	$0.3989 d\bar{x}/0.5$	$0.07978 d\bar{x}/0.5$	0.747
14	0.5	$0.0540 d\bar{x}/0.5$	$0.02700 d\bar{x}/0.5$	0.253
15	0.3	$0.000\ d\bar{x}/0.5$	$0.00000 d\bar{x}/0.5$	0.000
	1.0		$0.10678 d\bar{x}/0.5$	1.000

From Table 16.11 we find that the probability of there being a demand for size 13 is about 0.747; for size 14, it is about 0.253; and for size 15, it is about 0.000.

Note how the widths of the interval $d\bar{x}/0.5$ cancel out.

The point to note is how the likelihood of a sample is calculated by finding the probability of its sample mean from the sampling distribution of the sample mean; and how the unit normal distribution and the ordinate table have been used.

THE *t* DISTRIBUTION

17

In Chapter 8, the tests concerning means were based on large samples with known standard deviation. But in many practical cases, the sample is small and the standard deviation is not known. In such cases, it becomes necessary to estimate the standard deviation, usually from sample data, and perform a test.

The central limit theorem told us that the distribution of the sample mean $\bar{x}$ was approximately normal with mean μ (population mean) and variance σ^2/n (σ^2 is the population variance; n is the sample size). We also saw that the statistic z,

$$z = \frac{\bar{x} - \mu}{\dfrac{\sigma}{\sqrt{n}}}$$

had a normal distribution with mean 0 and variance 1. The probabilities of z were obtained from the normal area table.

But, if we use an estimate of σ^2, and n is small ($n < 50$), then z will not be normal. The question is: What is the distribution under such circumstances?

The statistician W. S. Gosset,* who wrote under the pseudonym "Student," derived an exact distribution in 1908 for the statistic t:

$$t = \frac{\bar{x} - \mu}{\dfrac{\hat{\sigma}}{\sqrt{n}}}$$

---

* W. S. Gosset, "The Probable Error of a Mean," *Biometrika*, 1908.

where $\bar{x}$ is the sample mean of a sample $x_1, x_2, \ldots, x_n$ taken from a normal distribution with μ and σ^2 (unknown). The $\hat{\sigma}$ is an estimate of σ. This distribution is called Student's distribution, or the t distribution. (The latter term is more commonly used.)

Our problem in this chapter is to study the applications of this t distribution.

17.1. Expected Value of Sample Variance

Consider a sample $x_1, x_2, \ldots, x_n$ of size n. The sample variance is defined as

(1)
$$s^2 = \frac{1}{n} \Sigma (x_i - \bar{x})^2$$

It can be shown that the expected value of s^2 is

(2)
$$E(s^2) = \frac{n-1}{n} \sigma^2 = \sigma^2 - \frac{\sigma^2}{n}$$

This shows that when all possible samples of size n have been taken from the population, the average of all sample variances will be equal to the population variance σ^2 plus a bias $(-\sigma^2/n)$. That is, s^2 is a biased estimator of σ^2.

As can be seen, since we assume that σ^2 is finite, if we let the sample size $n \to \infty$, then the bias $(-\sigma^2/n)$ approaches zero. Thus, for large samples, we may ignore this bias, but for small samples it is large. For example, if $n = 3$, then

$$E(s^2) = \frac{3-1}{3} \sigma^2 = \frac{2}{3} \sigma^2$$

That is, s^2 underestimates σ^2 by $1/3 = 33$ percent.

We can easily adjust s^2 so that it will be an unbiased estimator of σ^2. It will be

$$E\left(\frac{n}{n-1} s^2\right) = \left(\frac{n}{n-1}\right)\left(\frac{n-1}{n} \sigma^2\right) = \sigma^2$$

Thus $ns^2/(n-1)$ is an unbiased estimator of σ^2. Let us denote this by

(3)
$$\hat{\sigma}^2 = \frac{n}{n-1} s^2$$

By substituting equation (1) into (3), we find

(4)
$$\hat{\sigma}^2 = \frac{1}{n-1} \Sigma (x - \bar{x})^2$$

or

(5)
$$\hat{\sigma} = \sqrt{\frac{\Sigma (x - \bar{x})^2}{n - 1}}$$

Thus we have three expressions for the variances: σ^2 is the population variance; s^2 is the sample variance; and $\hat{\sigma}^2$ is the unbiased estimator of the population variance. In our subsequent discussion, we shall use $\hat{\sigma}$ as the estimator of σ. In some texts the letter s is used to indicate $\hat{\sigma}$. The student should make a mental note of these distinctions and adapt himself to the variations in notation of the standard deviation in different texts.

Obviously, when n is large, there will be very little difference between n and $n - 1$, and in such cases we may use n as an approximation. Then s and $\hat{\sigma}$ will be equal.

17.2. Pooled Variance

When we have several independent samples from the *same* population, it is natural that we wish to utilize all the information to estimate the population variance. We shall present the results without derivations. The simplest case is when there are two independent samples. Then an unbiased estimator of the population variance is

(1)
$$\hat{\sigma}^2 = \frac{n_1 s_1^2 + n_2 s_2^2}{n_1 + n_2 - 2}$$

where n_1 and n_2 are the sample sizes, and s_1^2 and s_2^2 are the variances of the samples. The expression $n_1 + n_2 - 2$ is called the degrees of freedom. (This is explained in the next section.) Note that

$$n_1 s_1^2 = n_1 \cdot \frac{\sum\limits^{n_1} (x_i - \bar{x})^2}{n_1} = \sum\limits^{n_1} (x_i - \bar{x})^2$$

$$n_2 s_2^2 = n_2 \cdot \frac{\sum\limits^{n_2} (x_i - \bar{x})^2}{n_2} = \sum\limits^{n_2} (x_i - \bar{x})^2$$

Thus $n_1 s_1^2 + n_2 s_2^2$ gives us the total sum of squared deviations of the two samples, and equation (1) can be considered as an operation of combining both samples into one large sample and estimating the variance.

This idea may be extended to k samples. When there are k independent samples from the same population, an unbiased estimator of σ^2 is

(2)
$$\hat{\sigma}^2 = \frac{Q}{U - k}$$

where

$$Q = n_1 s_1{}^2 + n_2 s_2{}^2 + \cdots + n_k k_k{}^2$$
$$U = n_1 + n_2 + \cdots + n_k$$

where $U - k$ is the degrees of freedom.

17.3.   Degrees of Freedom

Let us discuss this idea heuristically. Suppose we have two numbers, x_1 and x_2, where

$$\bar{x} = \frac{1}{2}(x_1 + x_2) = 5$$

Then, for example, we may have

$$x_1 + x_2 = 3 + 7 = 10$$
$$x_1 + x_2 = 4 + 6 = 10$$

and so forth. We can see that once the first number x_1 has been selected, the second number x_2 is automatically determined because the average has been set at 5. In terms of Fig. 17.1, we are not free to select any point in the 2-dimensional plane. Once the average $\bar{x} = 5$ (or total 10) has been selected, the points we can select are confined to a 1-dimensional line $x_1 + x_2 = 10$, as seen in Fig. 17.1.

Let us try it with three numbers:

$$x_1 + x_2 + x_3 = 15$$

Then the average is $\bar{x} = 5$. Graphically (Fig. 17.2) we have a 3-dimen-

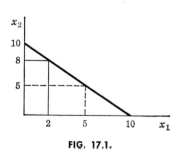

FIG. 17.1.

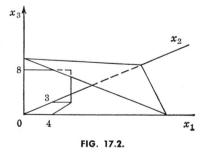

FIG. 17.2.

sional space, but we can select points only on the 2-dimensional plane, as the graph shows.

In similar fashion, if we have k numbers, $x_1, x_2, \ldots, x_k$ and are given the condition that the average is to be $\bar{x} = c$, where c is a constant, then we have a hyperplane of $k - 1$ dimensions in a k dimensional space. Once $k - 1$ numbers have been freely selected, the kth number is automatically determined. We say that there are $k - 1$ degrees of freedom.

Next let us consider the following situation:

$$(x_1 - \bar{x})^2 + (x_2 - \bar{x})^2 = 18$$

Assume $\bar{x} = 7$. Now let us select $x_1 = 4$. Then x_2 is automatically determined. In our present case,

$$(4 - 7)^2 + (x_2 - 7)^2 = 18$$
$$x_2 - 7 = \pm 3$$
$$x_2 = 10 \quad \text{or } x_2 = 4$$

The equation holds when $x_2 = 10$.

Likewise, if we have

$$(x_1 - \bar{x})^2 + (x_2 - \bar{x})^2 + \cdots + (x_k - \bar{x})^2 = c$$

where c is a constant and $\bar{x}$ is given, then $k - 1$ elements can be chosen freely, but the last element will be automatically determined. There are $k - 1$ degrees of freedom.

In general, we may say: The *number* of elements that can be chosen freely is called the degrees of freedom; or, the *number* of variables that can vary freely; or, the *number* of independent variables.

Thus, when we have the pooled variance

$$\hat{\sigma}^2 = \frac{n_1 s_1^2 + n_2 s_2^2}{n_1 + n_2 - 2}$$

the degrees of freedom are $n_1 + n_2 - 2$. This is because s_1^2 has n_1 variables, but a given mean, and thus $n_1 - 1$ free variables; likewise for s_2^2. Thus, the number of free variables is $(n_1 - 1) + (n_2 - 1)$. This reasoning extends to the general case where we had $U - k$ degrees of freedom.

As we shall see later, when a sum of squares is divided by its degrees of freedom, it is called the *mean square*. Thus the variance

$$\hat{\sigma}^2 = \frac{\Sigma (x - \bar{x})^2}{n - 1}$$

is a mean square. Conversely, mean squares can be thought of as variances.

Degrees of freedom will be pointed out and explained as the occasion arises.

17.4.   The *t* Distribution

(i)   Definition

Consider a sample $x_1, x_2, \ldots, x_n$ taken from a normal distribution with mean μ and variance σ^2. Let

(1)
$$y = \frac{x - \mu}{\sigma}$$

Then we know that y is normal with mean 0 and variance 1.

Next let us set

(2)
$$u = \sum_{i=1}^{n} \left(\frac{x_i - \bar{x}}{\sigma} \right)^2$$

As we shall explain in Chapter 20, this u has a Chi-square (χ^2) distribution. From our discussion in Section 17.3, we note that it has $n - 1$ degrees of freedom.

Using this y and u, we construct a statistic t as follows:

(3)
$$t = \frac{y}{\sqrt{\dfrac{u}{n-1}}}$$

W. S. Gossett showed that this t had an exact distribution, which was dependent on t and $k = n - 1$. It is called Student's distribution or the t distribution.

Let us now rewrite t as

(4)
$$t = \frac{\dfrac{x - \mu}{\sigma}}{\sqrt{\dfrac{1}{n-1} \sum \left(\dfrac{x - \bar{x}}{\sigma} \right)^2}} = \frac{x - \mu}{\sqrt{\dfrac{\sum (x - \bar{x})^2}{n-1}}}$$

Note that the denominator is the square root of the unbiased estimator for the variance. That is,

$$\hat{\sigma}^2 = \frac{\sum (x - \bar{x})^2}{n-1}$$

Of the _n_-squared deviations in the numerator of $\hat{\sigma}^2$, we have seen that $n-1$ will be independent, and hence $\hat{\sigma}^2$ has $k=n-1$ degrees of freedom. But, since in the _t_ distribution the _t_ is also dependent on $k=n-1$, we shall say that _t_ has $k=n-1$ degrees of freedom.

Let us now formally define the _t_ distribution as follows: Let _y_ be normally distributed with $E(y)=0$, $\mathrm{Var}(y)=1$. Let _u_ have a χ^2 distribution with _k_ degrees of freedom. If _y_ and _u_ are independently distributed, then the statistic

(5)
$$t = \frac{y}{\sqrt{\dfrac{u}{k}}}$$

has a _t_ distribution with _k_ degrees of freedom.

The implication of this theorem is: If we can find a statistic _y_ that is normal (0, 1) and a _u_ that is χ^2 with the appropriate degrees of freedom (say, _k_), then by forming the ratio shown by equation (5), we can find a variety of different ways of constructing the _t_ distribution. In the next several sections we shall show how the statistic _y_ can be constructed by sample means and also by differences of sample means. We shall also show how this provides us with various tests based on the _t_ distribution.

(ii)   Application to sample mean

Let us now apply this distribution to the sample mean. Let x_1, x_2, . . . , x_n be a sample from a normal distribution with mean μ and variance σ^2. Construct the statistic _y_:

$$y = \frac{\bar{x} - \mu}{\dfrac{\sigma}{\sqrt{n}}}$$

Then _y_ is normal with mean zero and unit variance. By letting _u_ be the same as in Section (i), we have

$$t = \frac{y}{\sqrt{\dfrac{u}{k}}} = \frac{\dfrac{\bar{x}-\mu}{\dfrac{\sigma}{\sqrt{n}}}}{\sqrt{\dfrac{1}{n-1}\Sigma\left(\dfrac{x-\bar{x}}{\sigma}\right)^2}} = \frac{\bar{x}-\mu}{\sqrt{\dfrac{\Sigma(x-\bar{x})^2}{n(n-1)}}}$$

From the definition we stated in Section (i), we know that this _t_ has a _t_ distribution with $k=n-1$ degrees of freedom.

To show the effect of $n \longrightarrow \infty$, let us rewrite this t as

$$t = \frac{\bar{x} - \mu}{\dfrac{\hat{\sigma}}{\sqrt{n}}}$$

$$\hat{\sigma}^2 = \frac{\Sigma (x - \bar{x})^2}{n - 1}$$

We know that as $n \longrightarrow \infty$, the estimator $\hat{\sigma} \longrightarrow \sigma$. Thus, as the sample size becomes larger, the statistic t will approach z, the standardized normal variate:

$$z = \frac{\bar{x} - \mu}{\dfrac{\sigma}{\sqrt{n}}}$$

That is, the t distribution will approach a normal distribution.

The characteristics of the t distribution may be summarized as follows.

1. It is an exact distribution.
2. $-\infty < t < \infty$
3. The distribution is unimodal and symmetric about 0.
4. It is flatter than the normal distribution (Fig. 17.3).

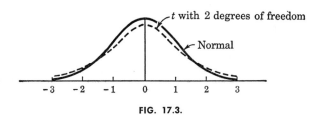

FIG. 17.3.

This means that the area near the tail is larger for the t distribution than for the normal distribution.

5. As the sample size n becomes larger, it approaches the normal distribution.
6. We need to know the degrees of freedom, $k = n - 1$, to obtain probabilities from the t table.

Let us next illustrate the use of the t table by a simple illustration. The t table is in the Appendix (Table 3).*

---

* Also in Fisher and Yates, *Statistical Tables,* 5th ed., New York: Hafner Publishing Company, 1957.

(iii)   *Use of the t table*

Consider a normally distributed population of monthly expenditures for maintenance of cars with mean μ dollars and variance σ^2. A sample of size $n = 16$ is taken, and we find $\bar{x} = \$34$. We wish to test the null hypothesis that

$$\text{Null hypothesis, } H_1: \qquad \mu = \$30$$
$$\text{Alternative hypothesis, } H_2: \qquad \mu > \$30$$

Let us set the risk of the type I error as $\alpha = 5$ percent. We have a one-tailed test and are considering only the upper tail of the distribution. But before we solve this problem, let us show how the t table is to be interpreted.

When we are given the degrees of freedom $k = n - 1 = 16 - 1 = 15$, we can find from the t table the values of t that correspond to various probabilities. The table is usually given in a two-tail form. For example, for 5 and 10 percent and $k = 15$ degrees of freedom, we have (from the table)

$$P(-2.131 < t < 2.131 \mid k = 15) = 0.95$$
$$P(-1.753 < t < 1.753 \mid k = 15) = 0.90$$

This is shown graphically in Figs. 17.4(a) and (b). The interpretation is

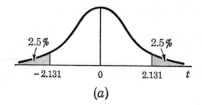 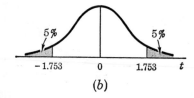

| (a) | (b) |

FIG. 17.4.

If $k = 15$ degrees of freedom, there are 95 chances in 100 that t will be between the two values -2.131 and 2.131. Or we may say that there are 5 chances in 100 that t will fall outside the two values -2.131 and 2.131.

If we are considering only the upper tail end, then there are $\alpha/2 = 2.5$ chances in 100 that t will exceed 2.131. This is shown as

$$P(t > 2.131 \mid k = 15) = 0.025$$

If we are considering the lower tail end, it is shown as

$$P(t < -2.131 \mid k = 15) = 0.025$$

Similarly, there are 10 chances in 100 of t falling outside -1.753 and 1.753 [Fig. 17.4(b)]. For the upper tail end, there are 5 chances in 100 of t exceeding 1.753, which is shown as

$$P(t > 1.753 \mid k = 15) = 0.05$$

In our present example, we are interested in this last case.

Let us assume that

$$\hat{\sigma}_{\bar{x}} = \sqrt{\frac{\Sigma (x - \bar{x})^2}{n(n-1)}} = \frac{\hat{\sigma}}{\sqrt{n}} = \$2$$

Then the t statistic becomes

$$t = \frac{\bar{x} - \mu}{\hat{\sigma}_{\bar{x}}} = \frac{34 - 30}{2} = 2$$

If we look at Fig. 17.5, we can see that there are *less* than 5 chances in

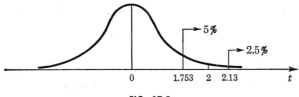

FIG. 17.5.

100 of t's being greater than 2, but *more* than 2.5 chances in 100 of it being greater than 2.

Thus, when we set the risk of the type I error at 5 percent, we conclude that the difference between $\bar{x} = \$34$ and $\mu = \$30$ is significant, and therefore we reject the null hypothesis.

If we select 2.5 percent as the risk of the type I error, then since the probability of $t \geq 2$ is more than 2.5 percent, we consider the difference to be not significant, and therefore we accept the null hypothesis.

17.5. Examples

Example 1. Two-tail test

A manufacturer packs sugar into small paper bags. Each bag is to hold 10 oz. When the production process is under control, it is found that each bag will contain, on the average, 10 oz. Periodically a sample of 9 bags is taken to check the process. If the sample mean $\bar{x}$ deviates significantly from 10 oz., the process will be considered not in control.

A sample of 9 bags is taken, and the sample mean is found to be $\bar{x} = 10.3$ oz. The $\hat{\sigma} = 0.45$ oz. Thus the test is

Null hypothesis, H_1: $\mu = 10.0$ oz.
Alternative hypothesis, H_2: $\mu \neq 10.0$ oz.

and we have a two-tail test. The t statistic is

$$t = \frac{\bar{x} - \mu}{\dfrac{\hat{\sigma}}{\sqrt{n}}} = \frac{10.3 - 10.0}{\dfrac{0.45}{\sqrt{9}}} = 2$$

This t has a t distribution with $k = 9 - 1 = 8$ degrees of freedom. Furthermore, assume the risk of the type I error will be less than 10 percent. That is, the probability of stopping the process when in fact $\mu = 10.0$ oz. will be less than 0.10.

Since $k = 8$ degrees of freedom, the t table in the Appendix gives us

$$P(-1.86 < t < 1.86 | k = 8) = 0.90$$

This is shown in Fig. 17.6. There are 10 chances in 100 of t falling outside

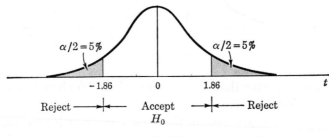

FIG. 17.6.

−1.86 and 1.86 and thus of rejecting the null hypothesis and stopping the process. Since we have found $t = 2$, we reject the null hypothesis.

Example 2. One-tail test

A new training program for secretaries claims to increase their typing speed by 10 words per minute. A random sample of 16 secretaries shows that the average increase has been 5 words per minute. The estimated standard deviation ($\hat{\sigma}$) is 8 words per minute. Does the sample finding support the claim?

The hypotheses are set up as

Null hypothesis, H_1: $\mu = 10$
Alternative hypothesis, H_2: $\mu < 10$

Let us construct the t statistic:

$$t = \frac{\bar{x} - \mu}{\frac{\hat{\sigma}}{\sqrt{n}}} = \frac{5 - 10}{\frac{8}{\sqrt{16}}} = -2.5$$

This t has a t distribution with $k = 16 - 1 = 15$ degrees of freedom. Since we are considering the lower tail of the distribution, we find from the t table, for $\alpha = 5$ percent (Fig. 17.7),

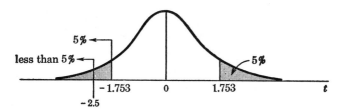

FIG. 17.7.

(1) $$P(-1.75 < t < 1.75 | k = 15) = 0.90$$

or

(2) $$P(t < -1.75 | k = 15) = 0.05$$

The $t = -2.5$ means that the probability of selecting a sample with a mean of $\bar{x} = 5$ words per minute or less from a population with a mean of 10 words per minute will be less than 5 chances in 100. Since we have set $\alpha = 5$ percent, we reject the null hypothesis and accept the alternative. That is, the data do not support the claim that the average typing speed will increase by 10 words per minute.

Example 3. Let us consider Example 2 again, but with the change that the training program claims that the typing speed will increase by 7 words per minute. Then the test is

$$\text{Null hypothesis, } H_1: \quad \mu = 7$$
$$\text{Alternative hypothesis, } H_2: \quad \mu < 7$$

The t becomes:

$$t = \frac{\bar{x} - \mu}{\frac{\hat{\sigma}}{\sqrt{n}}} = \frac{5 - 7}{2} = -1$$

We know from equation (1) and Fig. 17.7 that the probability of selecting a sample with $\bar{x} = 5$ words per minute or less from a population with a mean of $\mu = 7$ will be more than 5 chances in 100. In fact, from the _t_ table we find

$$P(-1.179 < t < 1.179 | k = 24) = 0.75$$

The $t = -1$ means that there are more than 12.5 chances in 100 of selecting a sample with $\bar{x} = 5$ or less from a population with $\mu = 7$.

Thus, if we set $\alpha = 5$ percent, we accept the null hypothesis that $\mu = 7$. That is, the data support the claim that the typing speed increases by 7 words per minute.

Example 4. It is claimed that students entering college have an average IQ higher than 100. A random sample of size 16 is taken and the sample mean is found to be $\bar{x} = 106$. The estimated standard deviation $(\hat{\sigma})$ is 10 points. Do the data support the claim? The test is as follows:

Null hypothesis, H_1: $\mu = 100$
Alternative hypothesis, H_2: $\mu > 100$

The _t_ statistic is

$$t = \frac{\bar{x} - \mu}{\dfrac{\hat{\sigma}}{\sqrt{n}}} = \frac{106 - 100}{\dfrac{10}{\sqrt{16}}} = 2.4$$

and has a _t_ distribution with $k = 16 - 1 = 15$ degrees of freedom. If we let $\alpha = 2.5$ percent, since this is a one-tail test, we find

$$P(-2.13 < t < 2.13 | k = 15) = 0.95$$

Since $t = 2.4$, the probability of selecting a sample with $\bar{x} = 106$ or higher from a population with $\mu = 100$ will be less than 2.5 percent. Thus, the difference between $\bar{x}$ and μ is significant, and we reject the null hypothesis that $\mu = 100$ and accept the alternative that $\mu > 100$.

17.6. Tests Concerning the Difference of Two Means

Consider two groups of students A (high income group) and B (low income group). We wish to test whether there is a significant difference between their weekly allowances. Let the population means be μ_1 (average weekly allowance for group A) and μ_2. To compare μ_1 and μ_2, we take random samples of size n_1 and n_2, find the sample means $\bar{x}_1$ and $\bar{x}_2$, and make inferences about μ_1 and μ_2. We shall consider the following four cases:

1. When x_1 and x_2 are normally distributed and σ_1 and σ_2 are _known_.
2. When x_1 and x_2 are not normally distributed, σ_1 and σ_2 are _known_, and n_1 and n_2 are large.

3.   When x_1 and x_2 are not normally distributed, σ_1 and σ_2 are *unknown*, and n_1 and n_2 are large.

4.   When x_1 and x_2 are normally distributed, but σ_1 and σ_2 are *unknown*.

Of the four cases, (1), (2), and (3) will be based on the normal distribution. For case (4) we shall apply the t distribution by constructing a ratio that satisfies the requirements for a t distribution.

(i)   When x₁ and x₂ are normally distributed and σ₁ and σ₂ are known

We know that when x is normally distributed with mean μ and variance σ^2, the sample mean $\bar{x}$ from a sample of size n will also be normally distributed with mean μ and variance σ^2/n.

It can also be shown that if $\bar{x}_1$ and $\bar{x}_2$ are independent and normally distributed, then $\bar{x}_1 - \bar{x}_2$ is also normally distributed with mean $\mu_1 - \mu_2$ and variance $\sigma_1^2/n_1 + \sigma_2^2/n_2$. Let us set

$$d = \bar{x}_1 - \bar{x}_2$$

Then the distribution of d is as shown in Fig. 17.8.

By using these results, we can set up our test as follows: The null hypothesis is that there is no difference in the weekly allowances of group A and group B, and we write

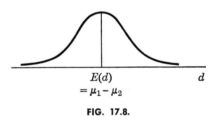

FIG. 17.8.

$$\text{Null hypothesis, } H_1: \quad \mu_1 = \mu_2$$
$$\text{Alternative hypothesis, } H_2: \quad \mu_1 > \mu_2$$

and the test statistic z becomes

$$z = \frac{(\bar{x}_1 - \bar{x}_2) - (\mu_1 - \mu_2)}{\sqrt{\dfrac{\sigma_1^2}{n_1} + \dfrac{\sigma_2^2}{n_2}}} = \frac{\bar{x}_1 - \bar{x}_2}{\sqrt{\dfrac{\sigma_1^2}{n_1} + \dfrac{\sigma_2^2}{n_2}}}$$

where z is the standardized normal variable of $d = \bar{x}_1 - \bar{x}_2$, and $E(z) = 0$ and $\mathrm{Var}(z) = 1$. Hence, we can use the normal area table to calculate probabilities.

Let us assume for illustrative purposes that $n_1 = 16$, $n_2 = 16$; $\bar{x}_1 = $

$17.50, \bar{x}_2 = \$15; \sigma_1 = \$3.00, \sigma_2 = \$4.00$. Then

$$z = \frac{17.50 - 15}{\sqrt{\dfrac{3^2}{16} + \dfrac{4^2}{16}}} = \frac{2.5}{\dfrac{5}{4}} = 2$$

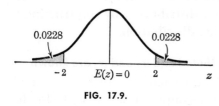

FIG. 17.9.

Thus, the probability that z will be as large as 2 is, from the normal area table (and Fig. 17.9),

$$P(z > 2) = 0.0228$$

If we adopt $\alpha = 5$ percent, we reject the null hypothesis and conclude that there is a significant difference between the weekly allowances of group A and B.

Before giving additional examples, let us consider the other cases.

(ii) When x_1 and x_2 are not normally distributed, σ_1 and σ_2 are known, and n_1 and n_2 are large

In the preceding case, we assumed x_1 and x_2 to be independent and normally distributed. When x_1 and x_2 are not normally distributed, but n_1 and n_2 are large (greater than 30), we can apply the central limit theorem and say that $\bar{x}_1$ and $\bar{x}_2$ are asymptotically normal. Then the theorem that was presented in the preceding section will apply to these sample means $\bar{x}_1$ and $\bar{x}_2$. In other words, we can state as follows: If n_1 and n_2 are large so that $\bar{x}_1$ and $\bar{x}_2$ may be considered independent and asymptotically normally distributed, then $\bar{x}_1$ and $\bar{x}_2$ will also be normally distributed with mean $\mu_1 - \mu_2$ and variance $\sigma_1^2/n_1 + \sigma_2^2/n_2$. Thus, the test procedure is the same as in the preceding case.

(iii) When x_1 and x_2 are not normally distributed, σ_1 and σ_2 are unknown, and n_1 and n_2 are large

If n_1 and n_2 are sufficiently large, we can use the central limit theorem and consider $\bar{x}_1$ and $\bar{x}_2$ to be asymptotically normal. Furthermore, we can assume that $\hat{\sigma}_1$ and $\hat{\sigma}_2$ will be good approximations of σ_1 and σ_2. Thus we state: $\bar{x}_1 - \bar{x}_2$ will be asymptotically normal with mean $\mu_1 - \mu_2$ and variance $\hat{\sigma}_1^2/n_1 + \hat{\sigma}_2^2/n_2$. Thus, the test procedure is the same as that in the previous two cases.

(iv) When x_1 and x_2 are normally distributed, but σ_1 and σ_2 are unknown

This is the case where we need to use the t distribution, and it is of main interest to us. What we propose to do is to find y and u that satisfy the requirements of the ratio $t = y/\sqrt{u/k}$ for the t distribution. Let us consider two cases.

Case 1: $\sigma_1{}^2 = \sigma_2{}^2 = \sigma^2$. Consider as an illustration a large group of students who have an average grade of μ and variance σ^2. Assume that their grades are normally distributed. Two new methods of teaching, A and B, are to be tested. Let us assume that half of the students are taught by method A and the other half by B. Let the new means be μ_1 and μ_2, and the variances be $\sigma_1{}^2$ and $\sigma_2{}^2$.

Samples of size n_1 and n_2 are taken from the two groups; the sample means are $\bar{x}_1$, $\bar{x}_2$, and the sample variances are $s_1{}^2$ and $s_2{}^2$. The situation is shown schematically in Fig. 17.10.

We wish to test whether there is a significant difference between μ_1 and μ_2. The null hypothesis is set as $\mu_1 = \mu_2$ and may be interpreted in two ways: The first is that there has been no change and $\mu_1 = \mu_2 = \mu$. The second is that the teaching methods have had the same effect and μ_1 and μ_2 have increased from μ by the same amount.

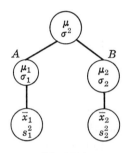

FIG. 17.10.

In either case, we wish to test whether group A and group B belong to the same population. Thus, the null hypothesis $\mu_1 = \mu_2$ can be interpreted as meaning: Do the two groups belong to the same population (which may be the original population or a new population)?

If this is the hypothesis, then $\sigma_1{}^2 = \sigma_2{}^2 = \sigma^2$ will also be part of the hypothesis. This may be explained as follows: Let x be the grades of the original population. Let x_1 be the grades of group A. Assume that the students in group A are affected uniformly and their grades have increased by 5 points; that is, $x_1 = x + 5$ for each student in group A. Then

$$\text{Var}(x_1) = \text{Var}(x + 5) = \text{Var}(x)$$

Similarly, $\text{Var}(x_2) = \text{Var}(x)$. Thus, if we can assume that the students will be affected uniformly, we have $\sigma_1{}^2 = \sigma_2{}^2 = \sigma^2$.

Generally speaking, μ_1 and μ_2 will be different from μ, and if we set up the hypothesis $\mu_1 = \mu_2$, $\sigma_1{}^2 = \sigma_2{}^2$, we are asking the question: Do the two groups A and B come from the same population (which may be different from our original one) or are they from two different populations?

With this much background, let us discuss the statistic necessary to perform the test of comparing μ_1 and μ_2. In the subsequent discussion, we assume the population to be normal unless otherwise stated.

Let $\bar{x}_1$ and $\bar{x}_2$ be the sample means of samples of size n_1 and n_2. Then $\bar{x}_1$ and $\bar{x}_2$ will also be normal with means μ_1 and μ_2 and variances σ_1^2/n_1 and σ_2^2/n_2, since x_1 and x_2 are normally distributed.

Let us set $d = \bar{x}_1 - \bar{x}_2$. Then we state without proof that d will have a normal distribution with

$$E(d) = E(\bar{x}_1 - \bar{x}_2) = E(\bar{x}_1) - E(\bar{x}_2)$$

$$= \mu_1 - \mu_2$$

$$\text{Var}(d) = \text{Var}(\bar{x}_1) + \text{Var}(\bar{x}_2)$$

$$= \frac{\sigma_1^2}{n_1} + \frac{\sigma_2^2}{n_2} = \sigma_{1-2}^2$$

Using these results, let us construct the y statistic as

$$y = \frac{(\bar{x}_1 - \bar{x}_2) - (\mu_1 - \mu_2)}{\sigma_{1-2}}$$

Then y will be normal with $E(y) = 0$ and $\text{Var}(y) = 1$, and thus it satisfies the y statistic that is to be the numerator of the t statistic.

Let us next find the denominator of the t statistic. When we had only $\bar{x}$, we set

$$u = \sum_{i=1}^{n} \left(\frac{x_i - \bar{x}}{\sigma} \right)^2$$

and found this to have a χ^2 distribution with $n - 1$ degrees of freedom. Now that we have $\bar{x}_1$ and $\bar{x}_2$, let us set

$$u = \sum^{n_1} \left(\frac{x_1 - \bar{x}_1}{\sigma_1} \right)^2 + \sum^{n_2} \left(\frac{x_2 - \bar{x}_2}{\sigma_2} \right)^2$$

Each term on the right side has a χ^2 distribution with $(n_1 - 1)$ and $(n_2 - 1)$ degrees of freedom. As we shall see in Chapter 20, the distribution is additive. That is, u will also have a χ^2 distribution with $(n_1 - 1) + (n_2 - 1) = n_1 + n_2 - 2$ degrees of freedom, and it satisfies the requirements of the u to be in the denominator of the t statistic. Let us rewrite this u, using the hypothesis that $\sigma_1^2 = \sigma_2^2 = \sigma^2$, as

$$u = \frac{1}{\sigma^2} \left[\sum^{n_1} (x_1 - \bar{x}_1)^2 + \sum^{n_2} (x_2 - \bar{x}_2)^2 \right]$$

$$= \frac{1}{\sigma^2} \left[n_1 s_1^2 + n_2 s_2^2 \right]$$

We did this because we wish to cancel out the σ^2, which is *unknown*, when we construct the t ratio, and also use the idea of a pooled variance, which we discussed in Section 17.2. The pooled variance is obtained by dividing u by its degrees of freedom:

$$\frac{u}{n_1 + n_2 - 2} = \frac{1}{\sigma^2} \cdot \frac{n_1 s_1^2 + n_2 s_2^2}{n_1 + n_2 - 2} = \frac{1}{\sigma^2} \cdot \hat{\sigma}^2$$

where $\hat{\sigma}^2$ is the pooled variance and is an unbiased estimator of σ^2.

Using these results, let us now construct the t statistic:

$$t = \frac{y}{\sqrt{\dfrac{u}{k}}} = \frac{\dfrac{(\bar{x}_1 - \bar{x}_2) - (\mu_1 - \mu_2)}{\sigma\sqrt{(1/n_1) + (1/n_2)}}}{\sqrt{\dfrac{\hat{\sigma}^2}{\sigma^2}}}$$

$$= \frac{(\bar{x}_1 - \bar{x}_2) - (\mu_1 - \mu_2)}{\hat{\sigma}} \sqrt{\frac{n_1 n_2}{n_1 + n_2}}$$

where

$$\hat{\sigma}^2 = \frac{n_1 s_1^2 + n_2 s_2^2}{n_1 + n_2 - 2}$$

This t has a t distribution with $n_1 + n_2 - 2$ degrees of freedom. We can see that the unknown population variance σ^2 has canceled out.

The test is usually set up as

Null hypothesis, H_1: $\mu_1 = \mu_2$
Alternative hypothesis, H_2: $\mu_1 \neq \mu_2$

$$t = \frac{\bar{x}_1 - \bar{x}_2}{\hat{\sigma}} \sqrt{\frac{n_1 n_2}{n_1 + n_2}}$$

Thus every term in the t statistic is obtained from the sample and is known. We shall give several examples to show how this is used.

Example 1.   Consider the following hypothetical example. There are two groups of students A and B who have been taught the same subject by different methods. We wish to know if there is a significant difference in the grades of the students when they are given the same examination.

To test this, we select a random sample of 5 students from each group and find their grades as shown in the table below. The test will be

$$\text{Null hypothesis, } H_1: \quad \mu_1 = \mu_2$$
$$\text{Alternative hypothesis, } H_2: \quad \mu_1 \neq \mu_2$$

However, observation of the data shows that the grades of class A are higher than class B, and hence we may also state the test as

$$\text{Null hypothesis, } H_1: \quad \mu_1 = \mu_2$$
$$\text{Alternative hypothesis, } H_2: \quad \mu_1 > \mu_2$$

The first approach is a two-sided test, and the second approach is a one-sided test. Let us work out the second approach.

x_1	x_2	$x_1{}^2$	$x_2{}^2$
60	40	3600	1600
60	40	3600	1600
70	50	4900	2500
80	60	6400	3600
80	60	6400	3600
$\overline{350}$	$\overline{250}$	$\overline{24{,}900}$	$\overline{12{,}900}$

We find

$$\Sigma (x_1 - \bar{x}_1)^2 = \Sigma x_1{}^2 - \frac{1}{n_1} (\Sigma x_1)^2 = 24{,}900 - \frac{1}{5} (350)^2 = 400$$

$$\Sigma (x_2 - \bar{x}_2)^2 = \Sigma x_2{}^2 - \frac{1}{n_2} (\Sigma x_2)^2 = 12{,}900 - \frac{1}{5} (250)^2 = 400$$

The worksheet is set up to correspond with the analysis of variance worksheet, which is discussed in Chapter 21.

Worksheet

Class	Number of Students	Degrees of Freedom	Sum of Squares	Mean Squares	Mean
A	5	4	400	100	70
B	5	4	400	100	50
		$\overline{8}$	$\overline{800}$		

Recall that the sum of the squares is

$$\Sigma (x_1 - \bar{x}_1)^2 = n_1 \frac{\Sigma (x_1 - \bar{x}_1)^2}{n_1} = n_1 s_1{}^2$$

$$\Sigma (x_2 - \bar{x}_2)^2 = n_2 \frac{\Sigma (x_2 - \bar{x}_2)^2}{n_2} = n_2 s_2{}^2$$

Thus the pooled variance is

$$\hat{\sigma}^2 = \frac{n_1 s_1{}^2 + n_2 s_2{}^2}{n_1 + n_2 - 2} = \frac{400 + 400}{5 + 5 - 2} = 100$$

and the t statistic becomes

$$t = \frac{70 - 50}{\sqrt{100}} \sqrt{\frac{5 \times 5}{5 + 5}} = 3.16$$

We have $k = n_1 + n_2 - 2 = 5 + 5 - 2 = 8$ degrees of freedom. From the t table we find

$$P(t > 2.90 | k = 8) = 0.01$$
$$P(t > 3.36 | k = 8) = 0.005$$

This is shown graphically in Fig. 17.11.

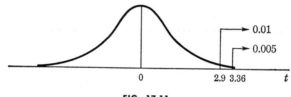

FIG. 17.11.

Since $t = 3.16$, the probability of such a t occurring is less than 1 percent. Thus, if we set $\alpha = 0.01$, the difference between $\bar{x}_1$ and $\bar{x}_2$ is significant, and we reject the null hypothesis.

The mean square was defined as, for example,

$$\frac{\Sigma (x_1 - \bar{x}_1)^2}{n_1 - 1} = \frac{400}{5 - 1} = 100$$

These mean squares are estimates of the variances for samples A and B. In our present case, the data are hypothetical and have been "doctored up" so that the mean squares have come out equal. In many practical cases, they will come out relatively close to each other. When this happens, it may be looked upon as evidence for supporting the assumption that $\sigma_1 = \sigma_2$. These points will be discussed in more detail in Chapter 21.

Example 2.   Let us now take a random sample of 5 students from group A and 7 students from group B. The hypothetical results are given in the table below. We wish to find if there is a significant difference between the grades of groups A and B, as in the preceding case.

We find

$$\Sigma (x_1 - \bar{x}_1)^2 = 400, \qquad \Sigma (x_2 - \bar{x}_2)^2 = 600$$

x_1	x_2	$x_1{}^2$	$x_2{}^2$
60	40	3600	1600
60	40	3600	1600
70	40	4900	1600
80	50	6400	2500
80	60	6400	3600
	60		3600
	60		3600
350	350	24,900	18,100

Worksheet

Class	Number of Students	Degrees of Freedom	Sum of Squares	Mean Squares	Mean $\bar{x}$
A	5	4	400	100	70
B	7	6	600	100	50
		10			

We have

$$\hat{\sigma}^2 = \frac{400 + 600}{5 + 7 - 2} = 100$$

and therefore

$$t = \frac{70 - 50}{10} \times \sqrt{\frac{5 \times 7}{5 + 7}} = 3.45$$

From the *t* table we find for 10 degrees of freedom,

$$P(t > 2.76 | k = 10) = 0.01$$
$$P(t > 3.17 | k = 10) = 0.005$$
$$P(t > 4.59 | k = 10) = 0.0005$$

Thus, the probability of $t \geqq 3.45$ is less than $\frac{1}{2}$ percent. That is,

$$P(t > 3.45 | k = 10) < 0.005$$

If we select $\alpha = 1$ percent as the level of significance, we reject the null hypothesis.

Note that the mean squares of *A* and *B* are equal and support the hypothesis that $\sigma_1 = \sigma_2$.

Case 2: $\sigma_1{}^2 \neq \sigma_2{}^2$. If there is reason to believe that the two samples came from two normally distributed populations where $\sigma_1{}^2 \neq \sigma_2{}^2$, we cannot use *t* distribution as in the preceding discussion. Let us investigate this problem.

Assume the two population means and variances to be μ_1 and μ_2, σ_1^2 and σ_2^2. Let the sample sizes, mean, and variances be n_1 and n_2, $\bar{x}_1$ and $\bar{x}_2$, s_1^2 and s_2^2. The test is set up similar to that for the previous cases:

$$\text{Null hypothesis, } H_1: \qquad \mu_1 = \mu_2$$
$$\text{Alternative hypothesis, } H_2: \qquad \mu_1 \neq \mu_2$$

The numerator of the t statistic, y, is shown by

$$y = \frac{(\bar{x}_1 - \bar{x}_2) - (\mu_1 - \mu_2)}{\sqrt{\dfrac{\sigma_1^2}{n_1} + \dfrac{\sigma_2^2}{n_2}}}$$

We know that this y is normal, and $E(y) = 0$ and $\mathrm{Var}(y) = 1$. Thus, it satisfies the requirements of the numerator of the t statistic.

The denominator u is shown by

$$u = \frac{\Sigma (x_1 - \bar{x}_1)^2}{\sigma_1^2} + \frac{\Sigma (x_2 - \bar{x}_2)^2}{\sigma_2^2}$$

This we know has a χ^2 distribution with $n_1 + n_2 - 2$ degrees of freedom, and it satisfies the requirements of the denominator. Noting that

$$\Sigma (x_1 - \bar{x}_1)^2 = (n_1 - 1) \frac{\Sigma (x_1 - \bar{x}_1)^2}{n_1 - 1} = (n_1 - 1) \hat{\sigma}_1^2$$

where $\hat{\sigma}_1^2$ is an unbiased estimator of σ_1^2, we can rewrite u as

$$u = \frac{(n_1 - 1) \hat{\sigma}_1^2}{\sigma_1^2} + \frac{(n_2 - 1) \hat{\sigma}_2^2}{\sigma_2^2}$$

Thus, the t statistic becomes

$$t = \frac{(\bar{x}_1 - \bar{x}_2) - (\mu_1 - \mu_2)}{\left\{\dfrac{\sigma_1^2}{n_1} + \dfrac{\sigma_2^2}{n_2}\right\}^{1/2}} \Bigg/ \left[\frac{\dfrac{(n_1 - 1) \hat{\sigma}_1^2}{\sigma_1^2} + \dfrac{(n_2 - 1) \hat{\sigma}_2^2}{\sigma_2^2}}{n_1 + n_2 - 2}\right]^{1/2}$$

In the previous case, where $\sigma_1^2 = \sigma_2^2$, this unknown population variance canceled out, and we were able to find t. Now it does not cancel out, and as a result we cannot find the value of t.

The natural thing to do is to substitute the unbiased estimators $\hat{\sigma}_1^2$ and $\hat{\sigma}_2^2$ for σ_1^2 and σ_2^2. But, then u becomes

$$u = (n_1 - 1) + (n_2 - 1) = n_1 + n_2 - 2$$

and will not have a χ^2 distribution. Thus t, which becomes

$$t = \frac{(\bar{x}_1 - \bar{x}_2) - (\mu_1 - \mu_2)}{\left\{\dfrac{\hat{\sigma}_1^2}{n_1} + \dfrac{\hat{\sigma}_2^2}{n_2}\right\}^{1/2}}$$

will not have a t distribution. Dixon and Massey[*] have shown that in such a case, the t will be approximately distributed as a t distribution, with the degrees of freedom (df) given by

$$\mathrm{df} = \frac{\left(\dfrac{\hat{\sigma}_1^2}{n_1} + \dfrac{\hat{\sigma}_2^2}{n_2}\right)^2}{\left(\dfrac{\hat{\sigma}_1^2}{n_1}\right)^2 \dfrac{1}{n_1 + 1} + \left(\dfrac{\hat{\sigma}_2^2}{n_2}\right)^2 \dfrac{1}{n_2 + 1}} - 2$$

When the degrees of freedom are not an integer value, take the closest integer value.

17.7. Confidence Intervals for a Mean

Confidence intervals were discussed in Chapter 10. As was pointed out there, we can use the method of maximum likelihood and find estimators of such parameters as the population mean or population proportion; this was called point estimation. In some cases, however, we are interested in finding limits within which we should expect to find the parameter with certain probability. For example, we may wish to know the upper (α_1) and lower (α_2) limits between which the average IQ (μ) of students at a certain college will fall, given a certain probability, say, of 95 percent. In symbols,

$$P(\alpha_1 < \mu < \alpha_2) = 0.95$$

Let us show how such intervals (which we called *confidence intervals*) are found when estimating the mean.

Let X be a random variable that is normally distributed with mean μ and variance σ^2, which is *unknown*. Consider a sample of size n with mean $\bar{x}$ and variance s^2. The t statistic was

(1)
$$t = \frac{\bar{x} - \mu}{\sqrt{\dfrac{\Sigma (x - \bar{x})^2}{n(n - 1)}}}$$

---

[*] W. J. Dixon and F. J. Massey, Jr., *Introduction to Statistical Analysis*, New York: McGraw-Hill Book Co., 1951, p. 105.

where t has a t distribution with $n - 1$ degrees of freedom. Let t be such that

(2) $$P(-t_a < t < t_a \mid k = n - 1) = 0.95$$

For example, let $n = 12$. Then from the t table in the Appendix we find

(3) $$P(-2.20 < t < 2.20 \mid k = 11) = 0.95$$

This shows that the probability of t falling between the two limits

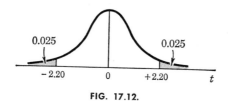

0.025   0.025

-2.20 0 $+2.20$ t

FIG. 17.12.

± 2.20 is 0.95 (Fig. 17.12). Substituting equation (1) into (2) we find

$$P\left(-t_a < \frac{\bar{x} - \mu}{\sqrt{\dfrac{\Sigma (x - \bar{x})^2}{n(n-1)}}} < t_a \right) = 0.95$$

$$P\left(\bar{x} - t_a \sqrt{\frac{\Sigma (x - \bar{x})^2}{n(n-1)}} < \mu < \bar{x} + t_a \sqrt{\frac{\Sigma (x - \bar{x})^2}{n(n-1)}} \right) = 0.95$$

Recall that this statement meant: If we take repeated samples of size n, calculate the sample mean, and construct confidence intervals

$$\bar{x} - t_a \sqrt{\frac{\Sigma (x - \bar{x})^2}{n(n-1)}} < \mu < \bar{x} + t_a \sqrt{\frac{\Sigma (x - \bar{x})^2}{n(n-1)}}$$

we may expect that 95 out of 100 such intervals will contain the true mean μ. In our present case, where $n - 1 = 11$, the $\pm t_a$, as we saw, was ± 2.20. This is for a 95 percent confidence interval; in similar manner, we can construct 90, 98, or other percent confidence intervals.

If an actual sample mean is calculated and it is found to be $\bar{x}_0$, then

$$P\left(\bar{x}_0 - t_a \sqrt{\frac{\Sigma (x - \bar{x})^2}{n(n-1)}} < \mu < \bar{x}_0 + t_a \sqrt{\frac{\Sigma (x - \bar{x})^2}{n(n-1)}} \right) = 0.95$$

is no longer a true probability statement. We know the μ must be either in or out of the interval, and thus the probability will be 1 or 0, but we can attach the 0.95 to this specific interval with the interpretation given above for the 95 percent confidence interval.

When σ^2 is known, we use the z statistic:

$$z = \frac{\bar{x} - \mu}{\dfrac{\sigma}{\sqrt{n}}} = \frac{\bar{x} - \mu}{\sigma_{\bar{x}}}$$

and the probability statement becomes

$$P(-z_a < \frac{\bar{x} - \mu}{\sigma_{\bar{x}}} < z_a) = 1.00 - \alpha$$

where α is the level of significance. z_a is the normalized deviation corresponding to α and is found from the normal area table. The probability statement becomes

$$P(\bar{x} - z_a \sigma_{\bar{x}} < \mu < \bar{x} + z_a \sigma_{\bar{x}}) = 1.00 - \alpha$$

and the $100(1 - \alpha)$ percent confidence interval is

$$\bar{x} - z_a \sigma_{\bar{x}} < \mu < \bar{x} + z_a \sigma_{\bar{x}}$$

Example 1. Assume we wish to find the 95 percent confidence interval for the average IQ of the students attending a certain college. A random sample of 100 students is selected, and the sample mean is found to be $\bar{x} = 110$. We shall assume that the IQ's are distributed normally and that the population variance σ^2 is *known* and is $\sigma = 20$ points. Let the normalized z statistic be

$$z = \frac{\bar{x} - \mu}{\dfrac{\sigma}{\sqrt{n}}} = \frac{\bar{x} - \mu}{\sigma_{\bar{x}}}$$

Then, from the normal area table,

$$P(-z < \frac{\bar{x} - \mu}{\sigma_{\bar{x}}} < z) = 0.95$$

when $z = 1.96$, and we find

$$P(\bar{x} - 1.96\, \sigma_{\bar{x}} < \mu < \bar{x} + 1.96\, \sigma_{\bar{x}}) = 0.95$$

Thus, the specific 95 percent confidence interval is

$$110 - 1.96 \times \frac{20}{\sqrt{100}} < \mu < 110 + 1.96 \times \frac{20}{\sqrt{100}}$$

$$106.08 < \mu < 113.92$$

In our present case, we assumed that the population variance σ^2 was known, and as a result that it was not necessary to use the t distribution. Let us next consider an example where σ^2 is *unknown*.

Example 2.   Assume we wish to find the 95 percent confidence interval for the average weight of students attending a certain college. A random sample of 5 students has been selected, and the results are shown in the following table.

X, Pounds	$X - \bar{X}$	$(X - \bar{X})^2$
160	−10	100
170	0	0
165	−5	25
175	5	25
180	10	100
Σ 850	0	250
$\bar{x}$ 170		

We find

$$\hat{\sigma}_{\bar{x}} = \sqrt{\frac{\Sigma (x - \bar{x})^2}{n(n-1)}} = \sqrt{\frac{250}{5 \times 4}} = 3.53 \text{ lb.}$$

The t statistic is

$$t = \frac{\bar{x} - \mu}{\hat{\sigma}_{\bar{x}}}$$

Thus the 95 percent confidence interval is, since we have $5 - 1 = 4$ degrees of freedom,

$$P\left(-2.78 < \frac{\bar{x} - \mu}{\hat{\sigma}_{\bar{x}}} < 2.78 \,\middle|\, k = 4\right) = 0.95$$

which becomes

$$\bar{x} - 2.78 \, \hat{\sigma}_{\bar{x}} < \mu < \bar{x} + 2.78 \, \hat{\sigma}_{\bar{x}}$$

For our present case, where $\bar{x} = 170$ lb. and $\hat{\sigma}_{\bar{x}} = 3.53$ lb., the confidence interval becomes

$$170 - (2.78 \times 3.53) < \mu < 170 + (2.78 \times 3.53)$$

$$160.2 < \mu < 179.8$$

17.8.   Confidence Interval for the Difference Between Means from Two Populations when the Standard Deviations are Known

(i)   When two populations are normal

Let X_1 and X_2 be two independent and normally distributed random variables with means μ_1, μ_2, and variance σ_1^2 and σ_2^2. Let $\bar{x}_1$ and $\bar{x}_2$ be sample means of random samples n_1 and n_2 taken from the first and second populations. Then the distribution of the difference $d = \bar{x}_1 - \bar{x}_2$ was found to be normal with mean $\mu_1 - \mu_2$ and variance $\sigma_1^2/n_1 + \sigma_2^2/n_2$. The statistic z was

(1)
$$z = \frac{(\bar{x}_1 - \bar{x}_2) - (\mu_1 - \mu_2)}{\sqrt{\dfrac{\sigma_1^2}{n_1} + \dfrac{\sigma_2^2}{n_2}}} = \frac{(\bar{x}_1 - \bar{x}_2) - (\mu_1 - \mu_2)}{\sigma_{1-2}}$$

and z was $N(0, 1)$.

Using this result, the confidence interval becomes

$$P\left(-z_a < \frac{(\bar{x}_1 - \bar{x}_2) - (\mu_1 - \mu_2)}{\sigma_{1-2}} < z_a\right) = 1 - \alpha$$

$$P((\bar{x}_1 - \bar{x}_2) - z_a\, \sigma_{1-2} < \mu_1 - \mu_2 < (\bar{x}_1 - \bar{x}_2) + z_a\, \sigma_{1-2}) = 1 - \alpha$$

Thus the $100(1 - \alpha)$ percent confidence interval becomes

(2)
$$(\bar{x}_1 - \bar{x}_2) - z_a\, \sigma_{1-2} < \mu_1 - \mu_2 < (\bar{x}_1 - \bar{x}_2) + z_a\, \sigma_{1-2}$$

Example. Two groups of pigs were fed different diets. A random sample of 9 pigs was selected from each group and their sample means were found to be $\bar{x}_1 = 80$ lb., $\bar{x}_2 = 90$ lb. It is assumed that the weights are normally distributed and the standard deviations are $\sigma_1 = 9$ lb., $\sigma_2 = 18$ lb. Find the 90 percent confidence interval for the difference of the means.

$$(80 - 90) - 1.64\sqrt{\frac{9^2}{9} + \frac{18^2}{9}} < \mu_1 - \mu_2 < (80 - 90) + 1.64\sqrt{\frac{9^2}{9} + \frac{18^2}{9}}$$

$$-20.988 < \mu_1 - \mu_2 < 0.989$$

(ii) Two populations not normal but when the samples are large

When the samples n_1 and n_2 are large (greater than 50), even though the populations are not normally distributed, the z in equation (1) will be approximately normally distributed. Then the procedure in section (i) applies to such cases and the confidence interval is given by equation (2).

17.9. Confidence Interval for the Difference Between Means from Two Normal Populations when the Standard Deviations are Unknown

Two cases of comparing means from normal populations when the standard deviations are unknown have been considered. One was where the variances were equal ($\sigma_1^2 = \sigma_2^2$), the other where they were un-equal. Let us now find the confidence interval for these two cases.

(i) $\sigma_1^2 = \sigma_2^2$ equal but unknown

The statistic t was given as

$$t = \frac{(\bar{x}_1 - \bar{x}_2) - (\mu_1 - \mu_2)}{\hat{\sigma} \sqrt{\dfrac{1}{n_1} + \dfrac{1}{n_2}}}$$

where $\hat{\sigma}^2$ was the pooled variance

$$\hat{\sigma}^2 = \frac{n_1 s_1^2 + n_2 s_2^2}{n_1 + n_2 - 2}$$

This t had a t distribution with $n_1 + n_2 - 2$ degrees of freedom. Thus, the confidence interval is obtained as

$$P(-t_a < t < t_a) = 1 - \alpha$$

$$P\left((\bar{x}_1 - \bar{x}_2) - t_\alpha \cdot \hat{\sigma} \sqrt{\frac{1}{n_1} + \frac{1}{n_2}} < (\mu_1 - \mu_2) \right.$$

$$\left. < (\bar{x}_1 - \bar{x}_2) + t_a \cdot \hat{\sigma} \sqrt{\frac{1}{n_1} + \frac{1}{n_2}} \right) = 1 - \alpha$$

and the $100(1 - \alpha)$ percent confidence interval becomes

$$(\bar{x}_1 - \bar{x}_2) - t_a \cdot \hat{\sigma} \sqrt{\frac{1}{n_1} + \frac{1}{n_2}} < (\mu_1 - \mu_2)$$

$$< (\bar{x}_1 - \bar{x}_2) + t_a \cdot \hat{\sigma} \sqrt{\frac{1}{n_1} + \frac{1}{n_2}}$$

(ii) $\sigma_1^2 \neq \sigma_2^2$ and unknown

The test statistic for this case was

$$t' = \frac{(\bar{x}_1 - \bar{x}_2) - (\mu_1 - \mu_2)}{\sqrt{\dfrac{\hat{\sigma}_1^2}{n_1} + \dfrac{\hat{\sigma}_2^2}{n_2}}}$$

This t' had an approximate t distribution when both populations were normally distributed and the null hypothesis was $\mu_1 = \mu_2$. This distribution of t' for $\mu_1 \neq \mu_2$ is not known. The degrees of freedom were given by

$$df = \frac{\left(\dfrac{\hat{\sigma}_1{}^2}{n_1} + \dfrac{\hat{\sigma}_2{}^2}{n_2}\right)^2}{\dfrac{\left(\dfrac{\hat{\sigma}_1{}^2}{n_1}\right)^2}{n_1 + 1} + \dfrac{\left(\dfrac{\hat{\sigma}_2{}^2}{n_2}\right)^2}{n_2 + 1}} - 2$$

Keeping in mind that we can use the t distribution only when x_1 and x_2 are normally distributed, and $\mu_1 = \mu_2$, we find the confidence interval as

$$(\bar{x}_1 - \bar{x}_2) - t_a \sqrt{\frac{\hat{\sigma}_1{}^2}{n_1} + \frac{\hat{\sigma}_2{}^2}{n_2}} < \mu_1 - \mu_2$$

$$< (\bar{x}_1 - \bar{x}_2) + t_a \sqrt{\frac{\hat{\sigma}_1{}^2}{n_1} + \frac{\hat{\sigma}_2{}^2}{n_2}}$$

THE BINOMIAL DISTRIBUTION

18

The important discrete distributions we shall discuss in this book are the binomial distribution, multinomial distribution, hypergeometric distribution, and Poisson distribution. The binomial distribution discussed in this chapter is sometimes called the Bernoulli distribution in honor of the Swiss mathematician Jakob Bernoulli (1654–1705) who derived it. We shall first discuss Bernoulli trials, define the binomial distribution and its properties, and explain the sampling distribution of the sample proportion and its application.

18.1. Bernoulli Trials

Consider an experiment of tossing a coin. Each throw (trial) has two possible outcomes, heads or tails. Assuming a fair coin, the probability of heads is $\frac{1}{2}$, and similarly for tails. Furthermore, no matter how many times this experiment is repeated, the probability of a head or tail remains the same.

Let us express this experiment in statistical terminology as follows: We have an experiment E of tossing a coin. Each toss is called a *trial* and has two possible outcomes: success, S, and failure, F. In our example, heads may be considered success and tails may be considered failure. The probability of a success or failure is denoted by

$$P(S) = p$$
$$P(F) = 1 - p = q$$

The trials are independent, which implies that no matter how many times the experiment is repeated, the probabilities of a success or failure remain the same.

Repeated independent trials that have the characteristics that (1) there are only two possible outcomes, and (2) the probabilities of the outcomes remain the same for all trials are called Bernoulli trials.

Example 1. Suppose we have an urn with 4 red and 6 green balls. A ball is selected at random and then returned. This experiment has only 2 possible outcomes: red (say, success) and green (say, failure); the probabilities of success or failure remain the same no matter how many times the experiment is repeated. Hence this experiment may be considered as a Bernoulli trial.

4 red

6 green

Example 2. A die is tossed and we are interested in the events odd or even number. Let the occurrence of an odd number be called a success and the occurrence of an even number be called a failure. The probabilities of success and failure are, respectively, $3/6$, and these remain the same throughout all the trials. Hence, we have Bernoulli trials.

The definition of Bernoulli trials gives us a theoretical model and the two examples above satisfy the conditions for Bernoulli trials. However, in most practical applications, we have situations that may be considered as approximately satisfying Bernoulli trials. Let us give several examples.

Example 3. Suppose 100 families are randomly selected from New York City and checked to see whether they have seen an advertisement of soap A. Let p be the proportion of families in New York City that have seen the advertisement. We may consider selecting a sample of size 100 as repeating an experiment of selecting a family 100 times. There are two possible outcomes for each trial, namely, a family has seen the ad or it has not seen it.

The probability that the first family saw the ad is p. If the selected family is replaced each time, the probability will remain the same for all subsequent families. However, in many practical cases, samples are selected without replacement; in such cases, theoretically, the probability changes each time a family is drawn.

But when the population is very large, and the sample is relatively small, the change in p will be very small, and for practical purposes may be considered to remain unchanged.

When this assumption is made, the selection of 100 families may be considered as repeated independent Bernoulli trials where the probability of success (a family has seen the ad) is p and the probability of a failure is $1 - p = q$ for each trial.

Example 4.   Suppose we have a production process of producing light bulbs that are classified as either defective (success) or nondefective (failure). A selection of a sample of size $n = 20$ may be considered as 20 repeated independent Bernoulli trials where the probability of success is p and that of failure is $1 - p = q$.

If, during the production process, there is a change in the adjustment of machines, or a change in the laborers producing the bulbs, we may argue theoretically that the p will not remain the same. However, if we may consider the change to be small enough to assume that p remains practically the same, the selection of the sample may be considered as a sequence of Bernoulli trials.

18.2.   A Geometrical Interpretation

Let us next interpret Bernoulli trials geometrically. We shall start with a simple case of 2 Bernoulli trials and then discuss the case of 3 Bernoulli trials, and finally give a general interpretation.

Suppose a coin is tossed twice. Then there are $2^2 = 4$ possible outcomes, which may be shown as

$$(H, H), \quad (H, T), \quad (T, H), \quad (T, T)$$

This may also be shown as a 2-dimensional sample space (Fig. 18.1).

The probabilities associated with the sample points are

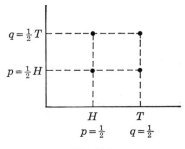

$$P(H, H) = pp$$
$$P(H, T) = pq$$
$$P(T, H) = qp$$
$$P(T, T) = qq$$

FIG. 18.1.

When a coin is tossed 3 times, we have a 3-dimensional sample space with $2^3 = 8$ sample points, as shown in Fig. 18.2. The 8 sample points are

$$(H, H, H), \quad (H, H, T), \quad (H, T, H), \quad (T, H, H)$$
$$(H, T, T), \quad (T, H, T), \quad (T, T, H), \quad (T, T, T)$$

and the probabilities associated with these sample points are, for example,

$$P(H, H, H) = ppp$$
$$P(H, H, T) = ppq$$
$$P(H, T, T) = pqq$$
$$P(T, T, T) = qqq$$

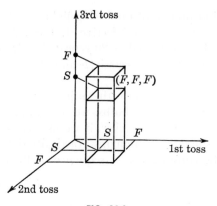

FIG. 18.2.

We see that if a coin is tossed n times, we have n repeated Bernoulli trials, and this generates an n dimensional sample space with 2^n sample points.

Each sample point gives a possible sequence of heads (H) and tails (T), and there are 2^n possible sequences when we have n repeated Bernoulli trials. The probabilities associated to these sample points may be shown as

$$p^k q^{n-k}$$

where k is the number of heads. In our previous example of 2 tosses, we may have 0, 1, or 2 heads. Thus, the probabilities may be shown as

$$p^k q^{n-k} \qquad k = 0, 1, 2$$

For (H, H) we have

$$P(H, H) = p^2 q^{2-2} = p^2$$

For (H, T) we have

$$P(H, T) = p^1 q^{2-1} = pq$$

and so forth.

For the example of 3 tosses, we may have 0, 1, 2, or 3 heads. Thus, the probability may be shown as

$$p^k q^{n-k} \qquad k = 0, 1, 2, 3$$

and, for example, for (H, T, H) we have

$$P(H, T, H) = p^2 q^{3-2} = p^2 q$$

We may state in general that when we have n repeated Bernoulli trials, an n dimensional sample space with 2^n sample points is generated. Each sample point is a possible sequence of S's and F's and the probabilities associated with these sample points are shown by

$$p^k q^{n-k}$$

where k is the number of successes.

18.3. Finding the Binomial Distribution

In Section 18.2, k was the number of successes in n Bernoulli trials, and it was $k = 0, 1, \ldots, n$. Let us now consider this k as a random variable, which is sometimes called a binomial variable. Then, for example, for $n = 2$, the random variable k has 3 possible outcomes: $k = 0, 1, 2$. The question we now ask is: What is the probability of there being k successes in n trials?

Let us reproduce our geometrical interpretation for $n = 2$ as Fig. 18.3. As we saw previously, the probabilities associated to the sample points are

$$p^k q^{n-k} \qquad k = 0, 1, 2$$

According to our new interpretation, where k is the random variable, for the point (H, H) we have $k = 2$, and hence

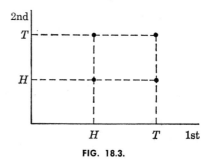

FIG. 18.3.

$$P(k = 2) = P(H, H) = p^2 q^{2-2} = p^2$$

For the points (H, T) and (T, H), which are distinct sample points, we have $k = 1$ for both points. Hence, the probability for $k = 1$ is

$$P(k = 1) = P(H, T \text{ or } T, H) = 2p^1 q^{2-1} = 2pq$$

and for (T, T) we have $k = 0$ and

$$P(k = 0) = P(T, T) = p^0 q^{2-0} = q^2$$

Viewed from a different standpoint, we may interpret these results as follows: When $n = 2$ and $k = 1$, how many possible ways are there of 1 success occurring in 2 trials? There are

$$\binom{n}{k} = \binom{2}{1}$$

different ways, and for any one way, the probability is

$$p^k q^{n-k} = p^1 q^{2-1} = pq$$

and hence

$$P(k = 1) = \binom{2}{1} pq$$

For $k = 0$ case, we ask: How many different ways are there of selecting 0 successes in $n = 2$ trials? Recalling that $0! = 1$, we have

$$\binom{n}{k} = \binom{2}{0} = 1$$

and hence,

$$P(k = 0) = \binom{2}{0} p^0 q^{2-0} = q^2$$

Finally, for $k = 2$, we ask: How many different ways are there of selecting 2 successes in $n = 2$ trials? This is shown by

$$\binom{n}{k} = \binom{2}{2} = 1$$

and hence,

$$P(k = 2) = \binom{2}{2} p^2 q^{2-2} = p^2$$

Let us apply this interpretation to the case of tossing a coin 3 times. The random variable k has 4 possible outcomes: $k = 0, 1, 2, 3$, and

$$P(k) = \binom{n}{k} p^k q^{n-k}$$

For example, when $k = 1$, we ask: How many different ways are there of selecting 1 success (S) in $n = 3$ trials? This is shown by

$$\binom{n}{k} = \binom{3}{1}$$

and hence,

$$P(k = 1) = \binom{3}{1} p^1 q^{3-1}$$

In general, when given n Bernoulli trials with k successes, the probability of k successes is

(1) $$P(k) = \binom{n}{k} p^k q^{n-k}$$

where p is the probability of a success and $q = 1 - p$ is the probability of a failure.

This $P(k)$ is also written as

$$b(k; n, p)$$

The b stands for binomial, and this expression shows explicitly the two parameters n and p.

The k is the random variable, and equation (1) is the distribution of k and is called the binomial distribution.

18.4.   Tables of the Binomial Probability Distribution

(i)   Individual probabilities

Suppose we have a box with 3 red and 7 black beads (Fig. 18.4). Let us select a random sample of size 5 with replacement. This sample may be interpreted as 5 repeated Bernoulli trials. The outcome of each trial is either a red or black bead with probabilities $p = 0.3$ and $q = 0.7$.

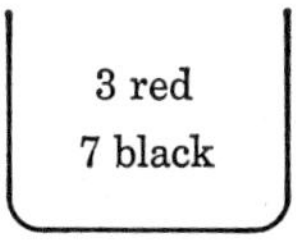

Let k be the random variable showing the number of red beads in the sample. Then $k = 0, 1, \ldots,$ 5. The probability of $k = 2$ red beads in $n = 5$ trials is

> 3 red
>
> 7 black

FIG. 18.4.

$$(1) \qquad P(k = 2 | n = 5,\, p = 0.3) = \binom{5}{2} (0.3)^2 (0.7)^{5-2}$$

Calculating such probabilities can become a difficult task. Fortunately, tables that have computed these probabilities for certain values are available; these are usually sufficient to cover our needs.* For samples of size less than 50 (that is, less than 50 trials, $n \leqslant 50$), the National Bureau of Standards table will usually be sufficient. For $50 \leq n \leq 100$, Romig** has provided values. These two tables will cover most practical cases because, as we shall see later, as n becomes large, we can use the normal distribution as an approximation. Table 11 of the Appendix has been extracted from the National Bureau of Standards table.

Using the National Bureau of Standards table, we may find the values for equation (1) for various k, which is given in Table 18.1.

TABLE 18.1.

$n = 5, \quad p = 0.3$

k	$P(k)$
5	0.0024300
4	0.0283500
3	0.1323000
2	0.3087000
1	0.3601500
0	0.1680700

---

* *Tables of the Binomial Probability Distribution*, National Bureau of Standards, Applied Mathematics Series 6, U.S. Dept. of Commerce, 1950.

** H. C. Romig, 50–100 *Binomial Tables*, New York: John Wiley and Sons, 1953.

The value for $k = 5$ is not given in the individual probability section of the table, but may be found by

$$1 - \sum_{k=1}^{4} P(k)$$

However, by using the partial sum section of the tables, we can find

$$\sum_{k=5}^{5} P(k) = P(k = 5) = 0.0024300$$

The tables provide values of p between $0.01 \leq p \leq 0.50$. When $p > 0.50$, we may convert the probabilities to corresponding equivalent formulas of $p < 0.50$ and use the tables. This conversion is illustrated as follows: In our preceding example, the proportion of red beads was $p = 0.3$. Suppose the proportion is $p = 0.7$. (That is, we have 7 red and 3 black beads.) Then, for $k = 3$,

(2) $$b(k = 3; n = 5, p = 0.7) = \binom{5}{3} (0.7)^3 (0.3)^{5-3}$$

But

$$\binom{5}{3} = \binom{5}{5-3}$$

and, in general,

$$\binom{n}{k} = \binom{n}{n-k}$$

Also note that

$$(0.7)^3 (0.3)^{5-3} = (0.7)^{5-2} (0.3)^2$$

Substituting these results in (2), we find

$$b(k = 3; n = 5, p = 0.7) = \binom{5}{3} (0.7)^3 (0.3)^{5-3}$$

(3) $$= \binom{5}{5-3} (0.7)^{5-2} (0.3)^2$$

$$= b(k = 2; n = 5, p = 0.3)$$

Hence, by using $p = 0.3$ and equation (3), we may find the probability for (2).

We may say: The probability of 3 successes in 5 trials, where $p = 0.7$, is equal to the probability of $5 - 3 = 2$ successes in 5 trials, where $p = 1 - 0.7 = 0.3$. In general,

(4) $$b(k; n, p) = b(n - k; n, 1 - p)$$

(ii)   Cumulative probabilities

Suppose we are interested in finding the probability of selecting *at least* 3 red beads in 5 trials. This means finding the probability of selecting 3, 4, or 5 red beads and summing these three probabilities. That is,

$$P(k \geqq 3 | n = 5, p = 0.3) = P(k = 3) + P(k = 4) + P(k = 5)$$

$$= \sum_{k=3}^{5} \binom{5}{k} (0.3)^k (0.7)^{5-k}$$

and, in general, we have

$$P(k \geqq 3 | n, p) = \sum \binom{n}{k} p^k q^{n-k}$$

Both sources have cumulative probability tables. The National Bureau of Standards tables are on a "more than" basis, and the Romig tables are on a "less than" basis. Since $p = 0.3$ and $n = 5$ in our example, we find from the National Bureau of Standards table:

$$P(k \geqq 3 | n = 5, p = 0.3) = 0.1630800$$

When $p > 0.50$, we perform a transformation similar to the case of individual probabilities and find a corresponding equivalent formula where $p < 0.50$. Let us illustrate by letting $p = 0.7$ and finding the probability of at least 3 successes in $n = 5$ trials. This is shown as

$$P(k \geqq 3 | n = 5, p = 0.7) = P(k = 3) + P(k = 4) + P(k = 5)$$

$$= 1 - P(k = 0) - P(k = 1) - P(k = 2)$$

$$= 1 - \binom{5}{0} p^0 q^{5-0} - \binom{5}{1} p^1 q^{5-1} - \binom{5}{2} p^2 q^{5-2}$$

Recalling that $\binom{n}{k} = \binom{n}{n-k}$, this becomes

$$P(k \geqq 3 | n = 5, p = 0.7) = 1 - \binom{5}{5} q^5 p^{5-5} - \binom{5}{4} q^4 p^{5-4} - \binom{5}{3} q^3 p^{5-3}$$

$$= 1 - \sum_{k=5-3+1}^{5} \binom{n}{k} q^k p^{n-k}$$

$$= 1 - P(k \geqq 5 - 3 + 1 | n, q)$$

The reasons this rather roundabout procedure is developed are (1) the $q = 1 - p = 1 - 0.7 = 0.3 < 0.5$, and (2) the National Bureau of Standards table is on a "more than" cumulative basis. From the cumulative table we find

$$1 - P(k \geq 3 \mid n = 5, q = 0.3) = 1 - 0.1630800$$
$$= 0.8369200$$

In general, we may state that

$$P(k \geq k_0 \mid n, p) = 1 - P(k \geq n - k_0 + 1 \mid n, q)$$

where $q = 1 - p$.

Example 1. What is the probability of selecting at least 2 red beads, where $n = 5$, $p = 0.7$?

$$P(k \geq 2 \mid n = 5, p = 0.7) = 1 - P(k \geq 5 - 2 + 1 \mid n = 5, q = 0.3)$$
$$= 1 - 0.0307800$$
$$= 0.9692200$$

The interpretation is: The probability of selecting at least 2 red beads in 5 trials where $p = 0.7$ is equal to 1 minus the probability of selecting at least 4 black beads in 5 trials with $q = 0.3$, and the probability is 0.969.

Example 2. Suppose $p = 0.40 = 40$ percent of a large number of families in a certain county use soap A. Let us take a sample of size $n = 30$. What is the probability that 15 families will be using soap A?

Since we assume a large number of families, we shall assume that p does not change, even if we do not sample with replacement. The probability will be, using the binomial table,

$$P(k = 15 \mid n = 30, p = 0.4) = 0.0783$$

There are about 8 chances in 100 of selecting a sample of 30 families with 15 using soap A.

Example 3. Using the data of Example 2, find the probability of there being at least 15 families using soap A in a sample of $n = 30$. From the National Bureau of Standards tables,

$$P(k \geq 15 \mid n = 30, p = 0.4)$$
$$= 0.175369$$

Example 4. In Example 3, let $p = 0.6$ and find the probability of at least 15 families using soap A.

$$P(k \geq 15 \mid n = 30, p = 0.6)$$
$$= 1 - P(k \geq 30 - 15 + 1 \mid n = 30, q = 0.4)$$
$$= 1 - 0.097057$$
$$= 0.902943$$

18.5. The Sampling Distribution of the Sample Proportion p

Many practical problems are concerned with a proportion of the population that has a certain characteristic. For example, a market researcher may be interested in the proportion of families using a certain brand of coffee, or a buyer of radios may be interested in the proportion of defectives per shipment. A population that is classified into two classes may be called a twofold, or binomial, population.

Let the units in one class be N_1 (say, a male, or defective) and the units in the other class be N_2 (say, a female, or nondefective). Then

$$N = N_1 + N_2$$

where N is the total population size. The population proportion of, say, males is defined as

$$\frac{N_1}{N} = \pi$$

We may be interested in estimating, or testing, hypotheses about this π, or comparing two π's. For this, we usually select a sample and find the sample proportion p to estimate or test hypotheses about π.

To estimate or perform tests about π, using p, we need to know the sampling distribution of p. In our previous discussion (Chapters 7 and 8), we assumed that the sample size n was large enough to use the normal approximation. However, when n is not large, we have to use the sampling distribution of p. It turns out that the sampling distribution of p is the same as the binomial distribution.

We may show this relation between the sampling distribution of p and the binomial distribution directly. However, we shall first digress and discuss various alternative ways of viewing a Bernoulli process and then derive the sampling distribution of p. The reason for discussing these various alternative ways of viewing the Bernoulli trials is that each is useful in certain situations, and we shall use these various approaches whenever necessary.

(i) Three ways of interpreting a sequence of n Bernoulli trials

Suppose a coin is tossed 10 times with the following results:

(1)	(2)	(3)	(4)	(5)	(6)	(7)	(8)	(9)	(10)
H	H	T	H	T	T	T	H	H	H

Assuming a fair coin, let us assign probability $\pi = \frac{1}{2}$ to heads and $1 - \pi = \frac{1}{2}$ to tails.

Let X be the random variable assigned to a toss where

$$X = \begin{cases} 1 & \text{for heads} \\ 0 & \text{for tails} \end{cases}$$

Then the sequence of 10 tosses may be shown as

(1)	(2)	(3)	(4)	(5)	(6)	(7)	(8)	(9)	(10)
H	H	T	H	T	T	T	H	H	H
1	1	0	1	0	0	0	1	1	1
x_1	x_2	x_3	x_4	x_5	x_6	x_7	x_8	x_9	x_{10}

The sum of the x's is

$$\Sigma x_i = 6$$

which is the number of heads in 10 tosses, and in terms of our previous notation, we may write

$$k = \Sigma x_i$$

where k was called the binomial variable. With this much background, let us distinguish the following approaches.

1. The first approach is to consider the 10 tosses as a sequence of 10 Bernoulli trials and the random variable k as the total number of successes in the 10 trials. The probability distribution was

(1) $$b(k : n, \pi) = \binom{n}{k} \pi^k (1 - \pi)^{n-k}$$

where $k = 0, 1, \ldots, 10$.

2. A second approach is to consider a discrete variable X, defined as

(2) $$X = \begin{cases} 1 & \text{for heads with } \pi = \frac{1}{2} \\ 0 & \text{for tails with } 1 - \pi = \frac{1}{2} \end{cases}$$

Then the 10 tosses will generate a sequence of 10 independent random variables:

$$X_1, X_2, \ldots, X_{10}$$

From the distribution above we can find the expected value and variance of X as follows:

(3) $$E(X) = \pi \cdot 1 + (1 - \pi) \cdot 0 = \pi$$

(4) $$\text{Var}(X) = E(X - \pi)^2$$
$$= \pi(1 - \pi)^2 + (1 - \pi)(0 - \pi)^2$$
$$= \pi(1 - \pi)$$

Using these results, let us find the mean and variance of the random variable k of the first approach. We know that

(5) $$k = X_1 + X_2 + \cdots + X_{10}$$

Hence, using the results of (3) and (4), the expected value and variance of k are, letting $n = 10$,

(6) $\qquad E(k) = \pi + \pi + \cdots + \pi = n\pi$

(7) $\quad \text{Var}(k) = \pi(1 - \pi) + \pi(1 - \pi) + \cdots + \pi(1 - \pi) = n\pi(1 - \pi)$

And from approach 1, we know the k to have the binomial distribution (1). That is, the random variable k of the first approach has the distribution given in (1) with mean and variance (6) and (7).

3.   The first approach considered k as the random variable. The second approach considered a sequence of independent random variables X_i and redefined k in terms of these X_i. The third approach we shall discuss considers the distribution of X_i.

To explain this third approach, we shall first assume a *population* and a *sample*. Let the population be the 10 values

$$X_1, X_2, \cdots, X_{10}$$

where the distribution is defined as

$$X = \begin{cases} 1 & \text{with probability } \pi \\ 0 & \text{with probability } 1 - \pi \end{cases}$$

Thus, density of X is

$$f(x) = \pi^x(1 - \pi)^{1-x} \qquad x = 0, 1$$

Let us define:

$$K = X_1 + X_2 + \cdots + X_{10}$$

Then, since $X = 0$ or 1, K is the total (or aggregate) of the population. In our present example, we have $K = 6$, whereas before we had 6 heads.

The population mean is

(8) $$\mu = \Sigma \frac{X}{N} = \frac{K}{N} = \pi$$

and is equal to the population proportion. The π may be considered as a special case of μ.

Let us now take a simple random sample of size $n = 4$ from the population and assume that it is

$$
\begin{array}{cccc}
H & H & T & H \\
1 & 1 & 0 & 1
\end{array}
$$

Then the sample total (aggregate) and the sample mean are

$$\Sigma x = 1 + 1 + 0 + 1 = 3 = k$$

(9)
$$\bar{x} = \Sigma \frac{x}{n} = \frac{3}{4} = p$$

and the sample mean is equal to the sample proportion.

The sample variance is

$$s^2 = \frac{1}{n} \Sigma (x - \bar{x})^2$$

(10)
$$= \frac{1}{n} [\Sigma x^2 - 2x \Sigma x + nx^2]$$

But we have

$$\bar{x} = p, \quad \Sigma x = np, \quad \Sigma x^2 = np$$

and substituting this into the equation above, we find

(11)
$$s^2 = pq$$

In Chapter 17 we saw that an unbiased estimate of the population variance σ^2 was

(12)
$$\hat{\sigma}^2 = \frac{\Sigma (x - \bar{x})^2}{n - 1} = \frac{n}{n - 1} s^2$$

Substituting (11) in (12), we find

(13)
$$\hat{\sigma}^2 = \frac{n}{n - 1} pq$$

as the unbiased estimate of σ^2.

(ii) *An illustration*

Let us illustrate these results with our example.

x	$x - \bar{x}$	$(x - \bar{x})^2$
1	1/4	1/16
1	1/4	1/16
0	−3/4	9/16
1	1/4	1/16
$\overline{3}$	0	12/16

$$\bar{x} = \frac{3}{4}$$

$$s^2 = \frac{1}{n} \, \Sigma \, (x - \bar{x})^2 = \frac{1}{4} \times \frac{12}{16} = \frac{3}{16}$$

The sample proportion is

$$p = \bar{x} = \frac{3}{4}$$

$$q = 1 - p = \frac{1}{4}$$

From (11), we find the variance s^2 as

$$s^2 = pq = \left(\frac{3}{4}\right)\left(\frac{1}{4}\right) = \frac{3}{16}$$

and it is the same as that we have obtained from the table.

(iii)   The sampling distribution of p

Let us next consider the sampling distribution of the sample proportion p. We have taken a sample of size 4, and since the random variable x has only 2 outcomes (which have probability π and $1 - \pi$), we have a 4-dimensional sample space with $2^4 = 16$ sample points. Let us enumerate these 16 sample points (Table 18.2).

TABLE 18.2.

(1)	1	1	1	1	(9)	0	1	0	1
(2)	1	1	1	0	(10)	0	0	1	1
(3)	1	1	0	1	(11)	0	1	1	0
(4)	1	0	1	1	(12)	1	0	0	0
(5)	0	1	1	1	(13)	0	1	0	0
(6)	1	1	0	0	(14)	0	0	1	0
(7)	1	0	1	0	(15)	0	0	0	1
(8)	1	0	0	1	(16)	0	0	0	0

Since the probability of 1 is π and the probability of 0 is $1 - \pi$, the density function associated with each of these points is shown as

$$f(x_1, x_2, x_3, x_4) = \pi^{\Sigma x} (1 - \pi)^{n - \Sigma x}$$

where Σ is over the sample and $n = 4$. For sample (1) in the preceding table, the density function is

$$f(x_1, x_2, x_3, x_4) = \pi^4 (1 - \pi)^{4-4} = \pi^4$$

For the sample (5), we have

$$f(x_1, x_2, x_3, x_4) = \pi^3 (1 - \pi)^{4-3}$$

and so forth.

Although we have 16 distinct sample points, in terms of samples the points (1, 1, 1, 0) and (1, 1, 0, 1), for instance, are the same sample. Let us regroup the samples in terms of the number of 1's, which we denote by k.

k	Sample Point	f
4	(1)	1
3	(2), (3), (4), (5)	4
2	(6), (7), (8), (9), (10), (11)	6
1	(12), (13), (14), (15)	4
0	(16)	1

The number of sample points corresponding to k may also be found by using the formula

$$\binom{n}{k}$$

For example, for $k = 2$,

$$\binom{n}{k} = \binom{4}{2} = 6$$

which shows that there are 6 ways of ordering two 1's in 4 places.

The probability distribution of k is thus

$$P(k) = \binom{n}{k} \pi^k (1 - \pi)^{n-k}$$

which is the binomial probability distribution.

Since the sample proportion p is $p = k/n$, we may replace the k by p in the table; hence, as is seen, the probability distribution of p is the same as k. This may be written as

$$P\left(\frac{k}{n}\right) = \binom{n}{k} \pi^k (1 - \pi)^{n-k}$$

This is the sampling distribution of p, and it is the binomial probability distribution. The results for our example are given in Table 18.3 and also graphically in Fig. 18.5.

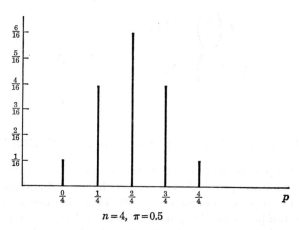

$n=4, \;\; \pi=0.5$

FIG. 18.5.

TABLE 18.3.

$p = k/n$	f	$P(k) = P(p)$
4/4	1	$\binom{4}{4} \pi^4$
3/4	4	$\binom{4}{3} \pi^3 (1 - \pi)$
2/4	6	$\binom{4}{2} \pi^2 (1 - \pi)^2$
1/4	4	$\binom{4}{1} \pi (1 - \pi)^3$
0/4	1	$\binom{4}{0} (1 - \pi)^4$
	$\overline{16}$	

(iv)   The mean and variance of the sampling distribution of p

From equations (1), (6), and (7) we find that the binomial variable k has a binomial distribution

(14) $$P(k) = \binom{k}{n} \pi^k (1 - \pi)^{n-k}$$

with mean and variance

(15) $$E(k) = n\pi$$

(16) $$\text{Var}(k) = n\pi(1 - \pi)$$

We know that the sample proportion is $p = k/n$. Hence, from equations (15) and (16), we find

(17) $$E\left(\frac{k}{n}\right) = E(p) = \pi$$

(18) $$\text{Var}\left(\frac{k}{n}\right) = \text{Var}(p) = \frac{n\pi(1 - \pi)}{n^2}$$

$$= \frac{\pi(1 - \pi)}{n}$$

which are the mean and variance of the sampling distribution of p.

Example 1. Suppose we have a large population of smokers and nonsmokers and let the population proportion of smokers be $\pi = 0.4$ and nonsmokers be $1 - \pi = 0.6$. Let us take a sample of $n = 10$. Then the number of smokers k (which is the random variable) can take on the values $k = 0, 1, 2, \ldots, 10$. The random variable k can also be expressed by the sample proportion p as

$$p = \frac{0}{10}, \quad \frac{1}{10}, \quad \cdots, \quad \frac{9}{10}, \quad \frac{10}{10}$$

The probabilities associated with these sample proportions are found in the National Bureau of Standards table, as shown in Table 18.4.

TABLE 18.4.

$P(p = 0/10) = 0.0060$	$P(p = 6/10) = 0.1115$
$P(p = 1/10) = 0.0403$	$P(p = 7/10) = 0.0425$
$P(p = 2/10) = 0.1209$	$P(p = 8/10) = 0.0106$
$P(p = 3/10) = 0.2150$	$P(p = 9/10) = 0.001572$
$P(p = 4/10) = 0.2508$	$P(p = 10/10) = 0.0001049$
$P(p = 5/10) = 0.2006$	

Figure 18.6 is the graphical presentation of this distribution. $P(p = 0.4) = 0.2508$, for example, means that if we took a sample of size 10, the probability of having $k = 4$ smokers ($p = 4/10 = 0.4$) is 0.2508. Or, to put it another way, if we selected 100 samples of size 10 from the population, we should expect that about 25 of these samples will have $k = 4$ smokers in it. The height of the bars indicates the relative frequency with which we can expect samples with k smokers in it to occur.

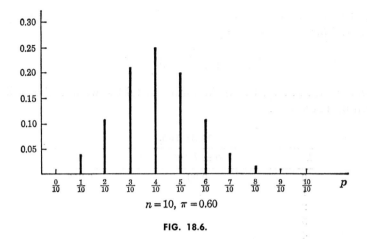

$n = 10, \; \pi = 0.60$

FIG. 18.6.

The mean and variance of this distribution is

$$E(p) = \pi = 0.4$$

$$\mathrm{Var}(p) = \frac{\pi(1 - \pi)}{n}$$

$$= \frac{(0.4)(0.6)}{10} = 0.024$$

Since $E(p) = 0.4 < 0.5$, we see that the distribution is skewed to the right. When $\pi > 0.5$ it will be skewed to the left, and when $\pi = 0.5$ it will be symmetrical.

Example 2. Suppose $\pi = 0.25$ (Fig. 18.7) of the families use soap A. Take a

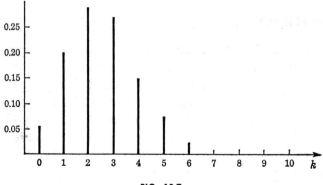

FIG. 18.7.

sample of $n = 10$ and let p be the proportion of families in the sample that use soap A. Then the probability distribution of p is

$$P(p) = \binom{n}{np} \pi^k (1 - \pi)^{n-k}$$

where $n = 0, 1, \ldots, 10$. Using the binomial tables, we find the probability as shown in Table 18.5.

TABLE 18.5.

k	$p = k/n$	$P(k)$
0	0.00	0.056
1	0.1	0.188
2	0.2	0.282
3	0.3	0.250
4	0.4	0.146
5	0.5	0.058
6	0.6	0.016
7	0.7	0.003
8	0.8	0.0004
9	0.9	0.00003
10	1.00	0.0
		1.00000

The mean and variance of the sampling distribution of p is

$$E(p) = \pi = 0.25$$

$$\text{Var}(p) = \frac{\pi(1 - \pi)}{n}$$

$$= \frac{(0.25)(0.75)}{10} = 0.01875$$

18.6. Tests of Hypotheses, Using the Binomial Distribution

In Chapters 7 and 8, tests of hypotheses concerning proportions were made, using the normal approximation. In this section we shall perform tests of hypotheses of proportions, using the sampling distribution of the sample proportion p that was derived in Section 18.5. The rationale involved in the tests is the same as that of Chapters 7 and 8. What differs is the way in which the rejection regions are computed.

We shall first give a simple illustration of tests of hypotheses and then explain the Clopper and Pearson charts.

(i) Testing hypotheses

Suppose a company will reject shipment of a certain product if more than 25 percent are defective and will accept shipment if less than or equal to 25 percent are defective. The company is anxious to avoid the error of rejecting the shipment when it should not. Then the null and alternative hypotheses are

$$H_1: \quad \pi \leq 20\%$$
$$H_2: \quad \pi > 20\%$$

Let us also assume that $n = 10$ and the level of significance is $\alpha = 10$ percent. The problem is shown schematically as follows:

Decision	$\pi \leq 0.25$	$\pi > 0.25$
A_1, accept		$\beta = P(A_1\|\pi > 25\%)$
A_2, reject	$\alpha = P(A_2\|\pi = 25\%)$	

The probability for different p's, given $\pi = 0.25$, has already been found in Table 18.5. It is reproduced here as Table 18.6 with additional cumulative and decumulative columns.

TABLE 18.6.

k	$p = k/n$	$P(k)$	Cumulative	Decumulative
0	0.0	0.056	0.056	
1	0.1	0.188	0.244	
2	0.2	0.282		
3	0.3	0.250		
4	0.4	0.146		0.223
5	0.5	0.058		0.077
6	0.6	0.016		0.019
7	0.7	0.003		0.003
8	0.8	0.0004		0.0
9	0.9	0.00003		0.0
10	1.0	0.0		0.0
		1.0000		

The hypotheses show that the critical value p^* will be in the upper (right) tail of the sampling distribution of p. Hence, we use the decumulative column of Table 18.6 to determine p^*. As this decumulative column shows,

$$P(p \geq 0.4) = 0.223$$
$$P(p \geq 0.5) = 0.077$$

Hence, 0.5 satisfies the requirement $\alpha = 0.1$, whereas 0.4 does not. Since p is a discrete variable, we cannot choose a value between 0.4 and 0.5. Hence, the critical value p^* is 0.5.

The conclusion (rule) is: Take a sample of size $n = 10$. If

$$p < 0.5 \qquad \text{accept shipment}$$
$$p \geqq 0.5 \qquad \text{reject shipment}$$

(ii) The Clopper and Pearson charts

The sampling distribution of p was

$$P(p) = \binom{n}{np} \pi^k (1 - \pi)^{n-k}$$

As this equation shows, $P(p)$ depends on n, p, and π. In our previous examples of testing hypotheses, we held n and π fixed and let p vary. What we wish to do now is to hold n fixed, let both π and p vary, and show how rejection regions and confidence intervals can be found. Let us start our discussion with a simple illustration.

We shall first construct a table (Table 18.7) where both p and π vary, holding the sample size at $n = 10$. We see that the values of Table 18.4, where $\pi = 0.4$, are found in the row corresponding to $\pi = 0.4$ of Table 18.7.

The results of Table 18.6, where we assumed $\pi = 0.25$ of the families used soap A, are found in the row corresponding to $\pi = 0.25$ of Table 18.7.

Let us now discuss some examples and show how this table may be used.

Example 1. A firm receives shipment of parts for production of TV sets. If 20 percent or less are defective, the firm will accept the shipment. If more than 20 percent are defective, the shipment will be rejected. The firm is anxious to avoid the error of rejecting the shipment when it should not and

Decision	$\pi \leqq 20\%$	$\pi > 20\%$
A_1, accept		
A_2, reject	$\alpha = P(A_2 \mid \pi \leqq 20\%)$	

sets the a risk at 10 percent and the sample size at $n = 10$. The null and alternative hypothesis are

$$H_1: \qquad \pi \leqq 20\%$$
$$H_2: \qquad \pi > 20\%$$

TABLE 18.7. $(n = 10)$

π/p	0	1	0.2	0.3	0.4	0.5	0.6	0.7	0.8	0.9	1.0
0.95							.001	.010	.075	.315	.599
0.90						.002	.011	.057	.194	.387	.349
0.85					.001	.008	.040	.130	.276	.347	.197
0.80				.001	.006	.026	.088	.201	.302	.268	.107
0.75				.003	.016	.058	.146	.250	.282	.188	.056
0.70			.001	.009	.037	.103	.200	.267	.233	.121	.028
0.65		.001	.004	.021	.069	.154	.238	.252	.176	.072	.013
0.60		.002	.011	.042	.111	.201	.251	.215	.121	.040	.006
0.55		.004	.023	.075	.160	.234	.238	.166	.076	.021	.003
0.50	.001	.010	.044	.117	.205	.246	.205	.117	.044	.010	.001
0.45	.003	.021	.076	.166	.238	.234	.160	.075	.023	.004	
0.40	.006	.040	.121	.215	.251	.201	.111	.042	.011	.002	
0.35	.013	.072	.176	.252	.238	.154	.069	.021	.004	.001	
0.30	.028	.121	.233	.267	.200	.103	.037	.009	.001		
0.25	.056	.188	.282	.250	.146	.058	.016	.003			
0.20	.107	.268	.302	.201	.088	.026	.006	.001			
0.15	.197	.347	.276	.130	.040	.008	.001				
0.10	.349	.387	.194	.057	.011	.002					
0.05	.599	.315	.075	.010	.001						

To perform this test, we need to find the sampling distribution of p corresponding to $\pi = 20$ percent of the table. Let us show these probabilities graphically, as in Fig. 18.8, as a visual aid.

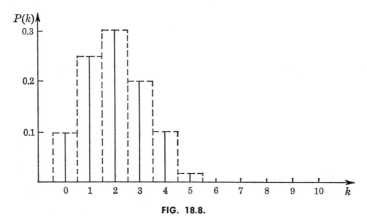

FIG. 18.8.

According to our test, we wish to find the critical value p^* in the upper tail beyond which we have 10 percent of the area (probability). From Fig. 18.8 and Table 18.7, we see that the probability beyond $p = 0.5$ is

$$0.026 + 0.006 + 0.001 = 0.033 \ (= 3.3\%)$$

The probability beyond $p = 0.4$ is

$$0.088 + 0.033 = 0.121 \; (= 12.1\%)$$

The interpretation of these probabilities is: When the population proportion $\pi = 0.20$, the probability of selecting samples of size $n = 10$ with sample proportions $p \geq 0.5$ is about 3.3 percent. The probability of selecting samples with $p \geq 0.4$ is about 12.1 percent.

Hence, if the $\alpha = 10$ percent is strictly adhered to, the critical value is $p^* = 0.5$, and in this case, the α-risk becomes 3.3 percent and is much less than the 10 percent which the firm was willing to allow.

If the firm feels this is too severe and is willing to relax the risk and let it be 12 percent instead of 10 percent, the critical value will be $p^* = 0.4$.

Using this second critical value, the decision rule is: Take a sample of size $n = 10$. If

$$p \geq 0.4 \qquad \text{reject hypotheses}$$
$$p < 0.4 \qquad \text{accept hypotheses}$$

Then the α-risk is about 12 percent. The β-risk is not calculated.

Example 2.   The α-risk in our previous example was 10 percent in the upper right tail. Let us now consider a two-tail case with 5 percent in each tail, given the population proportion $\pi = 0.25$. For the lower (left) tail, the value 0.056 is larger than 5 percent. But the variable p is discrete, and $p = 0$ is the smallest value it can take; we shall use the approximate value 0.056 to satisfy the requirement that $\alpha = 5$ percent.

For the upper tail, the value corresponding to $p = 0.6$ (that is, $k = 6$) has been circled. As Table 18.7 shows, the probability in the upper tail becomes

$$0.016 + 0.003 = 0.019$$

which is considerably smaller than 5 percent. However, the probability for $p = 0.5$ is 0.058; hence, when the rejection region starts at $p = 0.5$, the risk becomes

$$0.058 + 0.019 = 0.077$$

and becomes larger than 0.05 (= 5%). Hence, we shall let the critical region start from $p = 0.6$.

Let us look at the $\pi = 0.30$ row and perform the same operation. For the lower tail to be 5 percent or less, we circle the value 0.028 that corresponds to $p = 0$ (or $k = 0$). The value that corresponds to $p = 0.1$ (or $k = 1$) is 0.121, which exceeds 0.05 considerably and is excluded.

For the upper tail, the value 0.037, which corresponds to $p = 0.6$ (or $k = 6$), is circled and the cumulative sum for the upper tail is

$$0.037 + 0.009 + 0.001 + 0.000 + 0.000 < 0.05$$

The value that corresponds to $p = 0.5$ is 0.103 and is much larger than 0.05 and hence is excluded.

Circles have been put on the other values in Table 18.7 in a similar manner and the locus of these circled values gives us the boundary of the upper and lower critical regions.

In similar fashion we can find the boundaries when $\alpha = 5$ percent (that is, 2.5 percent in each tail) or 2 percent (that is, 1 percent in each tail) or some other value. When $\alpha = 15$ percent, for example, and is larger than 10 percent, then the boundary will lie inside the one we have drawn for $\alpha = 10$ percent. When $\alpha = 5$ percent, for example, and is smaller than 10 percent, the boundary will lie outside the one we have drawn for $\alpha = 10$ percent.

Furthermore, the boundary we have drawn is not smooth because the values of p and π we have been using are discrete. But, theoretically, as the values of p and π jump by small steps and approach a continuous variable, the boundaries will also become smooth curves.

Note that these curves assumed the sample size to be $n = 10$. In practice, however, the size of the sample will usually vary according to the problem. So let us next consider the case where $\alpha = 5$ percent is held constant but where n *varies*. We know that as the sample size becomes larger, the variance of the sampling distribution of p becomes smaller. That is,

$$\text{Var}(p) = \frac{\pi(1 - \pi)}{n}$$

becomes smaller as n becomes larger. Graphically (Fig. 18.9) this means the binomial curve becomes narrower and more pointed. This in turn

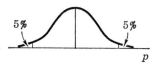 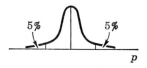

FIG. 18.9.

implies that the acceptance region becomes narrower, which means that when the sample is large, we may expect the sample proportion to be close to the population proportion π. Thus the boundary lines for n larger than $n = 10$ will lie inside the boundary lines for $n = 10$.

If we had a graph with boundary lines showing the rejection region for a given risk (say, $\alpha = 5$ percent) for various sample sizes, we should be able to read off from this graph the rejection regions. C. J. Clopper and E. S. Pearson have provided us with such a graph. This is reproduced in Fig. 18.10. It gives us the boundary lines for the rejection regions for $\alpha = 5$ percent and $n = 10, 15, 20, 30, 50, 100, 250,$ and 1000. Let us illustrate its use.

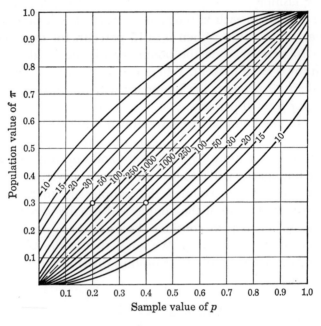

FIG. 18.10.

SOURCE: Reproduced by permission of the editor, from C. J. Clopper and E. S. Pearson, "The Use of Confidence or Fiducial Limits Illustrated in the Case of the Binomial," *Biometrika*, **26**, 1934, pp. 404–413.

Example 3.   Consider a population where $100\,\pi$ percent of the families use soap A. To test whether or not $100\,\pi = 30$ percent, the hypotheses are

$$H_1: \qquad \pi = 0.30$$
$$H_2: \qquad \pi \neq 0.30$$

A random sample of 100 families is taken and the sample proportion of families using soap A is found to be $p = 0.38$. Does this support the hypothesis that $\pi = 0.30$?

From Fig. 18.10 we find the row corresponding to $\pi = 0.30$. Then looking at the two curves that correspond to $n = 100$, we find for the lower and upper values, 0.20 and 0.40. The interpretation is as follows: If π were in fact $\pi = 0.30$, the probability of p falling outside the two limits 0.20 and 0.40 is $\alpha = 5$ percent. Assuming a level of significance of 5 percent, since $p = 0.38$, we accept the null hypothesis.

18.7   Calculation of the OC Curve

In Section 18.6, hypotheses were tested on the basis of the α-risk, but nothing was said about the β-risk. In this section, let us show how the β-risk is computed, and then, using these β-risks, we shall draw OC curves. The reasoning process is the same as that discussed in Chapter 8. What differs is the way the probabilities are computed, namely, we shall use the binomial tables to calculate the probabilities, which is quite a tedious process. Let us illustrate this process with an example.

Suppose we have a population of families and let π be the proportion that uses soap A. If π is 20 percent or less, management wishes to increase the amount of advertising, whereas if π is more than 20 percent, it wishes to leave the amount of advertising at the present level. Management is anxious to avoid the error of not advertising when it should. The situation is shown schematically as follows:

Decision	$\pi \leq 20\%$	$\pi > 20\%$
A_1, advertise		$\beta = P(A_1 \mid \pi > 0.20)$
A_2, do not advertise	$\alpha = P(A_2 \mid \pi = 0.20)$	

In terms of the null and alternative hypotheses, we have

$$H_1: \qquad \pi \leq 0.20$$
$$H_2: \qquad \pi > 0.20$$

Let management be willing to allow an α-risk of 5 percent. The problem is to find the critical value p^*, given a value of n such that the α-risk is satisfied. We shall find critical values p^* that correspond to sample sizes $n = 20, 40, 60, 80,$ and 100.

(i)   Calculation of p* for various n

Given $n = 20$, we find from the National Bureau of Standards tables the individual and cumulative binomial probabilities, as shown in Table 18.8

TABLE 18.8.

$s = k$	$p = k/n$ $= k/20$	$P(s = k)$	$P(s \geqq k)$
0	0	0.0115	
1	0.05	0.0576	
2	0.10	0.1369	
3	0.15	0.2054	
4	0.20	0.2182	
5	0.25	0.1746	
6	0.30	0.1091	
7	0.35	0.0545	0.0867
8	0.40	0.0222	0.0322
9	0.45	0.0074	0.0100
10	0.50	0.0020	0.0026
11	0.55	0.0005	0.0006
12	0.60	0.0001	0.0001

As this table shows, we have

$$P(k \geqq 7 \mid \pi = 0.20) = P(p \geqq 0.35 \mid \pi = 0.20)$$
$$= 0.0867$$
$$P(k \geqq 8 \mid \pi = 0.20) = P(p \geqq 0.40 \mid \pi = 0.20)$$
$$= 0.0322$$

Since we want $\alpha = 0.05$ or less, we shall take $k = 8$ or $p^* = 8/20 = 0.4$ as the critical value.

In similar fashion, we can find the critical values p^* for various n. The results are summarized in Table 18.9.

TABLE 18.9.

n	k	p^*	$P(k \geqq k_0 \mid \pi = 0.20)$	$\beta = P(k \leqq k_0 \mid \pi = 0.40)$
20	7		0.0867	
	8*	0.400	0.0321	0.5956
40	12		0.0878	
	13*	0.325	0.0432	0.2111
60	16		0.0773	
	17*	0.28	0.0427	0.0413
80	21		0.066	
	22*	0.275	0.039	0.0137
100	26		0.0558	
	27*	0.27	0.0342	0.0046

For example, for $n = 60$, we see that for

$$k = 16: \qquad \alpha = 0.0773$$
$$k = 17: \qquad \alpha = 0.0427$$

Hence, we take $k = 17$ or $p^* = 17/60 = 0.28$ as the critical value.

(ii) The OC curve

Once the critical value $p^* = 0.28$ is found, we may easily find the β-risks and hence the OC curve. Let us show the situation diagrammatically as a visual aid. Figure 18.11 shows the situation schematically.

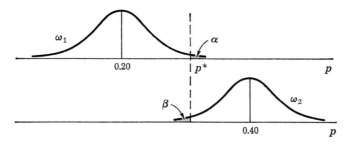

FIG. 18.11.

For example, when the alternative hypothesis is $\pi_2 = 0.40$, the β-risk is

$$\beta = P(p \leq p^* \mid \pi_2 = 0.40) = 0.0719$$

where $p^* = 0.28$, $n = 60$, and $\pi_2 = 0.40$. The various β-risks corresponding to the various alternative hypotheses are calculated in similar fashion and are shown in Table 18.10.

TABLE 18.10.

$$n = 60, \quad p^* = 0.28 = 17/60, \quad \beta = P(p \leq p^* \mid \pi_2)$$

π_2	β	$1 - \beta$
0.40	.04	.96
0.35	.17	.83
0.30	.45	.55
0.25	.78	.22
0.20	.96	.04
0.15	.99	.01
0.10	.99	.01

The $1 - \beta$ was called the power of the test in Chapter 8 and showed the probability of being correct, given the alternative hypothesis. Hence, the larger $1 - \beta$, the better the rule.

When the values of π_2 and β are graphed, we obtain the OC curve as shown in Fig. 18.12.

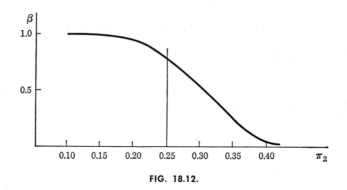

FIG. 18.12.

By applying the same procedure to $n = 20$, 40, 80, and 100, we find the corresponding OC curves. Table 18.11 gives the various values for different n. Figure 18.13 shows the OC curves corresponding to the various sample sizes.

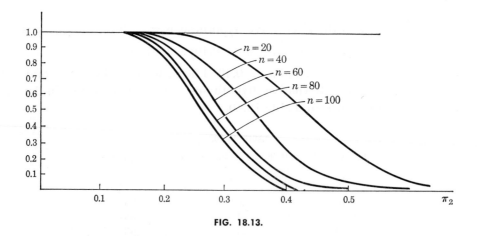

FIG. 18.13.

(iii)   Use of the OC curve

Now that we have an OC curve, it is natural to ask: How may it be used? The OC curve represents a decision rule and hence may be used to design a sampling procedure. Let us explain this with a hypothetical example. Suppose we have an OC curve as shown in Fig. 18.14. Recall how the horizontal scale shows the various alternative hypotheses π_2 and the vertical scale shows the β-values.

TABLE 18.11.

$$\beta = P(k \leq k^* \mid n, \pi_2) = 1 - P(k \geq k^* + 1 \mid n, \pi_2)$$

π_2	$n = 20$ $p^* = 8/20$	$n = 40$ $p^* = 13/40$	$n = 60$ $p^* = 17/60$	$n = 80$ $p^* = 22/80$	$n = 100$ $p^* = 27/100$
10	0.999	0.999	0.999	0.999	0.999
15	0.998	0.998	0.997	0.998	0.999
20	0.990	0.981	0.957	0.961	0.981
25	0.959	0.897	0.775	0.745	0.722
30	0.887	0.704	0.451	0.363	0.296
35	0.763	0.441	0.172	0.097	0.055
40	0.595	0.211	0.041	0.013	0.005
45	0.415	0.075	0.006	0.001	0.000
50	0.252	0.019	0.001	0.000	0.000

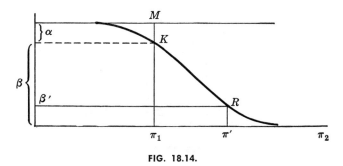

FIG. 18.14.

Let us denote the null hypothesis by π_1, which is also shown in Fig. 18.14. Then the height of the curve at π_1 shows

$$\beta = P(A_1 \mid \pi_2)$$

where, in this case, $\pi_2 = \pi_1$, and hence at this point on the horizontal scale we have

$$\beta = P(A_1 \mid \pi_1)$$

Thus the distance MK is

$$1 - \beta = 1 - P(A_1 \mid \pi_1)$$
$$= P(A_2 \mid \pi_1)$$
$$= \alpha$$

That is, MK is equal to the α-risk. In other words, the point on the horizontal scale (which shows π_2) where π_2 becomes equal to the null hypothesis π_1, the upper part of the OC curve MK, as we have shown it, will be equal to the α-risk. Thus the point K can be shown symbolically as $(\pi_1, \beta = 1 - \alpha)$.

Next let us select a value π' and find the corresponding point R on the OC curve, and let β be β'. Then this point R can be shown symbolically as (π', β').

Let us now reverse the procedure and suppose that we have a statistical test where

$$H_1: \qquad \pi = \pi_1$$
$$H_2: \qquad \pi = \pi_2$$

and α- and β-risks are given. Then we can plot two points on the OC graph, namely $(\pi_1, 1 - \alpha)$ and (π_2, β), as shown in Fig. 18.15. Find an

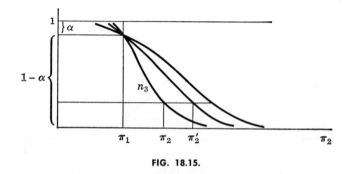

FIG. 18.15.

OC curve that passes through these two points and let it be shown by n_3.

This curve shows that when a sample of size n is taken, the probability of accepting the null hypothesis, when in fact the population proportion is π_2, will be β. We note that in this case the error tolerated is $\pi_2 - \pi_1 = e$.

We may continue our discussion of OC curves and consider the topic of sampling inspection. However, further discussion requires knowledge of the normal approximation to the binomial distribution and the Poisson distribution. So, let us consider these topics first and postpone further discussion of the OC curve.

18.8.   Estimators of π and σ_p

Up to now we have solved problems, using the binomial distribution and given the assumption that π is known. However, in many practical problems, π is not known; in this case, it is necessary to estimate π. In this section we shall first discuss the estimator of π and then estimators of the various variances.

(i)   Estimator of π

We mentioned in Chapter 10 that the sample proportion p is an unbiased maximum likelihood estimator of π. Hence, we may write

$$\hat{\pi} = p$$

and

$$E(p) = \pi$$

Thus, p is an unbiased, consistent, and sufficient estimator of π.

Example.   A random sample of 100 retailers was selected and it was found
that 20 of them experienced a decline in business during a given month.
Thus, an unbiased maximum likelihood estimate of the proportion of retailers that experienced a decline in business is

$$\hat{\pi} = p = \frac{20}{100} = 0.20$$

(ii)   Estimators of variances

We have seen that there are several ways of viewing a Bernoulli
process. One was to consider the number of successes k as a random
variable. A second was to view the Bernoulli process as a sequence of
random variable x_i, where $x_i = 1$ or 0, and let $k = x_1 + \cdots + x_N$. The
third approach was to consider the distribution of the x_i. We shall use
this third approach to discuss the various variances.

Suppose we have a twofold (or binomial, or dichotomous) population
$x_1, x_2, \ldots, x_N$, where

$$x_i = \begin{cases} 1 & \text{with probability } \pi \\ 0 & \text{with probability } 1 - \pi \end{cases}$$

A sample $x_1, x_2, \ldots, x_n$ of size n is taken.

We have seen that the aggregate of the population is

$$K = \overset{N}{\Sigma} x_i$$

For example, suppose the population is classified into smokers and nonsmokers. Let $x_i = 1$ be a smoker and $x_i = 0$ be a nonsmoker. Then K is
the total (or aggregate) number of smokers in the population. The
population mean and variance have been defined as

$$\mu = \frac{1}{N} \Sigma x = \frac{K}{N} = \pi$$

$$\text{Var}(x) = \sigma^2 = \frac{1}{N} \Sigma (x - \mu)^2 = \pi (1 - \pi)$$

For example, π is the proportion of smokers in the population, and σ^2 is the variance of the x_i in the population.

In similar manner we defined, for the sample,

$$k = \sum_{}^{n} x \qquad\qquad \text{sample aggregate}$$

$$\bar{x} = \frac{1}{n} \sum x = p \qquad \text{sample mean (i.e., sample proportion)}$$

$$s^2 = p(1 - p) = pq \quad \text{sample variance}$$

For example, k is the total number of smokers in the sample; p is the proportion of smokers in the sample; and s^2 is the variance of the distribution of the x in the sample.

For the sampling distribution of p, we have

$$E(p) = \pi$$

$$E(k) = n\pi$$

$$\mathrm{Var}(p) = \frac{\pi(1 - \pi)}{n} = \frac{\sigma^2}{n} = \sigma_p^2$$

From Chapter 17, we know that

$$\hat{\sigma}^2 = \frac{n}{n - 1} s^2$$

$$\hat{\sigma}_{\bar{x}}^2 = \frac{\hat{\sigma}^2}{n}$$

Using these relations and the results we obtained above, we find

$$\hat{\sigma}^2 = \frac{n}{n - 1} s^2$$

$$= \frac{n}{n - 1} pq$$

as an unbiased estimator of the population variance.

Using this result, we find, noting that $\bar{x} = p$,

$$\hat{\sigma}_p^2 = \frac{\hat{\sigma}^2}{n} = \frac{1}{n}\left(\frac{n}{n - 1} pq\right)$$

$$= \frac{pq}{n - 1}$$

as an unbiased estimator of the variance of p.

However, in practice, a simplified formula

$$\hat{\sigma}_p{}^2 = \frac{pq}{n}$$

is used. For most practical cases, the difference between using n and $n - 1$ is small. We shall use this simplified formula for $\hat{\sigma}_p{}^2$.

Example 1. A random sample of size 100 persons is selected, and it is found that 30 wear glasses. An estimate of the proportion of persons wearing glasses in the population is

$$\hat{\pi} = p = \frac{30}{100} = 0.3$$

An estimate of the population variance is

$$\hat{\sigma}^2 = \frac{n}{n - 1} pq$$

$$= \frac{100}{100 - 1} (0.3)(0.7)$$

$$= 0.21$$

An estimate of the variance of the sampling distribution of p is

$$\hat{c}_p{}^2 = \frac{pq}{n}$$

$$= \frac{(0.3)(0.7)}{100}$$

$$= 0.0021$$

Example 2. Consider a population of 10 students where 4 of them smoke. Then the population proportion is

$$\pi = \frac{4}{10} = 0.4$$

and the population variance is

$$\sigma^2 = (0.4)(1 - 0.4) = 0.24$$

Let us calculate this σ^2, using the definition

$$\sigma^2 = \frac{1}{N} \Sigma (x - \mu)^2$$

The calculations are shown in Table 18.12.

From Table 18.12 we find

$$\sigma^2 = \frac{1}{10}\,(2.4) = 0.24$$

which is the same as the result obtained above.

Let us now take a random sample of 5 students where we find 3 of them smoke. The sample proportion is $p = 3/5 = 0.6$. The sample variance is

$$s^2 = p(1 - p) = (0.6)(0.4) = 0.24$$

TABLE 18.12.

	x	$x - \mu$		$(x - \mu)^2$
1	1	$1 - 0.4 =$	0.6	0.36
2	1	$1 - 0.4 =$	0.6	0.36
3	1	$1 - 0.4 =$	0.6	0.36
4	1	$1 - 0.4 =$	0.6	0.36
5	0	$0 - 0.4 =$	-0.4	0.16
6	0	$0 - 0.4 =$	-0.4	0.16
7	0	$0 - 0.4 =$	-0.4	0.16
8	0	$0 - 0.4 =$	-0.4	0.16
9	0	$0 - 0.4 =$	-0.4	0.16
10	0	$0 - 0.4 =$	-0.4	0.16
			0	2.40

This may also be calculated as shown in Table 18.13.

TABLE 18.13.

x	$x - \bar{x}$		$(x - \bar{x})^2$
1	$1 - 0.6 =$	0.4	0.16
1	$1 - 0.6 =$	0.4	0.16
1	$1 - 0.6 =$	0.4	0.16
0	$0 - 0.6 =$	-0.6	0.36
0	$0 - 0.6 =$	-0.6	0.36
		0	1.20

From the table we find

$$s^2 = \frac{1}{5}\,(1.20) = 0.24$$

An unbiased estimate of the population variance $\hat{\sigma}^2$ is

$$\hat{\sigma}^2 = \frac{n}{n - 1}\,s^2$$

$$= \frac{5}{5 - 1}\,(0.6)(0.4) = 0.30$$

An estimate of the variance of p is

$$\widehat{\mathrm{Var}(p)} = \hat{\sigma}_p{}^2 = \frac{pq}{n}$$

$$= \frac{0.24}{5}$$

$$= 0.048$$

18.9. The Normal Distribution as an Approximation of the Binomial Distribution

As we have found in our previous discussion, computing binomial probabilities is in many cases a very difficult task. Fortunately, under certain conditions, the binomial distribution approaches the normal distribution and the Poisson distribution, which are easier to compute. In this section we shall explain the relation between the normal and binomial distribution by use of a simple illustration and show heuristically how the binomial distribution approaches a normal distribution as n becomes large. The Poisson approximation to the binomial distribution is explained in Chapter 19.

Suppose $\pi = 0.40$ of a population of students smoke. A sample of size $n = 10$ is taken with replacement, which can be considered as 10 repeated Bernoulli trials. Let k be the number of smokers (that is, successes) in the sample. Then the binomial probabilities $b(k; \; n = 10, \; \pi = 0.40)$ for $k = 0, 1, 2, \ldots, 10$ obtained from the National Bureau of Standards tables is given in Table 18.14 and a histogram of these probabilities is shown in Fig. 18.16.

We can see heuristically that as n becomes larger, the width of the rectangles and the steps in the histogram will become smaller, and the

TABLE 18.14.

k	$p = k/n$	$b(k; n = 10, \pi = 0.4)$
0	0	0.006
1	0.1	0.040
2	0.2	0.121
3	0.3	0.215
4	0.4	0.251
5	0.5	0.201
6	0.6	0.111
7	0.7	0.042
8	0.8	0.011
9	0.9	0.002
10	1.0	0.000
		1.000

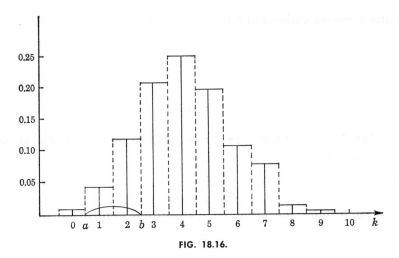

FIG. 18.16.

curve will approach a smooth curve. We state nonrigorously without proof that *as n* $\longrightarrow \infty$, *the smooth curve will approach a normal curve. That is, the binomial distribution will approach the normal distribution.*

When dealing with the normal distribution, we standardized it and used the normal area table. The standardized variable was shown as

$$z = \frac{x - \mu}{\sigma}$$

where μ and σ are the mean and standard deviation of the distribution.

For the binomial distribution, the random variable was k with mean and variance as

$$E(k) = n\pi, \qquad \text{Var}(k) = n\pi(1 - \pi)$$

Hence, the standardized binomial variable will be

$$k^* = \frac{k - n\pi}{\sqrt{n\pi(1 - \pi)}}$$

The theorem stated above implies that as $n \longrightarrow \infty$, this k^* may be treated as a standardized normal variable with mean 0 and variance 1.

The continuity correction we discussed in Chapter 6 may be applied to the random variable k. That is, the k should be adjusted by $+\frac{1}{2}$ or $-\frac{1}{2}$, depending on the problem. Hence, the normalized variable k^* should be

$$k^* = \frac{(k \pm \frac{1}{2}) - n\pi}{\sqrt{n\pi(1 - \pi)}}$$

In many problems, it is more convenient to use the sample proportion $p = k/n$ instead of k as the random variable. Then the normalized variable becomes

$$p^* = \frac{\dfrac{k \pm \frac{1}{2}}{n} - \pi}{\sqrt{\dfrac{\pi(1-\pi)}{n}}}$$

$$= \frac{\left(p \pm \dfrac{1}{2n}\right) - \pi}{\sqrt{\dfrac{\pi(1-\pi)}{n}}}$$

We see that

$$E(p) = \pi, \qquad \operatorname{Var}(p) = \frac{\pi(1-\pi)}{n}$$

Let us illustrate the use of these formulas with examples.

Example 1.   Past surveys show that 40 percent of the families in a certain county are Democrats. A random sample of 50 families is selected. What is the probability that there will be 25 or more Democrat families in this sample?

The situation is shown schematically in Fig. 18.17 as a visual aid.

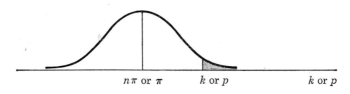

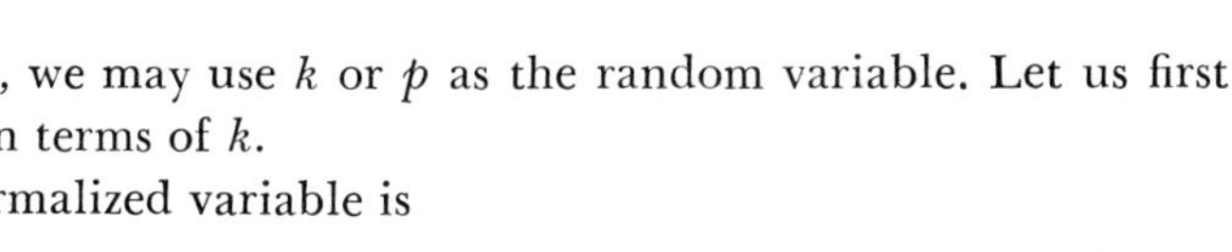

$$n\pi \text{ or } \pi \qquad k \text{ or } p \qquad\qquad k \text{ or } p$$

FIG. 18.17.

Obviously, we may use k or p as the random variable. Let us first solve the problem in terms of k.

The normalized variable is

$$k^* = \frac{(k - 1/2) - n\pi}{\sqrt{n\pi(1-\pi)}}$$

$$= \frac{(25 - 1/2) - 50 \times 0.4}{\sqrt{50(0.4)(0.6)}}$$

$$= 1.299$$

Thus, from the normal area table, we find the shaded area to be $0.0968 = 9.68$ percent. This means that there are about 9.68 chances in 100 of selecting a random sample of size 50 that will have 25 or more Democrat families.

To perform this in terms of proportions, we have

$$p^* = \frac{\left[p - \left(\dfrac{1}{2n} \right) \right] - \pi}{\sqrt{\dfrac{\pi(1 - \pi)}{n}}}$$

$$= \frac{(0.5 - 1/100) - 0.4}{\sqrt{\dfrac{(0.4)(0.6)}{50}}}$$

$$= 1.299$$

and the result is the same as when k is used. We can very easily see that both are algebraically equivalent.

The continuity correction for the second case is $\frac{1}{2}n = 1/100$. As is seen, as n becomes larger, the correction $\frac{1}{2}n$ becomes smaller. In our present case, when the continuity correction is not used, we have

$$p^* = \frac{0.5 - 0.4}{\sqrt{\dfrac{0.4 \times 0.6}{50}}} = 1.44$$

and the probability from the normal area table will be $0.0749 = 7.49$ percent.

Let us compare these results with the probability when computed by the binomial tables. Using the Romig table, we have

$$P(k \geq 25 | n = 50, \pi = 0.4)$$

$$= \sum_{k=25}^{50} \binom{50}{k} (0.4)^k (1 - 0.4)^{n-k}$$

$$= 1 - 0.90217$$

$$= 0.09783$$

Summarizing the results, we find

1. Using the binomial tables $= 9.78\%$
2. Using the normal approximation with the continuity correction $= 9.68\%$
3. Using the normal approximation without the continuity correction $= 7.49\%$

For applications, we are usually interested in the absolute differences of these various probabilities. When the continuity correction is used, the difference is

$$9.78\% - 9.68\% = 0.1\%$$

which for practical applications is very small and will have no effect. The difference when the continuity correction is not used is

$$9.78\% - 7.49\% = 2.29\%$$

which for practical applications may have an effect.

As the sample size becomes larger, the difference between the binomial distribution and the normal approximation decreases and the effect of the continuity correction also decreases. Let us investigate this by increasing the sample size to 100.

Example 2. Let the sample size be $n = 100$ and the number of Democrats be 50. The population proportion is still $\pi = 0.40$. Then, using the continuity correction, we find

$$p^* = \frac{\dfrac{50 - \frac{1}{2}}{100} - 0.4}{\sqrt{\dfrac{0.4(1 - 0.4)}{100}}} = 1.938 \doteq 1.94$$

Thus, the probability of selecting a random sample of $n = 100$ with 50 or more Democrats is, from the normal area table, $0.0262 = 2.62$ percent.

Without the correction for continuity, we have

$$p^* = \frac{\dfrac{50}{100} - 0.4}{\sqrt{\dfrac{0.4 \times 0.6}{100}}} = 2.04$$

Thus, the probability is $0.0207 = 2.07$ percent.

Next let us find the probability, using the Romig tables:

$$P(k \geq 50 | n = 100, \pi = 0.40) = 1 - \sum_{k=0}^{49} \binom{600}{k} (0.4)^k (1 - 0.4)^{100-k}$$
$$= 1 - 0.9729 = 0.0270$$

Summarizing the results, we have:

1. Using the binomial probability table $= 2.70\%$
2. Using the normal approximation
   with the continuity correction $= 2.62\%$
3. Using the normal approximation
   without the continuity correction $= 2.07\%$

Thus the absolute difference between the different probabilities has become smaller, and for practical purposes, the normal approximation without the continuity correction will suffice.

Example 3.   Consider a box with 10 beads of which 3 are red. Let us take a sample of 500 beads with replacement. What is the probability that there will be 145 or more or 155 or less red beads?

In symbols the probability will be

$$P(145 \leq k \leq 155)$$

Thus the normalized variable will be

$$p_1{}^* = \frac{\dfrac{145 - \frac{1}{2}}{500} - 0.3}{\sqrt{\dfrac{0.3 \times 0.7}{500}}}, \qquad p_2{}^* = \frac{\dfrac{155 + \frac{1}{2}}{500} - 0.3}{\sqrt{\dfrac{0.3 \times 0.7}{500}}}$$

We can ignore the continuity correction in this case. Then $p_1{}^* = -0.5$. Since the situation is symmetrical, $p_2{}^* = +0.5$. Thus, from the normal table, we find (Fig. 18.18)

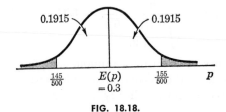

FIG. 18.18.

$$P(145 \leq k \leq 155) = 0.1915 + 0.1915 = 0.383$$

That is, there are about 38.3 chances in 100 of selecting a random sample of 500 beads that will have 145 or more, or 155 or less, red beads when the proportion is $\pi = 0.3$.

Note that for $p_2{}^*$, the continuity correction is $+\frac{1}{2}$ (and not $-\frac{1}{2}$), although we ignored it in our calculations.

18.10.   Confidence Interval

In many practical problems we are interested in estimating the population proportion. For example, we may wish to estimate the proportion of students in favor of a certain proposal, or the proportion of families with income less than $3000, and so forth. We have seen that the maximum likelihood estimator of π is the sample proportion p. However, this does not have a probability statement associated with it, and hence we do not have a measure of its reliability. What we wish to do now is to construct a confidence interval for π and associate a measure of reliability.

But before taking this up, let us very briefly review the confidence interval for the population mean. We know from Chapter 10 that the 0.95 confidence interval is obtained as follows:

$$(1) \qquad\qquad P\!\left(-z < \frac{\bar{x} - \mu}{\sigma_{\bar{x}}} < z\right) = 0.95$$

where z is the normal deviate, and in the present case is $z = 1.96$. By algebraic manipulation this becomes

$$P(\bar{x} - z\sigma_{\bar{x}} < \mu < \bar{x} + z\sigma_{\bar{x}}) = 0.95$$

and the confidence interval has been shown as

$$\bar{x} - z\sigma_{\bar{x}} < \mu < \bar{x} + z\sigma_{\bar{x}}$$

The point to note is that

$$\frac{\bar{x} - \mu}{\sigma_{\bar{x}}}$$

was (asymptotically) normally distributed, and hence z was easily obtained from the normal area table.

In finding the confidence interval for the binomial variable, we shall find that a confidence interval is not found so easily as the one above. This is because

1. The σ_p includes the unknown parameter π.
2. When π is close to zero or one, the distribution of p (or k) is skewed.
3. The variable p (or k) is discrete.

As a result, various persons have devised a number of ways of finding the confidence interval for π. Let us list these various methods as follows:

1.   When the sample is large and the normal approximation may be used, there are the following ways of computing the confidence interval.
   (a).   Follow the standard procedure as illustrated above with μ.
   (b).   Use an estimate of σ_p.

2.   When the sample is small and the normal approximation cannot be used.

(c). Use the limits of the binomial distribution computed from the binomial tables.

3. Use charts that have been prepared by various persons.
(d). The Clopper and Pearson charts
(e). The Chung and Delury charts
(f). Fisher and Yate's statistical tables

Let us very briefly discuss these methods.

(i) The method using the standard procedure

The sampling distribution of the sample proportion p is asymptotically normal with

$$E(p) = \pi, \qquad \text{var}(p) = \frac{\pi(1 - \pi)}{n}$$

Hence, the standardized sample proportion

$$p^* = \frac{p - \pi}{\sqrt{\dfrac{\pi(1 - \pi)}{n}}}$$

is asymptotically normal with mean 0 and variance 1.

Letting z be the normal deviate, we may state

$$P\left(-z < \frac{p - \pi}{\sqrt{\dfrac{\pi(1 - \pi)}{n}}} < z\right) = \gamma$$

where γ is the confidence coefficient. Since we want the confidence interval for π, we wish by algebraic manipulation to change this probability statement to

$$P(\theta_1 < \pi < \theta_2) = \gamma$$

so that θ_1 and θ_2 contain only known quantities. This can be done, but a rather complicated result will be obtained. We shall not present this result. Readers with a mathematical inclination are referred to the literature[*] for a mathematical discussion of this confidence interval.

We have mentioned this procedure because we wished to point out

---

[*] A. M. Mood, *Introduction to the Theory of Statistics*, Chap. 11, Sec. 11.7, New York: McGraw-Hill Book Co., Inc., 1950. J. F. Kenney and E. S. Keeping, *Mathematics of Statistics*, Chap. 6, Sec. 6.15, New York: D. Van Nostrand, Inc., 1951.

that the methods used to construct the confidence interval for the population mean may also be used for the population proportion. We also wish to use it as a background for our next discussion.

(ii)   The method using an estimate of σ_p

As we found in the preceding discussion, the algebraic difficulty of constructing a confidence interval for π was that σ_p includes the unknown population proportion π, which we wish to estimate.

Hence, instead of using a σ_p based on an unknown π, let us use an estimate of π. We have found that an unbiased estimate of σ_p^2 is

$$\hat{\sigma}_p^2 = \frac{p(1-p)}{n-1}$$

but, as mentioned previously, we may also use the biased form

$$\hat{\sigma}_p^2 = \frac{p(1-p)}{n}$$

which is simpler to calculate. Then the confidence interval for π is

$$(2) \qquad p - z\sqrt{\frac{p(1-p)}{n}} < \pi < p + z\sqrt{\frac{p(1-p)}{n}}$$

where z is the normal deviate to be determined from the confidence coefficient that is selected.

When a finite population correction is used, the confidence interval becomes

$$(3) \quad p - z\sqrt{\frac{p(1-p)}{n}}\sqrt{\frac{N-n}{N-1}} < \pi < p + z\sqrt{\frac{p(1-p)}{n}}\sqrt{\frac{N-n}{N-1}}$$

where N is the population size.

We may also adjust formula (3) by the continuity correction that was necessary because the variable is discrete. Formula (3) becomes

$$(4) \qquad \left(p - \frac{1}{2n}\right) - z\sqrt{\frac{p(1-p)}{n}}\sqrt{\frac{N-n}{N-1}}$$
$$< \pi < \left(p + \frac{1}{2n}\right) + z\sqrt{\frac{p(1-p)}{n}}\sqrt{\frac{N-n}{N-1}}$$

As formula (4) shows, the continuity correction increases the size of the confidence interval.

Example 1. A random sample of $n = 400$ dealers was selected and 20 reported that they had planned to increase their orders for a certain item. What is the 95 percent confidence interval for π?

$$\hat{\sigma}_p{}^2 = \frac{p(1 - p)}{n} = \frac{(0.2)(0.8)}{400}$$

$$\hat{\sigma}_p{}^2 = \frac{0.4}{20} = 0.02$$

Since $p = 0.2$ and z, which corresponds to the 95 percent confidence coefficient, is $z = 1.96$, we have

$$0.2 - (1.96)(0.02) \leq \pi \leq 0.2 + (1.96)(0.02)$$
$$0.1608 \leq \pi \leq 0.2392$$

As an exercise, recalculate the confidence interval, using the finite population correction and the continuity correction. Let $N = 2000$.

A question that we have left unanswered up to now is: How large must the sample be to be useful as the normal approximation? As we have seen, the sampling distribution is symmetrical when $p = 0.5$, but becomes more skewed as p approaches 0 or 1; as mentioned previously, when p approaches 0 or 1, the Poisson distribution may be preferable and more useful.

Table 18.15 presents working rules that have been developed by W. G. Cochran. For example, when the sample proportion p is 0.4 or 0.6, the sample size should be at least $n = 50$.

TABLE 18.15.

If p equals:	Use the normal approximation only if n is at least equal to:
0.5	30
0.4 or 0.6	50
0.3 or 0.7	80
0.2 or 0.8	200
0.1 or 0.9	600
0.05 or 0.95	1400

SOURCE: Reprinted from W. G. Cochran, *Sampling Techniques*, New York: John Wiley & Sons, Inc., 1953, p. 41.

(iii) *The method using binomial probabilities*

When the sample size is small and the normal approximation does not apply, the binomial probabilities are used to calculate confidence intervals. Let us illustrate this procedure with an example.

Suppose we wish to estimate the proportion π of students who prefer oral to written examinations. A sample of $n = 50$ students is selected and $k = 20$ are found to prefer oral exams. Then the confidence interval for the population proportion π, which is shown as

$$p_1 < \pi < p_2$$

is obtained as follows:

Assuming a confidence coefficient of 90 percent, the lower limit p_1 is found by solving the probability statement

(5) $$P(k \geq 20 | n = 50, p = p_1) = 0.05$$

This p_1 may be found from the Romig tables. Since the Romig tables are on a "less than" cumulative basis, we alter (5) as

$$P(k \geq 20 | n = 50, p = p_1)$$
$$= 1 - P(k \leq 19 | n = 50, p = p_1)$$

Therefore

$$P(k \leq 19 | n = 50, p = p_1) = 1 - 0.05 = 0.95$$

and from the Romig tables, we find p_1 is approximately 0.28.

In similar manner, to find p_2, we let

(6) $$P(k \leq 20 | n = 50, p = p_2) = 0.05$$

From the Romig tables we can see that p_2 is larger than 0.50. Hence, we perform the following algebraic change:

$$P(k \leq 20 | n = 50, p = p_2)$$
$$= 1 - P(k \leq 29 | n = 50, p = 1 - p_2)$$

Therefore

$$P(k \leq 29 | n = 50, p = 1 - p_2) = 1 - 0.05 = 0.95$$

and from the Romig tables we find

$$1 - p_2 \cong 0.49$$
$$p_2 \cong 0.51$$

Hence, the confidence interval we seek is

$$0.28 < \pi < 0.51$$

with confidence coefficient 0.90. Note that we have not interpolated for accurate values of p_1 and p_2, and hence the interval we have is only an approximation.

The interpretation of this confidence interval is: When a large number of confidence intervals have been constructed in this manner, we may expect about 95 percent to contain the true population proportion π.

In general, if we have a sample of size n with k_0 successes, the upper and lower limits of a 90 percent confidence interval is obtained by finding p_1 and p_2 that satisfy the binomial probabilities

$$P(k \geq k_0|n, p_1) = 0.05$$
$$P(k \leq k_0|n, p_2) = 0.05$$

The proof of this statement may be found in the literature.[*]

(iv)   The Clopper and Pearson charts

In our discussion of the first method, we found that the confidence interval was obtained from

$$(7) \qquad P\left(-z < \frac{p - \pi}{\sqrt{\dfrac{\pi(1 - \pi)}{n}}} < z\right) = \gamma$$

which was put in the form

$$(8) \qquad P(\theta_1 < \pi < \theta_2) = \gamma$$

Let us now partially solve (7) and show the quadratic that has to be solved for π, to find θ_1 and θ_2 of (8).

At the end points of the interval, the inequalities are set as equalities, and the π that satisfies these equalities will give us the end points of the interval. Hence, from (7), we find

$$\frac{p - \pi}{\sqrt{\dfrac{\pi(1 - \pi)}{n}}} = \pm z$$

Squaring both sides and arranging in terms of π, we find

$$(9) \qquad \pi^2(n + z^2) - \pi(2np + z^2) + np^2 = 0$$

When given the sample size n, the normal deviate z corresponding to the confidence coefficient, and the sample proportion p, we can solve for π. Then we shall find two values π_1 and π_2, which will be the lower and upper values of the confidence interval.

---

[*] A. Mood, *Introduction to the Theory of Statistics*, Secs. 11.5, 11.6, New York: McGraw-Hill Book Co., Inc., 1950. R. Schlaifer, *Statistics for Business Decisions*, Sec. 13.7, New York: McGraw-Hill Book Co., Inc., 1961. M. G. Kendall, *The Advanced Theory of Statistics*, Vol. 11, Chap. 19, London: Charles Griffin & Co., 1948.

In many practical cases, the sample size n has values such as $n = 10$, 20, 30, 50, 100, 250. The confidence coefficient also has standard values (such as 90 percent, 95 percent), which implies that the normal deviate z takes on given values such as 1.64 and 1.96. Hence, when given n and z, charts showing the relations between π and p may be constructed, and this will eliminate a great deal of computing. The Clopper and Pearson charts are charts that show the relation between π and p, based on equation (9) above.

We have already used the Clopper and Pearson charts to perform tests of significance. In that case, the charts were read *horizontally*. In our present case, where we wish to find confidence intervals, we shall read these charts *vertically*. Let us illustrate with an example, using Fig. 18.10, which is a Clopper and Pearson chart for determing the 95 percent confidence limits of π.

Example.   Suppose we wish to find a 95 percent confidence interval for the proportion of smokers among freshmen. A random sample of 250 students is selected, and it is found that the sample proportion of smokers is $p = 0.40$. Looking at the vertical line going through 0.4, we find that it cuts the two lines of $n = 250$ at approximately 0.34 and 0.46 of the vertical scale. Then the 95 percent confidence interval is approximately

$$0.34 < \pi < 0.46$$

We shall not explain the Chung and DeLury charts or the Fisher and Yates charts, since the interested student will find these in the literature.*

18.11.   Determining the Sample Size _n_ by Use of a Confidence Interval

A problem that frequently arises in market research is to arrive at the sample size that will obtain a required precision. We may interpret precision to mean the length of a confidence interval. For example, one may wish to estimate the proportion π of smokers who prefer brand A cigarettes to other brands. Suppose a 95 percent confidence interval is found to be

$$0.20 < \pi < 0.30$$

based on a sample of size n_1, and another confidence interval is found to be

$$0.24 < \pi < 0.26$$

---

* J. H. Chung and D. B. DeLury, *Confidence Limits for the Hypergeometric Distribution,* University of Toronto Press, 1950. R. A. Fisher and F. Yates, *Statistical Tables for Biological, Agricultural and Medical Research,* 5th ed., Edinburgh: Oliver and Boyd, 1957.

based on a sample of size n_2. As is seen, the second confidence interval is much smaller; that is, it is more precise than the first one. We also know that the confidence interval will become more precise as the sample size n increases. The problem is: How large must n be to obtain a confidence interval with a given precision?

The samples required in practical market research problems are usually large samples such that the normal approximation can be used. We shall use this normal approximation assumption and derive a formula for determining the size of the sample n for a given precision. We shall then explain a simple table (Appendix, Table 6) that has been compiled by the New York State Division of Housing which is a tabulation of the formula. Let us first derive the formula and then show how the table is used.

For a large n where the normal approximation is applicable, the 95 percent confidence interval is

(1) $$p - 1.96\sigma_p < \pi < p + 1.96\sigma_p$$

where σ_p is

$$\sigma_p = \sqrt{\frac{\pi(1 - \pi)}{n}}$$

Equation (1) may be rewritten as

(2) $$-1.96\sigma_p < p - \pi < 1.96\sigma_p$$

The difference $p - \pi$ shows the error of the estimation. For example, suppose $\pi = 0.25$ and $p = 0.28$. Then $p - \pi = 0.03$; that is, we have a 3 percent error.

Instead of using the term *error*, we may consider the difference $p - \pi = e$ as a measure of reliability. Hence, if we can determine the sample size such that $e = 0.03$, we shall say we have a reliability of 3 percent.

Using the notation $e = p - \pi$, we may rewrite (2) as

$$-1.96\sigma_p < e < 1.96\sigma_p$$

Since the situation is symmetrical, let us consider the upper tail. Then we can set

(3) $$e = 1.96\sigma_p$$

By squaring both sides, we find

(4) $$e^2 = (1.96)^2 \frac{\pi(1 - \pi)}{n}$$

If we consider the finite population correction, (4) becomes

$$e^2 = (1.96)^2 \, \frac{\pi(1-\pi)}{n} \cdot \frac{N-n}{N}$$

Since we are seeking the sample size *n*, let us solve this equation for *n*.
We find

(5)
$$n = \frac{(1.96)^2 \pi(1-\pi)N}{(1.96)^2 \pi(1-\pi) + Ne^2}$$

We see that we need to know π, N, and e in order to find *n*. The
error *e* is predetermined. The population *N* is also known in advance.
However, the population proportion π is usually unknown and hence
cannot be predetermined.

To circumvent this impasse, we first change formula (5) as follows:

(6)
$$n = \frac{(1.96)^2 N}{(1.96)^2 + \dfrac{Ne^2}{\pi(1-\pi)}}$$

and note that, given *N* and *e*, *n* is at a maximum when $\pi(1-\pi)$ is at a
maximum. We also know (p. 258) that $\pi(1-\pi)$ is at a maximum
when $\pi = \frac{1}{2}$.

Hence, if we set $\pi = \frac{1}{2}$, we know that the sample size will in general
be larger than necessary. Substituting $\pi = \frac{1}{2}$ into (5) gives us

(7)
$$n = \frac{(1.96)^2(0.5)^2 N}{(1.96)^2(0.5)^2 + Ne^2}$$

As a further simplification, let us use 2 normal deviates instead of 1.96
normal deviates. When 2 is used instead of 1.96, a larger sample will
be obtained, and the confidence coefficient becomes larger. Then 2
normal deviates will give us a 95.44 percent confidence interval instead
of a 95 percent confidence interval, but this slight difference will have
little if any effect in practical applications. Substituting this 2 into (7)
gives us

(8)
$$n = \frac{(2)^2(0.5)^2 N}{(2)^2(0.5)^2 + Ne^2}$$
$$= \frac{N}{1 + Ne^2}$$

which is a very simple formula to work with. Table 6 in the Appendix, compiled by the New York State Division of Housing, is a tabulation of this formula. Let us see how it works with several examples.

Example 1. Suppose we wish to estimate the proportion of families in a suburban development that listens to a certain TV program. There are about 1000 families, and it is quite a task to collect data from all these families. The researcher wishes to take a sample and estimate π with an error of $\pm$ 10 percent and with a confidence coefficient of 95 percent. How large a sample must he take? From (8) we find

$$n = \frac{1000}{1 + 1000(0.10)^2} \cong 91$$

That is, it is only necessary to take a sample of size 91 to construct a confidence interval to estimate π that satisfies the requirements of $e = 0.10$ and a confidence coefficient of 0.95. From Table 6 in the Appendix, we also find $n = 91$.

Example 2. If, instead of an error of $\pm$ 10 percent, the researcher wishes it to be $e = \pm 0.05$, the sample size is

$$n = \frac{1000}{1 + 1000(0.05)^2} \cong 286$$

which is also found in Table 6.

Example 3. Suppose there are 3000 families and the error is to be $e = \pm 0.03$. Then the sample size that will give us this reliability is

$$n = \frac{3000}{1 + 3000(0.03)^2} \cong 811$$

which is also found in Table 6.

For an error of $e = \pm 0.01$ and $N = 3000$, we find a letter "b" in Table 6. In this case we need to take 50 percent of the population as a sample. Since we have a finite population, then as the sample units are selected, the probability changes and we do not have a binomial distribution, but rather a hypergeometric distribution (see p. 579). But the normal distribution is a poor approximation of the hypergeometric distribution when n is more than 50 percent of the population, and therefore we cannot use formula (4). However, when 50 percent of the population is taken, the sample will give more than the required accuracy.

The values of Table 6 in the Appendix assumed a population proportion of $\pi = 0.50$. If there is prior information concerning π (say we know that $\pi = 0.3$), we may adjust the sample size and make it smaller. This is accomplished by substituting the value $\pi(1 - \pi)$ for $(0.5)^2$ in the numerator of formula (8). That is,

$$(9) \qquad n' = \frac{(2)^2\pi(1-\pi)N}{(2)^2(0.5)^2 + Ne^2}$$

As we can see, the $(0.5)^2$ in the denominator has been left unchanged, since this simplifies calculations and the effect on the sample size is small.

Noting that $4 \times (0.5)^2 = 1$, we may rewrite (9) as

$$n' = \frac{(2)^2\pi(1-\pi)N}{(2)^2(0.5)^2 + Ne^2} \cdot 4(0.5)^2$$

$$= \frac{(2)^2(0.5)^2 N}{(2)^2(0.5)^2 + Ne^2} \cdot 4pq$$

$$= n \cdot 4pq$$

where n' is the adjusted sample size, and n is the sample size in Table 6. Hence, for example, when $N = 1000$, $e = 0.10$, the sample size was $n = 91$, which was assuming $\pi = 0.5$. If we know that $\pi = 0.3$, then this n is adjusted as

$$n' = n4pq$$

$$= 91 \times 4(0.3)(1 - 0.3)$$

$$= 76$$

Let us now give an example and show how π may be estimated by using Table 6.

Example.   A marketing research firm wishes to estimate the proportion of families listening to a certain TV program in a small town that has 3000 families. It requires a precision of ± 3 percent and a 95 percent confidence interval. From Table 6 (Appendix) we find $n = 811$. This can be checked as follows:

$$n = \frac{N}{1 + Ne^2} = \frac{3000}{1 + 3000(0.0009)} \cong 811$$

After taking a random sample of 811 families, the research firm finds that 162 families were listening to the TV program. Thus the 95 percent confidence interval for the proportion of families listening is

$$p = \frac{162}{811} \cong 0.20$$

$$0.20 - 0.03 \leqq \pi \leqq 0.20 + 0.03$$

$$0.17 \leqq \pi \leqq 0.23$$

18.12.   Comparison of Two Percentages

Many problems take the form of comparing two percentages. For example, there may be two processes A and B where A has π_1 and B has π_2 percentage defective items. Is there a significant difference between process A and B? Let us first explain the model theoretically, and then illustrate with an example.

(i)   The model

Take two independent, random samples of items from process A and B. Let the sample sizes be n_1, n_2; the number of defectives k_1, k_2; then the sample proportions will be $p_1 = k_1/n_1$ and $p_2 = k_2/n_2$. We state the following theorem without proof: If n_1 and n_2 are sufficiently large, the sampling distribution of $p_1 - p_2$ will be asymptotically normal with mean and variance

$$E(p_1 - p_2) = \pi_1 - \pi_2$$

$$\mathrm{Var}(p_1 - p_2) = \frac{\pi_1(1 - \pi_1)}{n_1} + \frac{\pi_2(1 - \pi_2)}{n_2}$$

Thus the normalized variable may be shown as

$$(1) \qquad z = \frac{(p_1 - p_2) - (\pi_1 - \pi_2)}{\sqrt{\dfrac{\pi_1(1 - \pi_1)}{n_1} + \dfrac{\pi_2(1 - \pi_2)}{n_2}}}$$

where, when n_1 and n_2 are sufficiently large, z will be approximately normal, with $E(z) = 0$ and $\mathrm{Var}(z) = 1$.

The statistical test is usually of the form

$$H_1: \qquad \pi_1 = \pi_2$$
$$H_2: \qquad \pi_1 \neq \pi_2$$

Hence, the test statistic z becomes

$$(2) \qquad z = \frac{p_1 - p_2}{\sqrt{\dfrac{\pi_1(1 - \pi_1)}{n_1} + \dfrac{\pi_2(1 - \pi_2)}{n_2}}}$$

To perform this test, we need to know the variance in the denominator. But since π_1 and π_2 are usually unknown, we need to find an estimate of the variance.

(ii)   Estimate of Var($p_1 - p_2$)

An estimate of Var($p_1 - p_2$) may be obtained by finding estimates of π_1 and π_2. Since the test we are interested in is the equality of π_1 and π_2, we may set $\pi_1 = \pi_2 = \pi$. Using this hypothesis, we combine both samples into one and find the estimate of the population proportion π as

$$\hat{\pi} = \frac{k_1 + k_2}{n_1 + n_2}$$

Thus the estimates of $\hat{\sigma}_{p1-p2}^{2}$ becomes

(3)
$$\sigma_{p1-p2}^{2} = \frac{\hat{\pi}(1 - \hat{\pi})}{n_1} + \frac{\hat{\pi}(1 - \hat{\pi})}{n_2}$$

$$= \hat{\pi}(1 - \hat{\pi}) \left(\frac{1}{n_1} + \frac{1}{n_2} \right)$$

Using these results, (2) becomes

(4)
$$z = \frac{p_1 - p_2}{\sqrt{\hat{\pi}(1 - \hat{\pi}) \left(\dfrac{1}{n_1} + \dfrac{1}{n_2} \right)}}$$

There are several variations of (4) based on special considerations.

In the first variation, instead of using proportions, we can use the number of defectives to express (4), which in some cases will be easier to compute. Let us set

$$n = n_1 + n_2, \qquad k = k_1 + k_2$$

Then $\hat{\pi}$ and $\hat{\sigma}_{p1-p2}$ become

$$\hat{\pi} = \frac{k}{n}$$

$$\hat{\sigma}_{p1-p2}^{2} = \frac{k}{n} \left(1 - \frac{k}{n} \right) \left(\frac{1}{n_1} + \frac{1}{n_2} \right)$$

$$= \frac{k(n - k)}{n n_1 n_2}$$

Thus (4) becomes

(5)
$$z = \frac{\dfrac{k_1}{n_1} - \dfrac{k_2}{n_2}}{\sqrt{\dfrac{k(n - k)}{n n_1 n_2}}} = \frac{n_2 k_1 - n_1 k_2}{\sqrt{\dfrac{n_1 n_2 k(n - k)}{n}}}$$

The second variation is the case when $n_1 = n_2$. Then

$$\hat{\pi} = \frac{1}{2} (p_1 + p_2)$$

and (4) becomes, letting $n_1 = n_2 = n_0$,

(6)
$$z = \frac{(p_1 - p_2)\sqrt{n_0}}{\sqrt{(p_1 + p_2)\left(1 - \frac{p_1 + p_2}{2}\right)}}$$

Let us now illustrate the use of the models by examples.

(iii) Two-tail test

Consider two groups of children taken at random from two schools A and B. Of the 70 children from school A, 40 failed the test, and of the 100 from B, 45 failed. Is there a difference between the children of schools A and B?

Let π_1 and π_2 be the proportion of failures of schools A and B. Then

$$H_1: \qquad \pi_1 = \pi_2$$
$$H_2: \qquad \pi_1 \neq \pi_2$$

$$\hat{\pi} = \frac{40 + 45}{70 + 100} = 0.5$$

$$z = \frac{p_1 - p_2}{\sqrt{\hat{\pi}(1 - \hat{\pi})\left(\frac{1}{n_1} + \frac{1}{n_2}\right)}}$$

$$= \frac{0.40 - 0.45}{\sqrt{0.5 \times 0.5 \left(\frac{1}{70} + \frac{1}{100}\right)}}$$

$$= \frac{-0.05}{0.5 \times 0.1558} = -0.64$$

From the normal area table we find that there are about 26 chances in 100 of finding a difference of $p_1 - p_2 = -0.05$ in our problem. Thus we conclude that the difference is not significant and that it is due to chance. The null hypothesis $\pi_1 = \pi_2$ is accepted.

(iv) One-tail test

A random sample of 100 people was selected from the low income group and 60 were found to favor Democrats. A random sample of 100 people from the high income group showed that 40 favored the Democrats. Is the proportion favoring Democrats in the lower income group greater than the high income group?

Let π_1 and π_2 be the proportions in the low and high income groups. Then

$$H_1: \qquad \pi_1 = \pi_2$$
$$H_2: \qquad \pi_1 > \pi_2$$

$$\hat{\pi} = \frac{60 + 40}{100 + 100} = 0.5$$

Since $n_1 = n_2 = 100$ in this case, let us use formula (6):

$$z = \frac{(0.6 - 0.4)\sqrt{100}}{\sqrt{(0.6 + 0.4)\left(1 - \dfrac{0.6 + 0.4}{2}\right)}} = 2.8$$

There are less than 2.6 chances in 1000 of finding a difference as large as $0.6 - 0.4 = 0.2$. Thus, the difference is significant, and we accept the null hypothesis that $\pi_1 > \pi_2$.

THE POISSON DISTRIBUTION

<table>
<tr><td>

19

</td><td>

In Chapter 18 we saw how the normal distribution was a limiting form of the binomial distribution $b(k; n, p)$ when n became very large and p was near 0.5. We also mentioned that when p was near 0 or 1, the normal distribution could not be used as an approximation of the binomial, even when n was

</td></tr>
</table>

very large. But as we know, when n is large and p is small, calculation of the binomial probability becomes a prohibitive task. Fortunately, when n is large and p is very small, there is a limiting form of the binomial distribution that is easy to compute. This is the Poisson distribution, which was developed by a French mathematican, S. D. Poisson (1781–1840).

The Poisson distribution may be approached as a limiting form of the binomial distribution. However, it may also be approached on its own rights by considering a Poisson process. The Poisson process has applicability to a great variety of physical processes; as a result, along with the normal and binomial distribution, the Poisson distribution is one of the most widely used distributions. It is used in quality control statistics to count the number of defects of an item, or in biology to count the number of bacteria, or in physics to count the number of particles emitted from a radioactive substance, or in insurance problems to count the number of casualties, or in waiting-time problems to count the number of incoming telephone calls or incoming customers, and so forth. We shall first explain, nonmathematically, the Poisson distribution as a limiting form of the binomial; secondly we shall consider it in its own rights; and thirdly, give applications.

19.1.   The Poisson Distribution as the Limit of the Binomial Distribution

Suppose we have an urn with 99 white balls and 1 black ball. A random sample of size $n = 100$ is taken with replacement from this urn. This may be considered as a sequence of 100 Bernoulli trials where the probability of drawing a white ball is 0.99 and that of drawing a black ball is 0.01. From the binomial distribution, we may state that the probability of having k black balls in the sample is

$$b(k; n = 100, p = 0.01) = \binom{100}{k} p^k (1 - p)^{n-k}$$

Using the Romig tables, we find the probability as shown in Table 19.1.

TABLE 19.1.

k	$P(k)$	k or less
0	0.366	0.366
1	0.370	0.736
2	0.185	0.921
3	0.061	0.982
4	0.051	0.996
5	0.003	0.999
6	0.000	0.999
7	0.000	1.000
8	0.000	1.000
9	0.000	1.000
10	0.000	1.000

Figure 19.1 is a graph of the probabilities and, as is seen, it is skewed to the right. We can see graphically that although $n = 100$, the binomial distribution differs quite a bit from the normal distribution; in such cases, where p is very small, it is not appropriate to use the normal distribution as an approximation of the binomial distribution.

Let us increase the number of balls in the urn to 1000, of which 999 are white and 1 is black. When a random sample of $n = 1000$ is taken with replacement, we have 1000 repeated Bernoulli trials in which the probability of a black ball for each trial is $p = 0.001$. Then the probability of k black balls in $n = 1000$ trials is

$$b(k; n = 1000, p = 0.001) = \binom{1000}{k} p^k (1 - p)^{n-k}$$

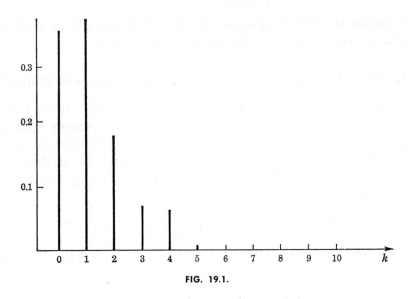

FIG. 19.1.

In this case, we do not have tables to find the binomial probabilities, and as seen above, the distribution is too skewed to get good results from a normal approximation.

Fortunately, it can be shown that as n becomes larger and p becomes proportionately smaller, where np remains unchanged, the binomial distribution approaches the Poisson distribution:

(1) $$b(k; n, p) \longrightarrow \frac{(np)^k}{k!} e^{-np}$$

In our example above we had

$$np = (100)(0.01) = 1$$
$$np = (1000)(0.001) = 1$$

where n becomes larger, p becomes smaller, and np remains unchanged. As (1) shows, the n and p appear together in the Poisson distribution, and hence we shall set

(2) $$\lambda = np$$

Then the Poisson distribution is shown as

(3) $$p(k; \lambda) = e^{-\lambda} \frac{\lambda^k}{k!}$$

The λ indicates the average (or expected) number of occurrences of the event. For example,

$$\lambda = np = (100)(0.01) = 1$$

means that the expected (or average) number of black balls per 100 draws is 1.

Similarly,

$$\lambda = np = (1000)(0.001) = 1$$

means that the expected (or average) number of black balls per 1000 draws is 1.

For most cases, when $np \leqslant 5$, we can use the Poisson distribution as an approximation of the binomial distribution. In this case, n should be greater than 20, which implies $p \leqslant 0.25$.

This Poisson distribution is relatively easy to compute and has been tabulated by Molina.* Table 12 of the Appendix has been extracted from Molina's tables.

Using Molina's tables, let us find the probability of the Poisson distribution for $\lambda = np = (100)(0.01) = 1$, and compare it with the binomial probability we obtained in Table 19.1. We find that the approximation is very good.

TABLE 19.2.

k	$b(k; n = 100, p = 0.01)$		$p(k; \lambda = 1)$	
0	0.366	032	0.367	879
1	0.369	730	0.367	879
2	0.184	865	0.183	940
3	0.060	999	0.061	313
4	0.014	942	0.015	328
5	0.002	898	0.003	066
6	0.000	463	0.000	511
7	0.000	063	0.000	073
8	0.000	007	0.000	009
9	0.000	001	0.000	001

When using the Poisson distribution as an approximation of the binomial distribution, we usually know p and n, and hence we can find $\lambda = np$. But, as will be seen later when the Poisson distribution is considered on its own, we usually do not know p and shall have to find λ by a different procedure.

Let us first give several examples where the Poisson distribution may be used as an approximation of the binomial distribution. The charac-

---

* E. Molina, *Poisson's Exponential Binomial Limit*, New York: D. Van Nostrand, Inc., 1942.

teristic of this type of application of the Poisson distribution is that we shall have a sequence of Bernoulli trials with p and n known, and from these data we shall find $\lambda = np$, and hence can use the Poisson distribution.

Example 1.   Suppose we have a production process of some item that is made in large quantities and we know that the proportion of defective items is $p = 0.01$. A random sample of 100 items is selected. What is the probability that there are k defective items in this sample?

In terms of a binomial distribution, this is

$$b(k;n = 100, p = 0.01) = \binom{100}{k} p^k(1 - p)^{n-k}$$

which is approximated by the Poisson distribution as

$$p(k;\lambda = np = 1) = e^{-\lambda} \frac{\lambda^k}{k!}$$

The results are the same as shown in Table 19.2. Hence, for example,

$$p(k = 2;\lambda = 1) = 0.185$$

That is, the probability is 0.185 that there will be 2 defective items in a random sample of $n = 100$.

Example 2.   Given 1000 students, what is the probability of there being k students with birthdays on a given day of the year? Here we have 1000 repeated Bernoulli trials with probability of success (the birthday of a student is on the given day) as $p = 1/365$. Hence, in terms of binomial probabilities, we have

$$b\left(k;n = 1000, p = \frac{1}{365}\right) = \binom{1000}{k} p^k(1 - p)^{n-k}$$

which will involve a large amount of computations. To find the Poisson approximation, we first calculate

$$\lambda = np = (1000)\left(\frac{1}{365}\right) = 2.7397$$

Using the Molina tables, we find

$$p(k = 0;\lambda = 2.74) = 0.067$$
$$p(k = 1;\lambda = 2.74) = 0.181$$
$$p(k = 2;\lambda = 2.74) = 0.225$$

The Molina tables jump from $\lambda = 2.7$ to $\lambda = 2.8$. We have used $\lambda = 2.7$, and hence the probabilities are approximate values.

Thus, the probability is about 0.181 (or 18.1 percent) that there will be a student with a birthday on the given day.

Example 3.   Suppose a lot is accepted if there is 1 or less defective item in a random sample of $n = 50$. What is the probability of accepting a lot whose incoming quality is 2 percent defective?

Using the binominal distribution and the Romig tables, we find

$$b(k \leq 1; n = 50, p = 0.02) = \sum_{k=0}^{1} \binom{50}{k} p^k (1 - p)^{n-k}$$

$$= 0.735771$$

To find the Poisson approximation, we first calculate

$$\lambda = np = (50)(0.02) = 1$$

and hence from the cumulative Molina tables we find

$$p(k \leq 1; \lambda = 1) = 1 - p(k \geq 2; \lambda = 1)$$

$$= 1 - 0.264241$$

$$= 0.735759$$

which is a good approximation of the true values. Hence, the probability of accepting the lot is about 0.736.

Example 4.   Suppose that, on the average, 1 house in 2000 in a certain district has a fire during a year. If 4000 houses are in that district, what is the probability that exactly 5 houses will have a fire during the year? We find

$$\lambda = np = 4000 \times \left(\frac{1}{2000}\right) = 2$$

Hence, the Poisson approximation is, from the Molina tables,

$$p(k = 5, \lambda = 2) = e^{-2} \frac{2^5}{5!} = 0.036$$

Example 5.   Consider a production process of making ball bearings where the probability of a defective bearing is 0.01. Then, for a box of 1000 ball bearings, λ will be

$$\lambda = np = 1000 \times 0.01 = 10$$

and the probability of k defective bearings will be

$$p(k; 10) = e^{-10} \frac{(10)^k}{k!}$$

Using the Molina tables, we find the results as shown in Table 19.3. Thus, the probability of 4 defectives in 1000 is 0.0189.

TABLE 19.3.

k	$p(k; 10)$
0	0.0000
1	0.0005
2	0.0023
3	0.0076
4	0.0189

The probability of at least $k = 3$ defectives is from the Molina tables:

$$\sum_{k=3}^{\infty} p(k; 10) = 0.9972$$

19.2. The Poisson Process

Let us now consider the Poisson distribution on its own. For this we shall first consider the Poisson process and then the Poisson distribution.

Suppose we are considering the arrival of telephone calls at a certain exchange. An incoming call is called an event, and each time a call comes in (that is, each time an event occurs), we shall say that there has been a *change* in the system.

A characteristic of this physical process is that the events are occurring over a *continuum of time*. Let us show this graphically, as in Fig. 19.2. The horizontal axis t shows time, and the dots on the line show

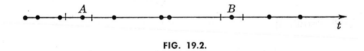

FIG. 19.2.

the incoming telephone calls (that is, the events, or the changes in the system).

In dealing with this process, we shall assume that:

1. The calls come in randomly.
2. The calls in any time interval are statistically independent of the calls in other time intervals.

By the term *random* in the first assumption, we do not mean haphazard. Rather, we shall use the term to mean that all events (changes) are of the same kind, or homogeneous; that is, the probability of an event's (change) occurring in any given very short time interval is the same, and the probability of more than one change occurring is very small.

The second assumption means that all previous or future calls have no effect on a call (event) occurring in a given time interval.

The interpretation of these two assumptions may also be shown graphically, as in Fig. 19.2. As is seen, we have two time intervals A and B of the same length, and we are assuming that there are no changes in the conditions of the experiment. Then the probability of an incoming call occurring in A or B is the same, and the probability of more than one call occurring is very small. Furthermore, no matter where these intervals may be taken, the probability remains the same.

We shall nonrigorously call a process with the above characteristics a *Poisson process.* Let us give several more examples of such physical processes.

Examples.   (a).   A continuous-conveyor production process producing a certain item in large quantities, where a defective item occurs randomly with small probability and independently, may be considered a Poisson process.

(b).   A radioactive substance emitting particles is another example. The particles are emitted randomly over a long period of time, and the occurrence of an emission is independent of other emissions.

(c).   Accidents in a large factory may occur randomly with small probability and be independent of each other over a continuum of time, in which case this process may be considered a Poisson process.

(d).   The arrival pattern of customers at a telephone booth.

(e).   The arrival pattern of airplanes at an airport.

(f).   The number of defects on the surface of a table.

(g).   The number of misprints on a page of a book.

(h).   The frequency of sudden thunderstorms in a certain region.

(i).   The scatter of raisins in raisin bread.

19.3.   Finding the Poisson Distribution

As we see in Fig. 19.2, we have a scatter of random points (incoming calls) along the time axis. What we wish to do now is to find the distribution of these random points or, as we may say, the density of these random points. The word "density" conveys more explicitly the idea that we are interested in the scatter of the points on a per unit interval basis.

How are we going to find the density of these random points? The Fig. 19.3 at first glance seems to give a completely haphazard situation. However, recall our assumptions of randomness and independence.

With these two assumptions, we shall turn this seemingly haphazard situation into a Poisson process, and this will enable us to derive the Poisson distribution.

We first start out with a given time interval t (say, $t = 5$ min.). As Fig. 19.3 shows, we have 3 such intervals in 15 min. Let us consider the first

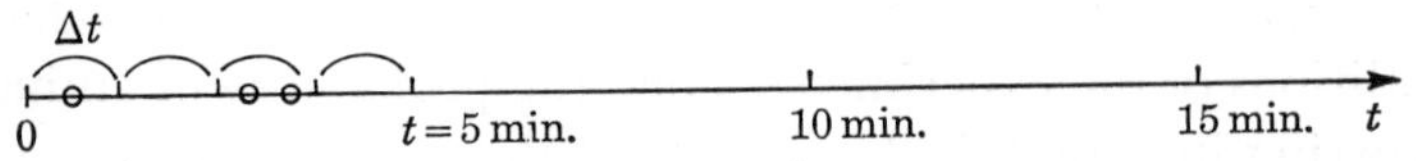

FIG. 19.3.

interval t from 0 min. to 5 min., and divide this into n (say, $n = 4$) subintervals as shown in the figure. We shall find in each subinterval no points, 1 point, or more than 1 point. As this subdividing process continues by letting n become larger, the subintervals become very short, and according to our assumption of randomness, the probability of having more than 1 point in the short subinterval becomes very small and may be considered negligible. Hence, we shall conclude that as the subdividing process continues, we shall reach a situation where we can say with (almost) probability 1 that there is either a point in the subinterval or there is not a point.

The second assumption of independence meant that the occurrence or nonoccurrence of an event in any preceding or subsequent subinterval has no effect on the occurrence or nonoccurrence of an event in the present subinterval.

Hence, we may conclude that we have a Poisson process. That is, given a time interval $t = 5$ min., we have, using our assumptions of randomness and independence, split this time interval into subintervals and constructed a Poisson process from these subintervals where the probability is almost 1 that a subinterval contains a point or does not. Hence, we shall ask the question: What is the probability of exactly k changes (points) during the given time interval of length t (in our present case $t = 5$ min.)?

We state without proof that the probability of finding exactly k points in a fixed interval of length t is

$$(1) \qquad\qquad p(k; \lambda t) = e^{-\lambda t}\,\frac{(\lambda t)^k}{k!}$$

where λ is a constant that shows the density of the random points on the time axis.

When the Poisson distribution was derived as an approximation of the binomial, we set

$$\lambda = np$$

where n was the number of Bernoulli trials, and p was the probability of a success. Hence, λ is the expected number of successes in n Bernoulli trials, or we may say that it shows the average number of successes in n trials. The interpretation of λt in (1) is that it shows the expected number of successes in the fixed interval t. Hence, λ in (1) shows the expected number of successes in a unit interval of time, and thus may be considered as showing the density of the random points on the horizontal time axis.

For example, λ may show the expected number of incoming phone calls per minute, or the expected number of defective items in a continuous production process per minute. Then λt shows the expected number of phone calls in t minutes, or the expected number of defective items in t minutes.

Hence, we may say: The larger λ, the larger the density of the random points, and the more probability of finding a point in a small interval.

A difference between the binomial and Poisson distribution is that in the former the number of trials n is known, whereas in the latter, it is usually unknown. In the binomial distribution, when we say k successes, we mean k successes in n Bernoulli trials. In the Poisson distribution, when we say k successes, we mean k successes in a given interval t. This interval t was divided into n subintervals to derive the Poisson distribution, and we let $n \longrightarrow \infty$ to make the length of the subintervals very small. The specific value of n is usually unknown, but as long as we know the constant λ, we do not need to know n in order to compute the probability of k successes.

However, in applications where we need to estimate λ, we shall in many cases find an appropriate n and use it to estimate λ.

Our next problem, then, is to show how λ is estimated in practical applications. But before we do that, let us state without proof that the mean and variance of the Poisson distribution are

$$E(k) = \lambda$$
$$\mathrm{Var}(k) = \lambda$$

and are equal to each other and also show the Poisson distribution graphically for several values of λ. In Table 19.4 we have values for the probability of k changes for $\lambda = 0.8$, 1, 2, 3, and 7, which were taken from Molina's tables. Figure 19.4 is a graph of these probabilities. The values have been rounded off, so they will not exactly add up to unity.

When $\lambda = 2$, for example, the mean and variance of the Poisson distribution is also 2.

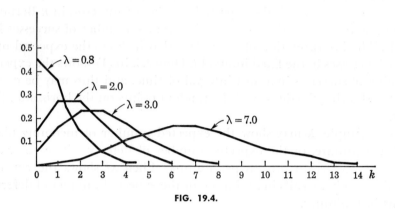

FIG. 19.4.

TABLE 19.4.

k	0.8	1.0	2.0	3.0	7.0
0	0.45	0.37	0.14	0.05	0.00
1	0.36	0.37	0.27	0.15	0.01
2	0.14	0.18	0.27	0.22	0.02
3	0.04	0.06	0.18	0.22	0.05
4	0.01	0.02	0.09	0.17	0.10
5			0.04	0.10	0.13
6			0.01	0.05	0.15
7				0.02	0.15
8				0.01	0.15
9					0.10
10					0.07
11					0.05
12					0.03
13					0.01
14					0.01
					0.00

Figure 19.4 shows that for $\lambda = 0.8$, the distribution curve is a reverse J type curve. For $\lambda > 1$, they gradually approach a normal curve as λ increases. Table 19.5 shows that the slope of the curve changes at the value $\lambda = 1$.

TABLE 19.5.

k	0.9	1.0	1.1
0	0.4066	0.3679	0.3329
1	0.3659	0.3679	0.3662
2	0.1647	0.1839	0.2014

In symbols we have

$$p(0; \lambda < 1) > p(1; \lambda < 1)$$
$$p(0; \lambda = 1) = p(1; \lambda = 1)$$
$$p(0; \lambda > 1) < p(1; \lambda > 1)$$

As we explained earlier, λ indicates the density of changes that occur in a given time interval. Thus, when λ is small, the density of changes is small, and this implies that changes do not occur frequently. The implication is, therefore, when λ is small, the probabilities associated with small values of k (say, $k = 0$, 1) are large, and as k increases, the probabilities associated with it decrease rapidly. Table 19.5 shows that $\lambda = 1$ is the dividing value of this trend. As λ increases beyond 1, the largest probabilities of occurrence become associated with values of $k > 1$.

19.4. Estimation of λ and Applications

Let us now show how λ is estimated, by using a simple illustration. We shall first determine an appropriate fixed interval t; then show how this fixed interval t is divided into subintervals that generate a Poisson process and a Poisson distribution; and then, recalling that λ was a constant that expressed the density of random points (events) on the time axis (or the expected value of the Poisson distribution), find the average number of random points in the fixed interval and consider it as an estimate of λt.

For example, suppose we have a time interval of 60 min., as shown in Fig. 19.5. The 60 min. are divided into 12 fixed intervals, where each

FIG. 19.5.

interval is $t = 5$ min. The dots show the incoming calls. As can be seen, there are $N_0 = 3$ intervals with no phone calls; $N_1 = 5$ intervals with 1 phone call; and $N_2 = 4$ intervals with 2 phone calls. The total number of these fixed intervals is shown by

$$N_0 + N_1 + N_2 = 3 + 5 + 4 = 12 = N$$

The total number of phone calls (that is, random points) is

$$1 \times N_1 + 2 \times N_2 = 13 = T$$

Each of these intervals of $t = 5$ min. is then divided into n sub-intervals. If we can assume that the assumption of randomness and independence apply to these subintervals, each fixed interval of $t = 5$ min. is split up into a Poisson process, and hence the points in the fixed interval ($t = 5$ min.) can be expressed by the Poisson distribution. That is,

$$p(k; \lambda t) = e^{-\lambda t} \frac{(\lambda t)^k}{k!}$$

is the probability of exactly k phone calls in the fixed interval of $t = 5$ min.

The λ shows the density of the random points on the time axis. To estimate this, we reason as follows: If we can assume the conditions of the experiment to remain unchanged, the 12 intervals of $t = 5$ min. in the 60 min. may be considered as repeating the experiment 12 times. There is a total of $T = 13$ points in the $N = 12$ intervals. Hence, the average number of points per interval of $t = 5$ min. is $T/N = 13/12 = 1.09 \cong 1.1$. In our present illustration, N is only $N = 12$, and the amount of data is small; but when N is large, we may consider T/N as representative of the average number of random points in a fixed interval of length t, and hence set it as

$$\lambda t = \frac{T}{N}$$

The values of the Poisson distribution for $\lambda t = 1.1$, from the Molina tables, are shown in Table 19.6.

In the following examples, the objective is to be able to find the fixed

TABLE 19.6.

k	$p(k; \lambda t = 1.1)$
0	0.333
1	0.366
2	0.201
3	0.074
4	0.020
5	0.004
6	0.0008

intervals, then determine whether these fixed intervals may be divided into n subintervals and whether a Poisson process can be constructed, and then to see if there are enough fixed intervals (that is, to see if the experiment has been repeated enough times) to estimate λt.

Example 1. Data of deaths due to a kick from a horse, based on the records of 10 army corps for 20 years (compiled by Bortkewitsch), are given in Table 19.7.

TABLE 19.7.

k	N_k	$p(k; \lambda t = 0.60)$	Np
0	109	0.55	110
1	65	0.32	64
2	22	0.10	20
3	3	0.02	4
4	1	0.003	0.6
5	0	0.0004	0
	200		198.6

We find that there are 200 readings; that is, 200 fixed intervals. Each fixed interval is a per-year, per-corps unit. This may also be interpreted as 200 repetitions of an experiment.

We are also assuming that the opportunity of an event's (a death due to a kick from a horse) occurring is continuously present. This means that if we consider the occurrence of an event as a success and the nonoccurrence as a failure, the proportion of successes is very small.

Let us now divide each fixed interval (per year per corps) into n subintervals where n is very large. Then we shall assume that the probability of occurrence or nonoccurrence in a subinterval is close to 1. The probability of more than 1 occurrence is very small. Furthermore, we shall assume that the occurrence of an event in any subinterval is independent of the occurrence in any other subinterval. Thus, we have a Poisson process in the fixed interval (per year per corps), and hence we have

$$p(k; \lambda t) = e^{-\lambda t} \frac{(\lambda t)^k}{k!}$$

where k is the number of deaths in a fixed interval (per year per corps); λt is the expected number of deaths $E(k)$ in the fixed interval; and t indicates the fixed interval (per year per corps).

The problem now is to estimate λt. We have 200 fixed intervals (that is, 200 repetitions of the experiment), and the total number of deaths in the 200 intervals is

$$\begin{aligned}
T &= N_1 + 2N_2 + 3N_3 + 4N_4 + 5N_5 \\
&= 65 + 2 \times 22 + 3 \times 3 + 4 \times 1 + 5 \times 0 = 122
\end{aligned}$$

Hence, the average number of deaths per year per corps is

$$\lambda t = \frac{T}{N} = \frac{122}{200} = 0.61$$

which shows the density of deaths on a fixed-interval basis. Hence, the Poisson distribution is

$$p(k; \lambda t = 0.61) = e^{-0.61} \frac{(0.61)^k}{k!}$$

Using the Molina tables, we find the probability as shown in Table 19.7. Since the tables do not have $\lambda t = 0.61$, we have used $\lambda t = 0.60$ as an approximate value. Thus, for example, the probability of $k = 2$ deaths is 0.32. As the table shows, we have a good fit.

Example 2.   A total of 1000 students participated in a spelling contest. T indicates the total number of misspelled words and N_k indicates the number of students with k misspelled words. The results are given in Table 19.8. What is the probability of a student having k misspelled words?

TABLE 19.8.

k	N_k	kN_k	$p(k; 2.98)$	$Np(k; 2.98)$
0	50	0	0.050	50
1	150	150	0.149	149
2	220	440	0.224	224
3	230	690	0.224	224
4	170	680	0.168	168
5	100	500	0.101	101
6	50	300	0.050	50
7	20	140	0.022	22
8	10	80	0.008	8
9	0	0	0.003	3
	1000	2980		999

We find

$$\lambda t = \frac{T}{N} = \frac{2980}{1000} = 2.98$$

Thus, the Poisson distribution becomes

$$p(k; 2.98) = e^{-2.98} \frac{(2.98)^k}{k!}$$

The probabilities can be found from the Molina tables. They are given in Table 19.8. Since the Molina tables do not have values for $\lambda = 2.98$, we have used $\lambda = 3.0$ as an approximation.

In quality control statistics, the terms *defective* and *defect* are distinguished. For example, we may have a defective radio that has 3 defects. An item is defective or nondefective. A defective item may have 1 or more defects.

When we are concerned with *defective* and *nondefective* items, and the probability of a defective item is small, we may use the Poisson distribution as an approximation to the binomial distribution. If, however, we are concerned with the number of *defects,* and the probability of a defect is small, it is appropriate to use the Poisson distribution. Let us illustrate with an example.

Example 3. Suppose 1000 radios are inspected as they come off a production line and the number of defects per radio are found as shown in Table 19.9.

TABLE 19.9.

k	N_k	$p(k; \lambda = 0.05)$	Np
0	950	0.951	951
1	47	0.048	48
2	2	0.001	1
3	1	0.000	0
4	0	0.000	0
	$\overline{1000}$		$\overline{1000}$

As the table shows, there are 950 radios with no defects; 47 with 1 defect; 2 with 2 defects; and 1 with 3 defects. The total number of defects is

$$T = 1N_1 + 2N_2 + 3N_3 + 4N_4$$
$$= 47 + 4 + 3 = 54$$

Hence, the average number of defects per radio is

$$\lambda t = \frac{T}{N} = \frac{54}{1000} = 0.054 \cong 0.05$$

From the Molina tables, using $\lambda t = 0.05$ as an approximation, we find the probabilities as shown in Table 19.9. As the table shows, the fit is good.

In Example 3, a radio is the fixed interval and a defect is the occurrence of an event and may be called a success. A nondefect is the nonoccurrence of an event and may be called a failure. We may assume that the opportunity of the occurrence of an event is continuously present, which implies in our present case that the probability of an occurrence of an event is very small.

Let us now theoretically divide the fixed interval (radio) into n subintervals where n is large. The subintervals may be considered as the possible places where 1 or more defects may occur in a radio. Then we shall assume that the probability of no defect or 1 defect occurring in a subinterval is close to 1, and the probability of more than 1 defect is very small. We shall also assume that the occurrence of a defect in a subinterval is independent of the occurrence of defects in other subintervals. Hence, we have a Poisson process in the fixed interval, and the probability of exactly k defects in a radio is

$$p(k; \lambda t) = e^{-\lambda t} \frac{(\lambda t)^k}{k!}$$

$$= e^{-0.05} \frac{(0.05)^k}{k!}$$

Note that we did not actually need to know the number of subintervals n to find the Poisson distribution. All we needed was the possibility of dividing the radio into a large number n of subintervals that could have 0, 1, or more defects.

Example 4. Assume a 1000-page book with k misprints per page. A misprint may be considered as 1 defect. Each page is considered as 1 interval. The distribution of misprints is given in Table 19.10. N_k is the number of pages with k misprints.

TABLE 19.10.

k	N_k	kN_k	$p(k; 0.71)$	$Np(k; 0.71)$
0	500	0	0.497	497
1	340	340	0.348	348
2	120	240	0.122	122
3	30	90	0.028	28
4	10	40	0.005	5
	1000	710		1000

What is the probability of k misprints on a page? We fit the Poisson distribution by first estimating λt:

$$\lambda t = \frac{T}{N} = \frac{710}{1000} = 0.71$$

Then the Poisson distribution is

$$p(k; 0.71) = e^{-0.71} \frac{(0.71)^k}{k!}$$

From the Molina tables we find the probabilities as shown in Table 19.10. The values are for $\lambda = 0.7$, which was the closest value of λ near 0.71. $Np(k; 0.71)$ gives us the theoretical results, and as we see, the fit is good.

In Example 4, we may theoretically divide a page into n subintervals where, in this case, a subinterval will be a subarea. If n is sufficiently large, we may assume that the probability of more than 1 misprint in a subarea is very small. We are also tacitly assuming that the number of misprints on a page is small. Furthermore, the occurrence of a misprint in any subarea is assumed to be independent of the occurrence in other subareas. Hence, we have a Poisson process in each interval (page) and the probability of exactly k defects per interval (page) is as given above.

The 1000 pages may be considered as 1000 repetitions of the experiment.

Example 5.   From a shipment of rice, samples of a pound of rice are taken to check the amount of small pebbles it contains. Suppose 50 samples of a pound of rice are taken at random, and the number of pebbles are found to be as shown in Table 19.11.

TABLE 19.11.

k	N_k	$p(k; \lambda t = 0.06)$
0	48	0.942
1	1	0.057
2	1	0.002
3	0	0
4	0	0
	$\overline{50}$	

The table shows that there are $N_0 = 48$ samples that have no pebbles; $N_1 = 1$ sample that has 1 pebble; $N_2 = 1$ sample that has 2 pebbles, and so forth.

As is seen in this case, each sample is the fixed interval t, and we may think that each sample is divided into subintervals that contain a few grains of rice. Hence, we may think that the probability of a subinterval's containing no pebbles or 1 pebble is almost 1, whereas there is a very small probability that it will contain more than 1 pebble. Furthermore, the probability of a sample's containing 1 pebble is very small. Hence, for each sample, we have a Poisson process.

The estimate of λt is obtained by

$$\lambda t = \frac{T}{N} = \frac{3}{50} = 0.06$$

where T is the total number of pebbles and N is the total number of samples.

The Poisson distribution we seek is

$$p(k; \lambda t = 0.06) = e^{-0.06} \frac{(0.06)^k}{k!}$$

and, for example, the probability of 2 pebbles in a pound of rice is

$$p(k = 2; \lambda t = 0.06) = 0.002$$

We have obtained this from the Molina tables.

Note that in this case we do not know the number of grains of rice in a sample, but we do know that it is a large number and the number of pebbles is relatively very small.

19.5. The Multinomial Distribution

Two other discrete distributions, the multinomial and hypergeometric distribution, will be mentioned primarily for purposes of reference. We shall discuss the multinomial distribution in this section and the hypergeometric distribution in Section 19.6.

The multinomial distribution can be looked upon as an extension of the binomial distribution, but instead of only two outcomes, there may be more than two. We shall first discuss the multinomial coefficient and then explain the multinomial distribution.

(i) The multinomial coefficient

Assume that there are $n = 5$ students and that we wish to form 3 groups: 2 in the first and second group, and 1 in the third group. Let $n_1 = 2, n_2 = 2, n_3 = 1$ indicate the numbers in the groups. Then

$$n_1 + n_2 + n_3 = n = 5$$

There are

$$\binom{n}{n_1} = \binom{5}{2} = 10$$

different ways of selecting the first group of 2 students.

After this first group has been selected, there are $n - n_1 = 5 - 2 = 3$ students remaining. From $n - n_1$, there are

$$\binom{n - n_1}{n_2} = \binom{3}{2} = 3$$

different ways of selecting n_2 students.

Finally, we have

$$\binom{n - n_1 - n_2}{n_3} = \binom{n_3}{n_3} = 1$$

way of selecting the remaining group.

Thus, the total number of ways of selecting these three groups will be

$$\binom{n}{n_1}\binom{n-n_1}{n_2}\binom{n-n_1-n_2}{n_3}$$

This turns out to be

$$\frac{n!}{n_1!\,(n-n_1)!}\cdot\frac{(n-n_1)!}{n_2!\,(n-n_1-n_2)!}\cdot 1$$

$$=\frac{n!}{n_1!\,n_2!\,n_3!}=\frac{5!}{2!\,2!\,2!}=30$$

This may be generalized as follows: Let a collection of n elements be grouped into k groups such that

$$n_1+n_2+\cdots+n_k=n$$

where $n_1, n_2, \ldots, n_k$ is the number of elements in each group. Then there are

$$\frac{n!}{n_1!\,n_2!\cdots n_k}$$

different ways of grouping the n elements into these k groups.

Example 1. Ten students are to be divided into 2 groups of 5 each to play basketball. How many different teams can be made?

$$\binom{10}{5}\binom{10-5}{5}=\frac{10!}{5!\,5!}=252$$

Example 2. Fifteen students are to be divided into 3 groups of 5 each to play basketball. How many different teams can be made?

$$\binom{15}{5}\binom{15-5}{5}\binom{15-5-5}{5}=\frac{15!}{5!\,5!\,5!}=756{,}756$$

Example 3. A deck of 52 cards is distributed among 4 players, each with 13 cards. How many different ways can the cards be distributed?

$$\binom{52}{13}\binom{52-13}{13}\binom{52-13-13}{13}\binom{52-13-13-13}{13}$$

$$=\frac{52!}{13!\,13!\,13!\,13!}$$

(ii)   The multinomial distribution

We know that if the probability of selecting a smoker is p and that of selecting a nonsmoker is $1-p$, then the probability of selecting k

smokers in n Bernoulli trials is

$$b(k;\, n,\, p) = \binom{n}{k} p^k \, (1-p)^{n-k}$$

Let us now assume that the probability of selecting a heavy smoker, an average smoker, and a nonsmoker is p_1, p_2, and p_3, where

$$p_1 + p_2 + p_3 = 1$$

Let us select n smokers, of which x_1, x_2, and x_3 is the number of heavy, average, and nonsmokers, where

$$x_1 + x_2 + x_3 = n$$

What is the probability of selecting n smokers who can be grouped in this manner?

We have a sequence of n independent trials, each having 3 possible outcomes. For example, let us assume $n = 5$ and $x_1 = 2$, $x_2 = 2$, $x_3 = 1$. Then, one such sequence will be

$$(HS) \quad (HS) \quad (AS) \quad (AS) \quad (NS)$$

where HS, AS, and NS are for heavy, average, and nonsmoker groups, respectively. The probability of selecting such a sequence is, because we assume independence of the trials,

$$p_1 \cdot p_1 \cdot p_2 \cdot p_2 \cdot p_3 = p_1^2 p_2^2 p_3$$

No matter what the ordering, the probability will be the same. Since there are

$$\frac{n!}{x_1!\, x_2!\, x_3!}$$

different ways of selecting n smokers, the probability of selecting such a grouping will be

$$\frac{n!}{x_1!\, x_2!\, x_3!}\, p_1^{x_1} p_2^{x_2} p_3^{x_3}$$

This can be generalized as follows: Let $E_1, E_2, \ldots, E_k$ be the possible outcomes of a trial with probabilities $p_1, p_2, \ldots, p_k$. Let there be n trials with $x_1, x_2, \ldots, x_k$ outcomes of $E_1, E_2, \ldots, E_k$. Then,

$$x_1 + x_2 + \cdots + x_k = n$$

The probability of having $x_1, x_2, \ldots, x_k$ occurrences in n trials will be

$$\frac{n!}{x_1! x_2! \cdots,\, x_k!}\, p_1^{x_1} p_2^{x_2} \cdots p_k^{x_k}$$

Note that x_k is automatically determined by $x_1, x_2, \ldots, x_{k-1}$ and n. Thus, we have only $k-1$ independent random variables, namely, x_1, $x_2, \ldots, x_{k-1}$. Likewise, p_k is automatically determined, since

$$\sum_{i}^{k} p_i = 1$$

Thus, the density function for the multinomial distribution can be written as

$$f(x_1, x_2, \cdots, x_{k-1}) = \frac{n!}{x_1! x_2! \cdots x_k!} \, p_1^{x_1} p_2^{x_2} \cdots p_k^{x_k}$$

But, in many cases this is written $f(x_1, x_2, \ldots, x_k)$ with the understanding that x_k is not an independent random variable.

Example 1.   Consider a box of 100 beads, of which 50 are red, 30 are green, and 20 are black. After 5 beads have been selected, they are replaced each time. What is the probability of selecting 5 beads such that 3 are red, 1 is green, and 1 is black? Since selections are made with replacement, the probability of selecting 1 red, 1 green, and 1 black bead will be, respectively, $p_1 = 0.5$, $p_2 = 0.3$, and $p_3 = 0.2$. Thus, the probability of selecting 5 beads with the given composition will be

$$\frac{n!}{n_1! \, n_2! \, n_3!} \, p_1^{n_1} p_2^{n_2} p_3^{n_3} = \frac{5!}{3! \, 1! \, 1!} (0.5)^3 (0.3)^1 (0.2)^1$$

(iii)   The mean and variance

Let us find the mean and variance of the multinomial distribution, using the following simple case of 3 variables:

$$f(x_1, x_2, x_3) = \frac{n!}{x_1! x_2! x_3!} \, p_1^{x_1} p_2^{x_2} p_3^{x_3}$$

The expected value of x_1 will be

$$E(X_1) = \Sigma \, x_1 f(x_1, x_2, x_3)$$

where the sum is over all possible combinations of x_1, x_2, and x_3. This becomes

$$\Sigma x_1 \frac{n!}{x_1! x_2! x_3!} \, p_1^{x_1} p_2^{x_2} p_3^{x_3}$$

$$= n p_1 \, \Sigma \, \frac{(n-1)}{(x_1 - 1)! x_2! x_3!} \, p_1^{x_1-1} p_2^{x_2} p_3^{x_3}$$

$$= n p_1$$

Thus the expected value of x_1 is np_1. In general the expected value of x_i will be np_i.

The variance is defined as

$$Var(X_1) = E(X_1 - np_1)^2$$
$$= E(X_1^2) - 2np_1E(X_1) + n^2p_1^2$$
$$= E(X_1^2) - n^2p_1^2$$

The $E(X_1^2)$ is

$$E(X_1^2) = \Sigma \, x_1^2 f(x_1, x_2, x_3)$$

$$= np_1 \, \Sigma \, x_1 \frac{(n-1)!}{(x_1-1)!x_2!x_3!} \, p_1^{x_1-1} p_2^{x_2} p_3^{x_3}$$

The summation part can be changed as

$$\Sigma \, x_1 \frac{(n-1)!}{(x_1-1)!x_2!x_3!} \, p_1^{x_1-1} p_2^{x_2} p_3^{x_3}$$

$$= \Sigma \, (x_1 - 1 + 1) \frac{(n-1)!}{(x_1-1)!x_2!x_3!} \, p_1^{x_1-1} p_2^{x_2} p_3^{x_3}$$

$$= \Sigma \, (x_1 - 1) \frac{(n-1)!}{(x_1-1)!x_2!x_3!} \, p_1^{x_1-1} p_2^{x_2} p_3^{x_3}$$

$$+ \Sigma \, \frac{(n-1)!}{(x_1-1)!x_2!x_3!} \, p_1^{x_1-1} p_2^{x_2} p_3^{x_3}$$

$$= (n-1)p_1 + 1$$

Thus if we put the results together, we find

$$Var(X_1) = np_1\{(n-1)p_1 + 1\} - n^2p_1^2$$
$$= np_1(1 - p_1)$$

In general the variance for x_i is $np_i(1 - p_i)$.

Example. Let

$$f(x_1, x_2, x_3) = \frac{20!}{10! \, 5! \, 3! \, 2!} \, (0.4)^{10} \, (0.3)^5 \, (0.2)^3 \, (0.1)^2$$

Then

$$E(X_1) = np_1 = (20)(0.4) = 8$$
$$Var(X_1) = np_1(1 - p_1) = (20)(0.4)(0.6) = 4.8$$

19.6.   The Hypergeometric Distribution

When sampling is without replacement, the hypergeometric distribution is used instead of the binomial distribution. As a result, it is finding increasing use in quality control statistics. A new table of this distribution has been published* which should facilitate its application. Let us sketch the derivation by use of an illustration.

(i)   The hypergeometric distribution

Consider a box that has 100 beads in it, of which $n_1 = 60$ are red and $n_2 = 40$ are black. $r = 10$ beads are selected. What is the probability that there will be $x = 4$ red beads? Since there are $n_1 = 60$ red beads, there are

$$\binom{n_1}{x}$$

possible ways of selecting $x = 4$ red beads. Of the $r = 10$ beads, $r - x = 10 - 4 = 6$ are black. Hence there are

$$\binom{n_2}{r - x}$$

possible ways of selecting $r - x = 6$ black beads. Thus, the total number of ways of selecting 10 beads that have exactly $x = 4$ red and $r - x = 6$ black beads is

$$\binom{n_1}{x}\binom{n_2}{r - x}$$

There are

$$\binom{n}{r} = \binom{100}{10}$$

possible ways of selecting 10 beads from 100 beads. Thus, the probability of selecting 10 beads that have $x = 4$ red beads is

$$f(x) = \frac{\binom{n_1}{x}\binom{n_2}{r - x}}{\binom{n}{r}} = \frac{\binom{60}{4}\binom{40}{10 - 4}}{\binom{100}{10}}$$

Note that in this case, since $r - x = 6$ black beads is determined by r and x, the random variable is x.

---

* G. J. Lieberman and D. B. Owen, *Tables of the Hypergeometric Distribution*, Stanford University Press, 1960.

Example 1. Consider 10 students where 6 are Democrats and 4 are Republicans. A sample of size 5 has been selected. What is the probability that there will be 3 Democrats in this sample?

$$f(x) = \frac{\binom{n_1}{x}\binom{n_2}{r-x}}{\binom{n_1+n_2}{r}} = \frac{\binom{6}{3}\binom{4}{5-3}}{\binom{6+4}{5}} \cong 0.50$$

THE CHI-SQUARE DISTRIBUTION

20

Suppose an experiment of tossing a die is repeated 60 times with the following results (Table 20.1), and we are asked: Is this a fair die?

In statistical terminology, the fair die represents a theoretical probability distribution, which we shall call our hypothesis H. We shall assume that this probability distribution is $p_i = 1/6 (i = 1, 2, \ldots, 6)$ for each outcome. The 60 observed values are a sample of $n = 60$ observed values of the random variable X, which takes on the 6 outcomes. Then the question may be restated as: Do the observed sample data support (or are consistent with) the hypothesis H?

TABLE 20.1.

X	
	0
1	8
2	11
3	11
4	12
5	9
6	9
	$\overline{60}$

Problems of testing whether the sample data support (or are in agreement with) the hypothetical distribution are called *tests of goodness of fit*.

The statistical technique used to test such problems is based on the χ^2 distribution. We shall first define the χ^2 distribution, explain a few related theorems, and then discuss K. Pearson's approximation, which is used in applications.[*] We shall then consider tests of goodness of fit, tests of independence, and tests of homogeneity.

---

[*] K. Pearson, "On the criterion that a given system of deviations from the probable in the case of a correlated system of variables is such that it can be reasonably supposed to have arisen from random sampling," *Phil. Mag.*, **50** (1900) p. 157.

20.1.   The χ^2 Distribution and its Properties

(i)   Definition of the χ^2 distribution

Suppose we have a sequence of normally distributed random variables $Y_1, Y_2, \ldots, Y_n$ with mean and variance

$$E(Y) = \mu, \qquad \text{Var}(Y) = \sigma^2$$

These variables may be standardized as

$$X_i = \frac{Y_i - \mu}{\sigma}$$

where X_i will be normally distributed with mean and variance

$$E(X) = 0, \qquad \text{Var}(X) = 1$$

Let us now construct the following statistic:

$$u = X_1{}^2 + X_2{}^2 + \cdots + X_n{}^2$$

and ask the question: Does u have a distribution, and if it does, what kind of a distribution?

The answers to these queries are: Yes, u has a distribution, and the distribution is the χ^2 distribution, which has the following density function:

$$f(u) = \frac{1}{\left(\frac{n}{2} - 1\right)!} 2^{(-n)/2} u^{(n/2)-1} e^{-(1/2)u} \qquad \text{for } u \geq 0$$

$$= 0 \qquad\qquad\qquad\qquad\qquad\qquad\qquad \text{otherwise}$$

The e is the natural number and n is the number of independent random variables that was summed. Note that the random variables are *independent*. Later in this chapter, there will be situations where we have n variables, but where only $n - k$ are independent. For our present case, there are n independent random variables, and we say that there are n degrees of freedom.

The derivation of the χ^2 distribution can be found in a mathematical statistics book such as Mood's.* We shall take the distribution as given, and mainly concern ourselves with the applications.

(ii)   The χ^2 table

Using the χ^2 table in the Appendix and Fig. 20.1 as a visual aid,

---

* A. Mood, *Introduction to the Theory of Statistics*, New York: McGraw-Hill Book Co., 1950, pp. 199–201.

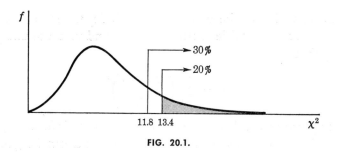

FIG. 20.1.

let us find a few values of χ^2. For $n = 10$ degrees of freedom, the value for 20 percent of the shaded area in the right-tail end is

$$P(13.4 < \chi^2 < \infty \,|\, n = 10) = 0.20$$

For 30 percent of the right-tail end, we find

$$P(11.8 < \chi^2 < \infty \,|\, n = 10) = 0.30$$

As can be seen, the χ^2 table is in cumulative form.

(iii)   The expected value and variance of the χ^2 distribution

We state without derivation that the mean and variance of a χ^2 distribution where all n variables are independent (that is, we have n degrees of freedom) are

$$E(\chi^2) = n$$
$$\mathrm{Var}(\chi^2) = 2n$$

(iv)   The distribution of $\sum \left(\dfrac{x_i - \mu_i}{\sigma_i} \right)^2$

In actual problems we usually do not have random variables that are independent and normally distributed with mean zero and variance unity. But when we have random variables with a normal distribution, we can always standardize the variables, as we have done above, and obtain normalized variables that have mean zero and variance unity.

Consider a sequence of random variables x_1, x_2, x_3 that are normal with means μ_1, μ_2, μ_3 and variance σ_1, σ_2, σ_3. Then the normalized variables will be

$$z_i = \frac{x_i - \mu_i}{\sigma_i} \qquad i = 1, 2, 3$$

The z_1, z_2, z_3 will then be a sequence of independent and normally distributed random variables with mean zero and variance unity. Thus, we can say that

$$u = \sum_{i=1}^{3} \left(\frac{x_i - \mu_i}{\sigma_i} \right)^2$$

has χ^2 distribution with three degrees of freedom. This form of presentation of u will be more useful for applications and can be generalized very easily to n degrees of freedom.

(v)   Additive nature of χ^2

A property that we shall use later is that when χ_1^2 and χ_2^2 are independent and have a χ^2 distribution with n_1 and n_2 degrees of freedom then $\chi_1^2 + \chi_2^2$ will also be distributed as a χ^2 distribution with $n_1 + n_2$ degrees of freedom. This additive property holds in general for k independent χ^2 variables.

20.2.   K. Pearson's Approximation

K. Pearson has shown how a discrete multinomial distribution may be transformed and made to approach a χ^2 distribution as $n \longrightarrow \infty$. By establishing this relationship between the multinomial and χ^2 distribution, the χ^2 distribution has become one of the most versatile distributions in applied statistics. Let us now explain this result.

Suppose a fair 4-sided die is tossed 40 times with the following results (Table 20.2). We have an experiment with 4 mutually exclusive events, E_1, E_2, E_3, and E_4, and we assume that the probability of an event E occurring is $p_i = 1/4$; n_i is the number of occurrences of the event E_i and $\Sigma n_i = n = 40$. We have seen that the joint distribution of n_1, n_2, n_3, and n_4 is called a multinomial distribution with density function

TABLE 20.2.

X	n_i
1	8
2	11
3	12
4	9
	40

$$f(n_1, n_2, n_3, n_4) = \frac{n!}{n_1! n_2! n_3! n_4!} \, p_1^{n_1} p_2^{n_2} p_3^{n_3} p_4^{n_4}$$

K. Pearson has shown that when

(1)
$$x_i = \frac{n_i - np_i}{\sqrt{np_i}}$$

and we set

(2) $$u = x_1{}^2 + x_2{}^2 + x_3{}^2 + x_4{}^2$$

the distribution of u approaches a χ^2 distribution with $4 - 1 = 3$ degrees of freedom as n becomes very large.

How large must n be in order to assume that the u is approximately distributed as a χ^2 distribution? As a rule, we shall state that when $np_i \geqq 5$, we may use the χ^2 distribution as an approximation. When $np_i < 5$, we may pool the smaller groups into larger ones so that $np_i \geqq 5$ is satisfied. This will be illustrated later.

Our problem now is to show how equations (1) and (2) may be applied to practical problems.

20.3.   The Goodness-of-Fit Test

The first application we shall consider is the goodness-of-fit test, which is a test of the agreement (or conformity, or consistency) between a hypothetical and sample distribution. Pearson's approximation, which was shown as

$$\chi^2 = \Sigma \frac{(n_i - np_i)^2}{np_i}$$

may be shown schematically as

$$\chi^2 = \Sigma \frac{(O_i - e_i)^2}{e_i}$$

where O_i is the observed and e_i is the expected frequency. As is seen, this χ^2 may be considered as a measure of discrepancy between O_i and e_i. If there is no discrepancy, then $\chi^2 = 0$. As the discrepancy becomes larger, the χ^2 becomes larger. These χ^2 values are evaluated by the χ^2 distribution.

The format of the goodness-of-fit tests is as follows:

1.   State the null hypothesis, which is usually: The sample distribution agrees with the hypothetical (theoretical) distribution.
2.   Determine the level of significance; that is, the risk of the type 1 error. We shall use $\alpha = 5$ percent in our examples.
3.   Calculate χ^2 and determine the number of degrees of freedom. The $\alpha = 5$ percent and the degrees of freedom will determine the region of rejection. We shall explain this procedure with examples.

Example 1. Suppose a coin is tossed 50 times with the results given in Table

TABLE 20.3.

Event	n_i
Heads	22
Tails	28
	50

20.3. Is this a fair coin? The null hypothesis is

$$H_1: \qquad n_i = np_i$$

where n_i is the number of observed frequencies and np_i is the expected frequencies in which the p_i are the theoretical probabilities. In our present case,

$$\Sigma\, n_i = n = 50, \quad p_1 = \frac{1}{2}, \quad \text{and} \quad p_2 = \frac{1}{2}$$

Using Pearson's approximation, we find

$$\chi^2 = \frac{(22 - 50 \times \frac{1}{2})^2}{50 \times \frac{1}{2}} + \frac{(28 - 50 \times \frac{1}{2})^2}{50 \times \frac{1}{2}}$$

$$= \frac{9}{25} + \frac{9}{25} = \frac{18}{25} = 0.72$$

There are $r - 1 = 2 - 1 = 1$ degree of freedom, and for $\alpha = 5$ percent level of significance, we find

$$P(3.841 < \chi^2 < \infty) = 0.05$$

and the rejection region is $\chi^2 \geq 3.84$. Hence, $\chi^2 = 0.72$ is not significant, and we accept the null hypothesis that the coin is fair.

Yates' correction for continuity. Yates' correction is analogous to the continuity correction that was applied to the normal approximation to the binomial distribution. In the χ^2 case, the χ^2 tables are calculated from the original theoretical distribution, which is continuous, whereas the approximations we are using are discrete.

There is a tendency to underestimate the probability, which means that the number of rejections of the null hypothesis will be increased. Thus, we wish to correct the χ^2 downward. Yates has shown that when

$$\chi^2 = \Sigma\, \frac{\left(|n_i - np_i| - \dfrac{1}{2} \right)^2}{np_i}$$

is used, the χ^2 approximation is improved. This adjustment is used only when there is one degree of freedom. When there is more than one degree of freedom, it is not used. It should also be omitted when several χ^2 values are combined.

Applying this to Example 1, we find

$$\chi^2 = \frac{\left(|22 - 25| - \dfrac{1}{2}\right)^2}{25} + \frac{\left(|28 - 25| - \dfrac{1}{2}\right)^2}{25}$$

$$= 0.5$$

The χ^2 in the example, without the continuity correction, was 0.72, and there has been a downward correction of the χ^2 value.

As is seen, when n (or np_i) is large, the $\frac{1}{2}$ correction has little effect, but becomes important when n is small. However, when $|n_i - np_i|$ is less than $\frac{1}{2}$, the continuity correction should be omitted.

Example 2.   There are 5 classes of freshman economics students, each having 50 students, and it is usually found that $1/5$ of a class fails the course. The results for the 5 classes are shown in Table 20.4.

TABLE 20.4.

Class	Failure	Pass	Expected Failure	Expected Pass	χ^2
1	8	42	10	40	0.31
2	5	45	10	40	2.53
3	13	37	10	40	0.78
4	15	35	10	40	2.53
5	5	45	10	40	2.53
	46	204	50	200	8.68

These 5 classes may be considered as 5 samples. We wish to test the hypothesis that the proportion of failures is $1/5$, using these 5 samples. That is, the null hypothesis is

$$H_1: \quad \text{Failure : pass} = 1 : 4$$

Let us first calculate the χ^2 values for each sample. For the first sample, we find

$$\chi^2 = \frac{(|8 - 10| - \frac{1}{2})^2}{10} + \frac{(|42 - 40| - \frac{1}{2})^2}{40} = 0.31$$

In similar manner we may find the χ^2 values for the other 4 samples, as shown in Table 20.4.

For the first sample, we have 1 degree of freedom. Hence, for $\alpha = 5$ percent level of significance, we find

$$P(3.841 < \chi^2 < \infty) = 0.05$$

and the rejection region is $\chi^2 \geqq 3.841$; hence, the $\chi^2 = 0.5$ is not significant. That is, the first sample supports the hypothesis. We can also see that the other χ^2 values also support the hypothesis.

Example 3.   Let us now suppose that the data in Example 2 are as given in Table 20.5.

TABLE 20.5.

Class	Failure	Pass	Expected Failure	Expected Pass	χ^2
1	8	42	10	40	0.31
2	5	45	10	40	2.53
3	7	43	10	40	0.78
4	5	45	10	40	2.53
5	5	45	10	40	2.53
	30	220	50	200	8.68

We see that the χ^2 values are exactly the same as those in Example 2. Hence, as far as the individual samples are concerned, they support the hypothesis that the ratio is 1:4.

However, a comparison of Table 20.4 and Table 20.5 shows that, whereas the proportion of the failures in Table 20.4 fluctuated around $\frac{1}{5}$, the proportion of failures in Table 20.5 are consistently lower than $\frac{1}{5}$.

The method we have used in computing the χ^2 for Examples 2 and 3 has removed the significance of the *direction* of the deviations of the observed from the expected frequencies because the deviations are squared. In Example 2, the deviations have no regularity, whereas in Example 3, the deviations are all in the same direction.

To take into consideration the *direction* of the deviations, we shall pool the samples into one large sample and find the χ^2 value for this pooled sample. Obviously, when we pool the samples of Example 2, the plus deviations and minus deviations will cancel out each other, whereas in Example 3, the minus deviations will cumulate and accentuate the deficiency. From Table 20.4 we see that the pooled χ^2 of Example 2 is

$$\chi^2 = \frac{\left(|46 - 50| - \dfrac{1}{2}\right)^2}{50} + \frac{\left(|204 - 200| - \dfrac{1}{2}\right)^2}{200}$$

$$= \frac{12.25}{50} + \frac{12.25}{200} = \frac{61.25}{200} = 0.31$$

whereas for Example 3, it is

$$\chi^2 = \frac{\left(|30 - 50| - \frac{1}{2}\right)^2}{50} + \frac{\left(|220 - 200| - \frac{1}{2}\right)^2}{200}$$

$$= \frac{380.25}{50} + \frac{380.25}{200} = 9.5$$

For one degree of freedom, the 5 percent level of significance is

$$P(3.841 < \chi^2 < \infty) = 0.05$$

and the rejection region is $\chi^2 \geqq 3.841$. Hence, for the 5 percent level of significance, $\chi^2 = 0.31$ is not significant.

However, the $\chi^2 = 9.5$ of Example 3 is significant for the 5 percent level of significance. It is seen that the pooling of the sample has accentuated the importance of the directions of the deviations.

Example 4.   The additive property of the χ^2 distribution may also be used as an additional test of significance. Let us add the individual χ^2 values of Example 2 as an illustration. For this, we must first omit the continuity corrections from each χ^2 value. The recalculated χ^2 values are given in Table 20.6.

TABLE 20.6.

Class	Failure	Pass	Expected Failure	Expected Pass	χ^2
1	8	42	10	40	0.5
2	5	45	10	40	3.1
3	13	37	10	40	1.1
4	15	35	10	40	3.1
5	5	45	10	40	3.1
	46	204			10.9

The sum of the χ^2 is $\chi^2 = 10.9$, and there are 5 degrees of freedom. Using the 5 percent level of significance, we find

$$P(11.07 < \chi^2 < \infty) = 0.05$$

and the rejection region is $\chi^2 \geqq 11.07$. Hence, $\chi^2 = 10.9$ is not significant.

A characteristic of the approach in Example 4 as compared to that of Example 3 is: Although the data of all five samples are combined, the directions of the deviations are not considered because, as we can see, the deviations are squared for each χ^2 value.

However, the summing process accentuated the deviations. Although the deviations may be small for each χ^2 value, the sum of the χ^2 values may accentuate the deviations, and as a result, the sum may produce a significant χ^2 value.

We may summarize the results of Examples 2, 3, and 4 and state as follows:

1.   For Example 2:

    (a).   The individual χ^2 values are not significant.

    (b).   The pooled χ^2 value is also not significant, indicating that the direction of the deviations are not significant.

    (c).   The sum of the values is also not significant, indicating that the cumulative effect of the deviations is not significant.

2.   For Example 3:

    (a).   The individual χ^2 values are not significant.

    (b).   The pooled χ^2 value is significant, indicating that the directions of the deviations are significant.

    (c).   The sum of the χ^2 values is not significant, indicating that the cumulative effect of the deviations is not significant.

Example 5.   The percent distribution of spending units in the United States in 1951 was as shown in Table 20.7.

TABLE 20.7.

Income Class	Percent, 1951
Under $1000	13
$1000–1999	15
$2000–2999	18
$3000–3999	18
$4000–4999	15
$5000–7499	14
$7500 and over	7
	100

A random sample of 200 spending units is selected in 1959 and the distribution is found as shown in Table 20.8.

Does the distribution of spending units in 1959 differ significantly from that of 1951? That is, has there been a change in the distribution of spending units?

We shall first change the percent distribution of 1951 into the actual number of families, as shown in Table 20.9.

TABLE 20.8.

Income Class	Number of Families, 1959
Under $1000	14
$1000–1999	24
$2000–2999	20
$3000–3999	22
$4000–4999	24
$5000–7499	52
$7500 and over	44
	200

TABLE 20.9.

Income Class	1959 O	1951 e	$O - e$	$(O - e)^2/e$
Under $1000	14	26	−12	5.5
$1000–1999	24	30	− 6	1.2
$2000–2999	20	36	−16	7.1
$3000–3999	22	36	−14	5.4
$4000–4999	24	30	− 6	1.2
$5000–7499	52	28	24	20.1
$7500 and over	44	14	30	64.3
	200	200		104.8

Observation of the deviations $O - e$ shows that in 1959 a large percentage of the families moved into the higher income brackets.

There are $7 - 1 = 6$ degrees of freedom, and hence the values of χ^2 for $\alpha = 5$ percent level of significance is

$$P(12.6 < \chi^2 < \infty) = 0.05$$

Since we have $\chi^2 = 104.8$, we shall conclude that there is a significant difference between the two distributions and that there has been a change in the distribution of spending units.

The χ^2 distribution is also used to test whether the sample distribution agrees with a hypothetical distribution that has a certain number of unknown parameters. For example, we may wish to test whether the sample distribution of IQ's of a class of children fits a normal distribution. We know that a normal distribution is specified by its mean and variance. If the mean and variance are unknown, it is necessary to estimate these parameters before we can use the χ^2 to perform the test.

When the mean and variance of the theoretical normal distribution are estimated from sample values, the degrees of freedom are reduced by $s = 2$. Hence, the total number of degrees of freedom are $r - s - 1$, where r is the number of groups and s is the number of restrictions on the theoretical distribution because the parameters are estimated by sample values.

For a Poisson distribution $p(k; \lambda)$, the parameter λ is estimated from sample values as we saw in Chapter 19. Hence, $s = 1$.

Let us now illustrate how the χ^2 distribution is used to test the goodness of fits of sample distributions when some of the parameters of the theoretical distributions have to be estimated.

Example 6. Table 19.10 is reproduced below as Table 20.10. The k was the

TABLE 20.10.

k	N_k	Np_k	$(N_k - Np_k)^2/Np$
0	500	497	0.02
1	340	348	0.18
2	120	122	0.03
3	30	28	0.14
4	10	5	5.0
	1000		5.37

number of misprints on a page of a 1000-page book. The Poisson distribution was calculated as

$$p(k; \lambda = 0.71) = e^{-0.71} \frac{(0.71)^k}{k!}$$

where λ was estimated as $\lambda = 0.71$.

The hypothesis we wish to test is that the misprints have a Poisson distribution. The N_k's are the observed frequencies and the Np_k's are the theoretical frequencies. The χ^2 is found as $\chi^2 = 5.37$. However, note that the contribution from $k = 0$ to $k = 3$ is 0.37, and for $k = 4$, it is 5. Also note that for $k = 4$, the frequency is only 5. It does not violate the rule that we should have $Np_k \geq 5$ in order to use the χ^2 approximation. However, let us first work it out as it is, and then pool the frequencies to get $Np_k > 5$.

Since λ was obtained from sample data, the degrees of freedom are $r - s - 1 = 5 - 1 - 1 = 3$. For the $\alpha = 5$ percent level of significance, we have

$$P(7.8 < \chi^2 < \infty) = 0.05$$

and the rejection region is $\chi^2 \geq 7.8$. Hence, $\chi^2 = 5.37$ is not significant, and we shall accept the hypothesis that the misprints have a Poisson distribution.

Let us now pool the frequencies of the last two brackets. That is, for $k \geqq 3$ we have $N_k = 40$, and $Np_k = 33$. Then the χ^2 value for this last bracket is

$$\frac{(40 - 33)^2}{33} = \frac{49}{33} = 1.48$$

Hence, the χ^2 value becomes

$$\chi^2 = 0.02 + 0.18 + 0.03 + 1.48 = 1.71$$

We now have $r - s - 1 = 4 - 1 - 1 = 2$ degrees of freedom, and we find

$$P(5.99 < \chi^2 < \infty) = 0.05$$

Hence $\chi^2 = 1.48$ is not significant.

20.4. Tests of Independence: Contingency Tables

The goodness-of-fit tests dealt with multinomial populations where:
1. We were given a hypothetical probability distribution of the population that was to be tested.
2. The population and sample were classified according to a *single* attribute.

For example, a group of individuals was classified according to the kind of soap they use, and we hypothesized the proportion of each group in the population. The problem was to test whether the observed data supported the hypothesis.

It was seen that we did not need to restrict ourselves to a multinomial population, but could apply this technique to other continuous distributions such as the normal distribution.

We now wish to apply the χ^2 distribution to tests of independence. The population and sample are now classified according to *several* attributes, but the probability distributions of these classifications are not given. For example, each individual may be classified according to his income and the kind of soap he uses. The proportion of each of these groups in the population is not known.

The problem in which we are interested is whether there is any dependency relationship between an individual's income and the kind of soap he uses. Hence, the hypothesis to be tested is as follows: A person's income and the soap he uses are independent of each other.

The test we shall develop will tell us only whether or not the two attributes are independent. It will not tell us the degree of association or the direction of dependency. For example, assume the result of the tests indicates dependency. The test will not tell us whether the choice of soap is dependent on income, or vice versa. Furthermore, it will not tell us the degree of dependency.

If the result indicates independence, it will tell us that the observed data support (or are consistent with) the hypothesis that the two attributes are independent.

Let us use an illustration and develop this test. We first explain the population, then the sample, and summarize this in a contingency table. We shall then discuss the sampling distribution to be used for the test.

(i) Population

The population is classified according to income and soap, as shown in Table 20.11. The capital N's indicate population values. N is the

TABLE 20.11.

	Soap		
Income	B (Good)	B (Poor)	Total, N_i
A_1 (high)	N_{11}	N_{12}	$N_1.$
A_2 (low)	N_{21}	N_{22}	$N_2.$
Total, N_j	$N_{.1}$	$N_{.2}$	N

total population, N_{11} is the number of individuals having income A (say, high income) and using soap B (say, good quality soap), and likewise for other cells. $N_i.$ indicates row totals. $N_{.j}$ indicates column totals.

This can also be shown in terms of proportions, as in Table 20.12.

TABLE 20.12.

	Soap		Total
Income	B_1	B_2	
A_1	$N_{11}/N = p_{11}$	$N_{12}/N = p_{12}$	$p_1.$
A_2	$N_{21}/N = p_{21}$	$N_{22}/N = p_{22}$	$p_2.$
	$p_{.1}$	$p_{.2}$	1

For example, $p_{11} = N_{11}/N$ is the proportion of persons with a high income (A_1) using good quality soap (B_1). Similar interpretations are given to the other p_{ij}.

The $p_{.1} = N_{.1}/N$ and $p_{.2} = N_{.2}/N$ show the proportion of persons using soap B_1 (good) and B_2 (poor), respectively. Hence,

$$p_{.1} + p_{.2} = \frac{N_{.1}}{N} + \frac{N_{.2}}{N} = 1$$

and similarly, for income,

$$p_1. + p_2. = 1$$

We do not actually know these probabilities, but they have been assumed for the purpose of investigating the theoretical implications of the independence of the attributes. This will be discussed in Par. (iii), on sampling distribution.

(ii) The sample and contingency table

A random sample of size n is selected from the preceding population and is classified as in Table 20.13, in which the lower case n's

TABLE 20.13. Sample (Observed Data)

Income	Soap B_1	B_2	Total, $n_i.$
A_1	n_{11}	n_{12}	$n_1.$
A_2	n_{21}	n_{22}	$n_2.$
Total, $n._j$	$n._1$	$n._2$	n

indicate sample values. n_{ij} indicates the frequency in the i–jth cell. $n_i.$ indicates the row totals and $n._j$ indicates the column totals. Note that

$$n._1 + n._2 = n$$
$$n_1. + n_2. = n$$

As an illustration, suppose a sample of $n = 300$ individuals is selected and it is found that $n_1. = 100$ have an income of A_1; $n_2. = 200$ have an income of A_2. Also $n._1 = 150$ use soap B_1; $n._2 = 150$ use soap B_2. This two-way classification is shown in Table 20.14.

TABLE 20.14.

Income	Soap B_1	B_2	Total, $n_i.$
A_1			$n_1. = 100$
A_2			$n_2. = 200$
Total, $n._j$	$n._1 = 150$	$n._2 = 150$	$n = 300$

Upon investigation, we find that $n_{11} = 40$ of the $n_1. = 100$ have income A_1 and also use soap B_1. Then, without any further investigation, we automatically find that $n_{12} = 60$ because

$$n_{12} = n_1. - n_{11} = 100 - 40 = 60$$

Likewise, $n_{21} = 110$, $n_{22} = 90$ are automatically determined. This result is shown in Table 20.15. We see that, once one of the n_{ij} have been

TABLE 20.15.

Income	Soap		Total
	B_1	B_2	
A_1	40	60	100
A_2	110	90	200
Total	150	150	300

determined, the remainder of the three n_{ij} are automatically determined in our present case.

(iii)   The sampling distribution and the test

Table 20.12 is reproduced as Table 20.16 for convenience. Let us now

TABLE 20.16.

Income		Soap	
		B_1	B_2
		$p_{\cdot 1}$	$p_{\cdot 2}$
A_1	$p_{1\cdot}$	p_{11}	p_{12}
A_2	$p_{2\cdot}$	p_{21}	p_{22}

ask the question: What is the probability that an individual will have the attributes A_1 and B_1? That is, have income A_1 and use soap B_1? If the hypothesis is true and A_1 and B_1 are independent, the probability of a person having high income and using good quality soap will be

$$P(A_1 \,\&\, B_1) = P(A_1)P(B_1) = (p_{1\cdot})(p_{\cdot 1})$$

Likewise, for A_1 and B_2, we have

$$P(A_1 \,\&\, B_2) = P(A_1)P(B_2) = (p_{1\cdot})(p_{\cdot 2})$$

and so forth.

But, since we have assumed that the probabilities in the cells are $p_{ij}(i, j = 1, 2)$ (see Table 20.16), we have

$$p_{11} = (p_{1\cdot})(p_{\cdot 1})$$
$$p_{12} = (p_{1\cdot})(p_{\cdot 2})$$

and so forth. In general, when we have independence,

$$p_{ij} = (p_{i\cdot})(p_{\cdot j})$$

The results may also be stated in terms of frequencies as follows: Since n is the sample size, the expected (theoretical) number of frequencies in each cell, np_{ij}, will be

$$np_{ij} = np_{i\cdot}p_{\cdot j}$$

assuming that the hypothesis of independence is true. The results are shown in Table 20.17.

TABLE 20.17.   Expected Frequencies

	B_1	B_2	Total
A_1	$np_1 \cdot p_{\cdot 1}$	$np_1 \cdot p_{\cdot 2}$	$np_1 \cdot$
A_2	$np_2 \cdot p_{\cdot 1}$	$np_2 \cdot p_{\cdot 2}$	$np_2 \cdot$
Total	$np_{\cdot 1}$	$np_{\cdot 2}$	

Recall that our object is to test the hypothesis that the attributes are independent, using observed sample data. Table 20.17 gives the theoretical frequencies when we assume independence. If the hypothesis is indeed true, we should expect the observed sample to be an image of the theoretical distribution, and the discrepancy between the theoretical and observed frequencies should be small.

Let us first find this discrepancy. Since the frequencies of the observed sample were shown in Table 20.13 to be n_{ij}, the discrepancies will be:

$$\text{Discrepancies} = n_{ij} - np_{i\cdot}p_{\cdot j}$$
$$= n_{ij} - np_{ij}$$

To obtain a measure to evaluate the discrepancy, we need to find its sampling distribution. It turns out that Pearson's approximation can be used. We state without proof that when

$$y_{ij} = \frac{n_{ij} - np_{ij}}{\sqrt{np_{ij}}}$$

and

$$u = y_{11}^2 + y_{12}^2 + y_{21}^2 + y_{22}^2$$
$$= \sum_{i=1}^{2} \sum_{j=1}^{2} \frac{(n_{ij} - np_{ij})^2}{np_{ij}}$$
$$= \sum_{i=1}^{2} \sum_{j=1}^{2} \frac{(n_{ij} - np_{i\cdot}p_{\cdot j})^2}{np_{i\cdot}p_{\cdot j}}$$

the u will approach a χ^2 distribution as n becomes large. Thus, by finding the value for u, we can use the χ^2 probability table and evaluate the probability of u, provided n is sufficiently large.

But, unfortunately, there is a slight catch; that is, *we do not know* the p_{ij} that were theoretical probabilities we assumed for purposes of analysis. Without the p_{ij}, we cannot calculate u. What should we do to solve this impasse?

By now the student should know enough statistics to answer immediately; estimate the p_{ij} from sample data and use the estimates to calculate u. The estimates of u will be found in the following heuristic manner: We know that

$$p_{i\cdot} = \frac{N_{i\cdot}}{N} \qquad i = 1, 2$$

$$p_{\cdot j} = \frac{N_{\cdot j}}{N} \qquad j = 1, 2$$

where $N_{i\cdot}$, $N_{\cdot j}$, and N are population values. For example, $p_{1\cdot} = N_{\cdot 1}/N$ is the proportion of persons in the population having high incomes.

The corresponding frequencies in the sample are $n_{1\cdot}/n$. In fact, as $n \longrightarrow N$, then

$$\frac{n_{1\cdot}}{n} \longrightarrow \frac{N_{1\cdot}}{N}$$

Thus, if we let $\hat{p}_{1\cdot}$ be an estimate of $p_{1\cdot}$, and set

$$\hat{p}_{1\cdot} = \frac{n_{1\cdot}}{n}$$

then,

$$\hat{p}_{1\cdot} \longrightarrow p_{1\cdot} \qquad \text{as} \quad n \longrightarrow N$$

In general,

$$\hat{p}_{i\cdot} \longrightarrow p_{i\cdot} \qquad \text{as} \quad n \longrightarrow N$$
$$\hat{p}_{\cdot j} \longrightarrow p_{\cdot j} \qquad \text{as} \quad n \longrightarrow N$$

We shall adopt these $\hat{p}_{i\cdot}$ and $\hat{p}_{\cdot j}$ as the estimators. It turns out that these estimators are the maximum likelihood estimators.

Thus, our test statistic becomes

$$u = \sum_{i=1}^{2} \sum_{j=1}^{2} \frac{(n_{ij} - n\hat{p}_{i\cdot}\hat{p}_{\cdot j})^2}{n\hat{p}_{i\cdot}\hat{p}_{\cdot j}}$$

Since $\hat{p}_{i\cdot} = n_{i\cdot}/n$, $\hat{p}_{\cdot j} = n_{\cdot j}/n$, the test statistic u may also be expressed in terms of sample frequencies as

$$u = n \sum_i \sum_j \frac{\left(n_{ij} - \dfrac{n_{i\cdot}.n_{\cdot j}}{n} \right)^2}{n_{i\cdot}.n_{\cdot j}}$$

We need to know two things. One is the number of degrees of freedom and the other is how large n has to be for a reliable approximation to the χ^2 distribution.

As for the number of degrees of freedom, for an $r \times s$ contingency table, it is $(r - 1) \times (s - 1)$. Looking at the first column of a contingency table, we note that when $r - 1$ of the values are determined, the rth value is automatically determined. That is, the rth value is dependent on the other $r - 1$ values in that column, and likewise for the other columns.

In similar fashion, for the first row, we note that when $s - 1$ of the values are determined, the sth value is automatically determined. Hence, there are $(r - 1)(s - 1)$ values that may be determined freely, while the remaining $rs - (r - 1)(s - 1)$ values will be determined automatically. Thus, there are $(r - 1)(s - 1)$ degrees of freedom. For a 2×2 contingency table, there are $(2 - 1)(2 - 1) = 1$ degree of freedom. For a 3×3 contingency table, there are $(3 - 1)(3 - 1) = 4$ degrees of freedom, and so forth.

As for the sample size n, various proposals have been made. Cramer states that when the expected frequencies are larger than 10, we have a good approximation.[*] Snedecor states that when the observed frequencies are less than 5 in any cell, the approximation to the χ^2 distribution becomes poor.[**] H. Walker sets up as a practical rule of thumb that when there are 2 or more degrees of freedom, and when each cell has 5 or more observations, the χ^2 table gives a good approximation to the exact probabilities.[†]

As mentioned earlier, we shall use the rule that the expected frequencies in each cell should be at least 5.

Example 1.   Using Tables 20.15 and 20.17, we obtain Table 20.18. The figures in the parentheses in the cells are the expected frequencies that have

---

[*] H. Cramer, *Mathematical Methods of Statistics*, Princeton University Press, 1946.
[**] H. Walker and J. Lev, *Statistical Inference*, New York: Henry Holt and Co., 1953.
[†] G. W. Snedecor, *Statistical Methods*, 5th ed., Ames, Iowa State University Press, 1956.

TABLE 20.18.

Income	Soap		Total
	B_1	B_2	
A_1	40(50)	60(50)	100
A_2	110(100)	90(100)	200
	150	150	300

been estimated from the sample data as follows:

$$n\hat{p}_{11} = n\hat{p}_1 . \hat{p}_{.1}$$

$$= n \times \frac{n_1.}{n} \times \frac{n_{.1}}{n}$$

$$= n_1 . \times \frac{n_{.1}}{n} = 100 \times \frac{150}{300} = 50$$

$$n\hat{p}_{12} = n_1 . \times \frac{n_{.2}}{n} = 100 \times \frac{150}{300} = 50$$

$$n\hat{p}_{21} = n_2 . \times \frac{n_{.1}}{n} = 200 \times \frac{150}{300} = 100$$

$$n\hat{p}_{22} = n_2 . \times \frac{n_{.2}}{n} = 200 \times \frac{150}{300} = 100$$

The test statistic u is

$$u = \sum_i \sum_j \frac{(n_{ij} - n\hat{p}_{ij})^2}{n\hat{p}_{ij}}$$

$$= \frac{(40 - 50)^2}{50} + \frac{(60 - 50)^2}{50} + \frac{(110 - 100)^2}{100} + \frac{(90 - 100)^2}{100} = 6$$

There is $(2 - 1)(2 - 1) = 1$ degree of freedom. From the χ^2 table, we find for the 5 percent level of significance,

$$P(3.841 < \chi^2 < \infty) = 0.05$$

and the rejection region is $\chi^2 \geqq 3.841$. Hence, we reject the hypothesis that a person's income and the kind of soap he uses are independent. Note that the test says only that the sample data do not support the hypothesis. It does not tell us anything about the degree of dependency or direction of dependency.

Since the expected frequencies were large, we have not used the continuity correction. Note the effect of the continuity correction in the next example.

Example 2. Noting that there was only 1 degree of freedom in Example 1, let us recalculate the χ^2 value, using Yates' correction for continuity.

$$u = \frac{\left(|40 - 50| - \dfrac{1}{2}\right)^2}{50} + \frac{\left(|60 - 50| - \dfrac{1}{2}\right)^2}{50}$$

$$+ \frac{\left(|110 - 100| - \dfrac{1}{2}\right)^2}{100} + \frac{\left(|90 - 100| - \dfrac{1}{2}\right)^2}{100}$$

$$= \frac{9.5}{50} + \frac{9.5}{50} + \frac{9.5}{100} + \frac{9.5}{100} = 5.415$$

As is seen, the χ^2 value has been reduced somewhat, but does not change the conclusion of rejecting the hypothesis.

Example 3.   Is there a relationship between sex and smoking? To test this question, we shall state the null hypothesis as: There is no relation between sex and smoking. Suppose we have selected a random sample of 100 persons and have found the results as shown in Table 20.19.

TABLE 20.19.

	Male	Female	
Smoker	30(20)	10(20)	$40 = n_{1\cdot}$
Nonsmoker	20(30)	40(30)	$60 = n_{2\cdot}$
	$50 = n_{\cdot 1}$	$50 = n_{\cdot 2}$	$100 = n$

Theoretical frequencies are found by estimating the $p_{i\cdot}$ and $p_{\cdot j}$, which are

$$\hat{p}_{1\cdot} = \frac{n_{1\cdot}}{n} = \frac{40}{100}$$

$$\hat{p}_{2\cdot} = \frac{n_{2\cdot}}{n} = \frac{60}{100}$$

$$\hat{p}_{\cdot 1} = \frac{n_{\cdot 1}}{n} = \frac{50}{100}$$

$$\hat{p}_{\cdot 2} = \frac{n_{\cdot 2}}{n} = \frac{50}{100}$$

The theoretical frequencies are

$$n\hat{p}_{11} = n(\hat{p}_{1\cdot})(\hat{p}_{\cdot 2}) = 100 \times \frac{40}{100} \times \frac{50}{100} = 20$$

The other theoretical frequencies are automatically determined, since the totals in the margins are given. These theoretical frequencies are shown within the parentheses.

Although we have estimated the $p_{i\cdot}$ and $p_{\cdot j}$ to find the theoretical frequencies, as is seen, the results may be shown very simply in terms of marginal totals as follows: For $n\hat{p}_{11}$, we have

$$n\hat{p}_{11} = n(\hat{p}_{1\cdot})(\hat{p}_{\cdot1})$$

$$= n \times \frac{n_{1\cdot}}{n} \times \frac{n_{\cdot1}}{n}$$

$$= n_{1\cdot} \times \frac{n_{\cdot1}}{n}$$

$$= 40 \times \frac{50}{100} = 20$$

Similarly, we find

$$n\hat{p}_{12} = n_{1\cdot} \times \frac{n_{\cdot2}}{n}$$

$$= 40 \times \frac{50}{100} = 20$$

This may be interpreted as follows: There are altogether 40 smokers. Of the 100 persons, 50/100 are males and 50/100 are females. If sex and smoking are independent, the proportion of male smokers and female smokers should be the same as the proportion of males and females. Hence,

$$40 \times \frac{50}{100} = 20 \text{ male smokers}$$

$$40 \times \frac{50}{100} = 20 \text{ female smokers}$$

In similar manner, we may argue that the proportion of smokers and non-smokers are 40/100 and 60/100. If sex and smoking are independent, then, of the 50 males we should expect as the theoretical frequencies

$$50 \times \frac{40}{100} = 20 \text{ smokers}$$

$$50 \times \frac{60}{100} = 30 \text{ nonsmokers}$$

We summarize: To find the theoretical frequencies, we need use only the marginal totals and calculate the proportions.

The χ^2 value is

$$u = \frac{\left(|30 - 20| - \frac{1}{2}\right)^2}{20} + \frac{\left(|10 - 20| - \frac{1}{2}\right)^2}{20}$$

$$+ \frac{\left(|20 - 30| - \frac{1}{2}\right)^2}{30} + \frac{\left(|40 - 30| - \frac{1}{2}\right)^2}{30}$$

$$= 15.04$$

For the 5 percent level of significance, since there is 1 degree of freedom,

$$P(3.841 < \chi^2 < \infty) = 0.05$$

and the rejection region is $\chi^2 \geqq 3.841$. Hence, we reject the hypothesis that sex and smoking are independent.

Example 4. Is there a relationship between sex and the preference of color? The null hypothesis in this case is: There is no relationship between sex and color. Suppose a sample of 100 persons is selected and we find the results shown in Table 20.20.

TABLE 20.20.

Color	Male	Female
Pink	10	20
White	20	10
Blue	30	10
	60	40

We see that we have $(r - 1)(s - 1) = (3 - 1)(2 - 1) = 2$ degrees of freedom in this 3×2 contingency table.

The theoretical frequencies that are obtained from the original totals are shown in Table 20.21.

TABLE 20.21.

Color	Male	Female
Pink	$30/100 \times 60 = 18$	$30/100 \times 40 = 12$
White	$30/100 \times 60 = 18$	$30/100 \times 40 = 12$
Blue	$40/100 \times 60 = 24$	$40/100 \times 40 = 16$
	60	40

The χ^2 value is

$$u = \frac{(10 - 18)^2}{18} + \frac{(20 - 12)^2}{12}$$

$$+ \frac{(20 - 18)^2}{18} + \frac{(10 - 12)^2}{12}$$

$$+ \frac{(30 - 24)}{24} + \frac{(10 - 16)^2}{16}$$

$$= 13.19$$

For 2 degrees of freedom and $\alpha = 5$ percent level of significance, we find

$$P(5.991 < \chi^2 < \infty) = 0.05$$

and the rejection region is $\chi^2 \geqq 5.991$. Since $u = 13.2$, we reject the null hypothesis that sex and color preference are independent.

Observation of the data shows that males prefer blue and females prefer pink, but the χ^2 test shows only that there is a dependency relation between sex and color preference.

Note that in this case we have 2 degrees of freedom and have omitted the continuity correction.

20.5. Test of Homogeneity

(i) The problem

Consider an academic test given to two different high schools. A sample of $n_1 = 100$ and $n_2 = 100$ students is taken from each school and the results of the grades are found to be as shown in Table 20.22.

TABLE 20.22.

		Sample		
Grade		1	2	
p_1	A	$n_{11} = 10$	$n_{12} = 10$	$m_1 = 20$
p_2	B	$n_{21} = 20$	$n_{22} = 10$	$m_2 = 30$
p_3	C	$n_{31} = 30$	$n_{32} = 40$	$m_3 = 70$
p_4	D	$n_{41} = 20$	$n_{42} = 30$	$m_4 = 50$
p_5	F	$n_{51} = 20$	$n_{52} = 10$	$m_5 = 30$
		$n_1 = 100$	$n_2 = 100$	$n = 200$

For example, there are $n_{11} = 10$ students with grade A in sample 1, which came from the first high school.

The question we ask is: Is there any difference between the grades of the two high schools? To investigate this question, we set up the null hypothesis: The two samples came from the same population.

This simply means there is no difference between the two high schools. Or, we can say that the two samples were drawn from the same population. The word "homogeneous" is used frequently in statistics to indicate "the same" or "equal." Thus we can say that we are interested in testing whether the data or samples are homogeneous in our present problem, and we call it a *test of homogeneity*.

We have dealt with a similar problem in a different way, namely, by comparing sample means. That is, we could find the sample means and test the difference by the t test. But when there were more than two samples, the t test for comparing means was not applicable, whereas in our present case, the test we shall develop will be applicable to any number of samples.

Since we are testing whether the samples came from the same population, there is a single probability distribution of the attribute in the population. For our present example, it is $p_1, p_2, \ldots, p_5$ as shown in Table 20.22. For example, p_1 indicates the proportion of A's in the population.

Let us now present the problem in general terms as shown in Table 20.23, where n_{ij} shows the number of observations in the ith class of the

TABLE 20.23.

Grade	Sample					
	1	2	3	$\cdots$	s	
p_1	n_{11}	n_{12}	n_{13}	$\cdots$	n_{1s}	m_1
p_2	n_{21}	n_{22}	n_{23}	$\cdots$	n_{2s}	m_2
$\vdots$	$\vdots$	$\vdots$	$\vdots$	$\vdots$	$\vdots$	$\vdots$
p_r	n_{r1}	n_{r2}	n_{r3}	$\cdots$	n_{rs}	m_r
	n_1	n_2	n_3	$\cdots$	n_s	n

sample and n_j shows the size of the jth sample. Thus

$$\sum_{i=1}^{r} n_{ij} = n_j$$

The probability distribution is shown by

$$\{p_1, p_2, \ldots, p_r\}$$

that is associated with the classification according to the criterion. Note that we do not actually know this probability distribution, but we have stated it theoretically so that we can use it to develop the test. Let us next develop the test.

(ii)   The test

Let us first re-examine the null hypothesis. It was: Are the two samples from the same population? Or, using the probability distribution of the hypothetical population, the null hypothesis may be stated: Both samples have the same probability distribution, which is the probability distribution of the population.

For purposes of constructing a test, we shall use the second way of expressing the null hypothesis in terms of probability distributions. Our aim will be to find the discrepancy between observations (that is, the samples) and the theoretical distribution, and then to find the sampling distribution of the discrepancy.

If we assume the probability distribution to be p_i $(i = 1, 2, \ldots, 5)$, then the expected number of frequencies will be

$$n_j p_i \qquad i = 1, 2, \ldots, 5, \quad j = 1, 2$$

The results are shown schematically in Table 20.24.

TABLE 20.24.

	Expected Frequencies		
	1	2	
p_1	$n_1 p_1$	$n_2 p_1$	m_1
p_2	$n_1 p_2$	$n_2 p_2$	m_2
p_3	$n_1 p_3$	$n_2 p_3$	m_3
p_4	$n_1 p_4$	$n_2 p_4$	m_4
p_5	$n_1 p_5$	$n_2 p_5$	m_5
	n_1	n_2	n

Note that

$$\sum_{i=1}^{5} p_i = 1$$

Thus, since n_{ij} are the observed frequencies, the discrepancy will be

$$n_{ij} - n_j p_i \qquad i = 1, 2, \ldots, 5, \quad j = 1, 2$$

From this we construct the test statistic

$$u = \sum_{i=1}^{5} \sum_{j=1}^{2} \frac{(n_{ij} - n_j p_i)^2}{n_j p_i}$$

We state without proof that when n is large, u approaches a χ^2 distribution with $(r-1)(s-1)$ degrees of freedom. Thus, we have a sampling distribution of u, which enables us to test whether or not the discrepancy is significant.

But since the p_i's are unknown, estimates need to be found. Similar to the estimates found in tests of independence, we find

$$\hat{p}_i = \frac{m_i}{n}$$

where $\hat{p}_i$ are estimates of p_i. We can see heuristically that

$$\hat{p}_i \longrightarrow p_i \quad \text{as} \quad n \longrightarrow N$$

where N is the population size. Thus, the test statistic u becomes

$$u = \sum_i^5 \sum_j^2 \frac{(n_{ij} - n_j \hat{p}_i)^2}{n_j \hat{p}_i}$$

$$= \sum_i \sum_j \frac{\left(n_{ij} - n_j \frac{m_i}{n}\right)^2}{n_j \frac{m_i}{n}}$$

$$= \sum_i \sum_j \frac{(O - e)^2}{e}$$

For our present illustration, we find

$$e_{11} = n_1 \frac{m_1}{n} = 100 \times \frac{20}{200} = 10$$

$$e_{12} = n_1 \frac{m_2}{n} = 100 \times \frac{30}{200} = 15$$

$$\cdot \quad \cdot \quad \cdot \quad \cdot \quad \cdot \quad \cdot \quad \cdot \quad \cdot \quad \cdot \quad \cdot$$

$$e_{21} = n_2 \frac{m_1}{n} = 100 \times \frac{20}{200} = 10$$

$$e_{22} = n_2 \frac{m_2}{n} = 100 \times \frac{30}{200} = 15$$

$$\cdot \quad \cdot \quad \cdot \quad \cdot \quad \cdot \quad \cdot \quad \cdot \quad \cdot \quad \cdot \quad \cdot$$

These expected values are shown within the parentheses in Table 20.25.

TABLE 20.25.

Grade	Sample		$\frac{(O-e)^2}{e}$	$\frac{(O-e)^2}{e}$
	1	2		
A	10(10)	10(10)	$0/10 = 0$	$0/10 = 0$
B	20(15)	10(15)	$25/15 = 1.6$	$25/15 = 1.6$
C	30(35)	40(35)	$25/35 = 0.7$	$25/35 = 0.7$
D	20(25)	30(25)	$25/25 = 1.0$	$25/25 = 1.0$
F	20(15)	10(15)	$25/15 = 1.6$	$25/15 = 1.6$
			4.9	4.9

Hence the χ^2 value is

$$u = 4.9 + 4.9 = 9.8$$

There are $(r-1)(s-1) = (5-1)(2-1) = 4$ degrees of freedom. For $\alpha = 5$ percent level of significance, we find

$$P(9.48 < \chi^2 < \infty) = 0.05$$

and the rejection region is $\chi^2 \geq 9.48$. Hence, we reject the null hypothesis that both samples came from the same population.

20.6. Confidence Interval for σ^2

We have seen that when a sample of size n is taken from a normal population, the statistic

$$u = \sum_{i=1}^{n} \frac{(x_i - \bar{x})^2}{\sigma^2}$$

has a χ^2 distribution with $n-1$ degrees of freedom. σ^2 is the population variance and $\bar{x}$ is the sample mean.

Thus we can easily find the values of a and b from the χ^2 table (Appendix) such that

$$P(a < u < b) = 0.90$$

If we assume $n = 21$, then there are 20 degrees of freedom. Furthermore, if there is to be 5 percent in each end of the tail, as shown in Fig. 20.2,

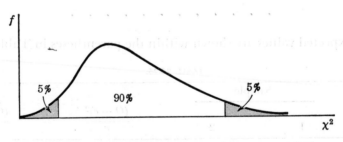

FIG. 20.2.

then

$$P(10.851 < u < 31.410) = 0.90$$

Now let us set

$$P\left(a < \frac{\Sigma(x - \bar{x})^2}{\sigma^2} < b\right) = 1 - \alpha$$

which becomes

$$P\left(\frac{\Sigma\,(x-\bar{x})^2}{b} < \sigma^2 < \frac{\Sigma\,(x-\bar{x})^2}{a}\right) = 1 - \alpha$$

Since $\Sigma\,(x-\bar{x})^2$ and a, b are values that can be obtained from the sample and from the χ^2 table, we have a confidence interval for σ^2:

$$\frac{\Sigma\,(x-\bar{x})^2}{b} < \sigma^2 < \frac{\Sigma\,(x-\bar{x})^2}{a}$$

and the a and b will be determined by confidence coefficient $(1 - \alpha)$.

THE F DISTRIBUTION

21

So far we have considered the normal, binomial, t, Poisson, multinomial, hypergeometric, and χ^2 distribution. But in all our previous discussion, we have never attempted to test two important hypotheses. One is the equality of variances, and the second is the equality of more than two means. Using the t distribution, for example, we have compared two sample means, but not three or more. As for the variances, in our previous discussion we usually assumed variances of different distributions to be equal without any proof. The F distribution we shall discuss in this chapter will give us a means of solving this problem. And it will, furthermore, open up a new method of statistical analysis called the analysis of variance which has wide applicability in many fields such as agriculture, industrial engineering, and psychology just to mention a few.

The F distribution was developed by R. A. Fisher in the early 1920s as the Z distribution, but was later transformed into the F distribution, which is easier to use. The F is in honor of R. A. Fisher.

In this chapter we shall explain the F distribution, show how it is used to test the equality of two variances, and then show how it is used in the analysis of variance.

21.1. The F Distribution

Example 1 of Section 17.6 is reproduced below for convenience. The problem involved two groups of students, A and B, who had been

	x_1	x_2	$x_1{}^2$	$x_2{}^2$
	60	40	3600	1600
	60	40	3600	1600
	70	50	4900	2500
	80	60	6400	3600
	80	60	6400	3600
Total	350	250	24,900	12,900
Mean	70	50		

taught the same subject by different methods. We wish to test whether there is a significant difference in grades between the 2 groups. A sample of 5 students is selected from each group, with the results as shown in the table above.

The test was set up as follows:

$$\text{Null hypothesis, } H_1: \qquad \mu_1 = \mu_2$$
$$\text{Alternative hypothesis, } H_2: \qquad \mu_1 > \mu_2$$

where the μ's are the average grades of the students. This test was carried out by applying the t distribution. But recall that this was possible only when we assumed $\sigma_1 = \sigma_2$. Based on this assumption, we found the pooled variance as

$$\hat{\sigma}^2 = \frac{n_1 s_1{}^2 + n_2 s_2{}^2}{n_1 + n_2 - 2} = 100$$

which was used to find the t value; this was

$$t = \frac{\bar{x}_1 - \bar{x}_2}{\hat{\sigma}} \sqrt{\frac{n_1 n_2}{n_1 + n_2}}$$
$$= \frac{70 - 50}{\sqrt{100}} \sqrt{\frac{5 \cdot 5}{5 + 5}}$$
$$= 3.16$$

The conclusion of the test was that there is a significant difference.

We now wish to raise the question: Is the assumption that $\sigma_1 = \sigma_2$ valid?

To answer this question, we shall first develop the F distribution in this section, explain the F table in Section 21.3, and then perform the test in Section 21.4.

Let x_i be normally distributed with mean μ_i and variance $\sigma_i{}^2$, and let

(1)
$$u = \sum_{i=1}^{k} \left(\frac{x_i - \mu_i}{\sigma_i} \right)^2$$

Then we know from Section 20.1 that u has a χ^2 distribution with k degrees of freedom.

If the values x_i are taken from the same population, then (1) becomes

(2) $$u = \sum_{i=1}^{k} \left(\frac{x_i - \mu}{\sigma} \right)^2$$

which has a χ^2 distribution with k degrees of freedom.

Now suppose we consider the k values of x_i to be a sample of size $n = k$. Let $\bar{x}$ be the sample mean and replace the μ in (2) by $\bar{x}$. Then (2) becomes

(3) $$u = \sum_{i=1}^{k} \left(\frac{x_i - \bar{x}}{\sigma} \right)^2$$

$$= \frac{k \dfrac{\Sigma (x_i - \bar{x})^2}{k}}{\sigma^2}$$

$$= \frac{ks^2}{\sigma^2}$$

Equation (3) has a χ^2 distribution with $k - 1$ degrees of freedom. In general, let the sample size be n. Then (3) may be rewritten as

(4) $$u = \frac{ns^2}{\sigma^2}$$

which has a χ^2 distribution with $n - 1$ degrees of freedom.

In terms of our example above, we may construct

(5) $$u = \frac{n_1 s_1^2}{\sigma_1^2}$$

(6) $$v = \frac{n_2 s_2^2}{\sigma_2^2}$$

and u and v will have χ^2 distributions with $n_1 - 1$ and $n_2 - 1$ degrees of freedom.

Using (5) and (6), let us form the ratio

(7) $$F = \frac{\dfrac{u}{n_1 - 1}}{\dfrac{v}{n_2 - 1}} = \frac{\dfrac{u}{m}}{\dfrac{v}{n}}$$

This F is the ratio of two quantities u and v, which have independent χ^2 distributions divided by their respective degrees of freedom, and is called the *variance ratio*.

It can be shown that the distribution of this F has the following density function:

$$(8) \quad g(F) = \frac{\left(\dfrac{m+n-2}{2}\right)!}{\left(\dfrac{m-2}{2}\right)!\left(\dfrac{n-2}{2}\right)!} \left(\frac{m}{n}\right)^{m/2} \frac{F^{(m-2)/2}}{\left(1+\dfrac{mF}{n}\right)^{(m+n)/2}} \geqq 0$$

where $m = n_1 - 1$ and $n = n_2 - 1$. This is called the *density function* of the F distribution. As can be seen, as m and n (that is, the degrees of freedom) vary, the distribution of F [that is, $g(F)$] will also vary. This formula (8) is a frightening looking formula. However, its values have been tabulated in tables so we need only to know the degrees of freedom in order to find values of the F distribution.

Before discussing the use of the F table, let us state a few character-istics of the F distribution. First, when $m > 2$, $n > 2$, the curve for the F distribution is a unimodal curve skewed to the right, as shown schematically in Fig. 21.1. Second, as the degrees of freedom m and n

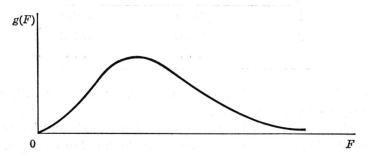

FIG. 21.1.

increase, the F distribution tends to normality. Third, the range of F is from 0 to infinity.

Let us now show how the F table is used.

21.2.   The F Table

As has been mentioned, R. A. Fisher first developed the Z distribu-tion, which was later transformed into the F distribution. The relation between the F and Z distribution is that

$$F = e^{2Z}$$

where e is the natural number; that is,

$$e = 2.71828$$

For example, if $Z = 1$, then

$$\begin{aligned}F &= e^{2Z} \\ &= (2.718)^2 \\ &= 7.39\end{aligned}$$

As formula (8) in the preceding section shows, the F depends on the degrees of freedom, and this is also true for the Z. Fisher and Yates have tabulated the Z distribution.* Their table gives the Z values for the 20, 10, 5, 1, and 0.1 percent right-tail points corresponding to various degrees of freedom. For example, a few values of the 5 percent right-tail points are given in the table below.

Z Values, 5 Percent Right-Tail Points

ν_2	ν_1	
	1	2
1	2.5421	2.6479
2	1.4592	1.4722
	. . .	. . .

The ν_1 and ν_2 show the degrees of freedom. Thus, for $\nu_1 = 1$, $\nu_2 = 2$ degrees of freedom, $Z = 2.5421$.

G. Snedecor has applied the transformation $F = e^{2Z}$ and has recalculated the Z table of Fisher and Yates as an F table. For example, the F table gives the following values:

F Values, 5 Percent Right-Tail Points

ν_2	ν_1	
	1	2
1	161	200
2	18.51	19.00

* R. A. Fisher and F. Yates, *Statistical Tables for Biological, Agricultural, and Medical Research*, New York: Hafner Publishing Company, 1957.

The 161 is found as follows: For $\nu_1 = 1$, $\nu_2 = 1$, the $Z = 2.5421$. Thus, using the transformation, F becomes

$$
\begin{aligned}
F &= e^{2Z} \\
&= e^{(2)\,(2.5421)} \\
&= (2.718)^{5.0842} \\
&= 161
\end{aligned}
$$

The student may check the other three values in a similar manner. For computations, use logarithms.

Snedecor has calculated the F values for the 5 and 1 percent right-tail points.* He has expanded the tables by including values of F corresponding to additional values of ν_1 and ν_2. These tables have been reproduced in the Appendix as Table 5.

(i)   Right-tail points

Let us now show how the F table is used. Suppose

$$
F = \dfrac{\dfrac{u}{m}}{\dfrac{v}{n}} = \dfrac{\dfrac{u}{\nu_1}}{\dfrac{v}{\nu_2}}
$$

and $\nu_1 = 10$, $\nu_2 = 7$ degrees of freedom. Then, schematically, the distribution of F will be as shown in Fig. 21.2. From the F table, we find for

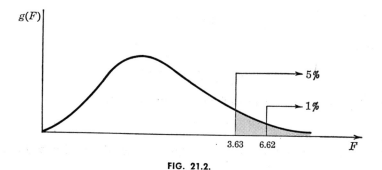

FIG. 21.2.

5 percent, $F = 3.63$; and for 1 percent we find $F = 6.62$. This means that the area under the tail end of the curve beyond $F = 3.63$ is 5 percent and beyond $F = 6.62$ is 1 percent.

---

* G. Snedecor, *Statistical Methods Applied to Experiments in Agriculture and Biology*, 5th ed., Ames, Iowa: The Iowa State College Press, 1956.

The counterpart of this is that the area from $F = 0$ to $F = 3.63$ is 95 percent, and from $F = 0$ to $F = 6.62$, it is 99 percent of the area.

In terms of probabilities it is

$$P[0 < F < 3.63 | \nu_1 = 10, \nu_2 = 7] = 0.95$$
$$P[0 < F < 6.62 | \nu_1 = 10, \nu_2 = 7] = 0.99$$
$$P[3.63 < F < 6.62 | \nu_1 = 10, \nu_2 = 7] = 0.04$$

(ii) Left-tail points

Figure 21.2 shows $F = 3.63$ and $F = 6.62$ for 5 and 1 percent in the right-tail, corresponding to $\nu_1 = 10$ (numerator) and $\nu_2 = 7$ (denominator) degrees of freedom. Is there any way by which the 5 and 1 percent critical points for the left tail can be found? The answer is "yes," and it is found as follows:

Let F_U denote the upper (right tail) values as shown in Fig. 21.3,

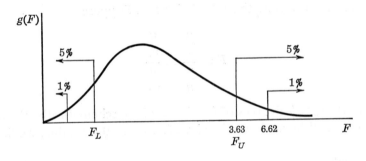

FIG. 21.3.

such that

(1) $$P[F > F_U] = 0.05$$

and let F_L denote the lower (left tail) values such that

(2) $$P[F < F_L] = 0.05$$

We know from the tables that $F_U = 3.63$, but we do not know F_L, which is what we wish to find.

Let us rewrite (2) as follows:

$$P[F < F_L] = P\left[\frac{1}{F_L} < \frac{1}{F}\right]$$

$$= P\left[\frac{1}{F} > \frac{1}{F_L}\right] = 0.05$$

Let $1/F = F'$. Then F' is

$$F' = \frac{1}{F} = \frac{\dfrac{v}{v_2}}{\dfrac{u}{v_1}}$$

and has an F distribution with $v_2 = 7$ (numerator) and $v_1 = 10$ (denominator). Note that the degrees of freedom have been reversed. From the F table, we find for the 5 percent right-tail point,

$$P[F' > 3.14] = 0.05$$

which is equal to

$$P\left[\frac{1}{F} > \frac{1}{F_L} = 3.14\right] = 0.05$$

Thus,

$$\frac{1}{F_L} = 3.14$$

$$F_L = \frac{1}{3.14} = 0.318$$

That is, the 5 percent left-tail F value we seek is $F_L = 0.318$.

In similar manner for the 1 percent left-tail point, we find for $v_2 = 7$ and $v_1 = 10$ degrees of freedom:

$$P\left[\frac{1}{F} > \frac{1}{F_L}\right] = P\left[\frac{1}{F} > 5.20\right]$$
$$= 0.01$$

which leads to

$$\frac{1}{F_L} = 5.21$$

$$F_L = \frac{1}{5.21} = 0.192$$

The procedure for finding the left-tail critical points may be summarized as follows: If F has an F distribution with v_1 (numerator) and v_2 (denominator) degrees of freedom, find the F values for, say, 5 percent right-tail critical points corresponding to v_2 (numerator) and v_1 (denominator), and then take the reciprocal value.

Example. Let F have an F distribution with $v_1 = 12$, $v_2 = 8$ degrees of freedom. Then the right-tail critical value is

$$P(F > 3.28 \mid v_1 = 12, \ v_2 = 8) = 0.05$$

For the left tail, first find the F value for $v_1 = 8$, $v_2 = 12$; which is, from the table,

$$P(F > 2.85 \mid v_1 = 8, \ v_2 = 12) = 0.05$$

Then the left-tail critical value is

$$F_L = \frac{1}{2.85} = 0.351$$

The results are shown graphically in Fig. 21.4.

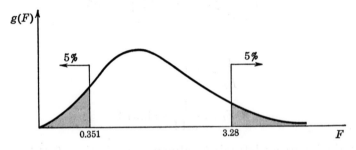

FIG. 21.4.

21.3. Testing the Equality of Variances

Let us now return to our original question. Is the assumption $\sigma_1 = \sigma_2$ valid? The test of this hypothesis may be divided into two cases. The first is a one-tail test, and the second is a two-tail test.

Case 1. One-tail test.   The null and alternative hypotheses are

$$\begin{aligned} H_1: & \qquad \sigma_1 = \sigma_2 \\ H_2: & \qquad \sigma_1 > \sigma_2 \end{aligned}$$

To test this, we construct the F statistic:

$$u = \frac{n_1 s_1^2}{\sigma_1^2}, \qquad v = \frac{n_2 s_2^2}{\sigma_2^2}$$

$$F = \frac{\dfrac{u}{m}}{\dfrac{v}{n}} = \frac{\dfrac{n_1 s_1^2}{m \sigma_1^2}}{\dfrac{n_2 s_2^2}{n \sigma_2^2}}$$

where $m = n_1 - 1$ and $n = n_2 - 1$. Since the null hypothesis is $\sigma_1 = \sigma_2$, the F becomes

(1)
$$F = \frac{\dfrac{n_1 s_1{}^2}{m}}{\dfrac{n_2 s_2{}^2}{n}} = \frac{\dfrac{\displaystyle\sum_{}^{n_1}(X - \bar{X})^2}{n_1 - 1}}{\dfrac{\displaystyle\sum_{}^{n_2}(X - \bar{X})^2}{n_2 - 1}}$$

$$= \frac{\hat{\sigma}_1{}^2}{\hat{\sigma}_2{}^2}$$

where $\hat{\sigma}_1{}^2$ and $\hat{\sigma}_2{}^2$ are unbiased estimates of $\sigma_1{}^2$ and $\sigma_2{}^2$.

In our example, calculations show that

$$\sum_{}^{n_1}(X - \bar{X})^2 = 400$$
$$\sum_{}^{n_2}(X - \bar{X})^2 = 400$$

and thus, since

$$m = n_1 - 1 = 5 - 1 = 4$$
$$n = n_2 - 1 = 5 - 1 = 4$$

the $\hat{\sigma}_1{}^2$ and $\hat{\sigma}_2{}^2$ are

$$\hat{\sigma}_1{}^2 = \frac{400}{4} = 100$$

$$\hat{\sigma}_2{}^2 = \frac{400}{4} = 100$$

Thus, the F is

$$F = \frac{100}{100} = 1$$

Since the alternative hypothesis is $\sigma_1 > \sigma_2$, we shall ask the question: Is the $F = 1$ significantly large? The degrees of freedom are $m = 4$ and $n = 4$, and thus the F value for the 5 percent critical point is 6.39; that is,

$$P[F \geqq 6.39] = 0.05$$

Thus, $F = 1$ is not significantly large and may be considered due to chance, and we accept the null hypothesis that $\sigma_1 = \sigma_2$.

Example 1. Suppose two different processes A and B are used to manufacture light bulbs. The life of the light bulbs of process A have a normal distribution with mean μ_a and standard deviation σ_a. Similarly, for B, it is μ_b and σ_b. We wish to compare the two means by taking a sample from each process. Let the samples be:

Sample A	Sample B
$n_a = 17$	$n_b = 21$
$\bar{X}_a = 1200$ hr.	$\bar{X}_b = 1300$ hr.
$s_a = 60$ hr.	$s_b = 50$ hr.

To compare the two means by use of the t test, we assume $\sigma_a = \sigma_b$. We wish to check this assumption.

For this, we first construct the F statistic:

$$F = \frac{\hat{\sigma}_a^2}{\hat{\sigma}_b^2} = \frac{\dfrac{n_a s_a^2}{n_a - 1}}{\dfrac{n_b s_b^2}{n_b - 1}}$$

$$= \frac{\dfrac{17(60)^2}{17 - 1}}{\dfrac{21(50)^2}{21 - 1}} = \frac{51}{35} = 1.5$$

Since $n_a - 1 = 16$, and $n_b - 1 = 20$, the value of F for the 5 percent critical point is 2.18; that is,

$$P[F > 2.18] = 0.05$$

Thus, $F = 1.4$ is not significantly large, and we accept the null hypothesis that $\sigma_a = \sigma_b$.

Note that, when constructing the F statistic, the larger $\hat{\sigma}^2$ is in the numerator.

Case 2. Two-tail test. This is where the hypotheses are:

$$
\begin{aligned}
H_1: & \quad \sigma_1 = \sigma_2 \\
H_2: & \quad \sigma_1 \neq \sigma_2
\end{aligned}
$$

In this case, we find

$$F = \frac{\hat{\sigma}_1^2}{\hat{\sigma}_2^2} \quad \text{and} \quad F' = \frac{\hat{\sigma}_2^2}{\hat{\sigma}_1^2}$$

and if $\hat{\sigma}_1^2 > \hat{\sigma}_2^2$, the F is compared to the right-tail critical point and the F' is compared to the left-tail critical point.

Example 2.   Using the data of Example 1, we found

$$F = \frac{\hat{\sigma}_a^2}{\hat{\sigma}_b^2} = \frac{51}{35} = 1.5$$

Then

$$F' = \frac{\hat{\sigma}_b^2}{\hat{\sigma}_a^2} = \frac{35}{51} = 0.69$$

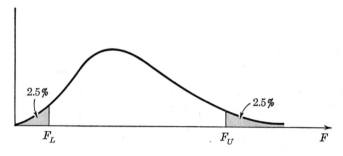

FIG. 21.5.

If the level of significance is 5 percent, then the right- and left-tail critical points are at the 2.5 percent points, as shown in Fig. 21.5. Since $n_a - 1 = 16$ and $n_b - 1 = 20$, the F value for 5 percent is 2.18; for 1 percent, 3.05. Thus, clearly,

$$P[F > 1.5] > 0.05$$

and the $F = 1.5$ is not significant.

As for $F' = 0.69$, we use $n_b - 1 = 20$ for the numerator and $n_a - 1 = 16$ for the denominator. From the F table, by reversing the degrees of freedom we find for 5 percent, 2.18; for 1 percent, 3.05.

Thus, the left- (lower) tail critical points become for 5 percent,

$$\frac{1}{2.18} = 0.46$$

and for 1 percent,

$$\frac{1}{3.05} = 0.33$$

As Fig. 21.6 shows, the $F' = 0.69$ is not significant, and thus we accept the null hypothesis.

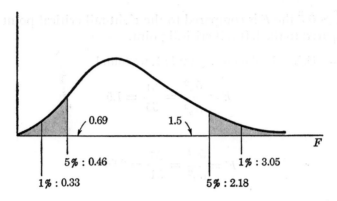

FIG. 21.6.

21.4.   Analysis of Variance

Our interest in the analysis of variance is as an example of the application of the F distribution. This section gives a simple explanation of the rationale of how an experiment is decomposed so that the F distribution can be applied, and in the subsequent two sections, illustrations describe two basic models, the fixed effects model and the random effects model.

The analysis of variance was developed by R. A. Fisher and was mainly used in agricultural research, but subsequently it has found application in almost every other scientific discipline and has become a very broad and technical subject.*

Instead of trying to define the basic idea of the analysis of variance at this point, we shall use a hypothetical example to show how the analysis of variance technique is developed and then give a definition.

(i)   Notation

Before starting our discussion of the analysis of variance, let us first introduce the standard notation that is used. Although it may look cumbersome at first, this roundabout method will prove more productive in the long run.

---

* The classic book is R. A. Fisher's *The Design of Experiments,* 4th ed., Edinburgh: Oliver and Boyd, 1947. Recently a number of books have appeared of which the following three are mentioned: W. G. Cochran and G. M. Cox, *Experimental Designs,* 2nd ed., New York: John Wiley & Sons, Inc., 1957; O. Kempthorne, *The Design and Analysis of Experiments,* New York: John Wiley & Sons, Inc., 1952; and W. T. Federer, *Experimental Design Theory and Application,* New York: The Macmillan Co., 1955. For those who do not wish to go so deeply into the subject, the chapters on analysis of variance in G. W. Snedecor, *Statistical Methods,* 5th ed., Ames: Iowa State University Press, 1956, are recommended.

Suppose there are 3 groups of freshmen students with grades as shown in Table 21.1.

TABLE 21.1.

Group 1	Group 2	Group 3
3	4	7
6	7	6
5	7	7
4	4	7
7	8	8
25	30	35

In terms of symbols, this is written as follows:

Group 1	Group 2	Group 3
x_{11}	x_{21}	x_{31}
x_{12}	x_{22}	x_{32}
x_{13}	x_{23}	x_{33}
x_{14}	x_{24}	x_{34}
x_{15}	x_{25}	x_{35}
Σx_{1j}	Σx_{2j}	Σx_{3j}
$\bar{x}_{1\cdot}$	$\bar{x}_{2\cdot}$	$\bar{x}_{3\cdot}$

An alternative way is to write the samples in rows. That is:

Group 1:	x_{11}	x_{12}	x_{13}	x_{14}	x_{15}
Group 2:	x_{21}	x_{22}	x_{23}	x_{24}	x_{25}
Group 3:	x_{31}	x_{32}	x_{33}	x_{34}	x_{35}

In general, a value is shown by x_{ij} which shows that it is the jth value in the ith group.

The sum of the values of the first group is shown by

$$\sum_{j=1}^{n_1} x_{1j} = x_{11} + x_{12} + x_{13} + x_{14} + x_{15} = 25$$

where $n_1 = 5$ shows the size of the first group. Similarly,

$$\sum_{j=1}^{n_2} x_{2j} = 30, \qquad \sum_{j=1}^{n_3} x_{3j} = 35$$

shows the sums of values of the second and third group.

The sum of all 15 values is shown by

$$\sum_{i=1}^{3}\sum_{j=1}^{n_i} x_{ij} = \sum_{j=1}^{n_1} x_{1j} + \sum_{j=1}^{n_2} x_{2j} + \sum_{j=1}^{n_3} x_{3j}$$

$$= 25 + 30 + 35$$

The arithmetic means of the groups are

$$\bar{x}_{1.} = \frac{1}{n_1}\sum_{j=1}^{n_1} x_{1j} = \frac{1}{5}(25) = 5$$

$$\bar{x}_{2.} = \frac{1}{n_2}\sum_{j=1}^{n_2} x_{2j} = \frac{1}{5}(30) = 6$$

$$\bar{x}_{3.} = \frac{1}{n_3}\sum_{j=1}^{n_3} x_{3j} = \frac{1}{5}(35) = 7$$

or in general

$$\bar{x}_{i.} = \frac{1}{n_i}\sum_{j=1}^{n_i} x_{ij}$$

The arithmetic mean of all 15 values is

$$\bar{x} = \frac{1}{n}\sum_{i=1}^{3}\sum_{j=1}^{n_i} x_{ij} = \frac{1}{15}(25 + 30 + 35) = 6$$

$$n = \sum n_i = n_1 + n_2 + n_3 = 5 + 5 + 5 = 15$$

(ii) The problem

Suppose 3 different methods of teaching mathematics are used on 3 groups of students and we wish to test whether these different methods have had an effect on the grades. Random samples of size 5 are taken from each group and the results are as shown in Table 21.2. The grades are on a 10-point maximum basis.

TABLE 21.2.

Group A	Group B	Group C
3	4	7
6	7	6
5	7	7
4	4	7
7	8	8
25	30	35

We shall assume that the grades are distributed normally with means μ_1, μ_2, and μ_3 for groups A, B, and C, respectively. The standard deviations of the distribution of grades for groups A, B, and C are assumed equal and constant. Let it be denoted by σ. This assumption implies that although the different teaching methods may affect the average grade, it does not affect the dispersion of the grades. That is, there may be merely a shift in the location of the distributions but no change in the dispersion. This is shown schematically in Fig. 21.7.

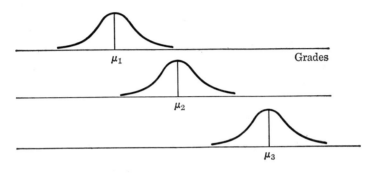

FIG. 21.7.

The question in which we are interested is: Is there a difference in the teaching methods? That is, have they produced different results (in terms of grades)? The null hypothesis corresponding to this question is

$$H_1: \qquad \mu_1 = \mu_2 = \mu_3$$

It is possible to test this null hypothesis by taking two means at a time and applying the t test. However, let us approach this test as follows:

First we note that the 3 groups of students may be considered as 3 populations that have a constant variance σ^2. If we assume $\mu_1 = \mu_2 = \mu_3 = \mu$, the 3 populations may be considered as one large population, and the 3 samples may be considered as samples from this one large population.

We have seen in Chapter 17 that an unbiased estimator of the population variance is obtained by pooling several sample variances. In our present case, the 3 sample variances may be shown as

$$s_1{}^2 = \frac{1}{n_1} \sum_{j=1}^{n_1} (x_{1j} - \bar{x}_{1\cdot})^2$$

$$s_2{}^2 = \frac{1}{n_2} \sum_{j=1}^{n_2} (x_{2j} - \bar{x}_{2\cdot})^2$$

$$s_3{}^2 = \frac{1}{n_3} \sum_{j=1}^{n_3} (x_{3j} - \bar{x}_{3\cdot})^2$$

and the pooled variance is

(1) $$\hat{\sigma}^2 = \frac{n_1 s_1{}^2 + n_2 s_2{}^2 + n_3 s_3{}^2}{n_1 + n_2 + n_3 - 3}$$

$$= \frac{\sum\limits_{j=1}^{n_1} (x_{1j} - \bar{x}_{1\cdot})^2 + \sum\limits_{j=1}^{n_2} (x_{2j} - \bar{x}_{2\cdot})^2 + \sum\limits_{j=1}^{n_3} (x_{3j} - \bar{x}_{3\cdot})^2}{n - 3}$$

$$= \frac{\sum\limits_{i=1}^{3} \sum\limits_{j=1}^{n_i} (x_{ij} - \bar{x}_{i\cdot})^2}{n - 3}$$

A second way of estimating the variance σ^2 is by using the relation

$$\sigma_{\bar{x}}{}^2 = \frac{\sigma^2}{n}$$

which becomes

$$\sigma^2 = n\sigma_{\bar{x}}{}^2$$

Hence, by estimating $\sigma_{\bar{x}}{}^2$, we may estimate σ^2. For the first sample we have

$$\sigma^2 = n_1 \sigma_{\bar{x}_1}{}^2 = n_1 (\bar{x}_{1\cdot} - \bar{x})^2$$

For the second and third samples, we have

$$\sigma^2 = n_2 \sigma_{\bar{x}_2}{}^2 = n_2 (\bar{x}_{2\cdot} - \bar{x})^2$$
$$\sigma^3 = n_3 \sigma_{\bar{x}_3}{}^2 = n_3 (\bar{x}_{3\cdot} - \bar{x})^2$$

Hence,

$$3\sigma^2 = \Sigma\, n_i (\bar{x}_{i\cdot} - \bar{x})^2$$

$$\sigma^2 = \frac{1}{3} \Sigma\, n_i (\bar{x}_{i\cdot} - \bar{x})^2$$

For an unbiased estimate, we use the degrees of freedom $3 - 1 = 2$

instead of 3. That is

(2) $$\hat{\sigma}^2 = \frac{1}{3-1} \sum_{i=1}^{3} n_i(\bar{x}_{i\cdot} - \bar{x})^2$$

is the second way of estimating σ^2.

Since both estimators (1) and (2) are estimating the population variance, we should expect that the values of (1) and (2) do not differ greatly. That is, we should expect that the ratio of (1) and (2) would be close to unity. This is shown as

(3) $$F = \frac{\dfrac{1}{3-1} \sum\limits_{i=1}^{3} n_i(\bar{x}_{i\cdot} - \bar{x})^2}{\dfrac{\sum\limits_{i=1}^{3} \sum\limits_{j=1}^{n_i} (x_{ij} - \bar{x}_{i\cdot})^2}{n-3}}$$

Now note that $\bar{x}_{i\cdot}$, that is, $\bar{x}_{1\cdot}$, $\bar{x}_{2\cdot}$, and $\bar{x}_{3\cdot}$ are the sample means of the 3 samples and are themselves maximum likelihood estimators of μ_1, μ_2, and μ_3. The null hypothesis was $\mu_1 = \mu_2 = \mu_3$, and hence, if this hypothesis should be true, the sample means $\bar{x}_{1\cdot}$, $\bar{x}_{2\cdot}$, and $\bar{x}_{3\cdot}$ should not vary significantly from each other and also from the overall mean $\bar{x}$.

This implies that if the hypothesis $\mu_1 = \mu_2 = \mu_3$ is not true, we should expect that the sample means $\bar{x}_{1\cdot}$, $\bar{x}_{2\cdot}$, and $\bar{x}_{3\cdot}$ should also differ from each other and from $\bar{x}$ by more than what may be attributed to chance. This, in turn, implies that the estimator (2) will become large because it includes the deviation $(\bar{x}_{i\cdot} - \bar{x})^2$. Furthermore, when the hypothesis is not true, (2) can no longer be considered as an estimator of σ^2.

However, the estimator (1), which is obtained by pooling the sample variances, is not affected by differences of $\bar{x}_{i\cdot}$ because the deviations $(x_{ij} - \bar{x}_{i\cdot})$ are only those within each sample.

Hence, the estimator (1) will not be affected when the null hypothesis is not true, but the estimator (2) will become larger. This implies that the ratio (3) will become larger than unity, and we may reason that the more the ratio F exceeds unity, the greater the variation between the sample means $\bar{x}_{i\cdot}$, and hence the population means μ_i.

The question now is: How large a value must F exceed to decide that the variation between the means is such that the null hypothesis $\mu_1 = \mu_2 = \mu_3$ should be rejected? To answer this question, we need to know the distribution of F. Before investigating this problem, let us explain one more preliminary matter.

(iii)   A fundamental identity

Given the null hypothesis $\mu_1 = \mu_2 = \mu_3$, there is a third way of estimating the population variance σ^2. Because of this hypothesis, we may consider the 3 samples together as 1 large sample of size $n = n_1 + n_2 + n_3$. Then an unbiased estimator of σ^2 is

$$(4) \qquad \hat{\sigma}^2 = \frac{\Sigma \Sigma (x_{ij} - \bar{x})^2}{n - 1}$$

It turns out that we may establish a relationship among the numerators of the three estimators (1), (2), and (4) of σ^2 as follows:

$$(5) \qquad \Sigma \Sigma (x_{ij} - \bar{x})^2 = \Sigma \Sigma (x_{ij} - \bar{x}_{i\cdot})^2 + \Sigma \Sigma (\bar{x}_{i\cdot} - \bar{x})^2$$

$$\text{Total} \qquad\qquad \text{Within} \qquad\qquad \text{Between}$$

$$= \Sigma \Sigma (x_{ij} - \bar{x}_{i\cdot})^2 + \Sigma\, n_i (\bar{x}_{i\cdot} - \bar{x})^2$$

The $\Sigma \Sigma (x_{ij} - \bar{x})^2$ is called the *total* sum of squared deviations. The $\Sigma \Sigma (x_{ij} - \bar{x}_{i\cdot})^2$ is called the sum of squares *within* groups. The $\Sigma\, n_i (\bar{x}_{i\cdot} - \bar{x})^2$ is called the sum of squares *between* groups. Formula (5) shows how the total sum of squared deviations is partitioned into two parts. In terms of regression analysis, the "between" sum of squared deviations corresponds to the "explained" and the "within" to the "unexplained" deviations.

We now show how (5) is obtained. We construct the identity

$$x_{ij} - \bar{x} = (x_{ij} - \bar{x}_{i\cdot}) + (\bar{x}_{i\cdot} - \bar{x})$$

Squaring both sides, we find

$$(x_{ij} - \bar{x})^2 = (x_{ij} - \bar{x}_{i\cdot})^2 + 2(x_{ij} - \bar{x}_{i\cdot})(\bar{x}_{i\cdot} - \bar{x}) + (\bar{x}_{i\cdot} - \bar{x})^2$$

Summing over all values, we find

$$(6) \qquad \sum_{i=1}^{r} \sum_{j=1}^{n_i} (x_{ij} - \bar{x})^2 = \Sigma \Sigma (x_{ij} - \bar{x}_{i\cdot})^2$$

$$+ 2 \Sigma \Sigma (x_{ij} - \bar{x}_{i\cdot})(\bar{x}_{i\cdot} - \bar{x})$$

$$+ \Sigma \Sigma (\bar{x}_{i\cdot} - \bar{x})^2$$

The cross-product term may be evaluated as follows:

$$2 \Sigma \Sigma (x_{ij} - \bar{x}_{i\cdot})(\bar{x}_{i\cdot} - \bar{x}) = 2 \Sigma \left[(\bar{x}_{i\cdot} - \bar{x}) \Sigma (x_{ij} - \bar{x}_{i\cdot}) \right]$$

But

$$\sum_{j}^{n_i} (x_{ij} - \bar{x}_{i\cdot})$$

is the sum of the deviations within a group, which is clearly zero. Thus the cross-product term drops out and (6) becomes the relation shown in equation (5). This identity holds, regardless of whether or not the null hypothesis $\mu_1 = \mu_2 = \mu_3$ holds.

Example 1. Using the example of grades, let us illustrate the various relations we have derived.

TABLE 21.3.

	Group 1	Group 2	Group 3
	3	4	7
	6	7	6
	5	7	7
	4	4	7
	7	8	8
Total	25	30	35
Mean	5	6	7

1. The first way of estimating the variance was the pooled variance method, which was

$$\hat{\sigma}^2 = \frac{\Sigma\Sigma (x_{ij} - \bar{x}_{i\cdot})^2}{n - 3}$$

The numerator may be written as

$$\underset{i\ j}{\Sigma\Sigma}(x_{ij} - \bar{x}_{i\cdot})^2 = \underset{j}{\Sigma}(x_{1j} - \bar{x}_{1\cdot})^2$$
$$+ \underset{j}{\Sigma}(x_{2j} - \bar{x}_{2\cdot})^2 + \underset{j}{\Sigma}(x_{3j} - \bar{x}_{3\cdot})^2$$

Using the data of Table 21.3, the calculations for the total sum of squared deviations is as shown in Table 21.4.

TABLE 21.4.

x_{1j}	$x_{1j} - \bar{x}_1$	$(x_{1j} - \bar{x}_1)^2$	x_{2j}	$x_{2j} - \bar{x}_2$	$(x_{2j} - \bar{x}_2)^2$	x_{3j}	$x_{3j} - \bar{x}_3$	$(x_{3j} - \bar{x}_3)^2$
3	-2	4	4	-2	4	7	0	0
6	+1	1	7	1	1	6	-1	1
5	0	0	7	1	1	7	0	0
4	-1	1	4	-2	4	7	0	0
7	2	4	8	2	4	8	1	1
		10			14			2

Using these results, the estimate becomes

$$\hat{\sigma}^2 = \frac{1}{15 - 3}(10 + 14 + 2)$$
$$= 2.17$$

The calculations may be simplified by using the relation

$$\Sigma (x - \bar{x})^2 = \Sigma x^2 - n\bar{x}^2$$

The worksheet is shown as Table 21.5.

TABLE 21.5.

	x_{1j}	x_{1j}^2	x_{2j}	x_{2j}^2	x_{3j}	x_{3j}^2
	3	9	4	16	7	49
	6	36	7	49	6	36
	5	25	7	49	7	49
	4	16	4	16	7	49
	7	49	8	64	8	64
Total	25	135	30	194	35	247
Mean	5		6		7	

We find

$$\Sigma (x_{1j} - \bar{x}_1.)^2 = 135 - (5)(5)^2 = 10$$

$$\Sigma (x_{2j} - \bar{x}_2.)^2 = 194 - (5)(6)^2 = 14$$

$$\Sigma (x_{3j} - \bar{x}_3.)^2 = 247 - (5)(7)^2 = 2$$

and, as is seen, the results are the same as those we obtained previously.

2. The second way of estimating the variance σ^2 was

$$\hat{\sigma}^2 = \frac{1}{3-1} \sum_{i=1}^{3} n_i(\bar{x}_i. - \bar{x})^2$$

Since $n_1 = n_2 = n_3 = 5$, this becomes

$$\hat{\sigma}^2 = \frac{1}{3-1} n_i \Sigma (\bar{x}_i. - \bar{x})^2$$

$$= \frac{1}{3-1} (5) [(\bar{x}_1. - \bar{x})^2 + (\bar{x}_2. - \bar{x})^2 + (\bar{x}_3. - \bar{x})^2]$$

$$= \frac{1}{3-1} (5) [(5 - 6)^2 + (6 - 6)^2 + (7 - 6)^2]$$

$$\doteq 5$$

3. The third way of estimating the variance σ^2 was

$$\hat{\sigma}^2 = \frac{1}{n-1} \Sigma \Sigma (x_{ij} - \bar{x})^2$$

$$= \frac{1}{n-1} (\Sigma \Sigma x_{ij}^2 - n\bar{x}^2)$$

$$= \frac{1}{15 - 1} \, (135 + 194 + 247 - (15)(6)^2)$$

$$= \frac{36}{14} = 2.57$$

To summarize, we have the following three estimates:

1. Using the "within" deviations, $\hat{\sigma}^2 = 2.17$
2. Using the "between" deviations, $\hat{\sigma}^2 = 5$
3. Using the "total" deviations, $\hat{\sigma}^2 = 2.57$

4. We also see from the results in Example 1 that

$$\Sigma \Sigma \, (x_{ij} - \bar{x})^2 = 36$$

$$\Sigma \Sigma \, (x_{ij} - \bar{x}_{i\cdot})^2 = 10 + 14 + 2 = 26$$

$$\Sigma \, n_i(\bar{x}_{i\cdot} - \bar{x})^2 = 5 \, (1 + 0 + 1) = 10$$

and hence the fundamental identity becomes

$$\Sigma \Sigma \, (x_{ij} - \bar{x})^2 = \Sigma \Sigma \, (x_{ij} - \bar{x}_{i\cdot})^2 + \Sigma \, n_i(\bar{x}_{i\cdot} - \bar{x})^2$$

$$36 \quad = \quad 26 \quad + \quad 10$$

The analysis of variance is a technique of partitioning the total sum of squared deviations and the degrees of freedom and locating the sources of variations. The importance of the fundamental identity will become apparent as our discussion develops.

Let us now return to our original problem of testing the equality of means. We have seen how the ratio

$$F = \frac{\dfrac{1}{3 - 1} \, \Sigma \, n_i(\bar{x}_{i\cdot} - \bar{x})^2}{\dfrac{\Sigma \Sigma \, (x_{ij} - \bar{x}_{i\cdot})^2}{n - 3}}$$

was considered as a measure of the variation of the means μ_i. We wish now to show how this ratio, the F distribution, and the fundamental identity tie together to produce a test of significance for the means μ_i.

(vi) *Application of the F distribution*

The ratio of two quantities, u and v, that have independent χ^2 distributions divided by their respective degrees of freedom m and n was called the variance ratio, and the distribution of this variance ratio was called an F distribution.

When applying this to testing, the equality of two variances, $\sigma_1^2 =$

$\sigma_2{}^2$, we found that the ratio of the unbiased estimators of $\sigma_1{}^2$ and $\sigma_2{}^2$ satisfied the conditions for the variance ratio and had an F distribution.

In terms of our present problem, in which we wish to test the equality of means, we constructed a ratio with the "within" and "between" sums of squares:

$$F = \frac{\dfrac{1}{3-1} \Sigma\, n_i(\bar{x}_{i\cdot} - \bar{x})^2}{\dfrac{\Sigma\,\Sigma\,(x_{ij} - \bar{x}_{i\cdot})^2}{n-3}}$$

where the numerator and denominator are unbiased estimators of the population variance σ^2. Hence, this ratio also has an F distribution. This ratio may be shown schematically as

$$F = \frac{\text{estimated variance from ``between''}}{\text{estimated variance from ``within''}}$$

Recall that the estimated variance from within, which is a pooled variance, estimates σ^2 regardless of whether or not the null hypothesis $\mu_1 = \mu_2 = \mu_3$ is true. But the estimated variance from the between sum of squares estimates σ^2 only when (a) the samples come from the same population, or (b) when the population means of the different populations are equal. As is seen, the (b) is equivalent to (a). When the population means are not equal, the estimated variance from the between sum of squares will be $\sigma^2 + c$ where $c > 0$ is a discrepancy due to the inequality of the population means, and the result is that the variance ratio F will become large. If we reverse the reasoning process, we may say that if F is significantly large, there is reason to doubt the equality of means, or that the samples came from the same population.

We shall now show how this test is formally worked out. But before we do that, there is one preliminary matter concerning the relationship among the various degrees of freedom we need to explain.

Let us take the expectation on both sides of the fundamental identity. For the term on the left we have

$$E \sum_i \sum_j (x_{ij} - \bar{x})^2 = (n-1)\sigma^2$$

For the first term on the right we have

$$E \sum_i \sum_j (x_{ij} - \bar{x}_{i\cdot})^2 = (n-r)\sigma^2$$

where r is the number of samples and is $r = 3$ in our present case.

For the second term on the right we have

$$E \sum_i n_i(\bar{x}_{i.} - \bar{x})^2 = (r - 1)\sigma^2$$

(The derivations are given in the Reference.)

Thus, the expectation of the fundamental identity leads to

$$(n - 1)\sigma^2 = (n - r)\sigma^2 + (r - 1)\sigma^2$$

$$\underset{\text{Total}}{} \quad \underset{\text{Within}}{} \quad \underset{\text{Between}}{}$$

If we divide through by σ^2, we find

$$(n - 1) = (n - r) + (r - 1)$$

$$\underset{\text{Total}}{} \quad \underset{\text{Within}}{} \quad \underset{\text{Between}}{}$$

which shows the relationship between the degrees of freedom.

These results may be summarized as shown in Table 21.6.

TABLE 21.6. Analysis of Variance Table

Source of Variation	Degrees of Freedom	Sum of Squares	Mean Square
Between	$r - 1$	$Q_1 = \sum_i n_i(\bar{x}_{i.} - \bar{x})^2$	$\hat{\sigma}_1^2 = \dfrac{Q_1}{r - 1}$
Within	$n - r$	$Q_2 = \sum_i \sum_j (x_{ij} - \bar{x}_{i.})^2$	$\hat{\sigma}_2^2 = \dfrac{Q_2}{n - r}$
Total	$n - 1$	$Q = \sum_i \sum_j (x_{ij} - \bar{x})^2$	$\hat{\sigma}^2 = \dfrac{Q}{n - 1}$

The sum of squares and mean squares in Table 21.6 are unbiased estimates of the population variance. That is,

$$E(\hat{\sigma}_1^2) = E(\hat{\sigma}_2^2) = E(\hat{\sigma}^2) = \sigma^2$$

Returning now to the main line of argument, the F test is performed by first finding the variance ratio

$$F_0 = \frac{\dfrac{Q_1}{r - 1}}{\dfrac{Q_2}{n - r}}$$

If the value of F_0 is such that $F_0 < F_{0.05}$ where

$$P[F > F_{0.05} \mid r - 1, n - r] = 0.05$$

then the difference between $Q_1/(r-1)$ and $Q_2/(n-r)$ is considered due to chance. Thus, we accept the null hypothesis that the samples came from the same population, or in other words, that the sample means are equal. (We are assuming a 5 percent level of significance.)

Example 2. Our example of grades may be summarized in an analysis of variance table as shown in Table 21.7.

TABLE 21.7.

Variation	Degrees of Freedom	Sum of Squares	Mean Square
Between	$3-1$	10	$\hat{\sigma}_1^2 = 10/2 = 5$
Within	$15-3$	26	$\hat{\sigma}_2^2 = 26/12 = 2.17$
Total	$15-1$	36	$\hat{\sigma}^2 = 36/14 = 2.57$

The variance ratio F is

$$F_0 = \frac{5}{2.17} = 2.3$$

Since F has an F distribution with 2 and 12 degrees of freedom, we find for $\alpha = 5$ percent,

$$P[F > 3.88 \mid 2{,}12] = 0.05$$

Since $F_0 = 2.3 < F_{0.05} = 3.88$, we conclude that the three samples came from the same population and that the three means are equal.

REFERENCE

$$(1) \quad E \sum_i \sum_j (x_{ij} - \bar{x})^2 = E\left[(n-1)\frac{\sum\sum(x_{ij}-\bar{x})^2}{n-1}\right]$$

$$= E[(n-1)\hat{\sigma}^2]$$

$$= (n-1)\sigma^2$$

$$(2) \quad E \sum_i \sum_j (x_{ij} - \bar{x}_{i\cdot})^2 = \sum_i E\left[(n_i-1)\frac{\sum_j(x_{ij}-\bar{x}_{i\cdot})^2}{n_i-1}\right]$$

$$= \sum_i E[(n_i-1)\hat{\sigma}_i^2]$$

$$= \sum_i (n_i-1)\sigma^2$$

$$= (n-r)\sigma^2$$

$$(3) \quad E \sum_i n_i (\bar{x}_{i\cdot} - \bar{x})^2 \; = E \sum_i n_i [(\bar{x}_{i\cdot} - \mu) - (\bar{x} - \mu)]^2$$

$$= E \sum_i n_i [(\bar{x}_{i\cdot} - \mu)^2 - 2(\bar{x}_{i\cdot} - \mu)(\bar{x} - \mu)$$
$$+ (\bar{x} - \mu)^2]$$

$$= E [\sum_i n_i (\bar{x}_{i\cdot} - \mu)^2 - 2n(\bar{x} - \mu)^2$$
$$+ n(\bar{x} - \mu)^2]$$

$$= \sum_i n_i E(\bar{x}_{i\cdot} - \mu)^2 - nE(\bar{x} - \mu)^2$$

$$= \sum_i n_i \frac{\sigma^2}{n_i} - n \frac{\sigma^2}{n}$$

$$= r \sigma^2 - \sigma^2 = (r - 1) \sigma^2$$

21.5.   Fixed Effects Model

In Section 21.4 the basic ideas of analysis of variance were discussed on a general level. In this and the next section, two specific models are presented as illustrations of this technique and use of the F distribution.

Suppose there are 3 machines $A, B,$ and C that produce a certain item that weighs x gram. We assume that:
1.   The outputs of each machine are normally distributed with mean μ_i and variance σ^2.
2.   The variances of the populations are equal.
   We wish to test the null hypothesis that

$$H_1: \quad \mu_1 = \mu_2 = \mu_3 = \mu$$

That is, the population means are equal to an overall mean μ.

Since we are interested in the differences of the means μ_i, we shall set up our model such that the differences are shown explicitly. This is best explained by use of a diagram. Figure 21.8 shows the 3 populations corresponding to the 3 machines. The diagram assumes that μ_1, μ_2, and μ_3 differ from μ by $\alpha_1, \alpha_2,$ and α_3. That is,

$$\mu_1 = \mu + \alpha_1 \qquad (= 100 - 5)$$
$$\mu_2 = \mu + \alpha_2 \qquad (= 100 + 2)$$
$$\mu_3 = \mu + \alpha_3 \qquad (= 100 + 3)$$

The α_i are called *effects* or *deviations* due to *treatments*. The analysis of variance was first used in agricultural research, and as a result, much of the terminology has agricultural overtones. For example, instead of machines, we may have a *plot* of land to which fertilizer is added. The

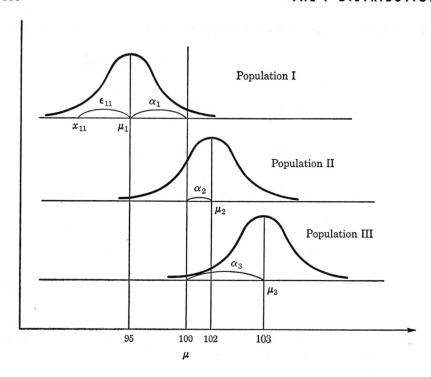

FIG. 21.8.

fertilizer is the *treatment* that is applied to the *plot,* and as a result, the *yield* may vary from an overall average. Then this variation is the *effect* that is due to the *treatments.* Other terms are also used, which will be clear from the context of the discussion.

Let x_{ij} be the jth output from the ith machine and let

$$\epsilon_{ij} = x_{ij} - \mu_i$$

or

$$x_{ij} = \mu_i + \epsilon_{ij}$$
$$x_{ij} = \mu + \alpha_i + \epsilon_{ij}$$

This is the basic model. For example, for the first machine, we have

$$x_{11} = \mu_1 + \epsilon_{11} = \mu + \alpha_1 + \epsilon_{11}$$
$$x_{12} = \mu_1 + \epsilon_{12} = \mu + \alpha_1 + \epsilon_{12}$$
$$\cdot \quad \cdot \quad \cdot \quad \cdot \quad \cdot \quad \cdot \quad \cdot \quad \cdot$$
$$x_{1n} = \mu_1 + \epsilon_{1n} = \mu + \alpha_1 + \epsilon_{1n}$$

and similarly for the other machines. From the assumptions that the populations are normally distributed with means μ_i and variance σ^2, we see that the ϵ_{ij} are normally distributed with

$$E(\epsilon_{ij}) = 0$$
$$\text{Var}(\epsilon_{ij}) = \sigma^2$$

In terms of regression analysis, the α_i are the explained deviations and the ϵ_{ij} are the unexplained deviations.

To test the null hypothesis about the equality of the means, a sample of outputs is taken from each machine, and the results are given in the table below.

Treatment	Individual Observations	Total	Mean
Machine A	$x_{11}, x_{12}, x_{13}, x_{14}, x_{15}$	$\sum_j x_{1j}$	$\bar{x}_{1\cdot}$
Machine B	$x_{21}, x_{22}, x_{23}, x_{24}, x_{25}$	$\sum_j x_{2j}$	$\bar{x}_{2\cdot}$
Machine C	$x_{31}, x_{32}, x_{33}, x_{34}, x_{35}$	$\sum_j x_{3j}$	$\bar{x}_{3\cdot}$

A random sample size $n_i = 5$ $(i = 1, 2, 3)$ is taken for each machine. Then we know from the fundamental identity that

$$\sum_i \sum_j (x_{ij} - \bar{x})^2 = \sum_i \sum_j (x_{ij} - \bar{x}_{i\cdot})^2 + \sum_i n_i(\bar{x}_{i\cdot} - \bar{x})^2$$

which is abbreviated as

$$Q = Q_2 + Q_1$$

Using these quantities, the analysis of variance table becomes as shown below.

Variation	Degrees of Freedom	Sum of Squares	Mean Square
Between	$3 - 1$	Q_1	$Q_1/(3 - 1)$
Within	$15 - 3$	Q_2	$Q_2/(15 - 3)$
Total	$15 - 1$	Q	$Q/(15 - 1)$

The variance ratio F_0 is

$$F_0 = \frac{\dfrac{Q_1}{3 - 1}}{\dfrac{Q_2}{15 - 3}}$$

This has an F distribution with $3 - 1 = 2$ and $15 - 3 = 12$ degrees of freedom. Setting $\alpha = 5$ percent, we find from the F table that

$$P[F > 3.88 \mid 2,12] = 0.05$$

Thus, if the variance ratio F_0 is greater than 3.88, we reject the null hypothesis that $\mu_1 = \mu_2 = \mu_3$. If F_0 is smaller than 3.88, we accept the hypothesis.

Let us now interpret the preceding example in different ways and illustrate some other uses. Let A, B, and C be three machines bought from different sources; we wish to check whether there is a difference in their performances. The test is the same as that used above, where the null hypothesis proposes that there is no difference in the machines; that is, the means are equal. Rejection of the null hypothesis implies that the machines are different.

As another example, let A, B, and C be three different kinds of fertilizer used for wheat production; we wish to test whether there are differences in the yields. The null hypothesis proposes that there is no difference in the yields; that is, the mean yields are equal for all cases.

As a third example, let A, B, and C be the morning, afternoon, and night classes studying economics. We wish to check whether there is any difference in the grades. Then the null hypothesis proposes that there are no differences; that is, the average grade is the same for all three classes, which is tested by the analysis of variance technique described previously.

21.6. Random Effects Model

The basic model for the fixed effects model was

$$x_{ij} = \mu + \alpha_i + \epsilon_{ij}$$

where the characteristic is that the α_i are fixed. That is, we had 3 machines, A, B, and C, with means μ_1, μ_2, and μ_3, which deviated from an overall mean μ by α_1, α_2, and α_3.

Let us now change our viewpoint and assume that machine A was selected from a large group of machines delivered by manufacturer A. Then, depending on the machine that is selected, the α_1 will vary. We shall assume that α_1 is normally distributed with mean and variance

$$E(\alpha_1) = 0$$
$$\text{Var}(\alpha_1) = \sigma_\alpha{}^2$$

In similar fashion, machines B and C are also considered selected from populations of machines B and C, and the α_2 and α_3 are considered random variables that are normally distributed with means 0 and variances σ_a^2.

The test and computation procedures are the same as the fixed effects model, but the interpretation is that we are inferring about the populations of A, B, and C machines, not just the single A, B, and C machines.

MULTIPLE LINEAR REGRESSION

22

In Chapter 13 a simple linear regression model with one independent variable (such as amount of fertilizer) and one dependent variable (such as yield of wheat) was discussed. However, we can very easily see that in practical problems there is usually more than one factor that effects a certain outcome. Not only fertilizer, but other factors such as rainfall and temperature will also have an effect on the yield of wheat.

The statistical technique of extending simple linear regression so that it considers two or more independent variables is called multiple linear regression. Sometimes as many as six independent variables are considered. It is quite obvious that multiple linear regression is a very useful technique and it is very frequently used in business and economic problems.

We shall consider only linear regression which is of the form

$$Y_c = a + b_1X_1 + b_2X_2 + b_3X_3$$

A natural extension of the linear regression model is the curvilinear model, an example of which is of the form

$$Y_c = a + b_1X_1 + b_2X_2{}^2$$

where the independent variables X_i may be expressed in powers. Those interested in curvilinear regression are recommended *Methods of Correlation and Regression Analysis* by M. Ezekiel and K. A. Fox.* Let us now start our discussion of multiple linear regression.

---

* M. Ezekiel and K. A. Fox, *Methods of Correlation and Regression Analysis,* 3rd ed., New York: John Wiley & Sons, Inc., 1959.

22.1.   Introduction

In Chapter 13 the basic linear regression model was

(1) $$E(Y \mid X) = A + BX$$

(2) $$Y = A + BX + \epsilon$$

for the population and

(3) $$Y_c = a + bX$$

(4) $$Y = a + bX + e$$

for the sample estimates. The coefficients A and B were estimated by the method of least squares and the normal equations were

(5) $$na + b \Sigma X = \Sigma Y$$

$$a \Sigma X + b \Sigma X^2 = \Sigma XY$$

Now we merely wish to extend this model so that there will be more than one independent variable. As an example, suppose the amount of sales (Y) is dependent on the amount of money spent on radio advertising (X_1) and newspaper advertising (X_2). The model is

(6) $$E(Y \mid X_1, X_2) = A + B_1X_1 + B_2X_2$$

$$Y = A + B_1X_1 + B_2X_2 + \epsilon$$

for the population and

(7) $$Y_c = a + b_1X_1 + b_2X_2$$

(8) $$Y = a + b_1X_1 + b_2X_2 + e$$

for the sample estimates. The coefficients are estimated by the method of least squares. That is, coefficients A, B_1, and B_2 are to be estimated such that

(9) $$\Sigma e^2 = \Sigma (Y - a - b_1X_1 - b_2X_2)^2 = \text{minimum}$$

The normal equations obtained from (9) are

$$na + b_1 \Sigma X_1 + b_2 \Sigma X_2 = \Sigma Y$$

(10) $$a \Sigma X_1 + b_1 \Sigma X_1^2 + b_2 \Sigma X_1X_2 = \Sigma X_1Y$$

$$a \Sigma X_2 + b_1 \Sigma X_1X_2 + b_2 \Sigma X_2^2 = \Sigma X_2Y$$

Solving these equations for a, b_1 and b_2, we find the estimated regression line (7). This regression line is, geometrically speaking, a regression plane in 3-dimensional space that has been fitted by the method of least squares to the points in the 3-dimensional space so that the sum of the squared deviations of the points from the plane is a minimum.

When there are k independent variables, the sample regression line is

$$(11) \qquad Y_c = a + b_1 X_1 + b_2 X_2 + \cdots + b_k X_k$$

and it is a hyper-regression plane in $k + 1$ dimensional space.

The normal equations necessary to find the coefficients $a, b_1, \ldots, b_k$ are

$$na + b_1 \Sigma X_1 + b_2 \Sigma X_2 + \cdots + b_k \Sigma X_k = \Sigma Y$$

$$(12) \quad a \Sigma X_1 + b_1 \Sigma X_1^2 + b_2 \Sigma X_1 X_2 + \cdots + b_k \Sigma X_1 X_k = \Sigma X_1 Y$$

$$\cdot \quad \cdot \quad \cdot \quad \cdot \quad \cdot \quad \cdot \quad \cdot \quad \cdot \quad \cdot \quad \cdot \quad \cdot$$

$$a \Sigma X_k + b_1 \Sigma X_k X_1 + b_2 \Sigma X_k X_2 + \cdots + b_k \Sigma X_k^2 = \Sigma X_k Y$$

and the pattern should be clear.

Various procedures have been devised to simplify calculations. These will be considered first. Then the interpretation of the regression line will be considered, which will be a discussion of the partial regression coefficients, the multiple correlation coefficient, the total correlation coefficient, and the partial correlation coefficient. After that we shall consider a graphic method of finding regression lines, one that is used frequently in economics.

22.2. Estimation of Parameters

As we have just seen, the ideas of multiple regression are relatively simple. What is troublesome is the process of computing the coefficients. In actual problems there may be 100 observations and from 2 to 6 independent variables. Solving such data for the coefficients may become quite a task, and any simplification of computational procedures is a big help. We shall first show how the normal equations are simplified.

By using the characteristic that

$$\Sigma (X - \bar{X}) = \Sigma X - n\bar{X} = \Sigma X - \Sigma X = 0$$

the normal equations (10) of Section 22.1 may be simplified by shifting the origin from $(0, 0, 0)$ to $(\bar{Y}, \bar{X}_1, \bar{X}_2)$. Then the terms $\Sigma X_1, \Sigma X_2, \Sigma Y$ become

$$\Sigma (X_1 - \bar{X}_1) = 0, \quad \Sigma (X_2 - \bar{X}_2) = 0, \quad \Sigma (Y - \bar{Y}) = 0$$

Hence, if we set

(1) $x_1 = X_1 - \bar{X}_1, \quad x_2 = X_2 - \bar{X}_2, \quad y = Y - \bar{Y}$

the normal equations become

(2)
$$b_1 \Sigma x_1^2 + b_2 \Sigma x_1 x_2 = \Sigma x_1 y$$
$$b_1 \Sigma x_1 x_2 + b_2 \Sigma x_2^2 = \Sigma x_2 y$$

Solving (2) gives us the b's and the regression line is

(3) $y_c = b_1 x_1 + b_2 x_2$

Substituting the relations of (1) in (3) gives us

$$(Y_c - \bar{Y}) = b_1(X_1 - \bar{X}_1) + b_2(X_2 - \bar{X}_2)$$

which becomes

$$Y_c = (\bar{Y} - b_1\bar{X}_1 - b_2\bar{X}_2) + b_1 X_1 + b_2 X_2$$

and, as is seen, the a coefficient is

$$a = \bar{Y} - b_1\bar{X}_1 - b_2\bar{X}_2$$

which is easily obtained since we have the values of b_1 and b_2.

Example.   Let us use hypothetical data to show the procedures clearly. Y is sales; X_1 is radio advertisement expenditures; X_2 is newspaper advertisement expenditures (all in thousands of dollars).

TABLE 22.1.

X_1	X_2	Y
4	1	7
7	2	12
9	5	17
12	8	20
Total 32	16	56
Mean 8	4	14

To find the terms Σx_1^2, $\Sigma x_1 x_2$, etc., in the normal equations, the computation formulas

$$\Sigma x_1^2 = \Sigma (X_1 - \bar{X}_1)^2 = \Sigma X_1 - n(\bar{X}_1)^2$$
$$\Sigma x_1 x_2 = \Sigma (X_1 - \bar{X}_1)(X_2 - \bar{X}_2) = \Sigma X_1 X_2 - n(\bar{X}_1)(\bar{X}_2)$$

will be used. The worksheet for this is given as Table 22.2.

TABLE 22.2.

$X_1{}^2$	$X_1 X_2$	$X_2{}^2$	$X_1 Y$	$X_2 Y$	Y^2
16	4	1	28	7	49
49	14	4	84	24	144
81	45	25	153	85	289
144	96	64	240	160	400
290	159	94	505	276	882

$$\Sigma x_1{}^2 = \Sigma X_1{}^2 - n(\bar{X}_1)^2 = 290 - 4(64) = 34$$

$$\Sigma x_1 x_2 = \Sigma X_1 X_2 - n\,(\bar{X}_1)(\bar{X}_2) = 159 - 4(8)(4) = 30$$

$$\Sigma x_2{}^2 = \Sigma X_2{}^2 - n(\bar{X}_2)^2 = 94 - 4(16) = 40$$

$$\Sigma x_1 y = \Sigma X_1 Y - n(\bar{X}_1)(\bar{Y}) = 505 - 4(8)(14) = 57$$

$$\Sigma x_2 y = \Sigma X_2 Y - n(\bar{X}_2)(\bar{Y}) = 276 - 4(4)(14) = 52$$

Thus the normal equations are

$$34b_1 + 30b_2 = 57$$
$$30b_1 + 40b_2 = 52$$

and solving for b_1 and b_2, we find

$$b_1 = \frac{36}{23}, \qquad b_2 = \frac{1}{8}$$

The value of a is

$$a = \bar{Y} - b_1 \bar{X}_1 - b_2 \bar{X}_2$$

$$= 0.9783$$

Hence, the regression line is

$$Y_c = 0.9783 + \frac{36}{23} X_1 + \frac{1}{8} X_2$$

22.3. Estimating σ^2

The population variance σ^2 of Y is defined as

(1) $$\mathrm{Var}(Y) = E[Y - E(Y|X)]^2 = \sigma^2$$

When the distribution of Y is normal, the maximum likelihood estimator of σ^2 is

(2) $$\breve{\sigma}^2 = \frac{1}{n} \Sigma (Y - Y_c)^2$$

where Y_c is the estimate of $E(Y|X)$ and n is the sample size. This maximum likelihood estimate is consistent and sufficient, but is biased, and hence we have used a ˅ to denote this. We state without proof that an unbiased estimator of σ^2 is

$$(3) \qquad \hat{\sigma}^2 = \frac{n}{n-k-1}\, \breve{\sigma}^2$$

$$= \frac{n}{n-k-1}\left(\frac{1}{n}\,\Sigma\,(Y-Y_c)^2\right)$$

$$= \frac{1}{n-k-1}\,\Sigma\,(Y-Y_c)^2$$

where $n-k-1$ is the number of degrees of freedom. The k is the number of b's in the sample regression equation. For example,

$$Y_c = a + b_1 x_1 + b_2 x_2$$

has $k+1=3$ restrictions because there are $k=2$ b coefficients and a may be considered a b coefficient of $X_0=1$. An alternative way of considering this is that

$$a = \bar{Y} - b_1 \bar{X}_1 - b_2 \bar{X}_2$$

and a is restricted by $\bar{Y}$ and thus takes away 1 degree of freedom. Thus we subtract $k+1$ from n.

Now that we have found the unbiased estimator of σ^2, our problem is to compute $\hat{\sigma}^2$ which, as can be seen, requires calculation of the Y_c's. This, in most cases, is a tedious process, but fortunately we may utilize the relation

$$(4) \qquad \Sigma\,(Y-\bar{Y})^2 = \Sigma\,(Y-Y_c)^2 + \Sigma\,(Y_c-\bar{Y})^2$$
$$\quad (n-1) \qquad\quad (n-k-1) \qquad\quad (k)$$

which was explained in Chapter 13, to find $\hat{\sigma}^2$. We see from (4) that

$$(5) \qquad \Sigma\,(Y-Y_c)^2 = \Sigma\,(Y-\bar{Y})^2 - \Sigma\,(Y_c-\bar{Y})^2$$

The $\Sigma\,(Y-\bar{Y})^2$, which is called the *total* deviations, may be rewritten as

$$(6) \qquad \Sigma\,(Y-\bar{Y})^2 = \Sigma\,Y^2 - n(\bar{Y})^2$$

and is easily calculated from the original data. This has $n-1$ degrees of freedom.

The $\Sigma\,(Y_c-\bar{Y})^2$, which is called the sum of squared deviations *due to regression,* may be obtained as follows: Since

$$Y_c = \bar{Y} + b_1(X_1 - \bar{X}_1) + b_2(X_2 - \bar{X}_2)$$
$$= \bar{Y} + b_1 x_1 + b_2 x_2$$

we find

$$Y_c - \bar{Y} = b_1 x_1 + b_2 x_2$$

Substituting this into $\Sigma (Y_c - \bar{Y})^2$, we get

$$\Sigma (Y_c - \bar{Y})^2 = \Sigma (b_1 x_1 + b_2 x_2)^2$$
$$= \Sigma [b_1^2 x_1^2 + b_1 b_2 x_1 x_2$$
$$+ b_1 b_2 x_1 x_2 + b_2^2 x_2^2$$
$$= b_1[b_1 \Sigma x_1^2 + b_2 \Sigma x_1 x_2]$$
$$+ b_2[b_1 \Sigma x_1 x_2 + b_2 \Sigma x_2^2]$$

But the normal equations are

$$b_1 \Sigma x_1^2 + b_2 \Sigma x_1 x_2 = \Sigma x_1 y$$
$$b_1 \Sigma x_1 x_2 + b_2 \Sigma x_2^2 = \Sigma x_2 y$$

Substituting these results into the above equations, we find

(7) $\Sigma (Y_c - \bar{Y})^2 = b_1 \Sigma x_1 y + b_2 \Sigma x_2 y$

Since the b's, $\Sigma x_1 y$, and $\Sigma x_2 y$ are already calculated, the $\Sigma (Y_c - \bar{Y})^2$ is easily obtained.

Now that $\Sigma (Y - \bar{Y})^2$ and $\Sigma (Y_c - \bar{Y})^2$ are found, $\Sigma (Y - Y_c)^2$ is easily obtained from (5). These results may be shown in compact form by an analysis of variance table.

Analysis of Variance Table

Source of Variation	Degrees of Freedom	Sum of Squares	Mean Square
Due to regression	k	$Q_1 = \Sigma (Y_c - \bar{Y})^2$	Q_1/k
Residuals	$n - k - 1$	$Q_2 = \Sigma (Y - Y_c)^2$	$Q_2/n - k - 1$
Total	$n - 1$	$Q = \Sigma (Y - \bar{Y})^2$	

Since Q_2 is usually obtained by $Q - Q_1$, an alternative way of presenting the analysis of variance table is as follows:

Analysis of Variance Table

Source of Variation	Degrees of Freedom	Sum of Squares	Mean Square
Total	$n-1$	$Q = \Sigma(Y-\bar{Y})^2$	
Due to regression	k	$Q_1 = \Sigma(Y_c-\bar{Y})^2$	Q_1/k
Residual	$n-k-1$	$Q_2 = \Sigma(Y-Y_c)^2$	$Q_2/n-k-1$

The mean square

$$(8) \qquad \frac{Q_2}{n-k-1} = \hat{\sigma}^2$$

is the unbiased estimate of σ^2 we seek.

An example of the computations is given in Section 22.8.

Note that we have three estimates of σ^2:

$$(9) \qquad \frac{Q}{n-1}$$

$$(10) \qquad \frac{Q_1}{k}$$

$$(11) \qquad \frac{Q_2}{n-k-1}$$

Example 1. Let us illustrate this procedure with our hypothetical data. The $\Sigma(Y-\bar{Y})^2$ is

$$\Sigma(Y-\bar{Y})^2 = \Sigma Y^2 - n(\bar{Y})^2$$
$$= 882 - 4(14)^2 = 98$$

The $\Sigma(Y_c-Y)^2$ is

$$\Sigma(Y_c-Y)^2 = b_1 \Sigma x_1 y + b_2 \Sigma x_2 y$$
$$= \frac{36}{23}(57) + \frac{1}{8}(52)$$
$$= 89.21.74 + 6.5 = 95.714$$

Hence the analysis of variance is as shown in Table 22.3.

Example 2. Let us check this result by actually calculating $\Sigma(Y-Y_c)^2$. The values of Y_c are calculated in Table 22.4 from

$$Y_c = 0.9783 + \frac{36}{23}X_1 + \frac{1}{8}X_2$$

TABLE 22.3.

Source of Variation	Degrees of Freedom	Sum of Squares	Mean Square
Total	$n-1=4-1$	98	
Due to regression	$k=2$	95.7174	
Residual	1	2.2826	2.2826

TABLE 22.4.

(1) $1.5652X_1$	(2) $0.125X_2$	(3) $(1)+(2)$	(4) $Y_c=(3)+0.9783$
6.2608	0.1250	6.3858	7.3641
10.9564	0.2500	11.2064	12.1847
14.0868	0.6250	14.7118	15.6901
18.7824	1.0000	19.7824	20.7607

TABLE 22.5.

Y	Y_c	$Y-Y_c$	$(Y-Y_c)^2$
7	7.3641	−0.3641	0.1326
12	12.1847	−0.1847	0.0341
17	15.6901	1.3099	1.7158
20	20.7607	−0.7607	0.5787
		0.0004	2.4612

Hence, the estimate is

$$\sigma^2 = \frac{\Sigma\,(Y-Y_c)^2}{n-k-1}$$

$$= \frac{2.4612}{4-2-1} = 2.4612$$

and is slightly larger than the 2.2826 we obtained from the analysis of variance table. The result obtained from the analysis of variance table is more accurate.

22.4.   Interpretation of the Regression Equation

(i)   Partial regression coefficients

The regression equation in the preceding example was

$$Y_c = 0.9783 + \frac{36}{23}\,X_1 + \frac{1}{8}\,X_2$$

The b's are called *partial regression coefficients* and show the average change in Y when there is a unit change in X, holding the other X's constant. For example, $b_1 = 36/23$ shows that sales increase by $(36/23)$ $\times \$1000$ when there is an $(X = 1)$ $\$1000$ increase in radio advertisement expenditures. Thus the units of b_1 and b_2 are

b_1:
$$\frac{\text{Sales, \$000}}{\text{Radio advertising expenditures, \$000}}$$

b_2:
$$\frac{\text{Sales, \$000}}{\text{Newspaper advertising expenditures, \$000}}$$

The b's show the slope of the regression plane.

The $a = 0.9783$ has the same unit as Y and shows the height (elevation) of the plane.

(ii) *Standard partial regression coefficients (β-coefficients)*

In many cases we may wish to compare the relative importance of radio advertisement (X_1) and newspaper advertisement (X_2) on increasing sales (Y). In our present example, the partial regression coefficients b_1 and b_2 showed the average change in sales (Y) per unit change in X_1 and X_2, which in our present case were $\$1000$ for each variable. That is, both X_1 and X_2 were in the same units, and hence b_1 and b_2 were comparable.

However, if we have a regression function where Y is yield of wheat in bushels, X_1 is rainfall in inches, and X_2 is fertilizer in pounds, the partial regression coefficients b_1 and b_2 cannot be compared directly because of different units. To overcome this impasse, the variables Y, X_1, and X_2 may be converted into units of standard deviations. For example, let the regression function be

$$(1) \qquad\qquad Y_c = a + b_1 X_1 + b_2 X_2$$

Divide each variable by its standard deviation and adjust the coefficients a, b_1, and b_2 as follows:

$$(2) \qquad\qquad \frac{Y}{\sigma_y} = \frac{a}{\sigma_y} + b_1 \cdot \frac{\sigma_1}{\sigma_y} \cdot \frac{X_1}{\sigma_1} + b_2 \frac{\sigma_2}{\sigma_y} \cdot \frac{X_2}{\sigma_2}$$

and, as is seen, equations (1) and (2) are identical.

Let us denote the coefficients as

$$(3) \qquad\qquad b_1{}^* = b_1 \frac{\sigma_1}{\sigma_y}$$

$$b_2{}^* = b_2 \frac{\sigma_2}{\sigma_y}$$

which are called β-coefficients, or standard partial regression coefficients. Then (2) becomes

(4)
$$\frac{Y}{\sigma_y} = \frac{a}{\sigma_y} + b_1{}^* \frac{X_1}{\sigma_1} + b_2{}^* \frac{X_2}{\sigma_2}$$

The interpretation of $b_1{}^*$ is as follows: Suppose $b_1{}^* = 0.6$. This means that when there is a 1 standard deviation change in X_1, there will be a 0.6 standard deviation change in Y. If 1 standard deviation of X_1 is $\sigma_1 = 3$ in. of rainfall, and 1 standard deviation of Y is 4 bushels, we are saying that when there are 3 in. of rainfall, there will be (4 bushels) $\times$ $(0.6) = 2.4$ bushels increase of yield. Also, $b_2{}^*$ shows the change in Y in terms of standard deviations per standard deviation change of X_2. Hence, we may compare $b_1{}^*$ and $b_2{}^*$ even though b_1 and b_2 may be of different units, such as inches of rainfall and pounds of fertilizer.

The equation (3) may be shown in terms of deviations (that is, $X - \bar{X} = x$), which sometimes facilitates comparison with other equations.

For this the relation

(5)
$$a = \bar{Y} - b_1\bar{X}_1 - b_2\bar{X}_2$$

and (3) are combined to find

(6)
$$a = \bar{Y} - b_1{}^* \frac{\sigma_y}{\sigma_1} \bar{X}_1 - b_2{}^* \frac{\sigma_y}{\sigma_2} \bar{X}_2$$

Substituting this (6) into (4) gives

(7)
$$\frac{y}{\sigma_y} = b_1{}^* \frac{x_1}{\sigma_1} + b_2{}^* \frac{x_2}{\sigma_2}$$

For computation purposes, (3) may be rewritten as

(8)
$$b_1{}^* = b_1 \sqrt{\frac{\Sigma x_1{}^2}{\Sigma y^2}}$$

$$b_2{}^* = b_2 \sqrt{\frac{\Sigma x_2{}^2}{\Sigma y^2}}$$

Example. Let us find the β-coefficient of our previous example. We have already calculated

$$\Sigma (X_1 - \bar{X}_1)^2 = 34, \qquad \Sigma (X_2 - \bar{X}_2)^2 = 40, \qquad \Sigma(Y - \bar{Y})^2 = 98$$

Hence,

$$b_1{}^* = b_1 \sqrt{\frac{34}{48}} = 0.8416$$

$$b_2{}^* = b_2 \sqrt{\frac{40}{98}} = 0.6388$$

Also, since

$$\hat{\sigma}_1{}^2 = \frac{1}{n-1} \, \Sigma \, (X_1 - \bar{X}_1)^2 = \frac{1}{4-1} \, (34) = 11.3$$

$$\hat{\sigma}_2{}^2 = \frac{1}{n-1} \, \Sigma \, (X_2 - \bar{X}_2)^2 = \frac{1}{4-1} \, (40) = 13.3$$

$$\hat{\sigma}_y{}^2 = \frac{1}{n-1} \, \Sigma \, (Y - \bar{Y})^2 = \frac{1}{4-1} \, (98) = 32.7$$

the regression function in terms of β-coefficients is

$$\frac{y}{32.7} = b_1{}^* \, \frac{x_1}{11.3} + b_2{}^* \, \frac{x_2}{13.3}$$

or

$$\frac{Y}{32.7} = \frac{a}{32.7} + b_1{}^* \, \frac{X_1}{11.3} + b_2{}^* \, \frac{X_2}{13.3}$$

22.5.   The Coefficient of Multiple Determination

Having found the regression function

$$Y_c = 0.9783 + \frac{36}{23} \, X_1 + \frac{1}{8} \, X_2$$

we should like to know (a) the closeness of the fit of the regression plane to the actual points, and (b) the significance of the partial regression coefficients. The first question is considered in this section and the second in Section 22.9.

A plane that is fitted to the actual points Y and which is horizontal and passes through the mean $(\bar{Y}, \bar{X}_1, \bar{X}_2)$ may be considered as the basic plane from which the improvement brought about by regression is measured. The deviations of the observed points Y from this plane are shown by $(Y - \bar{Y})$ and is called *total deviation.*

This total deviation may be partitioned into two parts. One is the deviation from Y_c to $\bar{Y}$; that is, $(Y_c - \bar{Y})$, which shows the improvement brought about by the regression plane. The second is $(Y - Y_c)$, which shows the part of the total deviation that remains unexplained after fitting the regression plane.

We have seen how these deviations are related by the fundamental identity

(1) $$\Sigma (Y - \bar{Y})^2 = \Sigma (Y - Y_c)^2 + \Sigma (Y_c - \bar{Y})^2$$

$$\underset{\text{Total}}{} \qquad \underset{\text{Unexplained}}{} \qquad \underset{\text{Explained}}{}$$

The ratio of the explained to the total, which is

(2) $$R^2_{y.12} = \frac{\Sigma (Y_c - \bar{Y})^2}{\Sigma (Y - \bar{Y})^2}$$

is called the *coefficient of multiple determination,* and it may be considered as showing the improvement of the closeness of the fit of the regression plane to the actual points relative to the fit of the plane going through the mean $(\bar{Y}, \bar{X}_1, \bar{X}_2)$.

For computation procedures, we shall use the relation

$$\Sigma (Y_c - \bar{Y})^2 = b_1 \Sigma x_1 y + b_2 \Sigma x_2 y$$

which was obtained in Section 22.3. Then the $R^2_{y.12}$ becomes

(3) $$R^2_{y.12} = \frac{b_1 \Sigma x_1 y + b_2 \Sigma x_2 y}{\Sigma y^2}$$

Using our previous example, the $R^2_{y.12}$ is

$$R^2_{y.12} = \frac{\dfrac{36}{23}(57) + \dfrac{1}{8}(52)}{98}$$

$$= \frac{95.7174}{98} = 0.9767$$

We shall express this result by saying that about 97.67 percent of the total deviation has been explained by the regression line.

The square root of $R^2_{y.12}$ is called the *coefficient of multiple correlation,* a term that was used frequently in the past but less used today.

Note that we have not considered $R_{y.12}$ as a measure of the covariation between variables, but merely as a measure of the goodness of fit of the regression plane. Hence, it is applicable to the case where the X's are fixed variables and the Y is a stochastic variable, and also to the case where the X's and Y are all stochastic variables.

But when Y and the X's are all variables, it may also be considered as a measure showing the correlation between Y and its best linear estimate Y_c. And since

$$Y_c = a + b_1 X_1 + b_2 X_2$$

the $R_{y.12}$ may be considered as the correlation coefficient between Y and the group of variables (X_1, X_2), and may be expressed by saying: $R_{y.12}$ is the correlation coefficient between Y and (X_1, X_2).

In the first case, where only Y is a stochastic variable, we can have only $R_{y.12}$, but in the second case, where Y, X_1, and X_2 are all stochastic variables, we may have $R_{y.12}$, $R_{1.y2}$, and $R_{2.y1}$.

22.6.   Partial Correlation

Consider the simple model where

(1) $$Y_c = a + b_1 X_1 + b_2 X_2$$

We have distinguished two cases conceptually. One is where Y_c is a stochastic (random) variable, and X_1 and X_2 are mathematical variables; that is, they have no distributions. The second case is where all three variables are random variables and have a multivariate distribution; in particular, a multivariate normal distribution.

When dealing with a multivariate normal distribution, we may wish to find the degree of covariation between variables. For example, let Y be the son's height; X_1 be the father's, and X_2 be the grandfather's height. Then we may wish to find the degree of covariation between Y (son's height) and X_1 (father's height). Do they vary together, and if so, to what degree?

When considering such a problem, two cases may be distinguished. One is seeking the covariation between Y (son's height) and X_1 (father's height), ignoring X_2 (grandfather's height); this is called the *total correlation* of Y and X_1 and is denoted by r_{y1}. This implies that, when seeking the covariation between Y (son's height) and X_1 (father's height), the X_2 (grandfather's height) is not held constant, and hence we may have a very tall grandfather or a very short grandfather. Hence, r_{y1} includes the effect, if any, of the grandfather's height, and we may assume that the effect will differ according to the grandfather's height. This r_{y1} is defined as

(2)
$$r_{y1} = \frac{\Sigma\, yx_1}{\sqrt{\Sigma\, y^2\, \Sigma\, x_1{}^2}}$$

and similarly for the total correlation between other variables.

A second measure of covariation between the variables Y and X_1 shows the correlation between Y and X_1 holding the other variables constant, and is called the *partial correlation coefficient* of Y and X_1, with respect to X_2. As an example, let Y be the yield of corn; X_1 be the amount of rainfall; and X_2 be temperature. Suppose that the *total* correlation coefficient r_{y1} between Y (yield) and X_1 (rainfall) is positive, which means: the more rain, the higher the yield. Suppose also that the *total* correlation coefficient r_{y2} between Y (yield) and X_2 (temperature) is negative, which means: the higher the temperature, the lower the yield. Generally speaking, we should expect: the higher (lower) the temperature, the greater (smaller) the yield, and hence have a positive r_{y2}.

What has happened in our illustration is that the effect of rain is included in r_{y2}. A large amount of rain is associated with low temperature, and the effect of rain on yield is more dominant than temperature. As a result, low temperature, accompanied by a large amount of rain increases yield and hence r_{y2} is negative.

However, if we eliminate the effect of rain (X_1) from r_{y2}, we may obtain a *partial* correlation between yield (Y) and temperature (X_2) that may be positive, showing that lower temperature brings about smaller yield.

The notation used to express the partial correlation coefficient is

$$r_{y2.1}$$

where the primary subscripts $_{y2}$ show that the coefficient is the partial correlation between Y and X_2; the secondary subscripts show the variables that are being held constant. The partial correlation coefficient $r_{y1.45}$, for example, shows the partial correlation between Y and X_1 holding X_4 and X_5 constant. However, X_2 and X_3 are not held constant.

Let us now develop this idea of partial correlation more formally.

Notation. In our previous discussion, the dependent variable was shown as Y, and the independent variables as X_1, X_2, ... A simpler, and in many cases more convenient, way of expressing the regression model is to let all the variables be denoted by X's. For a 3-variable case, the regression line is

$$X_{1c} = a + b_2 X_2 + b_3 X_3$$

The b coefficients are also written

$$X_{1c} = a + b_{12.3}X_2 + b_{13.2}X_3$$

to show that, for example, $b_{12.3}$ is the partial regression coefficient of X_1 on X_2 holding X_3 constant. In many cases where there is no confusion, the secondary subscripts are omitted and we simply write b_{12} and have

$$X_{1c} = a + b_{12}X_2 + b_{13}X_3$$

Similar to the previous case, we shall let $x_1 = X_1 - \bar{X}_1$, $x_2 = X_2 - \bar{X}_2$, and $x_3 = X_3 - \bar{X}_3$. Then the regression line becomes

$$x_{1c} = b_{12}x_2 + b_{13}x_3$$

and the normal equations are

$$b_{12} \Sigma x_2{}^2 + b_{13} \Sigma x_2x_3 = \Sigma x_1x_2$$

$$b_{12} \Sigma x_2x_3 + b_{13} \Sigma x_3{}^2 = \Sigma x_1x_3$$

This may be thought of as a subsection of the following set of equations:

$$b_{11} \Sigma x_1{}^2 + b_{12} \Sigma x_1x_2 + b_{13} \Sigma x_1x_3 = \Sigma x_1{}^2$$

$$b_{11} \Sigma x_1x_2 + b_{12} \Sigma x_2{}^2 + b_{13} \Sigma x_2x_3 = \Sigma x_1x_2$$

$$b_{11} \Sigma x_1x_3 + b_{12} \Sigma x_2x_3 + b_{13} \Sigma x_3{}^2 = \Sigma x_1x_3$$

Let us now return to the main line of discussion.

There are several ways of defining the partial correlation coefficient. The first way is to define it in terms of deviations. Let the regression function be

$$x_{1c} = b_{12}x_2 + b_{13}x_3$$

Suppose we wish to find the partial correlation between x_1 and x_2, which means that we wish to remove the effect of x_3. To accomplish this, we shall deduct x_3 from x_1 and x_2 as follows:

$$d_{1.3} = x_1 - b_{13}x_3$$
$$d_{2.3} = x_2 - b_{13}x_3$$

The geometrical meaning of the deviations d may be explained heuristically by a 2-dimensional illustration, as shown in Fig. 22.1.

The x_1 was $x_1 = X_1 - \bar{X}_1$, and hence is the total deviation AC. The $b_{12}x_2 = BC$ shows the improvement brought about by the regression line. Hence, the process of $x_1 - b_{12}x_2$ may be thought of as removing the improvement brought about by x_2, and what remains is that part of the deviation that is still unexplained.

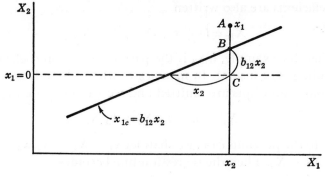

FIG. 22.1.

In terms of our previous notation, we had

$$Y - \bar{Y} = (Y - Y_c) + (Y_c - \bar{Y})$$

$$\underbrace{\qquad\qquad}_{\text{Unexplained}} \quad \underbrace{\qquad\qquad}_{\text{Explained}}$$

In our present notation, it is

$$x_1 - 0 = (x_1 - x_{1c}) + (x_{1c} - 0)$$

$$\underbrace{\qquad\qquad}_{\text{Unexplained}} \quad \underbrace{\qquad\qquad}_{\text{Explained}}$$

and the unexplained part is

$$x_1 - x_{1c} = x_1 - b_{12}x_2$$

The interpretation of $d_{1.3}$ is similar except that we are now dealing with three dimensions and $d_{1.3}$ may be considered as the unexplained part that remains after the effect (improvement) of x_3 has been removed. However, in this case, the effect of x_2 is not removed; similarly, for $d_{2.3}$. This interpretation is extended for cases where there are more variables.

Using the deviations $d_{1.3}$ and $d_{2.3}$, the population partial correlation coefficient is defined as

(3)
$$\rho_{12.3} = \frac{E(d_{1.3}d_{2.3})}{\sqrt{E(d^2_{1.3})E(d^2_{2.3})}}$$

We see that $E(d_{1.3}d_{2.3})$ is similar to the covariance between two variables and may be called a partial covariance between X_1 and X_2 holding X_3 constant. In similar manner, we may call $E(d^2_{1.3})$ as the partial covariance between X_1 and X_1 holding X_3 constant. It is also called the residual variance of x_1 after x_3 has been eliminated.

Our statistical problem is to estimate this population partial correlation coefficient by the method of maximum likelihood. This estimator turns out to be

(4)
$$r_{12.3} = \frac{r_{12} - r_{13}r_{23}}{\sqrt{(1 - r_{13}^2)(1 - r_{23}^2)}}$$

where

$$r_{ij} = \frac{\Sigma \, x_i x_j}{\sqrt{(\Sigma \, x_i^2)(\Sigma \, x_j^2)}}$$

is the total correlation coefficient between x_i and x_j.

In our previous illustration of sales (X_1), radio advertisement (X_2), and newspaper advertisement (X_3), we have calculated

$$r_{12} = \frac{\Sigma \, x_1 x_2}{\sqrt{\Sigma \, x_1^2 \, \Sigma \, x_2^2}} = \frac{57}{\sqrt{98 \times 34}} = 0.987295$$

$$r_{13} = \frac{\Sigma \, x_1 x_3}{\sqrt{\Sigma \, x_1^2 \, \Sigma \, x_3^2}} = \frac{52}{\sqrt{98 \times 40}} = 0.8305395$$

$$r_{23} = \frac{\Sigma \, x_2 x_3}{\sqrt{\Sigma \, x_2^2 \, \Sigma \, x_3^2}} = \frac{30}{\sqrt{34 \times 40}} = 0.8134887$$

$$r_{12.3} = \frac{0.987295 - (0.83053)(0.81348)}{\sqrt{[1 - (0.83053)^2][1 - (0.81348)^2]}}$$
$$= 0.96227$$

A second way of defining the partial correlation coefficient is as follows: The partial correlation coefficient between X_1 (sales) and X_2 (radio advertising) is the correlation between X_1 and X_2 holding X_3 (newspaper advertising) constant; say, at $5000. When we have a multivariate normal distribution, this second definition and the first definition will give us the same results. That is, the partial correlation coefficient is shown by equation (4). Holding the newspaper advertising expenditures constant eliminates its effect on sales.

A third way of defining the partial correlation coefficient is in terms of the amount of improvement brought about by the addition of another variable. In our present illustration, the regression of sales (X_1) on radio advertisement (X_2) may be shown by

$$x_{1.2c} = b_{12}x_2$$

The coefficient of determination for X_1 and X_2 is

(5)
$$R_{1.2}^2 = \frac{\Sigma\,(X_{1.2c} - \bar{X}_1)^2}{\Sigma\,(X_1 - \bar{X}_1)^2}$$

and shows the amount of improvement brought about by X_1 (radio advertisement). Hence, $1 - R_{1.2}^2$ may be considered as the amount that remains unexplained.

By adding the variable X_3 (newspaper advertisement), the regression function becomes

$$x_{1.23c} = b_{12.3}x_2 + b_{13.2}x_3$$

The coefficient of determination for X_1 and (X_2, X_3) becomes

(6)
$$R_{1.23}^2 = \frac{\Sigma\,(X_{1.23c} - \bar{X}_1)^2}{\Sigma\,(X_1 - \bar{X}_1)^2}$$

and shows the improvement brought about by X_2 and X_3. Hence, $1 - R_{1.23}^2$ may be considered as the amount that remains unexplained.

Thus, the difference

$$(1 - R_{1.2}^2) - (1 - R_{1.23}^2)$$

shows the amount of improvement brought about by the addition of X_3 (newspaper advertising). In relative terms, the improvement is shown by

(7)
$$r_{13.2}^2 = \frac{(1 - R_{1.2}^2) - (1 - R_{1.23}^2)}{1 - R_{1.2}^2}$$

and is the coefficient of partial determination between X_1 and X_3 holding X_2 fixed. Or, we may say, $r_{13.2}^2$ shows the relative amount of improvement that is brought about by adding the variable X_3.

The square root of the coefficient of partial determination (that is, $r_{13.2}$) is the coefficient of partial correlation between X_1 and X_3.

Substituting (5) and (6) into (7), we find,

(8)
$$r_{13.2}^2 = \frac{\Sigma\,(X_{1.23c} - \bar{X}_1)^2 - \Sigma\,(X_{1.2c} - \bar{X}_1)^2}{\Sigma\,(X_1 - \bar{X}_1)^2 - \Sigma\,(X_{1.2c} - \bar{X}_1)^2}$$

Substituting the relations

(9)
$$\Sigma\,(X_{1.23c} - \bar{X}_1)^2 = b_{12.3}\,\Sigma\,x_1x_2 + b_{13.2}\,\Sigma\,x_1x_3$$
$$\Sigma\,(X_{1.2c} - \bar{X}_1)^2 = b_{12}\,\Sigma\,x_1x_2$$

into (8) and then substituting the values of $b_{12.3}$, $b_{13.2}$, and b_{12} obtained from

$$b_{12.3} \Sigma x_2{}^2 + b_{13.2} \Sigma x_2 x_3 = \Sigma x_1 x_2$$
$$b_{12.3} \Sigma x_2 x_3 + b_{13.2} \Sigma x_3{}^2 = \Sigma x_1 x_3$$

and

$$b_{12} \Sigma x_2{}^2 = \Sigma x_1 x_2$$

we find

$$r_{13.2}^2 = \frac{(r_{13} - r_{12} r_{23})^2}{(1 - r_{23}{}^2)(1 - r_{12}{}^2)}$$

The square root of this is

$$r_{13.2} = \frac{r_{13} - r_{12} r_{23}}{\sqrt{1 - r_{23}{}^2}\sqrt{1 - r_{12}{}^2}}$$

which is the partial correlation coefficient between X_1 and X_3 holding X_2 constant and is of the same form as our first method of presentation.

For computation purposes, it is convenient to use the relations given in (9), since all the terms on the right-hand side are already calculated except for b_{12}. However, b_{12} is

$$b_{12} = \frac{\Sigma x_1 x_2}{\Sigma x_2{}^2}$$

and may be easily calculated.

Using our present example,

$$b_{12.3} \Sigma x_1 x_2 + b_{13.2} \Sigma x_1 x_3 = 95.7164$$

$$b_{12} \Sigma x_1 x_2 = \frac{(\Sigma x_1 x_2)^2}{\Sigma x_2{}^2} = \frac{57^2}{34}$$

$$\Sigma (X_1 - \bar{X}_1)^2 = 98$$

$$r_{13.2}^2 = \frac{95.7164 - \dfrac{(57)^2}{34}}{98 - \dfrac{(57)^2}{34}}$$

$$= \frac{95.7164 - 95.5588}{98 - 95.5588}$$

$$= 0.06456$$

$$r_{13.2} = 0.254$$

The coefficient of partial determination is about 6 percent and the coefficient of partial correlation is about 25 percent.

For $r_{12.3}^2$, since

$$\Sigma (X_{1.3c} - \bar{X}_1)^2 = b_{13} \Sigma x_1 x_3 = \frac{(\Sigma x_1 x_3)^2}{\Sigma x_3^2}$$

$$= \frac{52^2}{40}$$

we have

$$r_{12.3}^2 = \frac{\Sigma (X_{1.23c} - \bar{X}_1)^2 - \Sigma (X_{1.3c} - \bar{X}_1)^2}{\Sigma (X_1 - \bar{X}_1)^2 - \Sigma (X_{1.3c} - \bar{X}_1)^2}$$

$$= \frac{95.7164 - \dfrac{(52)^2}{40}}{98 - \dfrac{(52)^2}{40}}$$

$$= 0.9264$$

$$r_{12.3} = 0.9622$$

The $r_{12.3}$, using the first method, was 0.9623.

22.7. Gauss Multipliers

As we found in the previous sections, a major headache in regression analysis is the solution of the normal equations for the regression co-efficients. The Doolittle method* and variations of it are used to facilitate computations, but these are in most cases based on matrix algebra, although the matrix algebra is not explicitly used. This, however, seems to hinder a straightforward understanding of the procedures. In this section, we propose to use matrix algebra explicitly, although on an elementary level, and show how normal equations may be solved. This should also show how the Doolittle method and various variations of it are based on matrix algebra.

Since matrix algebra is being increasingly used in economics, business, and statistics, a slight detour into matrix algebra should not be a waste of time. For those not familiar with matrix algebra, an "instant" review is given in the Appendix to this chapter.

---

* M. H. Doolittle, "Method Employed in the Solution of Normal Equations and the Adjustment of a Triangulation," *U.S. Coast and Geodetic Survey Report*, 1878. Also see P. S. Dwyer, *Linear Computations*, New York: John Wiley and Sons, 1951.

As we shall see, the main problem is to find the inverse of a matrix. In our present case, the inverse matrix that is found consists of elements called Gauss multipliers. Once these Gauss multipliers have been found, formulas for the b's and the variances of the b's can easily be found. We shall find the b's in this section and the variances of b's in Section 22.9.

The normal equations

$$b_1 \Sigma x_1{}^2 + b_2 \Sigma x_1 x_2 = \Sigma x_1 y$$

$$b_1 \Sigma x_1 x_2 + b_2 \Sigma x_2{}^2 = \Sigma x_2 y$$

in matrix notation are

$$\begin{bmatrix} \Sigma x_1{}^2 & \Sigma x_1 x_2 \\ \Sigma x_1 x_2 & \Sigma x_2{}^2 \end{bmatrix} \begin{bmatrix} b_1 \\ b_2 \end{bmatrix} = \begin{bmatrix} \Sigma x_1 y \\ \Sigma x_2 y \end{bmatrix}$$

The b's are found by

(1)
$$\begin{bmatrix} b_1 \\ b_2 \end{bmatrix} = \begin{bmatrix} \Sigma x_2{}^2 & \Sigma x_1 x_2 \\ \Sigma x_1 x_2 & \Sigma x_2{}^2 \end{bmatrix}^{-1} \begin{bmatrix} \Sigma x_1 y \\ \Sigma x_2 y \end{bmatrix}$$

$$= \begin{bmatrix} c_{11} & c_{12} \\ c_{21} & c_{22} \end{bmatrix} \begin{bmatrix} \Sigma x_1 y \\ \Sigma x_2 y \end{bmatrix}$$

where the c's are called the Gauss multipliers. The matrix that has the $\Sigma x_i x_j$ as its elements will be called the *matrix of sum of squares*.

When the product of the last two matrices is written out, the b's are

(2)
$$b_1 = c_{11} \Sigma x_1 y + c_{12} \Sigma x_2 y$$

$$b_2 = c_{21} \Sigma x_1 y + c_{22} \Sigma x_2 y$$

Thus, the procedure of finding the b's is: first find the matrix of sum of squares; second, invert it and find the c_{ij}; and third, from (5) find the b's.

To find the matrix of the sum of squares, the following relationships are used:

$$\Sigma x_1{}^2 = \Sigma (X_1 - \bar{X}_1)^2 = \Sigma X_1{}^2 - n(\bar{X}_1)^2$$

$$\Sigma x_1 y = \Sigma (X_1 - \bar{X}_1)(Y - \bar{Y}) = \Sigma X_1 Y - n(\bar{X}_1)(\bar{Y})$$

and similar relationships hold for the other variables.

Using these results, let us find the matrix of sum of squares as in the following three steps.

Step 1. Find the matrix of sum of squares

X_1	X_2	Y	Sum
X_{11}	X_{21}	Y_1	S_1
X_{12}	X_{22}	Y_2	S_2
X_{13}	X_{23}	Y_3	S_3
X_{14}	X_{24}	Y_4	S_4
ΣX_1	ΣX_2	ΣY	ΣS

$$\Sigma X_1{}^2 \longrightarrow \Sigma X_1 X_2 \longrightarrow \Sigma X_1 Y = \Sigma X_1 S$$
$$\downarrow \qquad\qquad \downarrow$$
$$\Sigma X_2{}^2 \longrightarrow \Sigma X_2 Y = \Sigma X_2 S$$
$$\downarrow$$
$$\Sigma Y^2 = \Sigma YS$$

Example 1.

X_1	X_2	Y	Sum
1	2	12	15
2	3	14	19
3	7	16	26
4	10	18	32
$\Sigma 10$	22	60	92

$$30 \longrightarrow 69 \longrightarrow 160 = 259$$
$$\downarrow \qquad\qquad \downarrow$$
$$162 \longrightarrow 358 = 589$$
$$\downarrow$$
$$920 = 1438$$

Using the results obtained above, we find:

$$\Sigma x_1{}^2 = \Sigma X_1{}^2 - n(\bar{X}_1)^2 = 30 - 4\,(2.5)^2 = 5$$

$$\Sigma x_1 x_2 = \Sigma X_1 X_2 - n(\bar{X}_1)(\bar{X}_2) = 69 - (4)\left(\frac{10}{4}\right)\left(\frac{12}{4}\right) = 39$$

$$\Sigma x_2{}^2 = \Sigma X_2{}^2 - n(\bar{X}_2)^2 = 162 - 4\left(\frac{12}{4}\right)^2 = 126$$

$$\Sigma x_1 y = \Sigma X_1 Y - n(\bar{X}_1)(\bar{Y}) = 160 - 4\left(\frac{10}{4}\right)\left(\frac{60}{4}\right) = 10$$

$$\Sigma x_2 y = \Sigma X_2 Y - n(\bar{X}_2)(\bar{Y}) = 358 - 4\left(\frac{12}{4}\right)\left(\frac{60}{4}\right) = 178$$

Thus, the normal equations are

$$\begin{bmatrix} 5 & 39 \\ 39 & 126 \end{bmatrix} \cdot \begin{bmatrix} b \\ b \end{bmatrix} = \begin{bmatrix} 10 \\ 178 \end{bmatrix}$$

The next step is to invert the matrix of the sum of squares.

Step 2. Inversion of the matrix. Using the Gauss elimination technique, let us find the inverse matrix.

$$\begin{bmatrix} 5 & 39 \\ 39 & 126 \end{bmatrix} \quad \begin{bmatrix} 1 & 0 \\ 0 & 1 \end{bmatrix}$$

$$\begin{bmatrix} 1 & 7.8 \\ 1 & 3.2308 \end{bmatrix} \quad \begin{bmatrix} 0.2 & 0 \\ 0 & 0.02564 \end{bmatrix}$$

$$\begin{bmatrix} 1 & 7.8 \\ 0 & -4.5692 \end{bmatrix} \quad \begin{bmatrix} 0.2 & 0 \\ -0.2 & 0.02564 \end{bmatrix}$$

$$\begin{bmatrix} 1 & 7.8 \\ 0 & 1 \end{bmatrix} \quad \begin{bmatrix} 0.2 & 0 \\ 0.0438 & -0.0056 \end{bmatrix}$$

$$\begin{bmatrix} 1 & 0 \\ 0 & 1 \end{bmatrix} \quad \begin{bmatrix} -0.1416 & 0.04368 \\ 0.0438 & -0.0056 \end{bmatrix}$$

Let us check this:

$$\begin{bmatrix} 5 & 39 \\ 39 & 126 \end{bmatrix}\begin{bmatrix} -0.1416 & 0.0437 \\ 0.0438 & -0.0056 \end{bmatrix} = \begin{bmatrix} 1.0002 & 0.0001 \\ 0.0036 & .9987 \end{bmatrix}$$

$$\cong \begin{bmatrix} 1 & 0 \\ 0 & 1 \end{bmatrix}$$

Step 3. Find the b's

$$\begin{bmatrix} b_1 \\ b_2 \end{bmatrix} = \begin{bmatrix} c_{11} & c_{12} \\ c_{21} & c_{22} \end{bmatrix}\begin{bmatrix} \Sigma x_1 y \\ \Sigma x_2 y \end{bmatrix}$$

$$= \begin{bmatrix} -0.1416 & 0.0437 \\ 0.0438 & -0.0056 \end{bmatrix}\begin{bmatrix} 10 \\ 178 \end{bmatrix}$$

$$b_1 = (-0.1416)(10) + (0.0437)(178) = 6.3626$$
$$b_2 = (0.0438)(10) + (-0.0056)(178) = 1.4348$$

It is important to avoid computation errors, which in long computations become very costly in terms of time and effort. A simple procedure to check the computations at each stage may be constructed as follows. Suppose we have two numbers 5 and 7:

Numbers		Sum	Check
5	7	12	
1	1.4	$1 + 1.4 = 2.4$	$12/5 = 2.4$

The sum is $5 + 7 = 12$. Let us divide by 5, as shown in the second row. Then the sum is $1 + 1.4 = 2.4$. If we divide the sum in the first row, we get $12 \div 5 = 2.4$, which is clearly equal to the sum $1 + 1.4 = 2.4$. If it is not equal, there is a mistake. For example, let the second row be

Numbers		Sum	Check
1	1.3	$1 + 1.3 = 2.3$	$12/5 = 2.4$

where we have made an error in division; that is, $7/5 \neq 1.3$, and as a result, $1 + 1.3 = 2.3 \neq 12/5 = 2.4$.

By applying this simple principle to each stage of the calculations, we can detect computation mistakes. Let us illustrate with our example.

				Sum	Check
5	39	1	0	45	
39	126	0	1	166	
1	7.8	0.2	0	9	$45/5 = 9$
1	3.2308	0	0.02564	4.2564	$166/39 = 4.2564$
1	7.8	0.2	0		
0	−4.5692	−0.2	0.02564	−4.7436	−4.7436
1	7.8	0.2	0		9.0
0	1	0.0438	−0.0056	1.0382	1.0382
1	0	−0.1416	0.0437	0.9021	0.90204
0	1	0.0438	−0.0056		

In practice it is not necessary to write the "check" column.

In subsequent examples, this Gauss elimination method will be used to find the inverse matrix. It should be understood that one may start from any part of the matrix and develop the elimination process, but usually one may determine by observation which is the easiest starting point. It is also possible to combine several steps and seemingly simplify the procedures, but there is probably less confusion when all the steps are carried out as illustrated above because it clearly shows the elimination process. However, the computation process is a matter of individual preference, and it is recommended that instead of trying to memorize the various different procedures that are used by different people, you should understand the matrix algebra used above and devise your own method.

Another technique used to simplify calculations is to multiply the normal equations by n. That is:

$$\begin{bmatrix} n \Sigma x_1^2 & n \Sigma x_1 x_2 \\ n \Sigma x_1 x_2 & n \Sigma x_2^2 \end{bmatrix} \begin{bmatrix} b_1 \\ b_2 \end{bmatrix} = \begin{bmatrix} n \Sigma x_1 y \\ n \Sigma x_2 y \end{bmatrix}$$

The matrices that have been multiplied by n are sometimes called *moment matrices.* The advantage of this is, for example,

$$n \Sigma x_1{}^2 = n \Sigma X_1{}^2 - (\Sigma X_1)^2$$
$$n \Sigma x_1 y = n \Sigma X_1 Y - (\Sigma X_1)(\Sigma Y)$$

As is seen, the necessity of finding $\bar{X}_1$ and $\bar{Y}$ has been avoided, but the amount of savings in computations is not very great. However, let us illustrate this process with an example.

First, we shall denote the normal equations above by

$$\begin{bmatrix} G_{11} & G_{12} \\ G_{21} & G_{22} \end{bmatrix} \begin{bmatrix} b_1 \\ b_2 \end{bmatrix} = \begin{bmatrix} G_{1y} \\ G_{2y} \end{bmatrix}$$

and call the left-hand matrix the G matrix.

Example 2. Suppose the G matrix is

$$\begin{bmatrix} G_{11} & G_{12} & G_{13} \\ G_{21} & G_{22} & G_{23} \\ G_{31} & G_{32} & G_{33} \end{bmatrix} = \begin{bmatrix} 2 & 6 & 24 \\ 6 & 12 & 36 \\ 24 & 36 & 48 \end{bmatrix}$$

Then the inverse matrix is found as follows:

$$\begin{bmatrix} 2 & 6 & 24 \\ 6 & 12 & 36 \\ 24 & 36 & 48 \end{bmatrix} \begin{bmatrix} 1 & 0 & 0 \\ 0 & 1 & 0 \\ 0 & 0 & 1 \end{bmatrix} \begin{matrix} (1) \\ (2) \\ (3) \end{matrix}$$

$$(1) \div 2 \begin{bmatrix} 1 & 3 & 12 \\ 6 & 12 & 36 \\ 24 & 36 & 48 \end{bmatrix} \begin{bmatrix} \frac{1}{2} & 0 & 0 \\ 0 & 1 & 0 \\ 0 & 0 & 1 \end{bmatrix} \begin{matrix} (4) \\ (5) \\ (6) \end{matrix}$$

$$(5) - (4) \times 6 \begin{bmatrix} 1 & 3 & 12 \\ 0 & -6 & -36 \\ 24 & 36 & 48 \end{bmatrix} \begin{bmatrix} \frac{1}{2} & 0 & 0 \\ -3 & 1 & 0 \\ 0 & 0 & 1 \end{bmatrix} \begin{matrix} (7) \\ (8) \\ (9) \end{matrix}$$

$$(8) \div (-6) \begin{bmatrix} 1 & 3 & 12 \\ 0 & 1 & 6 \\ 24 & 36 & 48 \end{bmatrix} \begin{bmatrix} \frac{1}{2} & 0 & 0 \\ \frac{1}{2} & -\frac{1}{6} & 0 \\ 0 & 0 & 1 \end{bmatrix} \begin{matrix} (10) \\ (11) \\ (12) \end{matrix}$$

$$(12) - (10) \times 24 \begin{bmatrix} 1 & 3 & 12 \\ 0 & 1 & 6 \\ 0 & -36 & -240 \end{bmatrix} \begin{bmatrix} \frac{1}{2} & 0 & 0 \\ \frac{1}{2} & -\frac{1}{6} & 0 \\ -12 & 0 & 1 \end{bmatrix} \begin{matrix} (13) \\ (14) \\ (15) \end{matrix}$$

$$(15) + (14) \times 36 \begin{bmatrix} 1 & 3 & 12 \\ 0 & 1 & 6 \\ 0 & 0 & -24 \end{bmatrix} \begin{bmatrix} \frac{1}{2} & 0 & 0 \\ \frac{1}{2} & -\frac{1}{6} & 0 \\ 6 & -6 & 1 \end{bmatrix} \begin{matrix} (16) \\ (17) \\ (18) \end{matrix}$$

$$(18) \div (-24) \begin{bmatrix} 1 & 3 & 12 \\ 0 & 1 & 6 \\ 0 & 0 & 1 \end{bmatrix} \begin{bmatrix} \frac{1}{2} & 0 & 0 \\ \frac{1}{2} & -\frac{1}{6} & 0 \\ -\frac{1}{4} & \frac{1}{4} & -\frac{1}{24} \end{bmatrix} \begin{matrix} (19) \\ (20) \\ (21) \end{matrix}$$

$$(20) - (21) \times 6 \quad \begin{bmatrix} 1 & 3 & 12 \\ 0 & 1 & 0 \\ 0 & 0 & 1 \end{bmatrix} \begin{bmatrix} \frac{1}{2} & 0 & 0 \\ 2 & -\frac{5}{3} & \frac{1}{4} \\ -\frac{1}{4} & \frac{1}{4} & -\frac{1}{24} \end{bmatrix} \begin{matrix} (22) \\ (23) \\ (24) \end{matrix}$$

$$\begin{matrix} (22) - (23) \times 6 \\ - (24) \times 12 \end{matrix} \quad \begin{bmatrix} 1 & 0 & 0 \\ 0 & 1 & 0 \\ 0 & 0 & 1 \end{bmatrix} \begin{bmatrix} -\frac{5}{2} & 2 & -\frac{1}{4} \\ 2 & -\frac{5}{3} & \frac{1}{4} \\ -\frac{1}{4} & \frac{1}{4} & -\frac{1}{24} \end{bmatrix} \begin{matrix} (25) \\ (26) \\ (27) \end{matrix}$$

Thus the inverse matrix is

$$\begin{bmatrix} G_{11} & G_{12} & G_{13} \\ G_{21} & G_{22} & G_{23} \\ G_{31} & G_{32} & G_{33} \end{bmatrix}^{-1} = \begin{bmatrix} -\frac{5}{2} & 2 & -\frac{1}{4} \\ 2 & -\frac{5}{3} & \frac{1}{4} \\ -\frac{1}{4} & \frac{1}{4} & -\frac{1}{24} \end{bmatrix}$$

Check

$$\begin{bmatrix} 2 & 6 & 24 \\ 6 & 12 & 36 \\ 24 & 36 & 48 \end{bmatrix} \begin{bmatrix} -\frac{5}{2} & 2 & \frac{1}{4} \\ 2 & -\frac{5}{3} & \frac{1}{4} \\ -\frac{1}{4} & \frac{1}{4} & -\frac{1}{24} \end{bmatrix} = \begin{bmatrix} 1 & 0 & 0 \\ 0 & 1 & 0 \\ 0 & 0 & 1 \end{bmatrix}$$

All the steps have been carried out in detail, but several steps may be combined into one. Let us show one such procedure. We start with the original G matrix.

	X_1	X_2	X_3				
X_1	2	6	24	1	0	0	(1)
X_2	6	12	36	0	1	0	(2)
X_3	24	36	48	0	0	1	(3)

The first step is to make the $G_{11} = 2$ element become unity.

	2	6	24	1	0	0	(4)
$(4) \div 2$	1	3	12	$\frac{1}{2}$	0	0	(5)

The second step is to make the elements below 1 in the first column equal to zero. This is done in two steps. First, by making 6 of row (2) equal zero; and second, by making 24 of row (3) equal zero.

	6	12	36	0	1	0	(6)
$(5) \times 6$	6	18	72	3	0	0	(7)
	0	−6	−36	−3	1	0	(8)
	0	1	6	$\frac{1}{2}$	$-\frac{1}{6}$	0	(9)

In row (9) we have made the element in the G_{22} position equal to unity. Next:

	24	36	48	0	0	1	(10)
$(5) \times 24$	24	72	288	12	0	0	(11)
$(9) \times 36$		36	216	18	−6	0	(12)
$(10) - (11) + (12)$	0	0	−24	6	−6	1	(13)

Here, two steps have been combined. The first element of row (3) is made zero (that is, the 24 is made zero), and the second element of row (3) (in this case $36 - 72 = -36$) is also made zero. And from row (13) we find

$$
\begin{array}{ccc|ccc}
0 & 0 & 1 & -\frac{1}{4} & \frac{1}{4} & \frac{1}{24}
\end{array}
\qquad (14)
$$

From row (14) and row (9) we find row (15):

$$
\begin{array}{ccc|ccc}
0 & 1 & 0 & 2 & -\frac{5}{3} & \frac{1}{4} & \qquad (15)\\
0 & 0 & 1 & -\frac{1}{4} & \frac{1}{4} & \frac{1}{24} & \qquad (16)
\end{array}
$$

From rows (5), (15) and (16), we find row (17):

$$
\begin{array}{ccc|ccc}
1 & 0 & 0 & -\frac{5}{2} & 2 & \frac{1}{4} & \qquad (17)\\
0 & 1 & 0 & 2 & -\frac{5}{3} & \frac{1}{4} & \qquad (18) = (15)\\
0 & 0 & 1 & -\frac{1}{4} & \frac{1}{4} & \frac{1}{24} & \qquad (19) = (16)
\end{array}
$$

We may now summarize the process, including the check column, as shown on page 668.

22.8.   Example

Using a hypothetical example, let us recapitulate what we have done so far. Let X_1 be the number of cars (millions) in use, X_2 be the number of trucks (millions) in use, and let Y be gasoline consumption in millions of barrels. We wish to find the regression of Y on X_1 and X_2; that is,

$$
Y = a + b_1 X_1 + b_2 X_2
$$

The problem is to estimate a, b_1, and b_2 by the method of least squares. For simplicity let us use the data in the accompanying table.

X_1	X_2	Y
36	8	990
40	8	1140
44	9	1230
47	9	1320
50	10	1370

Note that with such a small amount of data, we cannot expect accurate results. However, our present object is to show the process of estimating the parameters, and it should be kept in mind that, in actual problems, there will usually be more data.

Row							Sum	Check
(1)	2	6	24	1	0	0	33	
(2)	6	12	36	0	1	0	55	
(3)	24	36	48	0	0	1	109	
(4)	2	6	24	1	0	0	33	
(5) (4)÷2	1	3	12	$\frac{1}{2}$	0	0	$16\frac{1}{2}$	$33 \div 2 = 16\frac{1}{2}$
(6) (2)	6	12	36	0	1	0	55	
(7) (5)×6	6	18	72	3	0	0	99	$16\frac{1}{2} \times 6 = 99$
(8)		-6	-36	-3	1	0	-44	$55 - 99 = -44$
(9) (8)÷(-6)		1	6	$\frac{1}{2}$	$-\frac{1}{6}$	0	$7\frac{1}{3}$	$(-44) \div (-6) = 7\frac{1}{3}$
(10) (3)	24	36	48	0	0	1	109	
(11) (5)×24	24	72	288	12	0	0	396	$16\frac{1}{2} \times 24 = 396$
(12) (9)×36		36	216	18	-6	0	264	$7\frac{1}{3} \times 36 = 264$
(13) (10)−(11)+(12)			-24	6	-6	1	-23	$109 - 396 + 264 = -23$
(14) (13)÷(-24)			1	$-\frac{1}{4}$	$\frac{1}{4}$	$-\frac{1}{24}$	$\frac{23}{24}$	$(-23) \div (-24) = \frac{23}{24}$
(15) (9)		1	6	$\frac{1}{2}$	$-\frac{1}{6}$	0	$7\frac{1}{3}$	
(16) (14)×6			6	$-\frac{3}{2}$	$\frac{3}{2}$	$-\frac{1}{4}$	$5\frac{3}{4}$	$\left(\frac{23}{24}\right) \times 6 = 5\frac{3}{4}$
(17) (15)−(16)		1	0	2	$-\frac{5}{3}$	$\frac{1}{4}$	$1\frac{7}{12}$	$7\frac{1}{3} - 5\frac{3}{4} = 1\frac{7}{12}$
(18) (5)	1	3	12	$\frac{1}{2}$	0	0	$16\frac{1}{2}$	
(19) (17)×3		3	0	6	-5	$\frac{3}{4}$	$4\frac{3}{4}$	$1\frac{7}{12} \times 3 = 4\frac{3}{4}$
(20) (14)×12			12	-3	3	$-\frac{1}{2}$	$11\frac{1}{2}$	$\frac{23}{24} \times 12 = 11\frac{1}{2}$
(21) (18)−(19)+(20)	1	0	0	$-\frac{5}{2}$	2	$-\frac{1}{4}$	$\frac{1}{4}$	$16\frac{1}{2} - 4\frac{3}{4} - 11\frac{1}{2} = \frac{1}{4}$
(22)	0	1	0	2	$-\frac{5}{3}$	$\frac{1}{4}$		
(23)	0	0	1	$-\frac{1}{4}$	$\frac{1}{4}$	$-\frac{1}{24}$		

We shall first estimate the a, b_1, and b_2 by solving the normal equations and then repeat the same process, using matrices.

(i)   Coding the data

From these data, we may find the b's, but as was discussed in Chapter 13, computations can be simplified by shifting the origin, which will not affect the slope of the regression plane. It will, however, affect the intercept value a. Let us subtract 36 from X_1; 8 from X_2; and 1000 from Y. Then the data become as shown in the table below.

X_1	X_2	Y
0	0	$-$ 10
4	0	140
8	1	230
11	1	320
14	2	370
37	4	1050

(ii)   Estimate a, b₁, and b₂

The normal equations are

$$na + b_1 \Sigma X_1 + b_2 \Sigma X_2 = \Sigma Y$$

$$a \Sigma X_1 + b_1 \Sigma X_1{}^2 + b_2 \Sigma X_1 X_2 = \Sigma X_1 Y$$

$$a \Sigma X_2 + b_1 \Sigma X_1 X_2 + b_2 \Sigma X_2{}^2 = \Sigma X_2 Y$$

and the various terms in the normal equations are found from the following worksheet.

Worksheet

$X_1{}^2$	$X_1 X_2$	$X_2{}^2$	$X_1 Y$	$X_2 Y$
0	0	0	0	0
16	0	0	560	0
64	8	1	1,840	230
121	11	1	3,520	320
196	28	4	5,180	740
397	47	6	11,100	1,290

Hence, the normal equations become

(1) $$5a + 37b_1 + 4b_2 = 1050$$

(2) $$37a + 397b_1 + 47b_2 = 11{,}100$$

(3) $$4a + 47b_1 + 6b_2 = 1290$$

To solve these equations, first eliminate a. This is performed as follows:

$$(1) \times 37 - (2) \times 5: \quad 616b_1 + 87b_2 = 16{,}650$$
$$(1) \times 4 - (3) \times 5: \quad 87b_1 + 14b_2 = 2250$$

Solving for b_1 and b_2 from these two equations gives us

$$b_1 = 35.4028$$
$$b_2 = -59.289$$

and using these results, the a is

$$a = -4.54$$

Note that the b_1 and b_2 values that have been found need no adjustment, but the a value needs to be adjusted because the data were coded.

The regression line is

$$Y_c - 1000 = -4.54 + 35.4028(X_1 - 36) - 59.289(X_2 - 8)$$

which becomes

$$Y_c = 195.46 + 35.4X_1 - 59.3X_2$$

(iii)   Estimate σ^2

To find an estimate of the variance σ^2 of Y around the regression line, we shall use the analysis of variance table of Section 21.3.

Analysis of Variance Table

Source of Deviation	Degrees of Freedom	Sum of Squares	Mean Square
Total	$n - 1$	$Q = \Sigma (Y - \bar{Y})^2$	
Due to regression	k	$Q_1 = \Sigma (Y_c - \bar{Y})^2$	Q_1/k
Residual	$n - k - 1$	$Q_2 = \Sigma (Y - Y_c)^2$	$Q_2/(n - k - 1)$

The estimate of σ^2 is

$$\hat{\sigma}^2 = \frac{Q_2}{n - k - 1}$$

and to find this, we first find Q and Q_1 and then calculate $Q_2 = Q - Q_1$.

The Q is

$$Q = \Sigma (Y - \bar{Y})^2$$
$$= \Sigma Y^2 - n(\bar{Y})^2$$
$$= 311{,}900 - 5 \left(\frac{1050}{5} \right)^2$$
$$= 91{,}400$$

The Q_1 is obtained by using the following relationship:

$$Q_1 = \Sigma (Y_c - \bar{Y})^2$$
$$= b_1 \Sigma x_1 y + b_2 \Sigma x_2 y$$

where x_1, x_2, and y are deviations from the respective means. Hence,

$$\Sigma x_1 y = \Sigma X_1 Y - n(\bar{X}_1 \bar{Y})$$
$$= 11{,}100 - 5 \times \frac{37}{5} \times \frac{1050}{5}$$
$$= 3330$$
$$\Sigma x_2 y = \Sigma X_2 Y - n(\bar{X}_2 \bar{Y})$$
$$= 1290 - 5 \times \frac{4}{5} \times \frac{1050}{5}$$
$$= 450$$
$$Q_1 = (35.4028)(3330) + (-59.289)(450)$$
$$= 91{,}211.274$$

Hence, the analysis of variance table is as follows:

Source	Degrees of Freedom	Sum of Squares	Mean Square
Total	$n - 1 = 4$	91,400	
Due to regression	$k = 2$	91,211.3	$91{,}211.3/2 = 45{,}605$
Residual	$n - k - 1 = 2$	188.7	$188.7/2 = 94.35$

Hence, the estimate of the variance is

$$\hat{\sigma}^2 = 94.35$$

Let us check the value:

$$Q_2 = \Sigma \, (Y - Y_c)^2 = 188.7$$

by actually computing the deviations $Y - \bar{Y}_c$. This is shown in Table 22.6.

TABLE 22.6.

X_1	X_2	Y	Y_c	$Y - Y_c$	$(Y - Y_c)^2$
36	8	990	995.5	− 5.5	30.25
40	8	1140	1137.1	2.9	8.41
44	9	1230	1219.4	10.6	112.36
47	9	1320	1325.6	− 5.6	31.36
50	10	1370	1372.5	− 2.5	6.25
					188.63

We see that

$$\Sigma \, (Y - Y_c)^2 = 188.63$$

and is in close agreement with the value we obtained from the analysis of variance table.

Let us next show how the parameters may be found by using matrix algebra.

(iv) Find a, b₁, and b₂ by using matrix algebra

The normal equations in moment matrix terms were

$$\begin{bmatrix} m_{11} & m_{12} \\ m_{21} & m_{22} \end{bmatrix} \begin{bmatrix} b_1 \\ b_2 \end{bmatrix} = \begin{bmatrix} m_{1y} \\ m_{2y} \end{bmatrix}$$

The first step is to find the moment matrix. Using the results of the previous worksheet, the m_{11}, m_{12}, and m_{22} are

$$m_{11} = n \, \Sigma \, X_1{}^2 - (\Sigma \, X_1)^2 = 5(397) - (37)^2 = 616$$

$$m_{12} = m_{21} = n \, \Sigma \, X_1 X_2 - (\Sigma \, X_1)(\Sigma \, X_2) = 5(47) - (37)(4) = 87$$

$$m_{22} = n \, \Sigma \, X_2{}^2 - (\Sigma \, X_2)^2 = 5(6) - (4)^2 = 14$$

and the moment matrix is

$$\begin{bmatrix} m_{11} & m_{12} \\ m_{21} & m_{22} \end{bmatrix} = \begin{bmatrix} 616 & 87 \\ 87 & 14 \end{bmatrix}$$

The m_{1y} and m_{2y} are

$$m_{1y} = n \Sigma X_1 Y - \Sigma X_1 \Sigma Y$$
$$= 5(11,100) - (37)(1050)$$
$$= 16,650$$
$$m_{2y} = 5(1290) - 4(1050)$$
$$= 2250$$

Thus, the normal equations in moment matrix terms become

$$\begin{bmatrix} m_{11} & m_{12} \\ m_{21} & m_{22} \end{bmatrix} \begin{bmatrix} b_1 \\ b_2 \end{bmatrix} = \begin{bmatrix} m_{1y} \\ m_{2y} \end{bmatrix}$$
$$\begin{bmatrix} 616 & 87 \\ 87 & 14 \end{bmatrix} \begin{bmatrix} b_1 \\ b_2 \end{bmatrix} = \begin{bmatrix} 16,650 \\ 2250 \end{bmatrix}$$

which is the same result as that obtained previously from the normal equations after a was eliminated.

To find b_1 and b_2, we use matrix algebra and set

$$\begin{bmatrix} b_1 \\ b_2 \end{bmatrix} = \begin{bmatrix} 616 & 87 \\ 87 & 14 \end{bmatrix}^{-1} \begin{bmatrix} 16,650 \\ 2,250 \end{bmatrix}$$

Hence, our next problem is to invert the moment matrix.

The inverse of the moment matrix may be obtained by using the method explained in Section 22.11, the Appendix to this chapter. We find

$$\begin{bmatrix} 616 & 87 \\ 87 & 14 \end{bmatrix}^{-1} = \frac{1}{\Delta} \begin{bmatrix} A_{11} & A_{21} \\ A_{12} & A_{22} \end{bmatrix}$$
$$= \frac{1}{1055} \begin{bmatrix} 14 & -87 \\ -87 & 616 \end{bmatrix}$$
$$= \begin{bmatrix} 0.01327014 & -0.0824644 \\ -0.0824644 & 0.5838863 \end{bmatrix}$$

where the A_{ij} are the cofactors and

$$\Delta = \begin{vmatrix} 616 & 87 \\ 87 & 14 \end{vmatrix} = (616 \times 14) - (87 \times 87) = 1055$$

Hence, the b_1 and b_2 are shown as

$$\begin{bmatrix} b_1 \\ b_2 \end{bmatrix} = \begin{bmatrix} 0.01327014 & -0.0824644 \\ -0.0824644 & 0.5838863 \end{bmatrix} \begin{bmatrix} 16,650 \\ 2,250 \end{bmatrix}$$

and

$$b_1 = (0.01327014)(16,650) + (-0.0824644)(2250)$$
$$= 35.40284$$

$$b_2 = (-0.0824644)(16{,}650) + (0.5838863)(2250)$$

$$= -59.28959$$

which is the same result as we obtained previously.

(v) Finding the inverse matrix by an alternative method

Using the computation scheme explained in Section 22.7, we may find the inverse matrix as follows:

616	87	1	0
87	14	0	1
7.0805	1	0.011494	0
6.2143	1	0	0.071428
0.8662	0	0.011494	−0.071428
1	0	0.013269	−0.082461
87	14	0	1
87	0	1.154403	−7.174107
	14	−1.154403	8.174107
	1	0.082457	0.583907
1	0	0.013269	−0.082461
0	1	−0.082457	0.583907

Hence, the inverse matrix is

$$\begin{bmatrix} 616 & 87 \\ 87 & 14 \end{bmatrix}^{-1} = \begin{bmatrix} 0.013269 & -0.082461 \\ -0.082457 & 0.583907 \end{bmatrix}$$

The inverse matrix found in the preceding section was

$$\begin{bmatrix} 0.013270 & -0.082464 \\ -0.082464 & 0.583869 \end{bmatrix}$$

22.9. Tests of Hypotheses of the Regression Coefficients

After a regression line, such as

$$Y_c = 195.46 + 35.4X_1 - 59.3X_2$$

is calculated, we may wish to know whether the partial regression coefficients $b_1 = 35.4$ and $b_2 = -59.3$ are significant, that is, whether they are significantly different from zero. If, for example, b_1 is not significantly different from zero, we may assume that there is no regression between Y and X_1. Or, if b_1 and b_2 are not significantly different from zero, Y may not be predicted any more accurately than by using a regression plane that goes through the mean $(\bar{Y}, \bar{X}_1, \bar{X}_2)$. Or, more simply, we may just as well predict Y by taking the average of the Y's.

To test whether or not the population partial regression coefficients B_i are zero, the null hypothesis may be stated in two ways. The first is to test each B_i separately; in this case, the null hypothesis and alternative hypothesis are

$$H_1 : \quad B_i = 0$$
$$H_2 : \quad B_i \neq 0$$

which is a two-tail test. However, in many cases, the sign of the B's is known from nonstatistical considerations, and in this case, the test may be

$$H_1 : \quad B_i = 0$$
$$H_2 : \quad B_i > 0$$

if B_i is positive; then the test becomes a one-tail test.

The second test is to find whether

$$B_1 = B_2 = \cdots = B_k = 0$$

which is an overall test of the significance of the regression line.

For the first case, the t test is used, and for the second case, the F test is used.

(i) Tests using the t distribution

To test the hypothesis

$$H_1 : \quad B_i = B_0$$
$$H_2 : \quad B_i \neq B_0$$

we need to know the sampling distribution of b_i. We state without proof that the sampling distribution of b_i is normal with mean and variance

$$E(b_i) = B_i$$
$$\mathrm{Var}(b_i) = c_{ii}\sigma^2$$

where c_{ii} is the Gauss multiplier and

$$\sigma^2 = E(Y - E(Y|X))^2$$

Thus, the procedure is to construct the statistic z:

$$(1) \qquad\qquad z = \frac{b_i - B_0}{\sqrt{c_{ii}\sigma^2}}$$

and if the null hypothesis is $B_i = B_0 = 0$, the z becomes

$$(2) \qquad z = \frac{b_i}{\sqrt{c_{ii}\sigma^2}}$$

which will be normal with mean 0 and variance 1.

But, since the population σ^2 is usually unknown, its unbiased estimator $\hat{\sigma}^2$ is used. Then the test statistic becomes

$$(3) \qquad t = \frac{b_i - B_0}{\sqrt{c_{ii}\hat{\sigma}^2}} = \frac{b_i}{\sqrt{c_{ii}\hat{\sigma}^2}}$$

which now has a t distribution with $n - k - 1$ degrees of freedom where k is the number of B's in the regression equation.

The estimate $\hat{\sigma}^2$ is

$$\hat{\sigma}^2 = \frac{1}{n - k - 1} \Sigma (Y - Y_c)^2$$

where n is the sample size and k is the number of B's.

Note that there is another estimate of σ^2. That is,

$$\hat{\sigma}^2 = \frac{1}{n - 1} \Sigma (Y - \bar{Y})^2$$

and if this is used, we have $n - 1$ degrees of freedom.

Using the example in Section 22.8, we have

$$\begin{bmatrix} b_1 \\ b_2 \end{bmatrix} = \begin{bmatrix} 0.0133 & -0.0824 \\ -0.0824 & 0.5838 \end{bmatrix} \begin{bmatrix} 16,650 \\ 2,250 \end{bmatrix}$$

where the inverse matrix is obtained from the moment matrix. Hence, to find the Gauss multipliers, we have to adjust the values by $1/n$. That is, the above inverse may be written as

$$\frac{1}{n} \begin{bmatrix} c_{11} & c_{12} \\ c_{21} & c_{22} \end{bmatrix} = \begin{bmatrix} 0.0133 & -0.0824 \\ -0.0824 & 0.5838 \end{bmatrix}$$

Then c_{11} and c_{22} are

$$c_{11} = 0.0133 \times n = 0.0133 \times 5 = 0.0665$$
$$c_{22} = 0.5838 \times n = 0.5838 \times 5 = 2.9190$$

We also know that $\hat{\sigma}^2 = 94.35$ with $n - k - 1 = 5 - 2 - 1 = 2$ degrees of freedom. Thus, the test for

$$H_1 : \qquad B_1 = 0$$
$$H_2 : \qquad B_1 > 0$$

is

$$t = \frac{b_1}{\sqrt{c_{11}\hat{\sigma}^2}}$$

$$= \frac{35.4}{\sqrt{0.0665 \times 94.35}}$$

$$= \frac{35.4}{2.50} = 14.16$$

The test for

$$H_1 : \quad B_2 = 0$$
$$H_2' : \quad B_2 < 0$$

is

$$t = \frac{b_2}{\sqrt{c_{22}\hat{\sigma}^2}}$$

$$= \frac{-59.3}{\sqrt{2.919 \times 94.35}}$$

$$= \frac{-59.3}{16.58} = -3.576$$

For a significance level of $\alpha = 5$ percent and $n - k - 1 = 5 - 2 - 1 = 2$ degrees of freedom, the value of t is $t = 2.92$ for a one-tail test. Since $t = 14.16$ for b_1 and $t = -3.576$ for b_2 in the example, we conclude that both $b_1 = 35.4$ and $b_2 = -59.3$ are not due to chance, and we reject the null hypotheses that $B_1 = 0$ and $B_2 = 0$, respectively.

In many cases, the standard deviations of b_1 and b_2 are written in brackets below the b coefficients of the regression equation as follows:

$$Y_c = a + b_1 X_1 + b_2 X_2$$
$$(\sigma_{b_1}) \qquad (\sigma_{b_2})$$

For our present example, it is

$$Y_c = 195.46 + 35.4 X_1 - 59.3 X_2$$
$$(2.50) \qquad (16.58)$$

In our example, there were only 5 observations, which in general are too few to expect accurate results. In practice, one will usually have over 10 observations, and in such a case, the degrees of freedom will usually be greater than 5. The t value for a one-tail test and level of significance of 5 percent is, for 5 degrees of freedom, $t = 2.02$; and for 1000 degrees of freedom, it is $t = 1.65$. Hence, as a rough rule of thumb, one may compare the b_1 value and the standard deviation σ_{b_1}, and if b_1/σ_{b_1} is greater than 2, one may conclude that b_1 is significantly different from zero. In our example above, one can see from observation that $35.4/2.5$ and $59.3/16.58$ are both greater than 2, and hence we may conclude that no matter what the degrees of freedom, the b's are significantly different from zero. That is, we reject the null hypothesis that $B_1 = 0$ and $B_2 = 0$.

(ii)   Tests using the F distribution

We now wish to test, for our example,

$$H_1 : \qquad B_1 = B_2 = 0$$

which is an overall test of whether or not the regression is significant. Geometrically speaking, if the regression is significant, the Y_c's will differ from the $\bar{Y}$ significantly, and

$$\Sigma\,(Y_c - \bar{Y})^2$$

will be large and the residual deviations $Y - Y_c$ will tend to be small relative to the improvement $Y_c - \bar{Y}$ brought about by the regression plane. This implies that

$$\Sigma\,(Y - Y_c)^2$$

will tend to be small. Thus, if we construct the ratio

$$F = \frac{\dfrac{\Sigma\,(Y_c - \bar{Y})^2}{k}}{\dfrac{\Sigma\,(Y - Y_c)^2}{n - k - 1}}$$

the F will be large when there is a significant regression.

Then, if there is no regression, that is, if $B_1 = B_2 = 0$, since

$$Y_c = \bar{Y} + b_1(X_1 - \bar{X}_1) + b_2(X_2 - \bar{X}_2)$$

the Y_c will be close to or equal to $\bar{Y}$, and hence the F will be close to or equal to zero.

Since the ratio F we constructed is the ratio of two unbiased estimates of σ^2, it has an F distribution with k and $n - k - 1$ degrees of freedom, and this allows us to test whether or not the F is significant.

In our present example,

$$F = \frac{45,605}{94.35} = 483.3$$

with 2 and 2 degrees of freedom. For $\alpha = 5$ or 1 percent, the F is significant. Thus, we conclude that there is regression in the population and the improvement brought about by fitting the regression plane was not due to chance.

22.10.   Graphic Correlation

Instead of finding a regression function mathematically, we may find it graphically. The advantage is, mainly, the avoidance of cumbersome calculations; the disadvantage is the sacrifice of accuracy. However, with practice, the degree of error from the standpoint of practical usefulness is usually not too great. Furthermore, in many cases, the data may be of such low accuracy that, even though refined mathematical methods are applied, the results may not be very reliable.

The graphic method was first developed by L. H. Bean in an article[*] and subsequently about nine other articles on this subject have appeared. A mathematical discussion of this method has also been presented by R. J. Foote.[**]

In this section we shall discuss the graphic method for an additive regression function such as

$$Y_c = a + b_1X_1 + b_2X_2$$

and in Section 22.11 we shall consider a multiplicative regression function such as

$$Y_c = aX_1^{b_1}X_2^{b_2}$$

Both are used frequently in economics and business.

Let us develop our discussion with simple hypothetical data. Suppose Y is sales; X_1 is radio advertising expenditures; and X_2 is newspaper advertising expenditures, all in units of $1000. Table 22.7 gives the data for a recent 5-year period.

---

[*] L. H. Bean, "A simplified method of graphic curvilinear correlation," *J. Amer. Statistical Assoc.* (1929).

[**] R. J. Foote, "The mathematical basis for the Bean method of graphic multiple correlation," *J. Amer. Statistical Assoc.* (1953).

TABLE 22.7.

Year	Y	X_1	X_2
1	130	1	2
2	155	2	3
3	165	3	1
4	205	4	5
5	220	5	4
	875	15	15
	175	3	3

We wish to find the regression of Y (sales) on X_1 (radio advertising) and X_2 (newspaper advertising). The procedure will be first to find the regression of Y on X_1, ignoring X_2. Let this be shown by

(1) $$Y_{X_1} = a + b_1 X_1$$

Then $Y - Y_{X_1}$ is the residual after the effect of X_1 (radio) has been removed and may be considered as showing the effect of X_2 on Y.

The second step is to find the regression function of $(Y - Y_{X_1})$ on X_2 (newspaper). Let this be shown by

(2) $$Y_{X_2} = a' + b_2 X_2$$

and in this case, we may consider the relation between Y and X_2 shown by this regression function as being net of the effect of X_1 (radio).

Since (1) included the effect of X_2, as a third step we may recalculate (1) by subtracting Y_{X_2} from Y (that is, $Y - Y_{X_2}$) and finding the regression of this on X_1 (radio). Let this be shown by

(3) $$Y_{X_1}{}^* = a'' + b_1{}^* X_1$$

which we may now consider to show the relation between Y (sales) and X_1 (radio) net of X_2 (newspaper).

The fourth and final step is to combine equations (2) and (3) and find the regression function of Y on X_1 and X_2. We find

(4) $$Y_c = (a' + a'') + b_1{}^* X_1 + b_2 X_2$$

Although we have shown the procedure algebraically, it may be worked out graphically, as we shall illustrate. So let us now, using the data of Table 22.7, find the regression function of Y on X_1 and X_2.

(i) Find equation (1)

Figure 22.2 is the scatter diagram of Y and X_1. As is seen, the points show a positive relationship, whereas a similar scatter diagram of Y and

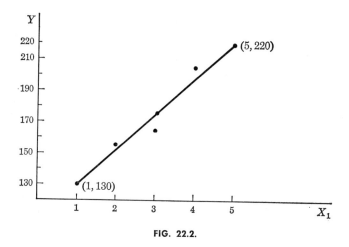

FIG. 22.2.

X_2 will show a rather irregular scatter. Let us fit a freehand straight line to the points in Fig. 22.2 such that the sum of the squared deviations is at a minimum. In our graph we have selected the two points (1, 130) and (5, 220), mainly to facilitate the explanation of the procedures. When drawing the freehand line, a criterion is to have it pass through the point $(\bar{X}_1, \bar{Y})$, which in our present case is (3, 175) as seen from Table 22.8, and have about an equal number of points above and below the line, giving more weight to the points with larger deviations.

Using the two points (1, 130) and (5, 220), the regression function is

$$Y_{X_1} = y_1 + \frac{y_2 - y_1}{x_2 - x_1}(X_1 - x_1)$$

$$= 130 + \frac{220 - 130}{5 - 1}(X_1 - 1)$$

(5)
$$Y_{X_1} = 107.5 + 22.5X_1$$

which shows the regression of Y on X_1 gross of X_2.

(ii)　Find the regression of $(Y - Y_{X_1})$ on X_2

The deviations $Y - Y_{X_1}$ may be obtained from the graph or may be calculated from equation (5). In our present illustration we have calculated the deviations $d_1 = Y - Y_{X_1}$, as shown in Table 22.8, column 5. In Fig. 22.3 we have plotted these deviations d_1 against the corresponding values of X_2 and have fitted a freehand regression line. As is seen, we have selected the two points (1, −8) and (5, 8) for simplicity and have

TABLE 22.8.

	(1) Year	(2) Y	(3) X_1	(4) X_2	(5) Y_{X_1}	(6) d_1	(7) Y_{X_2}	(8) Y_c	(9) $Y - Y_c$	Y/Y_c
	1	130	1	2	130.0	0	-4	126	4	103%
	2	155	2	3	152.5	2.5	0	152.5	2.5	102
	3	165	3	1	175.0	-10.0	-8	167	-2.0	99
	4	205	4	5	197.5	7.5	8	205.5	-0.5	99
	5	220	5	4	220.0	0	4	224	-4.0	98
		875	15			0	0			
		175	3							

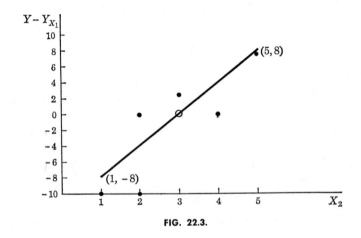

FIG. 22.3.

let the line approximately pass through the point $(\bar{X}_2 = 3, 0)$. Hence, the regression function is

$$Y_{X_2} = y_1 + \frac{y_2 - y_1}{x_2 - x_1}(X_2 - x_1)$$

$$= -8 + \frac{8 + 8}{5 - 1}(X_2 - 1)$$

(6) $$Y_{X_2} = -12 + 4X_2$$

which shows the relationship between Y (sales) and X_2 (newspaper) net of X_1 (radio). The values of Y_{X_2} are given in column 6 of Table 22.8.

(iii) Combine equations (5) and (6)

When the two equations (5) and (6) are combined, we find

$$Y_c = (107.5 - 12) + 22.5X_1 + 4X_2$$

(7) $$Y_c = 95.5 + 22.5X_1 + 4X_2$$

which shows the regression of Y_c (average sales) on X_1 (radio) and X_2 (newspaper). The values of Y_c are given in column 7.

Column 8 shows the deviations of the observations Y from Y_c and column 9 shows the ratio of Y to Y_c, which may be considered as a rough measure of the variability of Y around Y_c.

(iv)   Find the regression of $(Y - Y_{X_2})$ on X_1

Equation (5) was

$$(5) \qquad\qquad Y_{x_1} = 107.5 + 22.5X_1$$

and showed the regression of Y on X_1 gross of X_2. Hence, when equations (5) and (6) are combined to find equation (7), the effect of X_2 is entered in two ways: the first in the coefficient of X_1 and the second in the coefficient of X_2. To avoid this double counting, we may find the regression of Y on X_1 net of X_2 and combine this with equation (6). To find the regression of Y on X_1 net of X_2, we may calculate the regression of $(Y - Y_{X_2})$ on X_1. The values of Y_{X_2} and $(Y - Y_{X_2})$ are given in columns 4 and 5 of Table 22.9. These deviations $(Y - Y_{X_2})$ are graphed against X_1, as shown in Fig. 22.4.

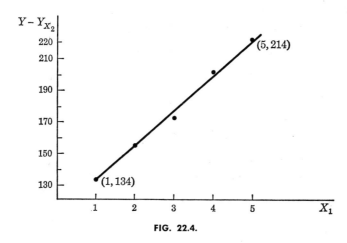

FIG. 22.4.

TABLE 22.9.

(1) Y	(2) X_1	(3) X_2	(4) Y_{X_2}	(5) $Y - Y_{X_2}$	(6) Y_c
130	1	2	−4	134	130
155	2	3	0	155	154
165	3	1	−8	173	166
205	4	5	8	197	202
220	5	4	4	216	218

The freehand regression line fitted to this scatter diagram shows the regression of Y (sales) on X_1 (radio) net of X_2 and has been fitted through the points $(1, 134)$ and $(5, 214)$ for simplicity. The calculated regression line is

$$Y_{X_1}{}^* = y_1 + \frac{y_2 - y_1}{x_2 - x_1}(X_1 - x_1)$$

$$= 134 + \frac{214 - 134}{5 - 1}(X_1 - 1)$$

(8) $$Y_{X_1}{}^* = 114 + 20X_1$$

(v) Combine equations (6) and (8)

The final step is to combine equations (6) and (8) as follows:

(8) $$Y_{X_1}{}^* = 114 + 20X_1$$

(6) $$Y_{X_2} = -12 + 4X_2$$

(9) $$Y_c = 102 + 20X_1 + 4X_2$$

The values of Y_c calculated from equation (9) are given in column 6 of Table 22.9.

The regression function obtained mathematically is

(10) $$Y_c = 103 + 20X_1 + 5X_2$$

and, as is seen, the regression function (9) that was obtained graphically is quite accurate.

22.11. Multiplicative Forms of Regression Functions

Two multiplicative forms of regression functions, which are used frequently in business and economics, are

(1) $$Y = ab^X$$

(2) $$Y = aX_1^{b_1}X_2^{b_2}$$

The logarithms of the functions are

(3) $$\log Y = \log a + X \log b$$

(4) $$\log Y = \log a + b_1 \log X_1 + b_2 \log X_2$$

and become linear functions, and hence the least squares procedures may be applied to find the coefficients.

Equation (1) is sometimes called a growth equation and is used to explain growth phenomena. For example, it has appeared in Chapter 3 as the compound interest formula

(5) $$P_n = P_0(1 + r)^n$$

where P_0 was the initial capital, r the rate of interest, n the number of years, and P_n the capital after n years. If we let $P_n = Y$, $P_0 = a$, $1 + r = b$, and $n = x$, equation (5) becomes equal to equation (1).

Equation (2) is used frequently in economics as demand functions. For example,

(6) $$Y = 0.00009058 X_1^{1.089} X_2^{0.439}$$

is a demand function of automobiles, where Y is the total private passenger car registration in thousands; X_1 is the number of households in millions; and X_2 is disposable personal income in billions of 1939 dollars. It was prepared by the U.S. Department of Commerce and published in the *Survey of Current Business*, April, 1952.

Another illustration is

(7) $$P = aL^a C^{1-a}$$
$$= 1.01 L^{0.75} C^{0.25}$$

which is a Cobb-Douglas production function, where P is production; L is labor; and C is capital.

An advantage of equations such as (2) is that the exponents are the elasticities. For example, in equation (6), the exponent 1.089 is the elasticity of Y with respect to X_1. That is, for a 1 percent change of X_1, there is a 1.089 percent change of Y.

In this section we shall consider regression functions similar to equation (2); equations similar to (1) will be considered in Chapter 23.

Let us set $\log Y = Y_L$, $\log X_1 = X_{1L}$, $\log X_2 = X_{2L}$, $\log a = a_L$. Then (4) becomes

(8) $$Y_L = a_L + b_1 X_{1L} + b_2 X_{2L}$$

and the procedure is to apply the method of least squares and solve for the coefficients a, b_1, and b_2. But, as is seen, the computations involve logarithms, and the calculation process is more cumbersome than in the ordinary case.

To avoid these calculations, the graphic process explained in Section 22.9 may be used. Let us illustrate with the data that were used in

Section 22.9. As in Section 22.10, we shall first find the regression of Y (sales) on X_1 (radio) gross of X_2 (newspaper). This is shown as

(9) $$Y = aX_1{}^{b_1}$$

which, in logarithms, is

(10) $$\log Y = \log a + b_1 \log X_1$$

When using double logarithmic paper, we merely plot the values of Y and X_1, fit a freehand straight line to these points, and we have the graphic expression of (10).

Using the data of Table 22.9, which is the same as that of Section 22.10, the values of Y and X_1 have been plotted as a scatter diagram in Fig. 22.5. A freehand straight line is fitted to these points and the slope

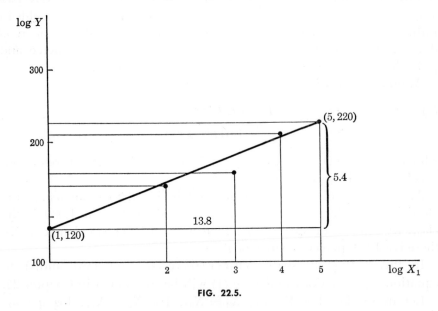

FIG. 22.5.

of this line b_1 is found. In our present case, the line has been drawn through the points (1, 120) and (5, 120) for simplicity. Then this line may be shown algebraically as

$$\log Y_{x_1} = \log y_1 + \frac{\log y_2 - \log y_1}{\log x_2 - \log x_1}(\log X_1 - \log x_1)$$

$$= \log 120 + \frac{\log 220 - \log 120}{\log 5 - \log 1}(\log X_1 - \log 1)$$

$$= \log 120 + 0.3755 \log X_1$$

(11) $$Y_{x_1} = 120 X_1{}^{0.3755}$$

The $X_1^{0.3755}$ may be considered as the average amount of variation in Y due to X_1. Hence, the difference between Y_{X_1} and $X_1^{0.3755}$ shows the residual of Y after the effect of X has been removed. Since we are dealing with logarithms, the difference between Y and $X_1^{0.3755}$ is obtained by dividing Y by $X_1^{0.3755}$. To find $X_1^{0.3755}$ of column 4, Table 22.10, set

$$\log M = \log X_1^{0.3755} = 0.3755 \log X_1$$

For $X_1 = 1$,

$$\log M = 0.3755 \times \log 1 = 0$$

and hence $M = 1$. For $X_1 = 2$,

$$\log M = 0.3755 \log 2 = (0.3755)(0.301) = 0.1130$$

Therefore

$$M = 1.197$$

and similarly for the other values of X_1.

The process of removing the effect of X_1 from Y is shown in column 5 and is merely a process of dividing the values of Y in column 1 by the values of $X_1^{0.3755}$ in column 4. Let us denote this process by

$$(12) \qquad Y_{X_1} = \frac{Y}{X^{0.3755}}$$

The residuals of Y_{X_1} are the Y's with the effect of X_1 (radio) removed. The next step is to find the regression of these Y_{X_1}'s on X_2 (newspaper). We first plot a scatter diagram of the values of Y_{X_1} and X_2, as shown in Fig. 22.6. The first point is (2, 130); the second point is (3, 129.5); and so forth. Then a freehand regression line is fitted to these points (Fig. 22.6).

The regression line has been drawn through the two points (1, 115) and (5, 130) for simplicity, and it may be shown as

$$\log Y_{X_2} = \log y_1 + \frac{\log y_2 - \log y_1}{\log x_2 - \log x_1} (\log X_2 - \log x_1)$$

$$= \log 115 + \frac{\log 130 - \log 115}{\log 5 - \log 1} (\log X_2 - \log 1)$$

$$= \log 115 + 0.0882 \log X_1$$

$$(13) \qquad Y_{X_2} = 115 X_2^{0.0882}$$

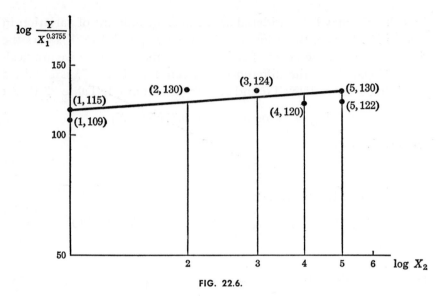

FIG. 22.6.

This equation may be considered as showing the average effect of X_2 on Y. The values of $X_2^{0.0882}$ are shown in column 6.

The equation (11), which showed the regression of Y on X_1, was gross of X_2. Hence, to find the regression of Y on X_1 net of X_2, we shall remove the effect of X_2 by using equation (13). This is performed by dividing Y by $X_2^{0.0882}$:

$$\frac{Y}{X_2^{0.0882}}$$

and this process is shown by column 7. That is, column 7 shows the values of Y net of the effect of X_2.

By finding the regression of the values of column 7 on X_1, we shall find the regression of Y on X_1 net of X_2. For this, we plot a scatter diagram of the values of columns 7 and 2 and fit a freehand regression line, as shown in Fig. 22.7. The regression line has been drawn through the points (1, 122) and (5, 190) and may be shown by

$$\log Y_{x_1}{}^* = \log 122 + \frac{\log 190 - \log 122}{\log 5 - \log 1} (\log X_1 - \log x_1)$$

$$= \log 122 + 0.275 \log X_1$$

Therefore

(14) $$Y_{x_1}{}^* = 122 X_1^{0.275}$$

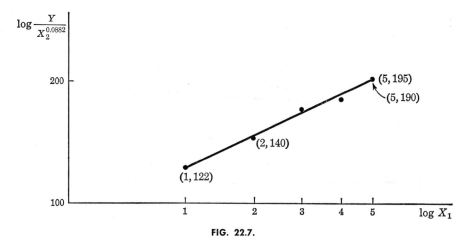

FIG. 22.7.

The values of $X_1^{0.275}$ are shown in column 8.

We may at this point combine equations (13) and (14) and find the regression of Y on X_1 and X_2. However, in obtaining equation (13) which shows the regression of Y on X_2, we used the residuals of Y_{X_1} of equation (12), which was not completely free of the effects of X_2. Hence, to find the regression of Y on X_1 net of X_2, we shall go one step farther and first remove the effect of X_1 (radio) from Y (sales) by

$$\frac{Y}{X_1^{0.275}}$$

as shown in column 9; second, we shall find the regression of $Y/X_1^{0.275}$ on X_2, which will give us the regression of Y on X_2 net of X_1.

The scatter diagram of $Y/X_1^{0.275}$ and X_2 and the freehand regression line is shown in Fig. 22.8. The regression line has been fitted through the points (1, 122) and (5, 140), and hence may be shown by

$$\log Y_{X_2}{}^* = \log y_1 + \frac{\log y_2 - \log y_1}{\log x_2 - \log x_1}(\log X_2 - \log x_1)$$

$$= \log 122 + \frac{\log 140 - \log 122}{\log 5 - \log 1}(\log X_2 - \log 1)$$

$$= \log 122 + 0.0854 \log X_1$$

(15) $$Y_{X_2}{}^* = 122 X_2^{0.0854}$$

The values of $X_2^{0.0854}$ are given in column 10.

Since

$$Y^* = \frac{Y}{X_1^{0.275}}$$

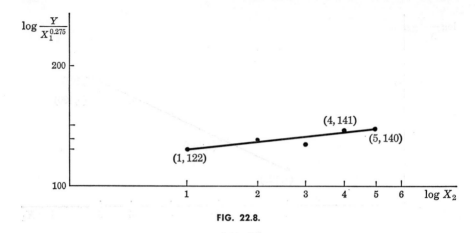

FIG. 22.8.

we may substitute this into (15) and find

(16) $Y_c = 122X_1^{0.275}X_2^{0.0854}$

which is the regression equation we seek. The values of Y_c are found in the table by multiplying the columns: $122 \times$ col. 8 $\times$ col. 10.

TABLE 22.10.

(1)	(2)	(3)	(4)	(5) $\dfrac{Y}{X_1^{0.3755}}$	(6)	(7) $\dfrac{Y}{X_2^{0.0882}}$	(8)	(9) $\dfrac{Y}{X_1^{0.275}}$	(10)	(11)
Y	X_1	X_2	$X_1^{0.3755}$		$X_2^{0.0882}$		$X_1^{0.275}$		$X_2^{0.0854}$	Y_c
130	1	2	1	130	1.063	122.3	1	130	1.06	130
155	2	3	1.197	129.5	1.102	149.7	1.21	128	1.098	163
165	3	1	1.51	109.3	1	165	1.353	122	1	166
205	4	5	1.68	122.0	1.153	177.8	1.464	140	1.147	206
220	5	4	1.83	120.2	1.13	194.7	1.557	141	1.126	216

$$\log Y_{X_1} = \log 130 + 0.3755 \log X_1$$
$$Y_{X_1} = 130 \, X_1^{0.3755}$$
$$Y_{X_2} = 115 \, X_2^{0.0882}$$
$$Y_{X_1}^* = 122 \, X_1^{0.275}$$

22.12. Appendix: Matrix Algebra

One of the obstacles in developing the discussion of multiple linear regression is the cumbersome algebra that accompanies systems of simultaneous equations. The best way to handle this problem is to learn a few elementary rules of matrix algebra. This roundabout process will, in the long run, prove to be productive.

(i) Vector

An ordered set of numbers is called a vector. For example:

$$V_1 = [1, 2]$$
$$V_2 = [3, 4]$$

These vectors are called *row vectors*. When the set of numbers are written in column form, they are called *column vectors*.

$$V'_1 = \begin{bmatrix} 1 \\ 2 \end{bmatrix} \quad V'_2 = \begin{bmatrix} 3 \\ 4 \end{bmatrix}$$

The column vectors are designated by a *prime*.

A vector with two numbers in it, as in the example, is called a *vector of order 2*. A vector with n numbers in it is called a vector of order n.

Vectors can be interpreted geometrically. For example, a vector of order 2, such as $V_1 = [1, 2]$, indicates a point $(1, 2)$ in a 2-dimensional space. A vector such as $V_3 = [1, 2, 4]$ indicates a point $(1, 2, 4)$ in 3-dimensional space. A row vector V_1 and its transpose V'_1 which is a column vector, indicate the same point.

(ii) Operations with vectors

Three operations, the sum, the differences, and the multiplication of vectors will be considered. Let $V_1 = [1, 2]$, $V_2 = [3, 4]$.

1. The addition of vectors:

$$V_1 + V_2 = [1, 2] + [3, 4]$$
$$= [1 + 3, 2 + 4] = [4, 6]$$
$$V'_1 + V'_2 = \begin{bmatrix} 1 \\ 2 \end{bmatrix} + \begin{bmatrix} 3 \\ 4 \end{bmatrix} = \begin{bmatrix} 1+3 \\ 2+4 \end{bmatrix} = \begin{bmatrix} 4 \\ 6 \end{bmatrix}$$

2. The difference of vectors:

$$V_1 - V_2 = [1, 2] - [3, 4]$$
$$= [1 - 3, 2 - 4] = [-2, -2]$$
$$V'_1 - V'_2 = \begin{bmatrix} 1 \\ 2 \end{bmatrix} - \begin{bmatrix} 3 \\ 4 \end{bmatrix} = \begin{bmatrix} -2 \\ -2 \end{bmatrix}$$

3. The multiplication of two vectors: When vectors V_1 and V_2 are to be multiplied, the rule is to multiply a row vector by a column vector of the same order. For example

$$V_1 \cdot V'_2 = [1, 2] \begin{bmatrix} 3 \\ 4 \end{bmatrix} \begin{matrix} = 1 \times 3 + 2 \times 4 \\ = 3 + 8 = 11 \end{matrix}$$

Notice that $V_1 \cdot V_2'$ has become a number (scalar) and not a vector. In general,

$$V_1 \cdot V_2' = [a_1 \quad a_2 \quad a_3] \begin{bmatrix} b_1 \\ b_2 \\ b_3 \end{bmatrix} = a_1 b_1 + a_2 b_2 + a_3 b_3$$

This result is called the *inner product* of two vectors V_1 and V_2.

Problems. Given the following vectors, carry out the operations and find the answers.

$$V_1 = [1, 3] \qquad V_2 = [4, 2]$$
$$V_3 = [1, 5, 2] \qquad V_4 = [2, -1, 3]$$

1. $V_1 + V_2$ 5. $V_2 \cdot V_1'$
2. $V_1 - V_2$ 6. $V_3 \cdot V_4'$
3. $V_3 + V_4$ 7. $V_4 \cdot V_3'$
4. $V_1 \cdot V_2'$ 8. $V_3 \cdot V_3'$

(iii)   A matrix

A matrix is a rectangular array of numbers. For example,

$$A = \begin{bmatrix} 1 & 2 \\ 3 & 4 \end{bmatrix}$$

Each row or column of the matrix A may be considered as a vector. For example, if the rows are considered vectors V_1 and V_2, the matrix A may be shown as

$$A = \begin{bmatrix} V_1 \\ V_2 \end{bmatrix}$$

The operations, sum difference, and multiplication of matrices are defined as follows:

1.   The sum of matrices:

$$A_1 + A_2 = \begin{bmatrix} 1 & 2 \\ 3 & 4 \end{bmatrix} + \begin{bmatrix} 5 & 6 \\ 7 & 8 \end{bmatrix}$$
$$= \begin{bmatrix} 1+5 & 2+6 \\ 3+7 & 4+8 \end{bmatrix} = \begin{bmatrix} 6 & 8 \\ 10 & 12 \end{bmatrix}$$

2.   The difference of matrices:

$$A_1 - A_2 = \begin{bmatrix} 1 & 2 \\ 3 & 4 \end{bmatrix} - \begin{bmatrix} 5 & 6 \\ 7 & 8 \end{bmatrix}$$
$$= \begin{bmatrix} 1-5 & 2-6 \\ 3-7 & 4-8 \end{bmatrix} = \begin{bmatrix} -4 & -4 \\ -4 & -4 \end{bmatrix}$$

3. The multiplication of matrices: The multiplication of matrices is different from the ordinary rules of multiplication and requires special attention. It is necessary to distinguish between premultiplication and postmultiplication. Let,

$$A = \begin{bmatrix} a_{11} & a_{12} \\ a_{21} & a_{22} \end{bmatrix}, \qquad B = \begin{bmatrix} b_{11} & b_{12} \\ b_{21} & b_{22} \end{bmatrix}$$

Premultiply B *by* A:

$$A \cdot B = \begin{bmatrix} a_{11} & a_{12} \\ a_{21} & a_{22} \end{bmatrix} \begin{bmatrix} b_{11} & b_{12} \\ b_{21} & b_{22} \end{bmatrix}$$
$$= \begin{bmatrix} a_{11}b_{11} + a_{12}b_{21} & a_{11}b_{12} + a_{12}b_{22} \\ a_{21}b_{11} + a_{22}b_{21} & a_{21}b_{12} + a_{22}b_{22} \end{bmatrix}$$

Note how the rows of matrix A are multiplied by the columns of matrix B. The results, which are the inner products, are placed in the appropriate places of the resulting matrix.

Postmultiply B *by* A:

$$B \cdot A = \begin{bmatrix} b_{11} & b_{12} \\ b_{21} & b_{22} \end{bmatrix} \begin{bmatrix} a_{11} & a_{12} \\ a_{21} & a_{22} \end{bmatrix}$$
$$= \begin{bmatrix} b_{11}a_{11} + b_{12}a_{21} & b_{11}a_{12} + b_{12}a_{22} \\ b_{21}a_{11} + b_{22}a_{21} & b_{21}a_{12} + b_{22}a_{22} \end{bmatrix}$$

Note that the rows of B are multiplied by the columns of A and the inner products are formed. Also note that $AB \neq BA$.

Two matrices A and B can be multiplied as long as the number of columns of the first matrix is equal to the number of rows of the second matrix. For example, let A be a $p \times n$ matrix and B be a $n \times q$ matrix. Then

$$A \cdot B \longrightarrow (p \times n)(n \times q) \longrightarrow (p \times q)$$

That is, $A \cdot B$ will be a $p \times q$ matrix. As an example, let

$$A = \begin{bmatrix} 1 & 2 \\ 3 & 4 \end{bmatrix}, \qquad B = \begin{bmatrix} 1 & 2 & 3 \\ 3 & 2 & 1 \end{bmatrix}$$

Then $A \cdot B$ will be a 2×3 matrix.

$$A \cdot B = \begin{bmatrix} 1 & 2 \\ 3 & 4 \end{bmatrix} \begin{bmatrix} 1 & 2 & 3 \\ 3 & 2 & 1 \end{bmatrix}$$
$$= \begin{bmatrix} 1+6 & 2+4 & 3+2 \\ 3+12 & 6+8 & 9+4 \end{bmatrix} = \begin{bmatrix} 7 & 6 & 5 \\ 15 & 14 & 13 \end{bmatrix}$$

4. Multiplying a matrix by a number (scalar): When a matrix A is pre- or post-multiplied by a scalar k, each element in the matrix is

multiplied by k. For example,

$$k \begin{bmatrix} a_{11} & a_{12} \\ a_{21} & a_{22} \end{bmatrix} = \begin{bmatrix} a_{11} & a_{12} \\ a_{21} & a_{22} \end{bmatrix} k = \begin{bmatrix} ka_{11} & ka_{12} \\ ka_{21} & ka_{22} \end{bmatrix}$$

5.   The transpose of a matrix: The transpose of a matrix A is obtained by interchanging the rows and columns of A. For example,

$$A = \begin{bmatrix} 1 & 2 & 3 \\ 4 & 5 & 6 \end{bmatrix} \qquad A^T = \begin{bmatrix} 1 & 4 \\ 2 & 5 \\ 3 & 6 \end{bmatrix}$$

The transpose of A is designated by A^T or A'.

Problems.   Given the following matrices, carry out the operations and find the answers.

$$A = \begin{bmatrix} 1 & 3 \\ 2 & 2 \end{bmatrix} \qquad B = \begin{bmatrix} 2 & 1 \\ -1 & 3 \end{bmatrix}$$

$$C = \begin{bmatrix} 3 & 0 & 1 \\ 4 & -1 & 2 \end{bmatrix} \qquad D = \begin{bmatrix} -1 & 2 & 1 \\ 3 & 1 & 2 \end{bmatrix}$$

1. $A + B$
2. $B - A$
3. AB
4. BA
5. AC
6. C'
7. $C'A$
8. $C + D$
9. $C \cdot D'$
10. $C' \cdot D$
11. $A \cdot C \cdot D'$
12. $C \cdot D' \cdot B$

(iv)   Determinants

A determinant is a number associated with a square matrix. For example, let

$$A = \begin{bmatrix} 1 & 2 \\ 2 & 6 \end{bmatrix}$$

Then the determinant of the matrix A is

$$|A| = \begin{vmatrix} 1 & 2 \\ 2 & 6 \end{vmatrix} = 1 \times 6 - 2 \times 2 = 6 - 4 = 2$$

The determinant is shown by two vertical lines. For the 2×2 matrix, we have a 2×2 determinant, and it was evaluated by cross-multiplying the numbers. But what if the matrix A is 3×3? For example, consider

$$A = \begin{bmatrix} 1 & 2 & 3 \\ 4 & 5 & 6 \\ 7 & 8 & 9 \end{bmatrix}$$

The determinant is

$$|A| = \begin{vmatrix} 1 & 2 & 3 \\ 4 & 5 & 6 \\ 7 & 8 & 9 \end{vmatrix}$$

Since we know how to evaluate a 2×2 determinant, if this 3×3 determinant A could be reduced to a combination of 2×2 determinants this would enable us to evaluate it. Fortunately, this can be done by use of signed minors. So let us discuss what is meant by signed minors.

1.   Minors and signed minors: Consider the 3×3 determinant A.

$$|A| = \begin{vmatrix} a_{11} & a_{12} & a_{13} \\ a_{21} & a_{22} & a_{23} \\ a_{31} & a_{32} & a_{33} \end{vmatrix}$$

The *minor* A_{ij} is defined as the determinant obtained from $|A|$ by deleting the ith row and jth column. For example,

$$A_{11} = \begin{vmatrix} a_{22} & a_{23} \\ a_{32} & a_{33} \end{vmatrix}$$

$$A_{32} = \begin{vmatrix} a_{11} & a_{13} \\ a_{21} & a_{23} \end{vmatrix}$$

A *signed minor* (which is also called a *cofactor*) is a minor with a sign attached to it according to the following rule:

$$\text{Signed minor} = (-1)^{i+j} A_{ij}$$

For example, the signed minors A_{11}, A_{32} are:

$$(-1)^{1+1}A_{11} = (-1)^{1+1} \begin{vmatrix} a_{22} & a_{23} \\ a_{32} & a_{33} \end{vmatrix} = \begin{vmatrix} a_{22} & a_{23} \\ a_{32} & a_{33} \end{vmatrix}$$

$$(-1)^{3+2}A_{32} = (-1)^{3+2} \begin{vmatrix} a_{11} & a_{13} \\ a_{21} & a_{23} \end{vmatrix} = - \begin{vmatrix} a_{11} & a_{13} \\ a_{21} & a_{23} \end{vmatrix}$$

2.   Expansion of a determinant by signed minors: A 3×3 determinant can be expanded by signed minors according to the following rule:

$$|A| = \begin{vmatrix} a_{11} & a_{12} & a_{13} \\ a_{21} & a_{22} & a_{23} \\ a_{31} & a_{32} & a_{33} \end{vmatrix}$$

$$= a_{11}(-1)^{1+1}A_{11} + a_{12}(-1)^{1+2}A_{12} + a_{13}(-1)^{1+3}A_{13}$$

$$= a_{11}(-1)^{1+1}A_{11} + a_{21}(-1)^{2+1}A_{21} + a_{31}(-1)^{3+1}A_{31}$$

That is, the determinant A has been expanded by its first row and also by its first column. Each element in the first row is multiplied by the signed minors associated with that element. When expanded by a column, each element in the column is multiplied by the signed minor associated with that element. Since each of the signed minors are 2×2 determinants, they can be easily evaluated. Let us illustrate with an example:

$$|A| = \begin{vmatrix} 1 & 2 & 3 \\ 4 & 3 & 6 \\ 7 & 8 & 9 \end{vmatrix}$$

$$= a_{11}(-1)^{1+1}A_{11} + a_{12}(-1)^{1+2}A_{12} + a_{13}(-1)^{1+3}A_{13}$$

$$= 1 \cdot (-1)^{1+1}\begin{vmatrix} 3 & 6 \\ 8 & 9 \end{vmatrix} + 2 \cdot (-1)^{1+2}\begin{vmatrix} 4 & 6 \\ 7 & 9 \end{vmatrix} + 3(-1)^{1+3}\begin{vmatrix} 4 & 3 \\ 7 & 8 \end{vmatrix}$$

$$= (27 - 48) - 2(36 - 42) + 3(32 - 21) = 24$$

Higher-order determinants are evaluated by repeating this process of expansion. For example, a 4×4 determinant is expanded by its 3×3 signed minors. Each of these 3×3 signed minors are in turn expanded by 2×2 signed minors.

When a determinant is expanded by signed minors of a different row, the value of the determinant is zero. The proof of this is beyond the scope of this book, but let us illustrate this with examples. Consider again the preceding matrix A. Let us expand it, using the elements of the first row, but with the signed minors associated with the elements of the second row. Then

$$a_{11}(-1)^{2+1}A_{21} + a_{12}(-1)^{2+2}A_{22} + a_{13}(-1)^{2+3}A_{23}$$

$$= 1(-1)^{3}\begin{vmatrix} 2 & 3 \\ 8 & 9 \end{vmatrix} + 2(-1)^{4}\begin{vmatrix} 1 & 3 \\ 7 & 9 \end{vmatrix} + 3(-1)^{5}\begin{vmatrix} 1 & 2 \\ 7 & 8 \end{vmatrix}$$

$$= -(18 - 24) + 2(9 - 21) - 3(8 - 14) = 0$$

Problems.
1. Evaluate the following determinant by expanding it according to its second row.

$$|A| = \begin{vmatrix} 1 & 2 & 3 \\ 4 & 3 & 6 \\ 7 & 8 & 9 \end{vmatrix}$$

2. Evaluate the determinant in problem 1 by its third column.
3. Evaluate the determinant by expanding by the elements of the second

row, but using the signed minors associated with the first row; check that
the result is zero.
4.   Evaluate the determinant by expanding by the elements of the second
column, but using the signed minors associated with the first column.

(v)   The inverse of a matrix

In algebra, the inverse of a number a is a^{-1}, and we know that
$a \times a^{-1} = 1$. A similar relationship between a matrix A and its inverse, which we denote by A^{-1}, can be established. For this, we first
define a unit matrix.

A unit matrix, which we denote by I, is a matrix with ones in the
main diagonal and zero elsewhere. For example, a 3×3 unit matrix is

$$I = \begin{bmatrix} 1 & 0 & 0 \\ 0 & 1 & 0 \\ 0 & 0 & 1 \end{bmatrix}$$

The characteristic of a unit matrix is that $AI = A$ or $IA = A$. For
example,

$$\begin{bmatrix} 1 & 2 & 3 \\ 4 & 3 & 6 \\ 7 & 8 & 9 \end{bmatrix} \cdot \begin{bmatrix} 1 & 0 & 0 \\ 0 & 1 & 0 \\ 0 & 0 & 1 \end{bmatrix} = \begin{bmatrix} 1 & 2 & 3 \\ 4 & 3 & 6 \\ 7 & 8 & 9 \end{bmatrix}$$

The inverse matrix of A is a matrix B such that

$$AB = I$$

This B is denoted by A^{-1}. Thus, we write

$$AA^{-1} = I$$

The problem now is to find the matrix A^{-1}. The derivation is beyond
the scope of this book. We shall present only the result. Let

$$A = \begin{bmatrix} a_{11} & a_{12} & a_{13} \\ a_{21} & a_{22} & a_{23} \\ a_{31} & a_{32} & a_{33} \end{bmatrix}$$

Then the inverse A^{-1} is as follows:

$$A^{-1} = \frac{1}{\Delta} \begin{bmatrix} A_{11}^0 & A_{21}^0 & A_{31}^0 \\ A_{12}^0 & A_{22}^0 & A_{32}^0 \\ A_{13}^0 & A_{23}^0 & A_{33}^0 \end{bmatrix}$$

where $\Delta = |A|$, and A_{ij}^0 are the signed minors.

Note two things: first, that the determinant $\Delta = |A|$ must not be
zero; second, that the signed minors are in transposed order.

Let us check our result.

$$AA^{-1} = \begin{bmatrix} a_{11} & a_{12} & a_{13} \\ a_{21} & a_{22} & a_{23} \\ a_{31} & a_{32} & a_{33} \end{bmatrix} \cdot \frac{1}{\Delta} \begin{bmatrix} A_{11}^{0} & A_{21}^{0} & A_{31}^{0} \\ A_{12}^{0} & A_{22}^{0} & A_{32}^{0} \\ A_{13}^{0} & A_{23}^{0} & A_{33}^{0} \end{bmatrix}$$

$$= \begin{bmatrix} (a_{11}A_{11}^{0} + a_{12}A_{12}^{0} & (a_{11}A_{21}^{0} + a_{12}A_{22}^{0} & (a_{11}A_{31}^{0} + a_{12}A_{32}^{0} \\ \quad + a_{13}A_{13}^{0}) & \quad + a_{13}A_{23}^{0}) & \quad + a_{13}A_{33}^{0}) \\ (a_{21}A_{11}^{0} + a_{22}A_{12}^{0} & (a_{21}A_{21}^{0} + a_{22}A_{22}^{0} & (a_{21}A_{31}^{0} + a_{22}A_{32}^{0} \\ \quad + a_{23}A_{13}^{0}) & \quad + a_{23}A_{23}^{0}) & \quad + a_{23}A_{33}^{0}) \\ (a_{31}A_{11}^{0} + a_{32}A_{12}^{0} & (a_{31}A_{21}^{0} + a_{32}A_{22}^{0} & (a_{31}A_{31}^{0} + a_{32}A_{32}^{0} \\ \quad + a_{33}A_{13}^{0}) & \quad + a_{33}^{0}A_{23}^{0}) & \quad + a_{33}A_{33}^{0}) \end{bmatrix}$$

$$= \frac{1}{\Delta} \begin{bmatrix} \Delta & 0 & 0 \\ 0 & \Delta & 0 \\ 0 & 0 & \Delta \end{bmatrix} = \begin{bmatrix} 1 & 0 & 0 \\ 0 & 1 & 0 \\ 0 & 0 & 1 \end{bmatrix} = I$$

Example

$$|A| = \begin{vmatrix} 1 & 2 & 3 \\ 4 & 3 & 6 \\ 7 & 8 & 9 \end{vmatrix} = 24$$

$$A_{11}^{0} = (-1)^{1+1} \begin{vmatrix} 3 & 6 \\ 8 & 9 \end{vmatrix} = 27 - 48 = -21$$

$$A_{12}^{0} = (-1)^{1+2} \begin{vmatrix} 4 & 6 \\ 7 & 9 \end{vmatrix} = -(36 - 42) = 6$$

In similar fashion we find:

$$A_{13}^{0} = 11, \quad A_{21}^{0} = 6, \quad A_{22}^{0} = -12, \quad A_{23}^{0} = 6$$

$$A_{31}^{0} = 3, \quad A_{32}^{0} = 6, \quad A_{33}^{0} = -5$$

Thus, the inverse matrix A^{-1} is

$$A^{-1} = \frac{1}{24} \begin{bmatrix} -21 & 6 & 3 \\ 6 & -12 & 6 \\ 11 & 6 & -5 \end{bmatrix}$$

Check

$$AA^{-1} = \frac{1}{24} \begin{bmatrix} 1 & 2 & 3 \\ 4 & 3 & 6 \\ 7 & 8 & 9 \end{bmatrix} \begin{bmatrix} -21 & 6 & 3 \\ 6 & -12 & 6 \\ 11 & 6 & -5 \end{bmatrix}$$

$$= \frac{1}{24} \begin{bmatrix} 24 & 0 & 0 \\ 0 & 24 & 0 \\ 0 & 0 & 24 \end{bmatrix} = \begin{bmatrix} 1 & 0 & 0 \\ 0 & 1 & 0 \\ 0 & 0 & 1 \end{bmatrix}$$

Problems.   Given the following matrix, find the inverse. Check your results.

1. $A = \begin{bmatrix} 1 & 2 \\ 3 & -1 \end{bmatrix}$

2. $A = \begin{bmatrix} 1 & 2 & 0 \\ 3 & 1 & 1 \\ 4 & 2 & 1 \end{bmatrix}$

(vi) Solving simultaneous equations

Our object in discussing matrices was to use them in solving simultaneous equations. Let us illustrate this procedure with an example. Consider the following simultaneous equations:

$$\begin{cases} 2x + y = 4 \\ x - 2y = -3 \end{cases}$$

This can be shown in matrix form as follows:

$$\begin{bmatrix} 2 & 1 \\ 1 & -2 \end{bmatrix} \begin{bmatrix} x \\ y \end{bmatrix} = \begin{bmatrix} 4 \\ -3 \end{bmatrix}$$

To find x and y, both sides of the equation are premultiplied by the inverse of the matrix of coefficients. We find

$$\begin{bmatrix} x \\ y \end{bmatrix} = \begin{bmatrix} 2 & 1 \\ 1 & -2 \end{bmatrix}^{-1} \begin{bmatrix} 4 \\ -3 \end{bmatrix}$$

After necessary calculations, we find

$$\begin{bmatrix} x \\ y \end{bmatrix} = \frac{1}{-5} \begin{bmatrix} -2 & -1 \\ -1 & 2 \end{bmatrix} \begin{bmatrix} 4 \\ -3 \end{bmatrix} = \frac{1}{-5} \begin{bmatrix} -5 \\ -10 \end{bmatrix}$$

$$\begin{bmatrix} x \\ y \end{bmatrix} = \begin{bmatrix} 1 \\ 2 \end{bmatrix}$$

Therefore, $x = 1$, $y = 2$.

This process may be generalized as follows:

$$\begin{cases} a_{11}x_1 + a_{12}x_2 + a_{13}x_3 = b_1 \\ a_{21}x_1 + a_{22}x_2 + a_{23}x_3 = b_2 \\ a_{31}x_1 + a_{32}x_2 + a_{33}x_3 = b_3 \end{cases}$$

$$\begin{bmatrix} a_{11} & a_{12} & a_{13} \\ a_{21} & a_{22} & a_{23} \\ a_{31} & a_{32} & a_{33} \end{bmatrix} \begin{bmatrix} x_1 \\ x_2 \\ x_3 \end{bmatrix} = \begin{bmatrix} b_1 \\ b_2 \\ b_3 \end{bmatrix}$$

Or, using matrix notation,

$$AX = B$$

If $|A| \neq 0$, then

$$X = A^{-1}B$$

Let

$$A^{-1} = \begin{bmatrix} c_{11} & c_{12} & c_{13} \\ c_{21} & c_{22} & c_{23} \\ c_{31} & c_{32} & c_{33} \end{bmatrix}$$

Then, the solution for x_1, x_2, x_3, will be

$$\begin{bmatrix} x_1 \\ x_2 \\ x_3 \end{bmatrix} = \begin{bmatrix} c_{11} & c_{12} & c_{13} \\ c_{21} & c_{22} & c_{23} \\ c_{31} & c_{32} & c_{33} \end{bmatrix} \begin{bmatrix} b_1 \\ b_2 \\ b_3 \end{bmatrix}$$

$$\begin{bmatrix} x_1 \\ x_2 \\ x_3 \end{bmatrix} = \begin{bmatrix} c_{11}b_1 + c_{12}b_2 + c_{13}b_3 \\ c_{21}b_1 + c_{22}b_2 + c_{23}b_3 \\ c_{31}b_1 + c_{32}b_2 + c_{33}b_3 \end{bmatrix}$$

As can be seen, the problem of solving systems of simultaneous equations becomes a problem of finding the inverse of the matrix of the coefficients. When the matrix is large, this becomes a tedious task. Various systematic schemes have been devised to cope with this problem. We have studied one of these schemes, the Doolittle method, in Section 22.7.

Problems. Solve the following systems of simultaneous equations by first finding the inverse of the matrix of coefficients.

1. $\begin{cases} x + 3y = 5 \\ 2x - y = 3 \end{cases}$

2. $\begin{cases} x - y = 1 \\ 3x + 2y = -7 \end{cases}$

3. $\begin{cases} 2x + y - z = 1 \\ x - 2y + z = 0 \\ x - y + 3z = 8 \end{cases}$

TIME SERIES (II)

23

In Chapters 11 to 13, a time series was decomposed into four components: trend (T), seasonal (S), cyclical (C), and irregular (I) movements. It was also assumed that these components were additive:

$$O = T + S + C + I$$

where O indicates the original series. This additive assumption implies that the causal factors affecting the four components are independent of each other.

In this chapter, this scheme will be modified and the components of the time series will be the trend, an oscillatory movement about the trend, and an irregular or random component.

The oscillation about the trend, in turn, is subdivided into cyclical movements that are periodic and oscillatory movements that are non-periodic.

Following this scheme, we shall first discuss several methods of finding a trend line, then consider such topics as serial correlation, cyclical fluctuations, and irregular movements.

23.1. The Trend Line

In Chapter 12, the trend line was

$$Y_c = a + bX$$

where the Y_c were the estimated trend values and the X's were the years. However, a number of other forms of trend lines are also used in business and economics to represent trends, although not so frequently as the simple linear trend line. They are

1. A second-degree parabola
2. A logarithmic (exponential) curve
3. A modified exponential curve
4. A logistic curve
5. A Gompertz curve
6. The moving average

(i) Second-degree parabola

When the original time series is plotted on a graph, it may show that a parabola fits more adequately than does a straight line. The simplest parabola is that of a second degree:

$$(1) \qquad\qquad Y_c = a + bX + cX^2$$

The coefficients a, b, and c may be found by the method of least squares. The normal equations in this case are

$$(2) \qquad \begin{aligned} \Sigma\, Y &= na + b\, \Sigma\, X + c\, \Sigma\, X^2 \\ \Sigma\, XY &= a\, \Sigma\, X + b\, \Sigma\, X^2 + c\, \Sigma\, X^3 \\ \Sigma\, X^2 Y &= a\, \Sigma\, X^2 + b\, \Sigma\, X^3 + c\, \Sigma\, X^4 \end{aligned}$$

and we solve for the a, b, and c of these equations. By shifting the origin to the center of the series, we may let $\Sigma\, X = 0$. Then the normal equations simplify to

$$(3) \qquad \begin{aligned} \Sigma\, Y &= na + c\, \Sigma\, X^2 \\ \Sigma\, XY &= b\, \Sigma\, X^2 \\ \Sigma\, X^2 Y &= a\, \Sigma\, X^2 + c\, \Sigma\, X^4 \end{aligned}$$

A question as to whether a linear equation, second-degree parabola equation, or a higher-degree equation should be used may be determined by investigating the differences of the series. By differences we mean

$$(4) \qquad\qquad \Delta Y_i = Y_i - Y_{i-1}$$

which is a first difference. For the linear trend, the first difference is equal to the parameter b. This is shown in Table 23.1.

The second difference of a series is

(5) $$\Delta^2 Y_i = \Delta Y_i - \Delta Y_{i-1}$$

TABLE 23.1.

X	$Y_c = a + bX$	$\Delta Y_i = Y_i - Y_{i-1}$
0	a	
1	$a + b$	$(a + b) - a \qquad = b$
2	$a + 2b$	$(a + 2b) - (a + b) = b$
3	$a + 3b$	$(a + 3b) - (a + 2b) = b$
. . .	. . .	. . .

For the linear case

$$\Delta^2 Y_i = \Delta Y_i - \Delta Y_{i-1}$$
$$= b - b = 0$$

and is always zero. The first and second differences for a second-degree parabola are as shown in Table 23.2.

TABLE 23.2.

X	$Y_c = a + bX + cX^2$	ΔY_i	$\Delta^2 Y_i$
0	a		
1	$a + b + c$	$b + c$	
2	$a + 2b + 4c$	$b + 3c$	$2c$
3	$a + 3b + 9c$	$b + 5c$	$2c$
. . .	. . .	. . .	. . .

For the first differences we have algebraically,

$$\Delta Y_i = (a + bX_i + cX_i^2) - (a + bX_{i-1} + cX_{i-1}^2)$$
$$= b(X_i - X_{i-1}) + c(X_i^2 - X_{i-1}^2)$$
$$= b + c(X_i + X_{i-1})$$

(Note that $X_i - X_{i-1} = 1$.)

For the second differences, we have

$$\Delta^2 Y_i = \Delta Y_i - \Delta Y_{i-1}$$
$$= c(X_i - X_{i-2})$$
$$= 2c$$

and the second differences are constant. In general, the nth differences of an nth-degree parabolic equation are constants.

Using these properties, we may reason that if the first differences of a series are approximately constant, we may use a linear trend line. If the second differences are approximately constant, we may use a second-degree parabolic equation.

The method of selected points or the method of semiaverages may also be used to find the parabola trend line. The procedure for the method of selected points is to draw a freehand curve, select 3 points on this curve, construct 3 equations using these points, and solve for the coefficients a, b, and c.

The method of semiaverages is similar to the method of selected points except that the 3 points are selected by splitting the time series into 3 groups, finding the average point of these groups, and using these to determine the coefficients.

The linear and second-degree parabolas usually suffice for most practical cases.

(ii) *The exponential (or logarithmic) trend line*
The exponential trend line is shown by the equation

$$(6) \qquad\qquad\qquad Y = ab^X$$

which was mentioned in Section 22.11 and shown to be similar to the compound interest formula. It may also be used to find the trend line of, for example, population, national income, or other phenomena that grow geometrically.

Observation of equation (6) shows that when $b > 1$, the value of Y will increase infinitely as X (time) becomes large; and when $b < 1$, it will approach zero.

By taking logarithms, (6) becomes a linear function:

$$(7) \qquad\qquad\qquad \log Y = A + BX$$

where $\log a = A$, $\log b = B$. When applying the method of least squares, we find the a and b that makes $\Sigma (\log Y - \log Y_c)^2$ a minimum.

When (7) is plotted on a semilog scale, we shall obtain a straight line. The slope of the line is $\log b$, where b may be considered as the rate of increase of Y.

Using this characteristic, we may plot data that show the behavior of a geometric sequence on a semilog scale, fit a straight line graphically, and estimate $\log b$ from the graph. From this, we can find b, which will be the rate of increase of Y.

The normal equations of (7) are

(8)
$$\Sigma \log Y = n \log a + (\log b) \Sigma X$$
$$\Sigma X \log Y = (\log a) \Sigma X + (\log b) \Sigma X^2$$

By selecting the origin so that $\Sigma X = 0$, the normal equations become

(8')
$$\Sigma \log Y = n \log a$$
$$\Sigma X \log Y = (\log b) \Sigma X^2$$

Using hypothetical data, let us illustrate the calculation procedures.

Example 1.   Let Y be sales of a new product that appears to be growing at a geometrical rate as follows:

Year	X	Y	$\log Y$	$X \log Y$	X^2
1955	−1	2	0.3010	−0.3010	1
1956	0	8	0.9031	0	0
1957	1	40	1.6021	1.6021	1
		50	2.8062	1.3011	2

We find

$$\log a = \frac{1}{n} \Sigma \log Y = \frac{1}{3} (2.8062) = 0.09354$$

Therefore

$$a = 8.62$$

$$\log b = \frac{\Sigma X \log Y}{\Sigma X^2} = \frac{1.3011}{2} = .6505$$

Therefore

$$b = 4.47$$

Thus the exponential trend line is

$$\log Y_c = 0.9354 + 0.6505X$$

or

$$Y_c = (8.62)(4.47)^X$$

Origin: $X = 0$ at 7/1/56

The Y_c values are calculated as follows:

X	$0.6505 X$	$\log Y_c$	Y_c	Y
−1	−0.6505	0.2849	1.93	2
0	0	0.9354	8.62	8
1	0.6505	1.5859	38.54	40

The computed equation can be shown in the compound-interest formula form as follows:

$$Y_c = 8.62 \,(1 + 3.47)^x$$

and $r = 3.47$ shows the rate of increase. That is, the rate of growth is 347 percent. This large rate of growth also suggests that even a small amount of extrapolation for purposes of forecasting may produce exaggerated results.

(iii)   Modified exponential trend

A variation of the exponential trend is obtained by adding a constant k as follows:

(9) $$Y_c = k + ab^x$$

For example, let $k = 32$, $a = -16$, $b = \frac{1}{2}$. Then

$$Y_c = 32 - 16 \,(\tfrac{1}{2})^x$$

Then, for $X = -1, 0, 1, 2, 3, 4$, we find

X	−1	0	1	2	3	4
Y	0	16	24	28	30	31

This is shown graphically in Fig. 23.1. We see that the curve gradually approaches $k = 32$ as $X \longrightarrow \infty$. This k is called the (upper) *asymptote*.

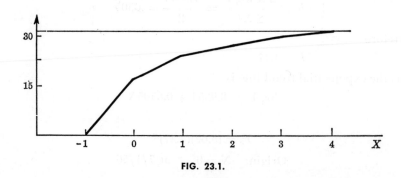

FIG. 23.1.

By combining different values of b and having the parameter a negative or positive, we have the four situations as shown in Fig. 23.2.

A characteristic of the exponential and modified exponential curve is that the ratio of the successive first differences is constant and equal to b.

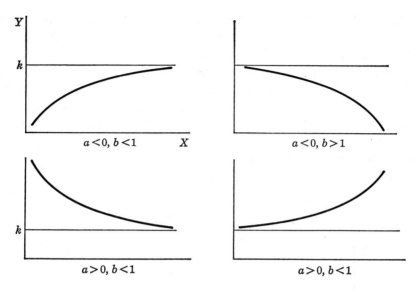

FIG. 23.2.

The first differences are

$$\Delta_1 = Y_{c2} - Y_{c1} = ab^2 - ab = ab \, (b - 1)$$
$$\Delta_2 = Y_{c3} - Y_{c2} = ab^3 - ab^2 = ab^2(b - 1)$$
$$\Delta_3 = Y_{c4} - Y_{c3} = ab^4 - ab^3 = ab^3(b - 1)$$

and so forth. The ratios of the first differences are

$$\frac{\Delta_2}{\Delta_1} = \frac{ab^2(b - 1)}{ab \, (b - 1)} = b$$

$$\frac{\Delta_3}{\Delta_2} = \frac{ab^3(b - 1)}{ab^2(b - 1)} = b$$

and this holds in general. As mentioned in the preceding section, this b may be considered as a measure of the rate of growth.

Since the modified exponential curve cannot be easily transformed into a linear form, the method of least squares is not used to find the coefficients k, a, and b. We shall present a simple method that fits a freehand curve to the scatter diagram, then selects three points and estimates k, a, and b. Two variations will be presented, the first using the method of selected points, and the second using the method of semiaverages. Let us illustrate this with simple examples.

We may first find the first differences of the given data and find the ratios, and then check to see if the ratios show a tendency to be constant. If, in addition, the freehand curve shows a tendency to approach an upper or lower limit, we may try to fit a modified exponential curve.

For purposes of illustration, let us assume that a curve, such as that shown in Fig. 23.3, has been fitted to the scatter diagram. The shape of the curve indicates that $a > 0$, $b > 1$. To develop the method of selected points, let us select the 3 points at $X = 0$, $X = 2$, and $X = 4$ on the curve. Then these points P_1, P_2, and P_3 are shown as

$$P_1 = k + a$$
$$P_2 = k + ab^2$$
$$P_3 = k + ab^4$$

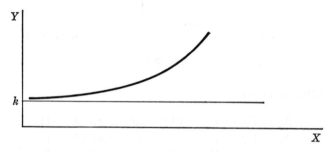

FIG. 23.3.

There are 3 equations and 3 unknowns, k, a, and b. Solving these equations, we find

$$b^2 = \frac{P_3 - P_2}{P_2 - P_1}$$

$$a = \frac{P_2 - P_1}{b^2 - 1}$$

$$k = P_1 - a$$

If the number of years between P_1, P_2, and P_3 are t years, respectively, the formulas become

(10a) $$b^t = \frac{P_3 - P_2}{P_2 - P_1}$$

(10b) $$a = \frac{P_2 - P_1}{b^t - 1}$$

(10c) $$k = P_1 - a$$

Let us use hypothetical data and illustrate the calculating procedures.

Example 2. Let the hypothetical data be as follows:

Year	X	Y		
1955	0	3	$\cdots$	P_1
1956	1	7		
1957	2	9	$\cdots$	P_2
1958	3	21		
1959	4	33	$\cdots$	P_3
1960	5	70		

The scatter diagram is shown in Fig. 23.4. Instead of selecting 3 points on the curve, let us use the values of Y for 1955, 1957, and 1959, for simplicity.

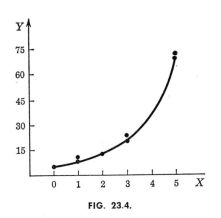

FIG. 23.4.

Then

$$b^2 = \frac{P_3 - P_2}{P_2 - P_1} = \frac{33 - 9}{9 - 3} = \frac{24}{6} = 4$$

$$a = \frac{P_2 - P_1}{b^2 - 1} = \frac{9 - 3}{4 - 1} = 2$$

$$k = P_1 - a = 3 - 2 = 1$$

$$b = \sqrt{4} = 2$$

Hence, the equation becomes

$$Y_c = 1 + 2(2)^X$$

Origin: $X = 0$ at $7/1/55$

The values of Y_c are

Year	X	Y_c
1955	0	3
1956	1	5
1957	2	9
1958	3	17
1959	4	33
1960	5	73

Let us now develop the method of semiaverages. We have

$$\left.\begin{array}{l} Y_0 = k + a \\ Y_1 = k + ab \end{array}\right\} \cdots S_1$$

$$\left.\begin{array}{l} Y_2 = k + ab^2 \\ Y_3 = k + ab^3 \end{array}\right\} \cdots S_2$$

$$\left.\begin{array}{l} Y_4 = k + ab^4 \\ Y_5 = k + ab^5 \end{array}\right\} \cdots S_3$$

The data are grouped into 3 groups and their sums are shown as S_1, S_2, and S_3 where

$$S_1 = 2k + a(b + 1)$$
$$S_2 = 2k + ab^2(b + 1)$$
$$S_3 = 2k + ab^4(b + 1)$$

There are 3 equations and 3 unknowns, k, a, and b. Solving for these unknowns, we find

$$b^2 = \frac{S_3 - S_2}{S_2 - S_1}$$

$$2k = S_1 - \frac{S_2 - S_1}{b^2 - 1}$$

$$a = \frac{S_2 - S_1}{(b^2 - 1)(b + 1)}$$

$$= (S_2 - S_1)\frac{b - 1}{(b^2 - 1)(b^2 - 1)}$$

If there are n observations per group, the formulas become

(11a)
$$b^n = \frac{S_3 - S_2}{S_2 - S_1}$$

(11b)
$$nk = S_1 - \frac{S_2 - S_1}{b^n - 1}$$

(11c)
$$a = (S_2 - S_1)\frac{b - 1}{(b^n - 1)(b^n - 1)}$$

Example 3. Using the following hypothetical data, let us fit a modified exponential curve by the method of semiaverages.

Year	X	Y	
1955	0	3 ⎫ ⋯	$S_1 = 10$
1956	1	7 ⎭	
1957	2	9 ⎫ ⋯	$S_2 = 30$
1958	3	21 ⎭	
1959	4	32 ⎫ ⋯	$S_3 = 102$
1960	5	70 ⎭	

We have

$$b^2 = \frac{S_3 - S_2}{S_2 - S_1} = \frac{102 - 30}{30 - 10} = \frac{72}{20} = 3.6$$

$$2k = S_1 - \frac{S_2 - S_1}{b^2 - 1} = 2.3$$

Therefore

$$k = 1.15$$

$$a = \frac{S_2 - S_1}{(b^2 - 1)(b + 1)} = 2.67$$

$$Y_c = 1.15 + 2.67 \, (1.89)^x \qquad (7/1/55)$$

(iv)   The logistic curve

A characteristic of the growth of the TV industry was that, once it got started, the rate of growth was very high during the early stages of development and then gradually declined and reached a saturation level. Similar growth patterns may be observed in various cases of biological and population growth. A curve that may be used to represent such growth patterns is the logistic curve. It became well known during the 1920's when two statisticans, Raymond Pearl and L. J. Reed, used it to analyze population and biological growth. It has been used to forecast the growth of industries, but usually the results have not been good. Today it is hardly ever used, but will be presented here mainly for historical interest.

The logistic curve in its general form is

$$Y_c = \frac{k}{1 + e^{f(X)}}$$

where k is a constant, and $f(X)$ is a polynomial of time X:

$$f(X) = a_0 + a_1 X + a_2 X^2 + \cdots + a_m X^m$$

The $f(X)$ is usually of the form $f(X) = a_0 + a_1 X$, and the logistic curve becomes

$$Y_c = \frac{k}{1 + e^{a_0 + a_1 X}}$$

Instead of the natural number e, the number 10 is usually used, and hence we have

(12) $$Y_c = \frac{k}{1 + 10^{a + bX}}$$

where b is usually $b < 0$. In this case, as $X \longrightarrow \infty$, the terms 10^{a+bX} $\longrightarrow 0$ and $Y_c \longrightarrow k$. That is, k becomes the upper asymptote.

The shape of the logistic curve is usually as shown in Fig. 23.4. Below

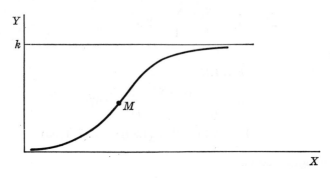

FIG. 23.5.

the point M, which is called the *point of inflexion*, the rate of growth is moving at an increasing rate; above M, it is moving at a decreasing rate.

The constants a, b, and k may be determined by the method of selected points or the method of semiaverages. Let us use hypothetical data and illustrate the procedures.

Case 1. Method of selected points. Suppose we have the following 6 years:

Year	X	Y		
1955	0	Y_0	$\cdots$	P_1
1956	1	Y_1		
1957	2	Y_2	$\cdots$	P_2
1958	3	Y_3		
1959	4	Y_4	$\cdots$	P_3
1960	5	Y_5		

The data are plotted as a scatter diagram and a freehand logistic curve is plotted.

The 3 points corresponding to $X = 0$, $X = 2$, $X = 4$ are selected on this curve. Let the Y value of these points be P_1, P_2, and P_3. Then, from equation (12), we find

(13a)
$$P_1 = \frac{k}{1 + 10^a}$$

(13b)
$$P_2 = \frac{k}{1 + 10^{a+2b}}$$

(13c)
$$P_3 = \frac{k}{1 + 10^{a+4b}}$$

There are 3 equations and 3 unknowns, a, b, and k. To find the b, we let

$$\frac{\dfrac{1}{P_3} - \dfrac{1}{P_2}}{\dfrac{1}{P_2} - \dfrac{1}{P_1}} = \frac{10^{a+4b} - 10^{a+2b}}{10^{a+2b} - 10^a} = 10^{2b}$$

Therefore

$$10^{2b} = \frac{P_1(P_3 - P_2)}{P_3(P_2 - P_1)}$$

Taking the common logarithm on both sides gives us

$$2b = \log \frac{P_1(P_3 - P_2)}{P_3(P_2 - P_1)}$$

To find the parameter a, let

$$\frac{P_1}{P_2} = \frac{1 + 10^{a+2b}}{1 + 10^a}$$

and solving for 10^a gives us

$$10^a = \frac{1 - P_2}{P_2 10^{2b} - P_1}$$

Taking the common logarithm on both sides gives us

$$a = \log \frac{1 - P_2}{P_2 10^{2b} - P_1}$$

Finally, k can be found from the equation (13a) as

$$k = P_1(1 + 10^a)$$

In general, if the 3 points are n years apart, the formulas become

(14a)
$$nb = \log \frac{P_1(P_3 - P_2)}{P_3(P_2 - P_1)}$$

(14b)
$$a = \log \frac{P_1 - P_2}{P_2 10^{nb} - P_1}$$

(14c)
$$k = P_1(1 + 10^a)$$

Example 4. Given the following hypothetical data, fit a logistic curve.

Year	X	Y		
1955	0	2	...	P_1
1956	1	4		
1957	2	6	...	P_2
1958	3	9		
1959	4	9	...	P_3
1960	5	10		

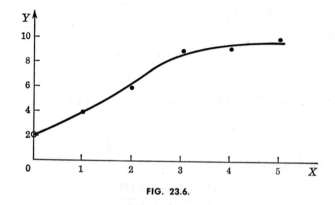

FIG. 23.6.

A curve is fitted to the scatter diagram as shown in Fig. 23.6. Note how it rises rapidly and then tapers off. Select 3 points on the curve that correspond to $X = 0$, $X = 2$, and $X = 4$. For simplicity, we shall use the 3 points $Y = 2$, $Y = 6$, and $Y = 9$. Using the formulas derived above, we find b as

$$2b = \log \frac{P_1 (P_3 - P_2)}{P_3 (P_2 - P_1)} = \log \frac{2 (9 - 6)}{9 (6 - 2)} = -0.7782$$

Therefore

$$b = -0.3891$$

The a is

$$a = \log \frac{P_1 - P_2}{P_2 10^{2b} - P_1} = \log \frac{2 - 6}{6 \left(\dfrac{1}{6}\right) - 2} = 0.6021$$

Finally, the k is

$$k = P_1(1 + 10^a) = 2(1 + 4) = 10$$

Thus, the logistic curve is

$$Y_c = \frac{10}{1 + 10^{0.6021 - 0.3891X}} \qquad b < 0$$

$$X = 0 \qquad \text{at } 7/1/55$$

Case 2. Method of semiaverages. A second way of finding the logistic curve is to apply the method of semiaverages. Starting from the logistic curve

$$Y_c = \frac{k}{1 + 10^{a + bX}}$$

we may invert this and let it be

(15) $$\frac{1}{Y_c} = \frac{1}{k} + \frac{1}{k} \times 10^{a + bX}$$

Let $1/k = k'$, $(1/k)(10^a) = a'$, $10^b = b'$, and $1/Y_c = Y'$. Then equation (15) becomes

$$Y'_c = k' + a'(b')^X$$

which is the form of the modified exponential curve. Hence, we may apply the formulas derived for the modified exponential curve. These are

(16a) $$(b')^n = \frac{S_3 - S_2}{S_2 - S_1}$$

(16b) $$nk' = S_1 - \frac{S_2 - S_1}{(b')^n - 1}$$

(16c) $$a' = (S_2 - S_1) \frac{b' - 1}{[(b')^n - 1][(b')^n - 1]}$$

where S_1, S_2, and S_3 are the sums of 3 evenly divided groups of data, each having n years in it. The computation procedures were explained in the preceding section.

(v) The Gompertz curve

The Gompertz curve is named after Benjamin Gompertz, who used it for work related to mortality tables in 1825. It is

(17) $$Y_c = ka^{b^X}$$

where a, b, and k are constants. For example, Y may be the number of survivors at age X.

To find the a, b, and k, we shall first take the logarithms.

$$\log Y_c = \log k + (\log a)(b^x)$$

Let $\log Y_c = Y'_c$, $\log k = k'$, $\log a = a'$. Then the equation becomes

$$Y'_c = k' + a'b$$

and it takes the same form as the modified exponential curve. Thus, procedures of estimating the coefficients of the modified exponential curve may be applied.

23.2. The Moving Average

In Chapter 12 a simple moving average scheme was presented to find the trend line. In Chapter 13, it was used to find seasonal indices. In this section we shall show that the simple moving average is the sequence of points obtained from the central value (the y-intercept) of straightline trend lines fitted by the method of least squares. We shall then extend this and discuss schemes of weighted moving averages.

(i)   The moving average and least squares

Suppose we have the following data for 7 years:

Year	X	Y
1955	0	Y_0
1956	1	Y_1
1957	2	Y_2
1958	3	Y_3
1959	4	Y_4
1960	5	Y_5
1961	6	Y_6

When applying a 3-year moving average to these data, we find

$$z_1 = \frac{1}{3}(Y_0 + Y_1 + Y_2)$$

$$z_2 = \frac{1}{3}(Y_1 + Y_2 + Y_3)$$

. . . .

and so forth.

Let us apply the method of least squares to 3 successive years, moving 1 year ahead each time That is, fit a straight line by the method of least squares to (Y_0, Y_1, Y_2) first; then repeat the process for the years (Y_1, Y_2, Y_3), and so forth. For the first 3 years, the worksheet is as follows:

Worksheet

	X	Y
1955	−1	Y_0
1956	0	Y_1
1957	1	Y_2

The normal equations are

$$\sum_{i=0}^{2} Y_i = na_1$$

$$\sum XY = b \sum X^2$$

and we find

$$a_1 = \frac{1}{n} \sum Y_i$$

$$= \frac{1}{3} (Y_0 + Y_1 + Y_2)$$

Hence, a is the 3-year average of the first 3 years.

When this is repeated for $(Y_1 + Y_2 + Y_3)$, we obtain

$$a_2 = \frac{1}{3} (Y_1 + Y_2 + Y_3)$$

and, as is seen, the sequence of $a_1, a_2, \ldots, a_5$ is the sequence of points that correspond to the points of the 3-year moving average points.

Instead of only 3 years, we may use any number of years. When the years are odd, the X's are numbered . . . , −3, −2, −1, 0, 1, 2, 3, . . . ; when the years are even, the X's are numbered . . . , −3, −1, 1, 3, ...

(ii)   Weighted moving average

The simple moving average was seen to correspond to fitting a straight line trend line $Y = a + bX$ to successive groups of n years by the method of least squares. In our example, we used $n = 3$. However, when n is, say, 12 months, a straight line may not be the adequate fit to show the trend line (or seasonal variation). We may wish to use a parabola and find a trend line by the moving average method such that the fit is best in the least-squares sense. We shall now investigate this problem.

We shall start with the straightline trend line and show how it may be expressed in a general form. The straight line is

$$Y = a_0 + a_1 X$$

and the normal equations are

$$\Sigma Y = n a_0 + a_1 \Sigma X$$
$$\Sigma XY = a_0 \Sigma X + a_1 \Sigma X^2$$

Assuming that we wish a 3-year moving average of Y_{-1}, Y_0, Y_1, we solve for a_0 and find, using determinants,

$$a_0 = \frac{\begin{vmatrix} \Sigma Y & \Sigma X \\ \Sigma XY & \Sigma X^2 \end{vmatrix}}{\begin{vmatrix} n & \Sigma X \\ \Sigma X & \Sigma X^2 \end{vmatrix}}$$

$$= \frac{1}{\Delta} [Y_{-1} (\Sigma X^2 - X_{-1} \Sigma X) + Y_0 (\Sigma X^2 - X_0 \Sigma X) + Y_1 (\Sigma X^2 - X_1 \Sigma X)]$$

$$= \frac{1}{\Delta} [Y_{-1} b_{-1} + Y_0 b_0 + Y_1 b_1]$$

where

$$\Delta = \begin{vmatrix} n & \Sigma X \\ \Sigma X & X^2 \end{vmatrix}$$

The sum of the b's are

$$b_{-1} + b_0 + b_1 = 3 \Sigma X^2 - (\Sigma X)^2$$

The determinant Δ is

$$\Delta = n \Sigma X^2 - (\Sigma X)^2 = 3 \Sigma X^2 - (\Sigma X)^2$$

since $n = 3$ for 3 years. Hence,

$$b_{-1} + b_0 + b_1 = \Delta$$

Thus, a is the weighted average of the Y's and the weights are the b's.

For $n = 3$, the X's are as follows:

X	X^2
-1	1
0	0
1	1
$\Sigma X = 0$	$\Sigma X^2 = 2$

Hence, the b's are

$$b_{-1} = \Sigma\, X^2 - X_{-1}\, \Sigma\, X = 2 - 0 = 2$$
$$b_0 = \Sigma\, X^2 - X_0\, \Sigma\, X = 2 - 0 = 2$$
$$b_1 = \Sigma\, X^2 - X_1\, \Sigma\, X = 2 - 0 = 2$$
$$\Delta = b_{-1} + b_0 + b_1 = 6$$

Thus a_0 becomes

$$a_0 = \frac{1}{6}\,(2Y_{-1} + 2Y_0 + 2Y_1)$$

$$= \frac{1}{3}\,(Y_{-1} + Y_0 + Y_1)$$

and is the simple moving average of the Y's.

For $n = 5$ years, calculations will show that

$$a_0 = \frac{1}{5}\,(Y_{-2} + Y_{-1} + Y_0 + Y_1 + Y_2)$$

and, in general, for the straightline linear trend, $Y = a + bX$, the moving average obtained from the least squares is the simple moving average.

The notation used to express the weights is

$$a_0: \qquad \frac{1}{5}\,(1,\, 1,\, 1,\, 1,\, 1)$$

and since the weights are symmetric, we shall write

$$a_0: \qquad \frac{1}{5}\,(1,\, 1,\, 1,\, \ldots)$$

where the last written term is the midvalue.

Let us now apply the procedure above to a second-degree parabola:

$$Y = a_0 + a_1 X + a_2 X^2$$

The normal equations are

$$\Sigma\, Y = na_0 + a_1\, \Sigma\, X + a_2\, \Sigma\, X^2$$
$$\Sigma\, XY = a_0\, \Sigma\, X + a_1\, \Sigma\, X^2 + a_2\, \Sigma\, X^3$$
$$\Sigma\, X^2 Y = a_0\, \Sigma\, X^2 + a_1\, \Sigma\, X^3 + a_2\, \Sigma\, X^4$$

and since the origin is taken so that $\Sigma\, X = 0$, the normal equations become

$$\Sigma\,Y = na_0 + 0 + a_2\,\Sigma\,X^2$$
$$\Sigma\,XY = 0 + a_{12}\,\Sigma\,X^2 + 0$$
$$\Sigma\,X^2 Y = a_0\,\Sigma\,X + 0 + a_2\,\Sigma\,X^4$$

For $n = 5$ years, we have Y_{-2}, Y_{-1}, Y_0, Y_1, Y_2, and a becomes

$$a_0 = \frac{1}{\Delta}\,[Y_{-2}\,(\Sigma\,X^2\,\Sigma\,X^4 - X_{-2}^{\,2}\,(\Sigma\,X^2)^2)$$

$$+ Y_{-1}\,(\Sigma\,X^2\,\Sigma\,X^4 - X_{-1}^{\,2}\,(\Sigma\,X^2)^2)$$

$$\cdot\quad\cdot\quad\cdot\quad\cdot\quad\cdot\quad\cdot\quad\cdot\quad\cdot\quad\cdot\quad\cdot\quad\cdot\quad\cdot$$

$$+ Y_2\,(\Sigma\,X^2\,\Sigma\,X^4 - X_2^{\,2}\,(\Sigma\,X^2)^2)]$$

$$= \frac{1}{\Delta}\,[Y_{-2}b_{-2} + Y_{-1}b_{-1} + Y_0 b_0 + Y_1 b_1 + Y_2 b_2]$$

$$\Delta = \begin{vmatrix} n & 0 & \Sigma\,X^2 \\ 0 & \Sigma\,X^2 & 0 \\ \Sigma\,X^2 & 0 & \Sigma\,X^4 \end{vmatrix}$$

$$= n\,\Sigma\,X^2\,\Sigma\,X^4 - (\Sigma\,X^2)^3$$

$$= 5\,\Sigma\,X^2\,\Sigma\,X^4 - (\Sigma\,X^2)^3$$

$$b_{-2} + b_{-1} + b_0 + b_1 + b_2 = 5\,\Sigma\,X^2\,\Sigma\,X^4 - (\Sigma\,X^2)^3 = \Delta$$

Furthermore,

$$\Sigma\,X^2 = (-2)^2 + (-1)^2 + (0)^2 + (1)^2 + (2)^2 = 10$$
$$\Sigma\,X^4 = (-2)^4 + (-1)^4 + (0)^4 + (1)^4 + (2)^4 = 34$$

Hence, the b's are

$$b_{-2} = \Sigma\,X^2\,\Sigma\,X^4 - X_{-2}^{\,2}\,(\Sigma\,X^2)^2$$
$$= 10 \times 34 - 4 \times 10^2 = -60$$
$$b_{-1} = 10 \times 34 - 1 \times 10^2 = 240$$
$$b_0 = 10 \times 34 - 0 \times 10^2 = 340$$
$$b_1 = 10 \times 34 - 1 \times 10^2 = 240$$
$$b_2 = 10 \times 34 - 4 \times 10^2 = -60$$
$$\Delta = -60 + 240 + 340 + 240 - 60 = 700$$

Thus, a_0 becomes

$$(1) \qquad a_0 = \frac{1}{700}\,[-60Y_{-2} + 240Y_{-1} + 340Y_0 + 240Y_1 - 60Y_2]$$

$$= \frac{1}{35}\,[-3Y_{-2} + 12Y_{-1} + 17Y_0 + 12Y_1 - 3Y_2]$$

Using the notation developed above, the weights are expressed as

(2) $\qquad\qquad a_0:\qquad \dfrac{1}{35}[-3, 12, 17, \cdots]$

We may compute weights for higher parabolas in similar manner. It turns out that the weights for a_0 obtained from parabolas of $2k$ degree and $2k + 1$ degree are the same. Hence, for example, the weights obtained from second- and third-degree parabolas will be the same. We list several weights for $n = 5, 7, 9, 11$, and 13:

$n = 5 \qquad \dfrac{1}{35}[-3, 12, 17, \cdots]$

$n = 7 \qquad \dfrac{1}{21}[-2, 3, 6, 7, \cdots]$

$n = 9 \qquad \dfrac{1}{231}[-21, 14, 39, 54, 59, \cdots]$

$n = 11 \qquad \dfrac{1}{429}[-36, 9, 44, 69, 84, 89, \cdots]$

$n = 13 \qquad \dfrac{1}{143}[-11, 0, 9, 16, 21, 24, 25, \cdots]$

Weights for other values of n and for fourth- and fifth-degree parabolas have been provided by Kendall.*

23.3.   Tests of Independence

One of the assumptions in time series is that the successive observations are statistically independent. For instance, if we are dealing with the output of steel, we are assuming that this year's output is independent of last year's output, which is usually not true. However, the degree of dependence between this year's steel output and the output of 3 years ago may be practically independent. In many cases where the time interval between successive observations is short, there may be dependence.

We should like to find a measure that will indicate the degree of dependence between terms of a time series. One such measure is called *serial correlation*. Using this serial correlation, we may test whether or not a series is random. There are also other tests of independence,

---

* M. G. Kendall, *The Advanced Theory of Statistics*, Vol. II, London: Charles Griffen and Co., 1948.

such as the Von Neuman ratio and Durbin-Watson test. We shall explain these tests briefly.

(i) Serial correlation

Given a time series $X_1, X_2, \ldots, X_n$, the correlation between successive terms of the series is defined as

$$(1) \qquad r_1 = \frac{\text{Cov}(X_i, X_{i+1})}{\sqrt{\text{Var}(X_i)\ \text{Var}(X_{i+1})}}$$

and is called the *serial correlation coefficient of order 1*. It is called "of order 1" because the time interval between X_i and X_{i+1} is 1 time interval. The serial correlation between X_i and X_{i+k} is called "of order k."

The terms autocorrelation, serial correlation, and lag correlation are sometimes distinguished, while on other occasions they are used interchangeably. When a distinction is made, the term *autocorrelation* is usually used to indicate the population serial correlation coefficient. The term *serial correlation* is usually used to indicate the sample serial correlation coefficient. And the term *lag correlation coefficient* is used to indicate the serial correlation between different time series. Since our discussion will be confined to sample data and a single time series, we shall use only the term serial correlation coefficient.

Let us now illustrate the serial correlation coefficient with hypothetical data as given in Table 23.3.

TABLE 23.3.

X_i	X_i^2	$X_i X_{i+1}$	$(X_{i+1} - X_i)^2$
2	4	10	9
5	25	20	1
4	16	24	4
6	36	48	4
8	64	16	36
25	145	118	54

The computation formula for the serial correlation coefficient is

$$(2) \qquad r_1 = \frac{\sum\limits_{i=1}^{n} x_i x_{i+1}}{\sum x_i^2} = \frac{\sum X_i X_{i+1} - \dfrac{(\sum X_i)^2}{n}}{\sum X_i^2 - \dfrac{(\sum X_i)^2}{n}}$$

where $x_i = X_i - \bar{X}$ and n is the sample size. We also set $x_{n+1} = x_1$. In terms of our example, $n = 5$, and hence $x_{n+1} = x_6 = x_1$. Hence, this definition is called the *circular definition* of the serial correlation coefficient. For our present example,

$$r_1 = \frac{118 - \dfrac{25^2}{5}}{145 - \dfrac{25^2}{5}} = -0.35$$

(ii) Tests of significance

Is this sample serial correlation coefficient significant? That is, may we conclude that serial correlation exists in the population time series? Or, to put it another way, is the series not random? To test the significance of $r = -0.35$, we may use the distribution of the serial correlation developed by R. L. Anderson* in his article. The table developed by Anderson is given at Table 9 in the Appendix. It gives the critical values of r for the 5 percent level of significance. If the value of r_1 exceeds the corresponding value (which depends on n) in the table, we conclude that there is serial correlation in the population. For $n = 5$, the value in the table is 0.253 (for positive values of r) or -0.753 (for negative values of r). Since the calculated serial correlation coefficient $r_1 = -0.35$ is smaller than -0.753, we conclude that there is no serial correlation in the population. That is, the series can be considered to be a random series.

(iii) Noncircular definition of serial correlation

The definition of the serial correlation coefficient in equation (1) assumed that $x_{n+1} = x_1$ and was called a *circular definition*. If the time series is detrended and long, this assumption $x_{n+1} = x_1$ may not affect the values of r_1. If, however, we apply this circular definition to a time series with a trend, there may be a large difference between the values x_1 and x_{n+1}, and hence may have a significant effect on r. It would, in such cases, be desirable to define a serial correlation coefficient that does not assume $x_1 = x_{n+1}$. A noncircular definition of a serial correlation

---

* R. L. Anderson, "Distribution of the serial correlation coefficient," *Annals of Mathematical Statistics* (1942).

coefficient of order k is

$$(3) \quad r_k = \frac{\sum\limits_{i=1}^{k} X_i X_{i+k} - \dfrac{1}{n-k}\left(\sum\limits_{i=1}^{n-k} X_i\right)\left(\sum\limits_{i=1}^{n-k} X_{i+k}\right)}{\left\{\sum\limits_{i=1}^{n-k} X_i^2 - \dfrac{1}{n-k}\left(\sum\limits_{i=1}^{n-k} X_i\right)^2\right\}^{1/2}\left\{\sum\limits_{i=1}^{n-k} X_{i+k} - \dfrac{1}{n-k}\left(\sum\limits_{i=1}^{n-k} X_{i+k}\right)^2\right\}^{1/2}}$$

and we define

$$r_0 = 1, \qquad r_{-k} = r_k$$

The distribution of (2), that is, Table 9 of the Appendix may be used as an approximation of the distribution of (3) to test the significance of the noncircular correlation coefficient. The critical values of r_k are obtained from the values corresponding to $n - k$. For example, using our hypothetical data, where $n = 5$, the critical value for r_1 corresponds to $n - 1 = 5 - 1 = 4$.

(iv) The mean square successive difference method

Another method of testing the independence of successive observations in a time series is the mean-square successive difference, which is sometimes called the Von Neuman ratio.*

Given a time series $X_1, X_2, \ldots, X_n$, the mean-square successive difference is defined as

$$\delta^2 = \frac{1}{n-1} \sum_{i=1}^{n-1} (X_{i+1} - X_i)^2$$

The sample variance is defined as

$$s^2 = \frac{1}{n} \sum_{i=1}^{n} (X_i - \bar{X})^2$$

The Von Neuman ratio is defined as

$$K = \frac{\delta^2}{s^2}$$

A table for the 1 and 5 percent significance points has been computed by Hart** and is Table 10 in the Appendix. Given a sample of

---

* J. Von Neuman, "Distribution of ratio of the mean square successive difference to the variance," *Annals of Mathematical Statistics* (1941), pp. 367 ff.

** B. I. Hart, "Significance levels for the ratio of the mean square successive difference to the variance," *ibid.*, Vol. 13, No. 4 (1942), p. 446.

size n (say, $n = 20$), and a level of significance of 5 percent, the table gives two critical values: $K_1 = 1.3680$ and $K_2 = 2.8425$. If the computed K is smaller than K_1, the value of K is considered significant, and it is concluded that a positive serial correlation exists. If the computed K is larger than K_2, the value of K is considered significant, and it is concluded that a negative serial correlation exists.

For other tests, such as the Durbin-Watson* test and Moran's** test, the reader is referred to the references in the footnote.

23.4 Stationary Time Series

A detrended time series is called a *stationary time series*. A stationary time series usually fluctuates, and a problem in which economists are interested is to test whether or not the fluctuations are random. If a stationary time series is not random, it is classified as cyclical or oscillatory. A cyclical time series is a series that is periodic, like a seasonal index. An oscillatory time series is one that is not random or cyclical; that is, one that is not random and nonperiodic. Most economic time series are oscillatory.

Assuming that the elements of a time series are additive, it may be shown schematically as

$$Y = T + O + R$$

where Y is the original time series, T is the trend, O is the oscillatory (and cyclical) component, and R is the random component. In analyzing time series, we are interested in determining the functional form of these components. We have already seen that the trend may be expressed as a linear trend, parabolic trend, exponential curve, etc.

After detrending a time series and obtaining a stationary time series, we may wish to investigate its form. First we shall test whether or not the series is random. The tests of serial correlation mentioned in Section 23.3 may be used for this. If the stationary time series is found not to be random, it may be cyclical or oscillatory.

A simple graph of the stationary time series may be used to detect whether it is cyclical. If the stationary time series is found not to be cyclical and does not have a regular period, we may conclude that it is

---

* J. Durbin and G. S. Watson, "Testing for serial correlation in least squares regression," *Biometrika*, Vol. 37 (1950), pp. 409 ff. J. Durbin, "Testing for serial correlation in systems of simultaneous regression equations," *Biometrika*, Vol. 44 (1957), pp. 370 ff.

** P. A. P. Moran, "A test for the serial independence of residuals," *Biometrika*, Vol. 37, (1950), pp. 178 ff.

oscillatory. Oscillatory movements are usually thought to be generated from three schemes. One is the moving average of a random series, a second is the sum of a number of cyclical time series, and a third is autoregressive system schemes. We shall only discuss the first and the third schemes.

(i) The Yule-Slutsky effect

It has been shown that the moving average of a random series oscillates, and that this is called the Yule-Slutsky effect.* Let the random series be

$$\epsilon_1, \epsilon_2, \cdots, \epsilon_n$$

where we assume $E(\epsilon_i) = 0$, $E(\epsilon_i)^2 = \sigma^2$. Take an $n = 3$ year moving average

$$\epsilon'_i = \frac{1}{3}(\epsilon_i + \epsilon_{i+1} + \epsilon_{i+2})$$

Then the variance of ϵ'_i is

$$E(\epsilon'_i)^2 = E\left\{\frac{1}{3^2}(\epsilon_i + \epsilon_{i+1} + \epsilon_{i+2})^2\right\}$$

$$= \frac{1}{3^2}E\{\epsilon_i^2 + \epsilon_{i+1}^2 + \epsilon_{i+2}^2 + 2\epsilon_i\epsilon_{i+1}$$

$$+ 2\epsilon_{i+1}\epsilon_{i+2} + 2\epsilon_{i+2}\epsilon_i\}$$

$$= \frac{1}{3^2}E\{\epsilon_i^2 + \epsilon_{i+1}^2 + \epsilon_{i+2}^2\}$$

because $E(\epsilon_i\epsilon_{i+j}) = 0$, where $i \neq j$. Since $E(\epsilon_i)^2 = \sigma^2$, we get

$$E(\epsilon'_i)^2 = \frac{1}{3^2}\cdot 3\sigma^2 = \frac{1}{3}\sigma^2 = \frac{1}{n}\sigma^2$$

The covariance is

$$\text{Cov}(\epsilon'_i, \epsilon'_{i+k}) = E(\epsilon'_i\epsilon'_{i+k})$$

$$= \frac{1}{3^2}E[(\epsilon_i + \epsilon_{i+1} + \epsilon_{i+2})(\epsilon_{i+k} + \epsilon_{i+k+1} + \epsilon_{i+k+2})]$$

If $n = 3 > k$ (say, $k = 2$), then

$$\text{Cov}(\epsilon'_i, \epsilon'_{i+k}) = \frac{1}{3^2}E[(\epsilon_i + \epsilon_{i+1} + \epsilon_{i+2})(\epsilon_{i+2} + \epsilon_{i+3} + \epsilon_{i+4})]$$

---

* E. Slutsky, "The summation of random causes as the source of cyclical processes," *Econometrica*, 5, 1937.

$$= \frac{1}{3^2} E[\epsilon_i \epsilon_{i+2} + \epsilon_i \epsilon_{i+3} + \epsilon_i \epsilon_{i+4}$$

$$+ \epsilon_{i+1} \epsilon_{i+2} + \epsilon_{i+1} \epsilon_{i+3} + \epsilon_{i+1} \epsilon_{i+4}$$

$$+ \epsilon_{i+2} \epsilon_{i+2} + \epsilon_{i+2} \epsilon_{i+3} + \epsilon_{i+2} \epsilon_{i+4}]$$

$$= \frac{1}{3^2} [E(\epsilon_{i+2})^2 + E(\epsilon_i \epsilon_{i+2} + \cdots + \epsilon_{i+2} \epsilon_{i+4})]$$

$$= \frac{1}{3^2} (3 - 2) \sigma^2$$

$$= \frac{1}{n^2} (n - k) \sigma^2$$

If $n = 3 \leqslant k$ (say, $k = 3$), then

$$\mathrm{Cov}(\epsilon'_i, \epsilon'_{i+k}) = \frac{1}{3^2} E[(\epsilon_i + \epsilon_{i+1} + \epsilon_{i+2})(\epsilon_{i+3} + \epsilon_{i+4} + \epsilon_{i+5})]$$

$$= \frac{1}{3^2} E[\epsilon_i(\epsilon_{i+3} + \epsilon_{i+4} + \epsilon_{i+5})$$

$$+ \epsilon_{i+1}(\epsilon_{i+3} + \epsilon_{i+4} + \epsilon_{i+5})$$

$$+ \epsilon_{i+2}(\epsilon_{i+3} + \epsilon_{i+4} + \epsilon_{i+5})]$$

$$= 0$$

Hence, the serial correlation coefficient between ϵ'_i and ϵ'_{i+k} is, for $n > k$,

$$\rho_{i, i+k} = \frac{\mathrm{cov}(\epsilon'_i, \epsilon'_{i+k})}{\sqrt{E(\epsilon'_i)^2 \, E(\epsilon'_{i+k})^2}}$$

$$= \frac{\dfrac{1}{n^2} (n - k) \sigma^2}{\sqrt{\dfrac{1}{n} \sigma^2 \cdot \dfrac{1}{n} \sigma^2}}$$

$$= \frac{n - k}{n} \sigma$$

For $n \leqslant k$,

$$\rho_{i, i+k} = \frac{0}{\sqrt{\dfrac{1}{n} \sigma^2 \cdot \dfrac{1}{n} \sigma^2}}$$

$$= 0$$

We see that as the lag k becomes larger, the coefficient $(n-k)/n$ becomes smaller, and the serial correlation coefficient becomes smaller and finally reaches 0 when $n \leqslant k$. This positive serial correlation coefficient between successive terms indicates that the terms are not independent, and the sequence of moving averages will generate an oscillatory series. This is known as the Yule-Slutsky effect.

The implication of this effect is that, when using the moving average to remove a trend from a time series, an oscillatory movement may be introduced even where none exists.

This effect may also be used to explain why various economic time series, such as national income and sales, oscillate. It may be thought that various economic phenomena contain weight averages of various random disturbances such as weather, strikes, political changes, institutional changes, and various economic disturbances, which generate oscillatory movements.

(ii)   Autoregressive scheme

Suppose we have a stationary time series X_t, X_{t-1}, X_{t-2}, ... Let

(1) $$X_t = aX_{t-1} + b + \epsilon_t$$

where a and b are constants and ϵ_t is a random disturbance. We assume that $E(\epsilon_t) = 0$ and $E(\epsilon_t^2) = \sigma^2$. Equations such as (1), which involve lagged variables, are called *autoregressive*. Equation (1) is a first-order, autoregressive, stochastic difference equation.

As an example, X_t may be considered as national income of time t. Then X_{t-1} is the national income of the previous period, and equation (1) shows that income of period t is dependent on income of period $t-1$. The variable X_t is sometimes called the *exogenous variable* and X_{t-1} is called the *endogenous variable*. The random term ϵ_t is a catchall variable and represents the various other factors that affect X_t and which are independent of X_{t-1}.

To simplify equation (1), let us express the X_t's as deviations from the mean $E(X_t)$. That is, let

$$x_t = X_t - E(X_t)$$

From (1), we find

$$E(X_t) = aE(X_{t-1}) + b$$

and hence,

$$x_t = (aX_{t-1} + b + \epsilon_t) - (aE(X_{t-1}) + b)$$
$$= a(X_{t-1} - E(X_{t-1})) + \epsilon_t$$

(2) $$\qquad x_t = ax_{t-1} + \epsilon_t$$

The term x_{t-1} in equation (2) may be shown as

$$x_{t-1} = ax_{t-2} + \epsilon_{t-1}$$

Substituting this into (2) and repeating this procedure for x_{t-2}, x_{t-3}, etc., we find

$$x_t = ax_{t-1} + \epsilon_t$$

$$= \epsilon_t + a(ax_{t-2} + \epsilon_{t-1})$$

$$= \epsilon_t + a\epsilon_{t-1} + a^2(ax_{t-3} + \epsilon_{t-2})$$

(3) $$\qquad x_t = \epsilon_t + a\epsilon_{t-1} + a^2\,\epsilon_{t-2} + a^3\epsilon_{t-3} + \cdots$$

This autoregressive equation shows that x_t is affected by the past random disturbances. It may be thought of as a moving average of past disturbances. The Yule-Slutsky effect tells us that (3) will show an oscillatory movement.

Although we have derived the result in terms of a first-order autoregressive equation, similar results may be obtained for higher-order autoregressive equations.

INDEX